STANLEY GIBBONS
GREAT BRITAIN SPECIALISED STAMP CATALOGUE

# Queen Elizabeth II
## Pre-decimal Issues

Volume 3

Four bromide photographic essays of unaccepted hand-painted alternative designs for the first Queen Elizabeth high value issues from the Farrar-Bell archive.

Stanley Gibbons
Great Britain Specialised
Stamp Catalogue

Volume 3

# Queen Elizabeth II
## Pre-decimal Issues

12th Edition

STANLEY GIBBONS LTD
London and Ringwood

By Appointment to Her Majesty The Queen
Stanley Gibbons Ltd, London
Philatelists

Published by Stanley Gibbons Ltd
Editorial, Publications Sales Offices
and Distribution Centre:
7 Parkside, Christchurch Road, Ringwood,
Hants BH24 3SH

1st edition – August 1970
2nd edition – October 1971
3rd edition – February 1976
Reprinted – October 1976
Reprinted – April 1977
4th edition – November 1978
5th edition – November 1980
6th edition – June 1984
7th edition – November 1987
8th edition – September 1990
9th edition – October 1993
10th edition – October 1998
11th edition – March 2006
12th edition – February 2011

British Library Cataloguing in
Publication Data.

A catalogue record for this book is available from the British Library.

Errors and omissions excepted. The colour
reproduction of stamps is only as accurate as
the printing process will allow.

ISBN-10: 0-85259-778-9
ISBN-13: 978-0-85259-778-1

Item No. R2810-11

Printed by Latimer Trend & Company Ltd, Plymouth

# Contents

# Preface

The period covered by this catalogue, from December 1952 to November 1970, just under 18 years, may be less than for any other volume in this Great Britain Specialised Catalogue series, but it is nevertheless one of the most interesting periods in British philately.

From the design point of view, the ornate 'Wildings' saw the return of a 'three-quarter' portrait of the monarch, only tried once before (with disastrous results), for the early stamps of King George V. The designs were successful enough, but 1967 saw the arrival of the elegantly simple 'Machins' – still with us today.

Technically, this was a period of rapid advances in mail-handling technology with experiments in the use of graphite and different phosphor inks to facilitate faster and more reliable letter sorting. Since the previous edition of this catalogue was published, much material from the trials carried out at the Post Office research laboratory at Dollis Hill, London, has come on to the market, with details and priced listings provided in this catalogue.

Then, of course, there was the introduction of regional stamps and the much expanded programme of commemorative issues. A period we now look back on as providing just the right number of new stamps for collectors to be excited by them without feeling exploited – and of course they were on sale at every post office too.

Happy days!

## This new edition

The catalogue has been completely redesigned with a larger page size and two-column format for the listings, which are now easier to use, thanks to the introduction of a second colour. We are also pleased to be able to revert to our earlier policy of providing a case binding for the Great Britain specialised volumes, making them more durable and able to lie open while in use.

As mentioned above, details are now provided of the "Dollis Hill" trial stamps, which have been priced for the first time. We are grateful to the late Mike Holt and to Ian Harvey for their help with this.

We must also thank Ian Harvey for his assistance in expanding the listings of Wilding and Machin booklet panes with the I(e) and AP(2E) perforation types now listed and priced for the first time.

He has also greatly expanded the information on stamp booklets with extended notes on the pattern books and advertiser voucher copies and new information on paste-up books and publicity proofs for booklets with pictorial covers – all backed by priced listings.

In preparation for the introduction of decimal stamps in 1971, colour trials were carried out using certain values in the pre-decimal series. Thanks to John Deering, the background details to these are now given, together with full listings of those now on the market.

Thanks are also due to Jean Alexander and Andrew McGavin for providing details of the encapsulated stamp cards produced by the Post Office from 1970 to promote certain new issues, and to the latter for showing us details of the scientific research he commissioned into the stamps enclosed within them, which demonstrates that they are printed on uncoated paper.

Much new information has been added to the "Castles" high values, following research by Peter Shaw, published in a series of articles in *Gibbons Stamp Monthly*.

Numerous other additions and amendments have been made to the listings, following information provided by collectors and members of the philatelic trade alike.

## Prices

Once again, prices have been carefully checked and updated in line with the current stamp market.

As reported here five years ago, in the preface to the 11th edition, the market for straightforward Wildings, pre-decimal Machins, commemoratives and regionals remains steady, but anything more unusual may have increased significantly. This includes cylinder blocks, booklets, booklet panes, errors and varieties.

We commented last time that there might be steep increases on the way for the previously popular plate flaws and varieties and this has certainly proved to be the case, with some of them increasing five or six-fold in five years – yet they remain difficult to track down, so further increases may be on the way!

We are once again grateful to all those who have assisted in ensuring that the prices given in this catalogue present an accurate picture of the market at the time of publication.

Hugh Jefferies
Vince Cordell

### Acknowledgements

We are grateful to the Great Britain Philatelic Society for allowing us to draw on information published in articles from *The GB Journal*, in particular *British Stamp Booklets* by Dr. Jean Alexander and the late Leonard F. Newbery. A special note of appreciation goes to J.R. Holman, former editor of the *British Philatelic Bulletin*. In addition to those mentioned above, we thank Ross Candlish, Tony Bellew, Richard Monteiro, Mark Brandon, Michael Mayall and many others for their contributions, expertise and advice.

# Introductory Notes

The aim of this catalogue is to classify in specialised form the Queen Elizabeth II pre-decimal stamps of Great Britain, to give distinguishing numbers to them and to quote prices which are current with Stanley Gibbons Ltd. at the time of going to press and at which they will supply if in stock.

## Detailed Introductory Notes

Before using the catalogue it is important to study the "General Notes" as these explain the technical background of the issues in question. They are to be found at the beginning of the relevant sections.

## Arrangement of Lists

The Wilding, Machin £.s.d. and Regional issues are dealt with value by value and Special issues in order of issue. The order of listing is as follows:

A.  Basic listing of single stamps from sheets, booklets and coils according to paper, phosphor and gum with errors and varieties.
B.  Illustrations of listed cylinder and plate varieties.
C.  List of cylinder blocks according to paper, phosphor and gum combinations and priced according to perforation types.
D.  Details of constant minor sheet flaws without illustrations and prices but quoting positions on stamps.
E.  Information relating to coils.
F.  Ancillary data relating to withdrawal dates, and quantities issued or sold.

If there is a deliberate change in the number of phosphor bands this is treated as a separate issue which is then listed in the order shown above.

Booklet panes are listed separately in Sections SB and UB according to paper and gum, with errors and cylinder varieties, and all priced according to perforation types. These are followed by illustrations of cylinder varieties and lists of booklet pane cylinder numbers appear at the end of each listing.

The Special issues (Section W) are listed on the same basis, set by set, with the addition of ancillary information about sheet format, method of printing, a list of the sheet markings, quantities sold and withdrawal dates from information published by the Post Office.

## Catalogue Numbering

Users of this Catalogue for the first time will doubtless be familiar with our other Great Britain catalogues, however, in order to understand the unique numbering system used throughout the Specialised catalogues an explanation may help.

The stamps are split up by issue, commencing with the 1840 1d. black as Section A. This volume starts with the Wilding issues as section S and goes on to cover the issues prior to decimalisation on 15 February 1971.

Unlike our other catalogues, the arrangement is by value rather than by set, so all ½d. Wilding stamps are grouped together as numbers S1-12 in chronological order of issue to include watermark and paper changes, graphites and phosphors, etc. Where Specialised Catalogue numbers relate directly to numbers in the current edition of the *Great Britain Concise Stamp* Catalogue, these are clearly shown and the

tables at the beginning of each section and will also be of consdiderable help. Shades are indicated by a number in brackets and varieties by a letter indication. For example "S25(2)e" indicates "S25" Wilding 1½d. Tudor Crown, "(2)" Deep green, "e" Butterfly flaw.

In Appendix HA the booklets have the same numbers and prefix letters as are used in the *Great Britain Concise Stamp Catalogue*. Varieties of booklets listed in the Specialised Catalogue only are shown with number in brackets, thus "(a)".

## Symbols and Abbreviations

| | |
|---|---|
| † | (after date of issue) date of issue in sheet format, but available earlier from coil or booklet source. See Dates of Issue, under General Notes |
| † | (in price column) does not exist |
| — | (in price column) may exist or is known to exist, but we are unable to quote a price (a blank conveys the same meaning) |
| * | (against the price of a cylinder block) price includes a listed variety |
| / | between colours means "on" and the colour following is that of the paper on which the stamp is printed. |
| Cyl. | Cylinder |
| GA | Gum arabic |
| mm. | Millimetres |
| No. | Number |
| OP | Ordinary and phosphor |
| Phos. | Phosphor |
| Pl. | Plate |
| PVA | Polyvinyl alcohol (gum) |
| R. | row (thus "R. 6/4" indicates the fourth stamp from the left in the sixth horizontal row from the top of a sheet of stamps) |
| Th. | Refers to the Stanley Gibbons "Thirkell" Position Finder. The letters and figures which follow (e.g. Th. E5) pinpoint the position of the flaw on the stamp according to the grid engraved on the Finder |

## Watermark Illustrations

The illustrations show watermarks as seen from the front of the stamp. This is important to remember when classifying sideways watermarks which also exist sideways inverted (i.e. Crown to right).

## Quantities Sold

The figures for quantities issued or sold are those published by the Post Office. Some figures for the Regionals, however, came from an article by Mr. E. C. Ehrmann in *Stamp Collecting*.

## Items Excluded

In dealing with varieties and minor constant flaws we record only those for which we can vouch, namely items we have seen and verified for ourselves. It should be recognised, however, that some flaws described as constant may be transient: they may develop in size to be sufficiently noticeable to be worth retouching.

Colour shifts due to faulty registration range from minor shifts to quite spectacular varieties. As it is very difficult to draw a line between major and minor shifts we have not listed any. We likewise exclude: doctor blade flaws; paper creases; partially omitted colours; negative offsets; and misplaced perforations.

We do not quote for traffic light blocks or positional blocks showing various sheet markings other than cylinder blocks, but when available they will be supplied at appropriate prices.

## National Postal Museum Archive Material, Sold 1984/5

During 1984 and 1985 surplus GB material from the National Postal Museum archives was included in three auction sales. The lots offered were mostly imprimaturs, which were handstamped on the reverse to indicate origin, and specimen overprints. In this catalogue items which are only known from the lots sold at these auctions are included in special entries, under headings clearly indicating their origin. Where items included in these sales had been previously listed a dagger is shown alongside the catalogue price.

> **To order from this Catalogue**
> Always quote the Specialised Catalogue number, mentioning Volume 3, 12th Edition, and where necessary specify additionally the precise item wanted.

## Prices

Prices quoted in this Catalogue are the selling prices of Stanley Gibbons Ltd., at the time the book went to press. They are for stamps in fine condition for the particular issue, unless otherwise indicated: those of lesser quality may be offered at lower prices. All prices are subject to change without prior notice and no guarantee is given to supply all stamps priced, since it is not possible to keep every catalogued item in stock.

In the case of unused stamps, our prices are for unmounted mint. Prices for used stamps refer to fine postally used examples.

If a variety exists in more than one shade it is priced for the commonest shade and will be worth correspondingly more in a scarcer shade. Except where otherwise stated, varieties are priced for single examples and extra stamps required to make up positional blocks would be valued as normals. All cylinder flaws and other varieties listed under booklet panes are priced for the complete pane.

Cylinder blocks containing varieties are indicated by an asterisk against the price (which includes the cost of the variety).

Cases can exist where a particular stamp shows more than one listed variety. It might, for example, have an inverted watermark as well as a broad phosphor band, both of which are listed but priced separately. It is not practical to cover every possible combination, but the value of such items may be established by adding the difference between the price of the basic stamp and the dearest variety to the catalogue price of the cheapest variety.

The prices quoted for booklet panes are for panes with good perforations and complete with the binding margin. Prices for complete booklets are for those containing panes with average perforations as it is unusual for all panes in the booklet to show full perforations on the guillotined sides.

Cylinder blocks are priced according to the type of perforator used. This takes account of the state of the perforations on all four sides of the sheet, not just the corner where the cylinder number appears. Note that a full specification of a cylinder block should quote the basic number of the stamp; cylinder number; with or without dot; perforation type; cream or white paper; gum arabic or PVA, wherever such alternatives exist.

## Guarantee

All stamps supplied by Stanley Gibbons Ltd., are guaranteed originals in the following terms:

If not as described, and returned by the purchaser, we undertake to refund the price paid to us in the original transaction. If any stamp is certified as genuine by the Expert Committee of the Royal Philatelic Society, London, or by B.P.A. Expertising Ltd., the purchaser shall not be entitled to make any claim against us for any error, omission or mistake in such certificate.

Consumers' statutory rights are not affected by the above guarantee.

## Expertisation

We do not give opinions as to the genuineness of stamps. Expert Committees exist for this purpose and enquiry can be made of the Royal Philatelic Society, 41 Devonshire Place, London W1N 1PE, or B.P.A. Expertising Ltd., P.O. Box 137, Leatherhead, Surrey KT22 0RG. They do not undertake valuations under any circumstances and fees are payable for their services.

> **Correspondence**
> Letters should be addressed to the Catalogue Editor, Stanley Gibbons Publications, Parkside, Christchurch Road, Ringwood, Hants BH24 3SH, and return postage is appreciated when a reply is sought. New information and unlisted items for consideration are welcomed.
> Please note we do not give opinions as to the genuineness of stamps, nor do we identify stamps or number them by our Catalogue.

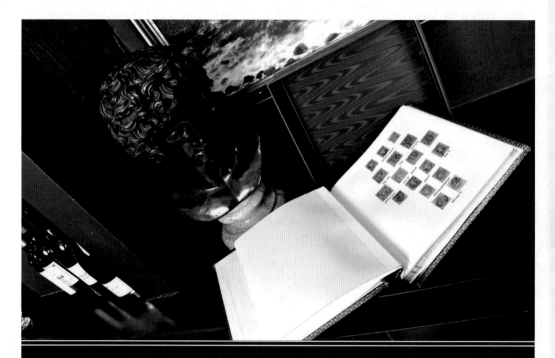

# Give your collection the home it deserves

Frank Godden albums are a labour of love, with each individual album beautifully handmade to an unmistakable and unmatchable quality.

All leaves are now made to the internationally recognised standard for archival paper, the type that is used and recommended by all major museums.

Revered throughout the philatelic world for their supreme quality and craftsmanship, Frank Godden albums are built to last a lifetime and to offer you a lifetime of enjoyment.

If you are passionate about your collection, then Frank Godden provides the home it deserves.

Whether you are looking for the best quality albums, exhibition cases, protectors, leaves or interleaving, you can find whatever you are looking for at Stanley Gibbons, the new home of Frank Godden.

For more information, visit **www.stanleygibbons.com/frankgodden**

Stanley Gibbons Publications
7 Parkside, Christchurch Road, Ringwood, Hampshire, BH24 3SH
Tel: +44 (0)1425 472 363 | Fax: +44 (0)1425 470 247
Email: orders@stanleygibbons.co.uk
www.stanleygibbons.com

Est 1856
STANLEY
GIBBONS

Edward Crown Inv Accent on 2 Spec SB7ah

Edward Crown Inv Accent on 2 Spec SB7ah

Butterfly Flaw

Watermark

Tudor Crown

One Band in Green both I/P and E/P Cylinder Blocks

# WILDING ISSUES

We have massive stocks, please contact us for details

SG614b both Dot and N0 Dot Cylinder 4 Blocks

SG605a Wmk Error
Variety Flaw on Upper Rose

One Band in Green

SG605a Wmk Error
Variety Flaw on Left d

# SECTION S
## Dorothy Wilding Issues
## 1952-68. Sheet and Coil Stamps in Gravure

## General Notes

**Introduction.** Queen Elizabeth II came to the throne on 6 February, 1952. By contrast with the King George VI series there were five different basic designs from five artists with a common feature consisting of the portrait of the Queen by Dorothy Wilding Ltd. enclosed in an oval. The Queen is shown wearing the Crown Jewels, whilst the policy of embodying various emblems representative of the different parts of the United Kingdom was continued. These and the intricacies of the Crown Jewels produced many minor varieties and there are probably more varieties and flaws on this issue than on any other issue since the Victorian Line-engraved stamps.

The stamps were issued value by value over a period, the first being the 1½d. and 2½d. which were placed on sale on the 5 December 1952, but it was not until February 1954 that the series was completed. During this period there was an interesting phase when booklets were issued containing panes of King George VI and Queen Elizabeth II stamps.

**Arrangement.** This section takes each value in turn and follows its history through the various watermarks, graphite lines, phosphors and papers, taking in the coils and on pages 6 and 7 there are tables setting out which values occurred in each state and quoting their catalogue numbers for easy reference.

The general arrangement of the catalogue is to show first the basic listing with errors and varieties, followed by illustrations of the listed cylinder flaws. These are priced, whereas the minor constant flaws are not, but they are included for reference. The sheet cylinder numbers and a record of the minor flaws follow. Where applicable the description of the coils and Imprimaturs and Specimens that were sold from the then National Postal Museum (now British Postal Museum and Archive (B.P.M.A.)) archives are dealt with. Quantities sold of the basic issue are included where known at the end of each listing although for the definitives this information was seldom available.

Booklet panes are dealt with in a similar manner in Section SB. For quantities issued or sold see under Appendix HA.

**Paper.** For the first ten years the definitives were printed on a creamy paper but in April 1962 a whiter paper was gradually introduced. It is always a difficult matter to maintain successive supplies of paper in exactly the same colour and so it is not surprising that there is some variation in the degree of whiteness in the whiter paper which sometimes makes it difficult to identify. Sometimes knowledge of the cylinder used can be decisive. Chalk-surfaced paper was used for the 2s. Holiday Booklet issued in 1963 which affected the ½d. and 2½d. values in the Crowns watermark.

In 1964 an experimental paper was used for the 3d. non-phosphor Crowns watermark which was slightly thicker. It can be distinguished by the fact that an additional watermark letter "T" lying on its side occurred about four times in the sheet.

Variations can also be found in the thickness of the paper used, a notable example being the 3d. Tudor Crown watermark (No. S67) on thick paper. As weight standards were applied to complete reels only, such differences on individual stamps were within acceptable tolerances.

**Paper Fluorescence.** Stamps printed on unsurfaced paper may show a varying fluorescence when viewed under a short-wave ultra-violet lamp. This is due to the presence, in the rags used in paper making, of optical brightening agents. Such fluorescent properties are outside the scope of this catalogue.

**Watermarks.** The first Queen Elizabeth stamps were printed on Tudor Crown watermarked paper. It is now known that the change to St. Edward's Crown paper followed damage to the Tudor Crown dandy roll in early 1955. The change to Multiple Crowns paper followed the decision to isssue regional stamps for Scotland and the possibility that protests could follow the use of the "E2R" cypher on its stamps. In the Crowns watermark differences in the spacing of the Crowns have been noticed, but it is believed that this is due to variations in the dandy roll and does not represent a different version of the watermark.

Errors, or replacement "bits", occur on most dandy rolls. For example during the period 1964 to 1966 the Crowns watermark can be found with one crown inverted. These errors have been seen on the ½d., No. S2b, and on various commemoratives.

**Watermark Varieties.** As the Wilding issues are all printed "on the web" inverted watermarks cannot occur on the counter sheet stamps, but they do occur on 50% of the booklet panes owing to the manner in which the sheets are arranged with half the columns having the images inverted on the cylinders. The booklets are guillotined before issue resulting in half the panes with the watermark inverted in relation to the image. Booklets are the only source of inverted watermarks in the Wilding issues.

Until 1961 all stamps with the watermark sideways came only from coils with left side delivery and these all show the top of the watermark pointing to left *as seen from the front of the stamp*. From 1961 all 2s. booklets on Crowns watermark had the watermark sideways and these, of course, have 50% of the panes with the crowns pointing to left and 50% to right and they are listed both ways.

**Sheet Perforators.** The perforator types are described and illustrated in Appendix G. Definitive cylinder blocks are from the bottom left corner of the sheet and the following abbreviations relate to the margins at left and the bottom margin. The perforation type is given last and further details on the type of comb and perforation feed are in Appendix G.

(AE/I) Alternate extension holes in left margin and imperf bottom margin. Perf. Type E no dot pane

(E/I) On extension in left margin, each row and imperf. bottom margin. Perf. Types A both panes, E dot pane and H no dot pane

(E/P) As last but bottom margin perforated through. Perf. Type C no dot and dot also A(T) dot pane

(I/P) Imperf. left margin and bottom margin perforated through. Perf. Types B and J no dot panes only

(I/E) As last but extension holes in each row, bottom margin. Perf. Type F(L) no dot pane

(P/E) Left margin perforated through and extension holes in bottom margin. Perf. Types F no dot and dot panes and F(L) dot pane

(P/I) Left margin perforated through and bottom margin imperf. Perf. Type H dot pane

**Experimental Graphite Issues.** The first Automatic Letter Facing machine (known as ALF) was introduced experimentally at Southampton on 19 December 1957. The machine, which prepares letters for the sorting process, is fed with letters having their long edges parallel but with stamps in any of four possible positions. The letters are reorientated so that the stamps are in one of two possible positions on one long edge. These two positions, together with First and Second Class mail, are separated into stacks, and the stamps are cancelled. Items which cannot be faced, due for example to the absence of a stamp, are rejected to receive manual treatment.

The prototype facing machine looked in the stamp corner for an area of dense printing ink, having the characteristics of a stamp, as a means of stamp detection. This system was inefficient as the machine s performance was influenced by stamp design and the occasional presence of misleading writing on the envelope. However, facing machines were equipped with this method as a secondary means of stamp detection in order to deal with O.H.M.S. and Business Reply items.

To improve the efficiency of facing it was necessary to give these stamps some unmistakable identity. The first attempt used stamps which were printed with electrically conducting vertical black graphite lines on the back under the gum. One line on the 2d., then the printed paper rate, and two lines on the other values. The use of electrically conducting lines was not a complete success as failures were caused by metallic paper fasteners and damp mail.

There were two graphite issues. The first in November 1957 on the ½d., 1d., 1½d., 2d., 2½d. and 3d. sheet stamps with the St. Edward's Crown watermark and also on coils. The second issue came out during 1958-59 on the same values, plus the 4d. and 4½d. in sheets with the Crowns watermark and here also there were coils and booklets.

Stamps showing faked graphite lines are known, especially on used examples.

**Phosphor Trials.** As the electrical conductivity of graphite line stamps was not a success, the Post Office decided to experiment with phosphor as the medium to help with letter facing and with sorting stamped mail. These experiments were carried out in the laboratory of the Post Office Research Station located at Dollis Hill, North-West London.

The experiments were started in 1957 by the Chief Chemist, Charles F. Forster, as original research since no other postal authority used phosphorescent materials for this purpose (until the first Canadian issue in 1962). Forster was the inventor of new organic phosphors and his work resulted in a patent, filed in 1959, granted in 1961. Consequently, Forster undertook many short-run experiments with a greater number of phosphor ink mixtures than those which were eventually used on issued stamps and in different formats, some being within the paper. As the Post Office was continually looking for greater efficiency and reduction in cost in the sorting office, the phosphor experiments by Forster and his department were continuous until at least 1972.

Substantially, all the known trial stamps, whether unused or used, derive from the estate of Forster and other material of a similar nature may be assumed to have come from the laboratory. The stamps are listed separately at the end of Section SA, as most were printed by Harrison & Sons on paper or in a format, probably in very short runs, not used for issued stamps. Additionally, whilst some of the phosphor reactions under ultra-violet light may be categorised into the colours described below for issued stamps, that is for easy identification and afterglow varies, which evidences different experimental mixtures – also other phosphor colour reactions are described.

Apart from some 3d. Deep lilac cylinder 11 blocks, the stamps appear to be low quality printing, probably by Harrison & Sons, and those with phosphor within the paper required hand made paper for the experiment prior to printing. Even the cylinder blocks do not equate with an issue of stamps as these trials are without graphite lines on the reverse whereas issued cylinder 11 printings were graphite lined stamps only. Additionally, the cylinder 11 printings used for trials have perf Type B (I/P) selvedges whereas the contemporary issued sheet stamps printed from other cylinders have Type A (E/I) selvedges, so trial stamps with attached selvedge can be distinguished.

**Phosphor-Graphite Issues.** In November 1959 existing graphite stamps were overprinted on the face with phosphorescent ink which, when exposed to ultra-violet (u.v.) light, releases energy in the form of visible light. The emission of visible light persists for some time after the exposure to u.v. light has ceased. These stamps were originally issued for further experiments at Southampton, November 1959 to February 1960, when the ALF operated with one electrical scanner and one phosphor scanner. Most countries which handle very large quantities of mail have followed the lead of Great Britain in the use of some form of luminescence on stamps to facilitate automatic facing.

The British Post Office used organic-resin phosphors containing an activator, the choice of activator affecting the optical properties.

Phosphor bands are not always easy to see, especially on used stamps, and it is usually necessary to hold the stamps up to the light at eye level when they become visible as broad bands.

The graphite lined stamps were overprinted with vertical phosphor bands on the face, again one band for the 2d. and two bands for the others. In sheets they appeared on the ½d., 1d., 1½d. and 2d. (in error) with St. Edward's Crown watermark and on the 2d., 2½d., 3d., 4d. and 4½d. with Crowns watermark. The substance used is commercially known as Lettalite B1 (the activator being Parahydroxydiphenyl) and it produces a greenish phosphorescence when reacting with u.v. light in the 2000 to 3000 Ångstrom range.

As the phosphor treatment of stamps at Southampton was successful, residual stocks having graphite lines were distributed as normal stock to other areas and a notice was sent to Post Office clerks to say that they should disregard the black lines. This applied also to the 5s. booklet No. H46g (Sept. 1960).

**Phosphor Issues.** The Southampton ALF was converted to scan phosphor only on 6 July 1960 and the ½d. to 4d. and 1s.3d. values with Crowns watermark with phosphor bands only were issued on 22 June 1960, the 6d. following on 27 June. Coils and booklets were issued later. The same phosphor reacting green was employed but in 1961 this was replaced as an interim measure by Lettalite B2 (Carbazole sulphonic acid being the activator) which reacts blue to u.v. in the 2000–4000 Ångstrom range. The advantage of this was that it gave a stronger signal.

At this time ALF machines were introduced into other areas and the "blue" phosphor was in use between 1961 and 1966 on the same values as for the "green" phosphor and with the addition of the 4½d. value. This period covered the changeover to the whiter paper and also two changes in postal rates so that the 2d., 2½d. and 3d. were each issued with one and two bands.

With the introduction of address coding and automatic letter sorting, at Norwich in 1965, it became necessary to use a phosphor for stamps which would not interfere with sorting. Thus another change was made, this time to Lettalite B3 (having Terephthalic acid as the activator) which was inert to the u.v. light of wavelength 3650 Ångstroms used in sorting machines but which has a bright visible light output when subjected to 2537 Ångstroms in the facing machine. This reacts violet under the lamp.

**Identification of Phosphor Colours.** Short wave ultra-violet lamps are available to enable collectors to identify the green, blue and violet phosphors. Please refer to the Stanley Gibbons Accessory list for information on these products currently available. Care should be taken when using such lamps as ultra-violet light can damage the eyes.

**Phosphor Band Widths.** Both the green and the blue bands measure 8 mm. except for the values used for the printed paper rate during the period, which had a single 4mm side band at left on the 2d. and 2½d. values and alternately at left and right on the 3d. by application of 8mm. bands across adjacent stamps.

There are two widths of the violet phosphor bands, the 8 mm. bands, issued in 1965 (½d., 1d., 1½d., 3d., 4d., 6d. and 1s.3d., plus coils and booklets) and the 9·5 mm. bands issued in 1966–67 (1d., 2d., 4d., 5d., 6d., 7d., 8d., 9d., 10d., 1s., 1s.3d. and 1s.6d. plus coils and booklets). As the bands overlap the stamps it is easier to distinguish these by measuring the space between the bands, this being approximately 12 mm. for the 8 mm. bands and 10·5 mm. for the 9·5 mm. bands. As with the "blue" bands the 3d. value has only one band and in the 8 mm. band series this is at the left or right of the stamp whilst in the 9·5 mm. band series it is a 4mm. band in the centre.

**Typographed 6 mm. and 8 mm. Phosphor Bands in Sheets.** For values with the phosphor applied by typography the bands along the left and right margins were only 6 mm. wide, instead of the normal 8 mm. Where these varieties exist they have been listed, the prices being for stamps with the vertical margin attached. Most booklet panes of four from the watermark Crowns sideways issues had the phosphor bands applied by Typography. Examples with 4mm. and 5½mm. side bands, similar to those on sheets, have been identified on panes also showing shifted phosphor bands.

**Phosphor Printed on Both Sides.** Instances have been reported of stamps with phosphor bands on both the front and the back. These can be caused by offsets from normal phosphor bands, but where there is a sharp phosphor impression, these are listed. Offsets, which appear indistinct and weak, are outside the scope of this Catalogue.

**Application of Phosphor Bands.** The choice of method for applying the phosphor bands is a matter for the printer and three different methods have been used: Gravure, Typography and Flexography.

To apply bands in Gravure sometimes an additional printing cylinder is brought into use so that it is done in the same operation as printing the stamps. In the case of multicoloured special issues there may not be a spare cylinder available as this would depend upon the colour capacity of the press and the number of colours to be used. The bands may then be applied by Typography or Gravure as a separate operation on a sheet-fed press.

Typography was used to apply the bands to cut graphite sheets to produce the phosphor-graphite issue; and for various later "emergency sheet" printings and all booklet panes of four except 4d. panes after January 1966.

Flexography is a typographic process but using a rubber cylinder (which does not indent the paper) to pick up the impression from a photo-etched inking cylinder. The screen pattern is usually blurred, although some traces of it remain. This method was employed for applying bands to stamps already printed "on the web" before being cut into counter sheets.

Gravure bands do not indent the paper, are screened (either 150 or 250 lines to the inch, but occasionally occur mixed), extend through the top and bottom sheet margins and cause a reflective appearance on the non-phosphor part of the paper, due to the pressure of the cylinder. Bands applied by Typography often indent the paper, as can be seen from the back, are solid and stop short of the edges of the sheet.

It is rather difficult to distinguish Flexography phosphor bands from those printed by Gravure, and for this reason they are not listed separately. Flexography is known to have been used to apply phosphor bands to early multicoloured special issues, when all the gravure cylinders had been used for the colour and a Flexographic cylinder was attached to apply the phosphor in the reel. Being a typographic process the non-phosphor part of the paper is not reflective. Currently, there is no evidence that Flexography was used on any other issues.

**Phosphor Reaction.** The "green" phosphor was overprinted by Typography on the graphite stamps but in Gravure on the first phosphor only issue. The "blue" phosphor was normally applied in Gravure, but some values also exist with typographic or flexographic application overprint. The violet 8 mm. bands are normally applied in Gravure but again some values exist with them typographed and the 9·75 mm. series exist with them only in Gravure except for the *se-tennant* booklet panes which were typographed.

**Misplaced Bands on Sheets, Coils and Booklet Panes.** Phosphor bands frequently appear misplaced but such varieties are outside the scope of this Catalogue except where the misplacement affects the number of bands, i.e. one band instead of two or two narrow bands over the vertical perforations, instead of one centre or side band.

**Cylinder Varieties.** Most of the more prominent varieties are listed and illustrated, but we have restricted ourselves to those we have actually seen. Others will be added to future editions as examples become available for illustration.

The position is always indicated by stating first the cylinder number (and where no full stop is shown this means the "no dot" cylinder, whereas a full stop means the "dot" cylinder) followed by the position indicated first by the horizontal row and then the position in it. Thus "Cyl. 15, R. 10/3" means cylinder 15 no dot, the third stamp in the tenth row down. Where the same cylinder is used on stamps with different watermark, paper or type of phosphor, etc. the varieties on that cylinder will recur, unless corrected by retouching, and these are then listed again with footnotes referring back to its first appearance where it is illustrated.

Unless otherwise stated the prices are for single stamps and extra copies needed to make positional blocks will be charged as normals.

***Tête-Bêche* Errors.** These derive from booklets due to faulty making-up; this is described in the introductory notes to Appendix HA.

**Minor Constant Flaws.** These are so numerous that they are merely recorded without illustrations. Their location on the stamp is indicated, where helpful, by reference to the S.G. "Thirkell" Position Finder, an essential tool for identifying flaws. The recording of these flaws, often insignificant in themselves, will prove an aid in identifying a particular cylinder and will also serve to show that the flaw has been considered for listing as a variety but rejected as being too minor. Again we have only recorded what we have actually seen but the picture is necessarily incomplete as we have not been able to view full sheets from every cylinder.

**Coils.** Coils are generally printed from double cylinders. In identifying their position the roll number is quoted (this is the number printed on the outer wrapper of the coil which corresponds to the row in the sheet before reeling) but where double cylinders are used only half the coils bearing the roll numbers will contain the variety. Hence there are twelve rolls (vertical delivery) and ten rolls (sideways delivery) from every sheet and varieties will be repeated on every 21st stamp on vertical rolls and on every 25th stamp on sideways delivery rolls.

**Shades.** Intended changes of colour such as the 2d. red-brown and light red-brown, the 6d. reddish purple and deep claret and the 4d. ultramarine and deep ultramarine are given full numbers and some of the more marked shades which were not made by design are shown as alternatives. In some cases, however, there is a whole range of shades which it would be meaningless to attempt to list. The colour descriptions given are based on the Stanley Gibbons Colour Key.

**Dates of Issue.** The dates given in bold type in the headings are those on which stamps in normal Post Office *sheets* were first issued, notwithstanding the fact that they may have appeared earlier in booklet form. A dagger is added to the sheet date where stamps were issued at an *earlier* date in booklets or coils. Stamps with inverted or sideways watermarks which appeared either earlier or later than those from ordinary sheets have the dates given after the listing of each item, and for stamps from booklets we have taken the earliest possible dated booklet, i.e. taking into account booklets containing panes with mixed watermarks. Where there is a change of watermark or type of phosphor or to the whiter paper, the dates given are generally those on which they were first issued by the Supplies Department to Postmasters.

**Withdrawal Date.** All the low value Wilding stamps not previously sold out were withdrawn from issue at the Philatelic Bureaux on 27 February 1970, and were invalidated as from 1 March 1972.

**Post Office Training School Stamps.** Examples of most stamps exist overprinted with two thick vertical bars. Some values on are also known overprinted "SCHOOL SPECIMEN" by handstamp. Stamps cancelled with various types of these overprints were used in Post Office Training Schools. Their acquisition by the public was unauthorised and whilst quite common, the simplicity of the overprint has resulted in the production of fakes.

**Sheet Markings.** Compared with the King George VI period a wide variety of markings of various kinds have been introduced in Elizabethan issues to facilitate new elements such as registration of multicoloured stamps, ensuring that the cylinders are applied in the correct sequence, aids to registration of perforation, colour dots to ease checking for omission of colours and so on.

We give below notes and illustrations of the markings which were used in the Wilding issues and those which apply to other issues are described in the General Notes relating to the other Sections. They are particularly helpful in establishing the position of varieties in the case of marginal blocks and can also help in identifying the type of perforator used or the type of machine employed for printing, etc.

Cylinder Number

**Cylinder Number.** This always occurs in the left-hand margin opposite Row 18 No. 1. In double pane cylinders the no dot pane is on the left and the dot pane on the right. Booklet cylinder numbers are described in Appendix HA.

**Varieties in Cylinder Blocks.** Where a cylinder block contains a listed variety the price is adjusted accordingly and bears an asterisk.

"V" shaped Hand engraved

"W" shaped Photo etched

**Marginal Arrows.** These occur against the middle rows of the sheet as an aid to Post Office Clerks when breaking up the sheets. They may be hand engraved or photo-etched. The earlier cylinders were "V" shaped (hand engraved) at the top and bottom of the sheet and "W" shaped (photo-etched) at both sides. Later cylinders were often "W" shaped (photo-etched) at top, bottom and sides but a number of combinations exist. In some cases they are accidentally missing from the cylinder and where these are known this is stated under the cylinder number listing. The 2½d. on Crowns watermarked paper, cylinder 55, exists with "V" shaped arrow in the correct position below rows 6/7 and a faint outline to the

right, below rows 8/9, where the mark had been placed in error.

Narrow Rule          Wide Rule          Damaged Rule

**Marginal Rules.** These are the solid bands of colour which appear below the bottom row of the sheet and which used to be called "Jubilee Lines" because they were first introduced in the so-called "Jubilee" issue of 1887. These are invariably co-extensive (with breaks between each stamp) and come in various widths.

Unboxed                              Boxed

In Double Box                     Black Bar

**Perforation Guide Holes on Sheets.** These large circular punched holes occur on reel-fed printings usually boxed opposite rows 14/15 at left (no dot) or right (dot) or unboxed opposite rows 1 and 7/8 at both sides. They are an indication of the type of perforator used and further reference to these is made in Appendix G. They also occur in double boxes, those illustrated being representative. They are liable to be trimmed off almost completely.

See also General Notes for Section W.

**Black Bar.** This was used alongside the marginal arrows at left on no dot sheets and at right on dot sheets on "green" and early "blue" phosphor printings. It was intended for easy recognition of phosphor stocks in the Post Office Supplies Department.

**Sheet Numbers.** Most sheets are serially numbered in black after printing for checking purposes but the numbers are liable to be placed anywhere in the margins and so are of no use for identifying a position. They are not of much help in establishing whether a sheet occurred early or late in a printing either, as a particular printing was not necessarily numbered from 1 and several machines may have been used.

**Checkers Marks.** These are small encircled numbers applied with a rubber stamp in a variety of colours. They are applied by Post Office checkers when counting the sheets delivered by the printer. As with sheet numbers they are liable to be placed anywhere in the sheet margins.

**Printers.** All the Wilding issues were printed in Gravure by Harrison & Sons. They were printed on continuous reels of paper "on the web" generally in double pane width, i.e. 480 stamps consisting of two panes (no dot and dot) each of 240 stamps arranged in twenty rows of twelve stamps, the panes being guillotined before issue. However, some printings were made from single cylinders printing sheets of 240 stamps (i.e. no dot panes only). For the method of printing booklet panes, see section SB.

## Table of Wilding Issues
References are to Specialised Catalogue Numbers

| Watermark / Paper / Phosphor | ½d. | 1d. | 1½d. | 2d. Red-brown | 2d. Light red-brown | 2d. 2 bands | 2½d. Type I | 2½d. Type II | 2½d. Type II One band | 2½d. Type II One band | 3d. | 4d. Ultramarine | 4d. Deep Ultramarine | 4½d. | 5d. | 6d. Reddish purple | 6d. Deep claret | 7d. | 8d. | 9d. | 10d. | 11d. | 1s. | 1s.3d. | 1s.6d. |
|---|---|---|---|---|---|---|---|---|---|---|---|---|---|---|---|---|---|---|---|---|---|---|---|---|---|
| Tudor Crown | S1 | S13 | S25 | S36 |  |  | S50 | S51 |  |  | S67 |  |  |  | S99 | S104 |  | S114 | S119 | S124 | S129 | S134 | S136 | S141 | S150 |
| St. Edward's Crown | S2 | S14 | S26 | S37 | S38 |  | S52 | S53 |  |  | S68 | S81 |  |  | S100 | S105 | S106 | S115 | S120 | S125 | S130 | S135 | S137 | S142 | S151 |
| Graphite. St. Edward's Crown | S3 | S15 | S27 |  | S39 |  | S54 |  |  |  | S69 | S82 |  |  |  |  |  |  |  |  |  |  |  |  |  |
| Crowns. Cream Paper | S4 | S16 | S28 |  | S40 |  | S56 | S55 |  |  | S70 | S83 |  | S93 | S101 |  | S107 | S116 | S121 | S126 | S131 |  | S138 | S143 | S152 |
| Crowns. Whiter Paper | S5 | S17 | S29 |  | S41 |  | S56c | S57 |  |  | S71 | S84 | S85 | S94 | S102 |  | S108 | S117 | S122 | S127 | S132 |  | S139 | S144 | S153 |
| Crowns. Chalky Paper | S6 |  |  |  |  |  |  | S58 |  |  |  |  |  | S95 |  |  |  |  |  |  |  |  |  |  |  |
| Graphite. Crowns | S7 | S18 | S30 |  | S42 |  |  | S59 |  |  | S72 | S86 |  | S96 |  |  |  |  |  |  |  |  |  |  |  |
| Phosphor-graphite | S8 | S19 | S31 |  | S43 |  |  | S60 |  |  | S73 | S87 |  |  |  |  |  |  |  |  |  |  |  |  |  |
| Green Phosphor | S9 | S20 | S32 |  | S44 |  |  | S61 |  |  | S74 | S88 |  |  |  |  | S109 |  |  |  |  |  |  | S145 |  |
| Blue Phosphor. Cream Paper | S10 | S21 | S33 |  | S45 | S46 |  | S62 | S63 | S64 | S75 | S89 |  | S97 |  |  | S110 |  |  |  |  |  |  | S146 |  |
| Blue Phosphor. Whiter Paper | S11 | S22 | S34 |  |  | S47 |  | S66 | S65 |  | S76 |  | S90 | S98 |  |  | S111 |  |  |  |  |  |  | S147 |  |
| Violet Phosphor. 8 mm. | S12 | S23 | S35 |  |  | S48 |  |  |  |  |  |  | S91 |  |  |  | S112 |  |  |  |  |  |  | S148 |  |
| Violet Phosphor. 9.5 mm. |  | S24 |  |  |  | S49 |  |  |  |  | S80 |  | S92 |  | S103 |  | S113 | S118 | S123 | S128 | S133 |  | S140 | S149 | S154 |
| 1 Side Band. Blue Phosphor |  |  |  |  |  |  |  |  |  |  | S77 |  |  |  |  |  |  |  |  |  |  |  |  |  |  |
| 1 Side Band. Violet Phosphor |  |  |  |  |  |  |  |  |  |  | S78 |  |  |  |  |  |  |  |  |  |  |  |  |  |  |
| 1 Centre Band. Violet Phosphor |  |  |  |  |  |  |  |  |  |  | S79 |  |  |  |  |  |  |  |  |  |  |  |  |  |  |
| Presentation Packs at end of Section SA |  |  |  |  |  |  |  |  |  |  |  |  |  |  |  |  |  |  |  |  |  |  |  |  |  |

Index to Coil Stamps

| Face Value | Watermark | Further description | Delivery | Stamp No. |
|---|---|---|---|---|
| ½d. | Tudor Crown | | V S | S1 |
| ½d. | St. Edward's Crown | | V S | S2 |
| ½d. | St. Edward's Crown | Graphite lines | V | S3 |
| ½d. | Crowns | Cream or whiter paper | V S | S6 |
| ½d. | Crowns | Graphite lines | V | S7 |
| ½d. | Crowns | Green phosphor | V | S9 |
| ½d. | Crowns | Blue phosphor, cream or whiter paper | V | S11 |
| ½d. | Crowns | Violet phosphor, 8 mm. | V | S12 |
| 1d. | Tudor Crown | | V S | S13 |
| 1d. | St. Edward's Crown | | V S | S14 |
| 1d. | St. Edward's Crown | Graphite lines | V | S15 |
| 1d. | Crowns | Cream or whiter paper | V S | S17 |
| 1d. | Crowns | Graphite lines | V | S18 |
| 1d. | Crowns | Green phosphor | V | S20 |
| 1d. | Crowns | Blue phosphor, cream or whiter paper | V | S22 |
| 1d. | Crowns | Violet phosphor, 8 mm. | V | S23 |
| 1d. | Crowns | Violet phosphor, 9·5 mm. | V | S24 |
| 1½d. | Tudor Crown | | V | S25 |
| 1½d. | Tudor Crown, sideways | | S | S25 |
| 1½d. | St. Edward's Crown | | V | S26 |
| 1½d. | St. Edward's Crown, sideways | | S | S26 |
| 1½d. | St. Edward's Crown | Graphite lines | V | S27 |
| 1½d. | Crowns | Cream paper | V | S29 |
| 1½d. | Crowns | Whiter paper | S | S29 |
| 2d. | Tudor Crown | Red-brown | V | S36 |
| 2d. | Tudor Crown, sideways | Red-brown | S | S36 |
| 2d. | St. Edward's Crown | Red-brown | V | S38 |
| 2d. | St. Edward's Crown, sideways | Red-brown | S | S38 |
| 2d. | St. Edward's Crown | Light red-brown | V | S38 |
| 2d. | St. Edward's Crown, sideways | Light red-brown | S | S38 |
| 2d. | St. Edward's Crown | Graphite lines | V | S39 |
| 2d. | Crowns | Cream or whiter paper | V | S41 |
| 2d. | Crowns, sideways | Cream or whiter paper | S | S41 |
| 2d. | Crowns | Graphite lines | V | S42 |
| 2d. | Crowns | Green phosphor | V | S44 |
| 2d. | Crowns | Blue phosphor, 1 left band | V | S45 |
| 2d. | Crowns | Blue phosphor, cream or whiter paper, 2 bands | V | S47 |
| 2d. | Crowns | Violet phosphor, 8 mm. | V | S48 |
| 2d. | Crowns | Violet phosphor, 9·5 mm. | V | S49 |
| 2d. | Crowns, sideways | Violet phosphor, 9·5 mm. | S | S49 |

| Face Value | Watermark | Further description | Delivery | Stamp No. |
|---|---|---|---|---|
| 2½d. | Tudor Crown | Type I | V | S50 |
| 2½d. | Tudor Crown, sideways | Type I | S | S50 |
| 2½d. | St. Edward's Crown | Type I | V | S52 |
| 2½d. | St. Edward's Crown, sideways | Type I | S | S52 |
| 2½d. | St. Edward's Crown | Type II, Graphite lines | S | S54 |
| 2½d. | Crowns | Type I. Cream or whiter paper | V | S56 |
| 2½d. | Crowns, sideways | Type I. Cream or whiter paper | S | S56 |
| 2½d. | Crowns, sideways | Type II. Whiter paper | S | S57 |
| 3d. | Tudor Crown | | V S | S67 |
| 3d. | St. Edward's Crown | | V S | S68 |
| 3d. | St. Edward's Crown, sideways | | S | S68 |
| 3d. | St. Edward's Crown | Graphite lines | S | S69 |
| 3d. | Crowns | Cream or whiter paper | V | S71 |
| 3d. | Crowns, sideways | Cream or whiter paper | S | S71 |
| 3d. | Crowns | Graphite lines | V S | S72 |
| 3d. | Crowns | Blue phosphor, cream or whiter paper, 2 bands | V | S77 |
| 3d. | Crowns | Blue phosphor, whiter paper, 1 side band | V | S77 |
| 3d. | Crowns | Violet phosphor, 1 side band | V | S80 |
| 3d. | Crowns | Violet phosphor, 1 centre band | V | S80 |
| 3d. | Crowns, sideways | Violet phosphor, 1 centre band | S | S80 |
| 4d. | Tudor Crown | Ultramarine | S | S81 |
| 4d. | St. Edward's Crown | Ultramarine | V S | S82 |
| 4d. | Crowns | Ultramarine, cream or whiter paper | V S | S85 |
| 4d. | Crowns | Deep ultramarine, whiter paper | V | S85 |
| 4d. | Crowns, sideways | Deep ultramarine, whiter paper | S | S85 |
| 4d. | Crowns, sideways | Violet phosphor, 9·5 mm. | S | S92 |
| 6d. | Tudor Crown | | V | S104 |
| 6d. | St. Edward's Crown | Reddish purple | V | S106 |
| 6d. | St. Edward's Crown | Deep claret | V | S106 |
| 6d. | Crowns | Cream or whiter paper | V | S108 |
| 6d. | Crowns | Violet phosphor, 9·5 mm. | V | S113 |

**Paper and Watermark.** All the following issues are printed on unsurfaced paper, except the ½d. and 2½d. values (Nos. S6 and S58) printed on chalk-surfaced paper.

The illustrations of the watermarks are *as seen from the front of the stamp*. The Tudor Crown was in use from 1952 to 1954, the St. Edward's Crown from 1955 to 1958 and the Multiple Crowns from 1958 onwards. No Wilding issues appeared on paper without watermark.

**Gum.** Only gum arabic has been used for the Wilding issues as PVA gum was not introduced until the Machin series.

**Perforation.** All stamps are comb perforated 15 × 14 as the King George VI issues. However, the horizontal perforation is very close to the three-quarters mark and so is sometimes described as 14½ × 14.

Perforation varieties such as double or misplaced perforations are not listed in this Catalogue.

Tudor Crown **W.22**

St. Edward's Crown **W.23**

Crowns **W.24**

S1     S2     S3

S4     S5     S6

S7

Portraits of Queen Elizabeth II and National Emblems

(Des. Miss Enid Marx (S1), Michael C. Farrar Bell (S2/3), George T. Knipe (S4), Miss Mary Adshead (S5), Edmund Dulac (S6/7))

(Portrait by Dorothy Wilding Ltd.)

## ◼ 1953-65 ½d. Orange-red, Type S1

### 1953 (31 August). ½d. Watermark Tudor Crown, Type W.22

**S1** (=SG 515)

| | | Mint | Used |
|---|---|---|---|
| ½d. | Orange-red | 10 | 15 |
| a. | Watermark inverted (3.54) | 1·00 | 60 |
| b. | Coil join (horiz. pair) | 4·00 | |
| c. | "A" flaw (Vert. coil, Roll 3) | 22·00 | |
| d. | Spot on "d" (Vert. coil, Roll 5) | 22·00 | |
| f. | Rose flaw (Cyls 1 & 3 Dot, R. 19/12) | 20·00 | |

S1c, S2g, S4k                           S1d, S2h, S4l

S1f, S2f Retouched on Crowns watermark

**Cylinder Numbers** (Blocks of Six)
Perforation Type B (I/P no dot) and C (E/P dot)

| Cyl. No. | No dot | Dot |
|---|---|---|
| 1 | 7·00 | 7·00 |

Perforation Type A(E/I)

| Cyl. No. | No dot | Dot |
|---|---|---|
| 1 | 5·00 | 5·00 |
| 3 | 5·00 | 5·00 |

**Minor Constant Sheet Flaws**

Cyl. 1  4/4  White smudge at left of upper left rose (Th. B1)
       5/6  White spot at end of stem of upper right shamrock (Th. C6)
       13/1  Large concealed retouch on Queen's cheek (Th. D3–4)

Cyl. 1.  1/7  Background retouch below upper left rose (Th. B1)
       1/10  Orange spot at top right of centre cross in crown (Th. A–B3–4)
       15/4  Retouched background between "OS" of "POSTAGE"
       18/8  Coloured dot in "P" of "POSTAGE"

Cyl. 3  4/4  As cyl. 1
       5/6  As cyl. 1

Cyl. 3.  18/8  As cyl. 1.

**Coils**
All coils have the watermark upright and Cylinder A1 or A2 was used. Vertical delivery printed in continuous reels

| Code No. | Number in roll | Face value |
|---|---|---|
| AA | 240 | 10/- |
| G | 480 | £1 |

| Code No. | Number in roll | Face value |
|---|---|---|
| W | 960 | £2 |
| D | 960 | £2 |
| Y | 1920 | £4 |

Sideways delivery made up from sheets with sheet margin joins

| | | |
|---|---|---|
| P | 480 | £1 |

**Imprimaturs from the National Postal Museum Archives**
Imperforate, watermark Type W.22

| Watermark upright | £2000 |
|---|---|
| Watermark inverted | £2000 |
| Tête-bêche pair | £8000 |

### 1955 (12 December). ½d. Watermark St. Edward's Crown, Type W.23

**S2** (=SG 540)

| | | Mint | Used |
|---|---|---|---|
| ½d. | Orange-red | 15 | 15 |
| b. | Watermark inverted (9.55) | 20 | 30 |
| c. | Coil join (horiz. pr.) | 3·50 | |
| d. | Flaw on shamrock stem (Cyl. 2 Dot, R. 18/8) | 20·00 | |
| e. | Major retouch (Cyl. 2 Dot, R. 19/2) | 25·00 | |
| f. | Rose flaw (Cyl. 2 Dot, R. 19/12) | 20·00 | |
| g. | "A" flaw (Vert. coil, Roll 3) | 22·00 | |
| h. | Spot on "d" (Vert. coil, Roll 5) | 22·00 | |
| i. | Shamrock flaw (Vert. coil, Roll 11) | 22·00 | |
| j. | "R" flaw (Vert. coil, Roll 11) | 22·00 | |

For illustrations of Nos. S2f/h, see Nos. S1c/d and S1f.

S2d, S4g                S2e, S4h Shows as retouched
                        area to design edge

S2i, S4m, S5g, S9b, S10g, S11f    S2j, S4n, S5i, S9c, S10h, S11g

**Cylinder Numbers** (Blocks of Six)
Perforation Type B (I/P no dot) and C (E/P dot)

| Cyl. No. | No dot | Dot |
|---|---|---|
| 1 | 5·00 | 5·00 |

Perforation Type A(E/I)

| Cyl. No. | No dot | Dot |
|---|---|---|
| 2 | 5·00 | 30·00* |
| 3 | 5·00 | 5·00 |

**Minor Constant Sheet Flaws**
Cyl. 1 no dot and dot. As for No. S1, cyl. 1.
Cyls. 2 and 3 no dot and dot. As for No. S1, cyl. 3 except that flaw on 4/4 is retouched on cyl. 3 no dot.
Cyl. 2. 20/2 Retouch by lower right thistle and rose (Th. F5–6).

**Coils**
All coils have the watermark upright and it is believed that the cylinder numbers used were A3 in double panes as well as cylinder A1 or A2. Vertical delivery printed in continuous reels

| Code No. | Number in roll | Face value |
|---|---|---|
| AA | 240 | 10/- |
| G | 480 | £1 |
| W | 960 | £2 |
| D | 960 | £2 |
| Y | 1920 | £4 |

**Sideways delivery made up from sheets with sheet margin joins**

| P | 480 | £1 |
|---|---|---|

**Imprimaturs from the National Postal Museum Archives**
Imperforate, watermark Type W.23

| Watermark upright | £2000 |
|---|---|
| Watermark inverted | £2000 |
| *Tête-bêche* pair | £8000 |

●————————————

**Graphite-lined Issues**

The graphite lines were printed in black on the back, beneath the gum. Two lines per stamp, except for the 2d. value which have one line

S8

●————————————

**1957 (19 November). ½d. with graphite lines, Type S8. Wmk. St. Edward's Crown**

**S3** (=SG 561)

| | | Mint | Used |
|---|---|---|---|
| ½d. | Orange-red | 25 | 25 |
| a. | "E" flaw (Cyl. 5 No dot, R. 17/9) | 10·00 | 20 |
| b. | Extra stem to thistle (Cyl. 5 No dot, R. 18/10) | 10·00 | 20 |

S3a, S8b        S3b, S8c

**Cylinder Numbers** (Blocks of Six)
Single pane cylinders
Perforation Type B (I/P no dot) and C (E/P dot)

| Cyl. No. | Perforation type | No Dot |
|---|---|---|
| 4 | B (I/P) | 5·00 ✓ |
| 4 | C (E/P) | 5·00 |

| Cyl. No. | Perforation type | No Dot |
|---|---|---|
| 5 | B (I/P) ✓ | 6·00 |
| 5 | C (E/P) | 6·00 |

**Minor Constant Sheet Flaw**
Cyl. 4 12/8 Orange spot in top thistle (Th. A4)

**Coils**
All have watermark upright, sheet Cylinder 4 having been converted to a 21-row cylinder. Vertical delivery printed in continuous reels

| Code No. | Number in roll | Face value |
|---|---|---|
| G | 480 | £1 |
| W | 960 | £2 |
| Y | 1920 | £4 |

**Imprimatur from the National Postal Museum Archives**
Imperforate, watermark Type W.23

| Watermark upright | £20·00 |
|---|---|

**Quantity Issued:** 22,508,400

●————————————

**1958 (25 November). ½d. Watermark Crowns, Type W.24**

**A. Cream Paper**

**S4** (=SG 570)

| | | Mint | Used |
|---|---|---|---|
| ½d. | Orange-red | 10 | 10 |
| c. | Watermark inverted (11-58) | 40 | 40 |
| d. | Watermark Crown to left (26.5.61) | 25·00 | 15·00 |
| e. | Watermark Crown to right | 25·00 | 15·00 |
| f. | Coil join (horiz. pair) | 3·50 | |
| g. | Flaw on shamrock stem (Cyl. 2 Dot, R. 18/8) | 20·00 | |
| h. | Major retouch (Cyl. 2 Dot, R. 19/2) | 25·00 | |
| k. | "A" flaw (Vert. coil, Roll 3) | 22·00 | |
| l. | Spot on "d" (Vert. coil, Roll 5) | 22·00 | |
| m. | Shamrock flaw (Vert. coil, Roll 11) | 22·00 | |
| n. | "R" flaw (Vert. coil, Roll 11) | 22·00 | |

**B. Whiter Paper (27 July 1962)†**
**S5**

| | | Mint | Used |
|---|---|---|---|
| ½d. | Orange-red | 10 | 10 |
| a. | Watermark Crown to left (5.6.62) | 30 | 40 |
| b. | Watermark Crown to right | 30 | 40 |
| c. | Watermark inverted (29.7.62) | 75 | 60 |
| f. | Large dot by daffodil (Vert. coil, Roll 4) | 22·00 | |
| g. | Shamrock flaw (Vert. coil, Roll 11) | 22·00 | |
| h. | "d" joined to shamrock (Vert. coil, Roll 11) | 22·00 | |
| i. | "R" flaw (Vert. coil, Roll 11) | 22·00 | |

***Tête-bêche***. No. S5 exists *tête-bêche* from booklet sheets which were not issued. (*Price £2250 pair.*)

**C. Chalky Paper. Booklets only (15 July 1963)**

**S6** (=SG 570k)

| | | Mint | Used |
|---|---|---|---|
| ½d. | Orange-red | 2·50 | 2·75 |
| a. | Watermark inverted | 2·75 | 3·00 |

†The earliest issue was in vertical coils on 30 April 1962.
For illustrations of No. S4g, see No. S2d; for No. S4h, see No. S2e; for No. S4k, see No. S1c; for No. S4l, see No. S1d; for Nos. S4m/n and S5g, S5i, see Nos. S2i/j.

S5f, S12e                    S5h, S12f

**Cylinder Numbers** (Blocks of Six)

**A. Cream Paper (No. S4)**
Perforation Type B (I/P no dot) and C (E/P dot)

| Cyl. No. | No dot | Dot |
|---|---|---|
| 1 | 5·00 | 5·00 |
| 3 | 5·00 | 5·00 |

Perforation Type A(E/I)

| Cyl. No. | No dot | Dot |
|---|---|---|
| 2 | 6·00 | 30·00* |
| 3 | 6·00 | 6·00 |

**B. Whiter Paper (No. S5)**
Perforation Type A(E/I)

| Cyl. No. | No dot | Dot |
|---|---|---|
| 1 | 5·00 | 5·00 |
| 3 | 5·00 | 5·00 |

**Minor Constant Sheet Flaws**

| Cyl. 1 | 4/4 | White smudge at left of upper left rose (Th. B1) |
|---|---|---|
| | 5/6 | White spot at end of stem of upper right shamrock (Th. C6), rather faint on this cylinder |
| | 13/1 | Large concealed retouch on Queen's cheek (Th. D3–4) |
| Cyl. 1. | 1/10 | Orange spot at top right of centre cross in crown (Th. A–B3–4) |
| Cyl. 2. | 18/8 | Coloured dot in "P" of "POSTAGE" (later retouched) |
| | 20/2 | Retouch by lower right thistle and rose (Th. F5–6) |
| Cyl. 3 | 5/6 | White spot at end of stem of upper right shamrock (Th. C6) |
| Cyl. 3. | 18/8 | Coloured dot in "P" of "POSTAGE" |

**Coils**
All have watermark upright and cylinder numbers A1, A2 and A3 were used for cream paper printings and numbers A3 and A4 for whiter paper issues.
Vertical delivery printed in continuous reels. Cream or whiter paper.

| Code No. | Number in roll | Face value |
|---|---|---|
| AA | 240 | 10/- |
| G | 480 | £1 |
| W | 960 | £2 |
| D | 960 | £2 |
| Y | 1920 | £4 |

Sideways delivery made up from sheets with sheet margin joins. Cream paper

| | | |
|---|---|---|
| P | 480 | £1 |

**Imprimaturs from the National Postal Museum Archives**
Imperforate, watermark Type W.24. Cream or whiter paper

| Watermark upright | £2000 |
|---|---|
| Watermark inverted | £2000 |
| Tête-bêche pair | £8000 |

**1959 (15 June). ½d. With graphite lines, Type S8. Watermark Crowns**

S7 (=SG 587)

| | | Mint | Used |
|---|---|---|---|
| ½d. Orange-red | | 9·00 | 9·00 |
| a. Watermark inverted (4.8.59) | | 3·25 | 4·00 |

No. S7/a was only issued in booklets and coils. For panes, see Section SB, Nos. SB14/a.

**Coils**
All have watermark upright, sheet cylinder 4 having been converted to a 21-row cylinder.

| Code No. | Number in roll | Face value |
|---|---|---|
| W | 960 | £2 |
| Y | 1920 | £4 |

**Imprimaturs from the National Postal Museum Archives**
Imperforate, watermark Type W.24

| Watermark upright | £2000 |
|---|---|
| Watermark inverted | £2000 |
| Tête-bêche pair | £8000 |

**Quantity Issued:** 4,161,840

**1959 (18 November). ½d. Phosphor-graphite issue. Wmk. St. Edward's Crown**

S8 (=SG 599)

| | | Mint | Used |
|---|---|---|---|
| ½d. Orange-red | | 4·00 | 3·75 |
| a. Narrow band at left or right (stamp with vert. margin) | | 10·00 | |
| b. "E" flaw (R. 17/9) | | 25·00 | |
| c. Extra stem to thistle (R. 18/10) | | 25·00 | |

This has two graphite lines, Type S8, on the back and two phosphor bands, applied by typography, on the front, which react green under the lamp.
The listed flaws are as illustrated for Nos. S3a/b.

**Cylinder Numbers** (Blocks of Six)

**Single pane cylinder**

| Cyl. No. | Perf type | No Dot |
|---|---|---|
| 5 | B(I/P) | 30·00 |
| 5 | C(E/P) | 30·00 |

**Imprimatur from the National Postal Museum Archives**
Perf. 15 × 14, watermark Type W.23

| Watermark upright | £2000 |
|---|---|

**Quantity Issued:** 707,040

**1960 (22 June). ½d. Two phosphor bands reacting green. Wmk. Crowns**

S9

| | | Mint | Used |
|---|---|---|---|
| ½d. Orange-red | | 1·75 | 1·50 |
| a. Watermark inverted (14.8.60) | | 6·00 | 6·00 |
| b. Shamrock flaw (Coil, Roll 11) | | 22·00 | |
| c. "R" flaw (Coil, Roll 11) | | 22·00 | |
| d. Coil join (vert. pair) | | 4·00 | |
| e. One 8 mm. phosphor band | | £140 | |

The bands were applied in Gravure.
For illustrations of Nos. S9b/c see Nos. S2i/j.

**Cylinder Numbers** (Blocks of Six)
Perforation Type B (I/P no dot) and C (E/P dot)

| Cyl. No. | No dot | Dot |
|---|---|---|
| 1 | 16·00 | 16·00 |

**Minor Constant Sheet Flaws**

| Cyl. 1 | 4/4 | White smudge at left of upper left rose (Th. B1) |
|---|---|---|
| | 5/6 | White spot at end of stem of upper right shamrock (Th. C6), rather faint on this cylinder |
| | 13/1 | Large concealed retouch on Queen's cheek (Th. D3–4) |
| Cyl. 1. | 1/10 | Orange spot at top right of centre cross in crown (Th. AB3–4), later retouched |
| | 19/12 | White bulge on upper right sepal of lower right rose (Th. E5–6) |

**Coils**
All have watermark upright and cylinder number A3 was used in double panes. Vertical delivery printed in continuous reels

| Code No. | Number in roll | Face value |
|---|---|---|
| G | 480 | 10/- |
| W | 960 | £2 |
| Y | 1920 | £4 |

Vertical delivery. Made up from sheets with sheet margin joins.

| | | |
|---|---|---|
| Y | 1920 | £4 |

**Imprimatur from the National Postal Museum Archives**
Imperforate, watermark Type W.24

| Watermark upright | £2000 |
|---|---|

---

## 1961 (5 June)†. ½d. Two phosphor bands reacting blue. Wmk. Crowns

S10

| A. Cream Paper | | Mint | Used |
|---|---|---|---|
| ½d. | Orange-red | 25 | 20 |
| a. | Watermark inverted (3.61) | 90 | 90 |
| b. | Watermark Crown to left (14.7.61) | 10·00 | 10·00 |
| c. | Watermark Crown to right | 10·00 | 10·00 |
| d. | One band (wmk. sideways) | 30·00 | |
| da. | One band (wmk. upright or inverted) | 90·00 | |
| g. | Shamrock flaw (Coil, Roll 11) | 22·00 | |
| h. | "R" flaw (Coil, Roll 11) | 22·00 | |

**B. Whiter Paper (21 June 1965)†**
**S11 (=SG 610)**

| ½d. | Orange-red | 10 | 15 |
|---|---|---|---|
| a. | Watermark Crown to left (15.8.62) | 12·00 | 12·00 |
| b. | Watermark Crown to right | 12·00 | 12·00 |
| c. | Watermark inverted (3.6.63) | 1·50 | 1·50 |
| f. | Shamrock flaw (Coil, Roll 11) | 22·00 | |
| g. | "R" flaw (Coil, Roll 11) | 22·00 | |

The bands were applied in Gravure on the stamps with upright and inverted watermark and by Typography on those with watermark sideways.
For illustrations of Nos. S10g and S11f see No. S2i and for S10h and S11g see No. S2j.

**Cylinder Numbers** (Blocks of Six)
Perforation Type A(E/I)

**Cream paper (No. S10)**

| Cyl. No. | No dot | Dot |
|---|---|---|
| 1 | 5·00 | 5·00 |

**Whiter paper (No. S11)**

| Cyl. No. | No dot | Dot |
|---|---|---|
| 1 | 5·00 | 5·00 |

**Minor Constant Sheet Flaws**
As for No. S9

**Coils**
All have watermark upright and cylinder number A3 was used in double panes. Vertical delivery printed in continuous reels. Cream or whiter paper.

| Code No. | Number in roll | Face value |
|---|---|---|
| G | 480 | 10/- |
| W | 960 | £2 (cream paper only) |
| Y | 1920 | £4 |

**Imprimaturs from the National Postal Museum Archives**
Imperforate, watermark Type W.24. Cream or whiter paper

| Watermark upright | £2000 |
|---|---|
| Watermark inverted | £2000 |
| *Tête-bêche* pair | £8000 |

---

## 1965 (13 August). ½d. Two 8mm. Phosphor bands reacting violet. Wmk. Crowns

S12

| | | Mint | Used |
|---|---|---|---|
| ½d. | Orange-red | 55 | 45 |
| a. | One 6 mm. band at left or right (stamp with vert. margin) | 3·50 | |
| b. | Typo. bands omitted* | 30·00 | |
| c. | One 8 mm. band (typo.) | 6·00 | |
| ca. | As c. but 6 mm. band | 4·00 | |
| d. | Bands applied photo. (15.10.65) | 1·25 | 50 |
| e. | Large dot by daffodil (Coil, Roll 4) | 22·00 | |
| f. | "d" joined to shamrock (Coil, Roll 11) | 22·00 | |

The bands were applied by Typography on the sheets and in Gravure on the coils.
*No S12b can be distinguished from a non-phosphor stamp by the fact that this shows a clear impression of the typo. plate with no reaction under the lamp.
For illustrations of Nos. S12e/f, see Nos. S5f/h.

**Cylinder Numbers** (Blocks of Six)
Perforation Type A(E/I)

| Cyl. No. | No dot | Dot |
|---|---|---|
| 1 | 13·00 | 25·00 |

**Minor Constant Sheet Flaws**
As for No. S9

**Coils**
All have the watermark upright and it is believed a new double pane cylinder number A4 was used.
Vertical delivery printed in continuous reels

| Code No. | Number in roll | Face value |
|---|---|---|
| G | 480 | 10/ |
| W | 960 | £2 |
| Y | 1920 | £4 |

## ■ 1953-67 1d. Ultramarine, Type S1

### 1953 (31 August). 1d. Watermark Tudor Crown, Type W.22

S13 (=SG 516)

|  | Mint | Used |
|---|---|---|
| ✓1d. Ultramarine | 20 | 20 |
| ✓ a. Watermark inverted (3.54) | 6·00 | 2·75 |
| b. Coil join (horiz. pair) | 10·00 | |
| c. Shamrock flaw (Cyl. 2 No dot, R. 18/2) | 25·00 | |

S13c, S14d, also SB22a, see Section SB
White flaw on top shamrock, later retouched on St. Edward's Crown watermark

**Cylinder Numbers (Blocks of Six)**
Perforation Type B (I/P no dot) and C (E/P dot)

| Cyl. No. | No dot | Dot |
|---|---|---|
| 1 | 5·00 | 5·00 |

Perforation Type A(E/I)

| Cyl. No. | No dot | Dot |
|---|---|---|
| 2 | 30·00* | 6·00 |

**Minor Constant Sheet Flaws**
Cyl. 2. 19/8 White flaw between thistle stem and lower right rose (Th. E6)

**Coils**
Single pane cylinders B1 or B2 were used for the Tudor Crown watermark. The watermark is always upright.

**Vertical delivery printed in continuous reels**

| Code No. | Number in roll | Face value |
|---|---|---|
| AB | 240 | £1 |
| E | 480 | £2 |
| X | 960 | £4 |
| Z | 1920 | £8 |

**Sideways delivery made up from sheets with sheet margin joins**

| | | |
|---|---|---|
| O | 480 | £2 |

**Imprimaturs from the National Postal Museum Archives**
Imperforate, watermark Type W.22

| Watermark upright | £2000 |
|---|---|
| Watermark inverted | £2000 |
| *Tête-bêche* pair | £8000 |

### 1955 (19 September)†. 1d. Watermark St. Edward's Crown, Type W.23

S14 (=SG 541)

|  | Mint | Used |
|---|---|---|
| 1d. Ultramarine | 30 | 15 |
| a. *Tête-bêche* (horiz. pair) | — | |

|  | Mint | Used |
|---|---|---|
| ✓b. Watermark inverted (8.55) | 65 | 60 |
| c. Coil join (horiz. pair) | 10·00 | |
| d. Shamrock flaw (Cyl. 2 No dot, R. 18/2) | 25·00 | |

† The earliest issue was from E coils, released on 23 August 1955.
For illustration of No. S14d see No. S13c.

**Cylinder Numbers (Blocks of Six)**
Perforation Type A(E/I)

| Cyl. No. | No dot | Dot |
|---|---|---|
| 1 | 5·00 | 5·00 |
| 2 | 30·00* | 5·00 |
| 4 | 5·00 | 5·00 |

Perforation Type B (I/P no dot) and C (E/P dot)

| Cyl. No. | No dot | Dot |
|---|---|---|
| 4 | 7·00 | 7·00 |

**Minor Constant Sheet Flaws**

| Cyl. 2 | 19/8 | White flaw between thistle stem and lower right rose (Th. E6) |
|---|---|---|
| Cyl. 4 | 11/9 | Blue spot in "E" of "POSTAGE" |
| | 19/8 | As cyl. 2 |
| Cyl. 4. | 14/11 | White spur to bottom leaf of shamrock above diadem (Th. A3) |

**Coils**
Single pane cylinders B1 or B2 were again used for the St. Edward's Crown watermark. The watermark is always upright.

**Vertical delivery printed in continuous reels**

| Code No. | Number in roll | Face value |
|---|---|---|
| AB | 240 | £1 |
| E | 480 | £2 |
| B | 960 | £4 |
| X | 960 | £4 |
| Z | 1920 | £8 |

**Sideways delivery made up from sheets with sheet margin joins**

| | | |
|---|---|---|
| O | 480 | £2 |

**Imprimaturs from the National Postal Museum Archives**
Imperforate, watermark Type W.23

| Watermark upright | £2000 |
|---|---|
| Watermark inverted | £2000 |
| *Tête-bêche* pair | £8000 |

### 1957 (19 November). 1d. With graphite lines, Type S8. Wmk. St. Edward's Crown

S15 (=SG 562)

|  | Mint | Used |
|---|---|---|
| 1d. Ultramarine | 40 | 40 |
| a. Flaw on thistle head (Cyls. 7 and 8 No dot, R. 6/1 and Coil, Roll 1) | 22·00 | |
| b. Daffodil stem flaw (Cyls. 7 & 8 No dot, R. 15/2 and Coil, Roll 2) | 22·00 | |
| ✓ c. Extra stop (Coil, Roll 2) | 30·00 | |
| ✓ d. Stop omitted (Coil, Roll 3) | 30·00 | |
| e. White flaw on shamrock leaf (Coil, Roll 8) | 25·00 | |

Flaw on top thistle occurs on sheets (Nos. S15a and S19b or coils (Nos. S16n, S18i, S20g and S21g)

S15b, S19c                    S15c Later retouched

S15d White stop omitted       S15e

### Cylinder Numbers (Blocks of Six)

**Single pane cylinders**

| Cyl. No. | Perf type | No Dot |
|---|---|---|
| 7 | B(I/P) | 5·50 |
| 7 | C(E/P) | 5·50 |
| 8 | B(I/P) | 11·00 |
| 8 | C(E/P) | 11·00 |

### Coils

Single pane cylinder B4 was used and all have the watermark upright. Vertical delivery printed in continuous reels

| Code No. | Number in roll | Face value |
|---|---|---|
| E | 480 | £2 |
| X | 960 | £4 |
| Z | 1920 | £8 |

**Imprimatur from the National Postal Museum Archives**
Imperforate, watermark Type W.23

| Watermark upright | £2000 |
|---|---|

**Quantity Issued:** 29,620,080

### 1959 (24 March). **1d. Watermark Crowns, Type W.24**

S16

| A. Cream Paper | Mint | Used |
|---|---|---|
| 1d.  Ultramarine | 25 | 20 |
| a.  Imperf. (vert. pair from coil) | — | |
| d.  Watermark inverted (11.58) | 25 | 20 |
| e.  Watermark Crown to left (26.5.61) | 1·50 | 1·25 |
| f.  Watermark Crown to right | 1·50 | 1·25 |
| g.  Coil join (horiz. pair) | 6·50 | |
| h.  Daffodil flaw (Cyl. 5 No dot, R. 10/11) | 20·00 | |
| n.  Flaw on thistle head (Coil) | 22·00 | |

### B. Whiter Paper (7 May 1962)
**S17** (=SG 571)

| 1d.  Ultramarine | 10 | 10 |
|---|---|---|
| a.  Watermark Crown to left (5.6.62) | 1·50 | 1·25 |
| b.  Watermark Crown to right | 1·50 | 1·25 |
| c.  Watermark inverted (29.7.62) | 40 | 30 |
| d.  Coil join (horiz. pair) | 3·00 | |
| e.  Daffodil flaw (Cyl. 5 No dot, R. 10/11) | 20·00 | |
| f.  *Tete-bêche* (horiz. pair) | — | |

For illustration of No. S16n, see No. S15a.

16h, S17e, S20c, S21e
Later retouched

### Cylinder Numbers (Blocks of Six)
**A. Cream Paper (No. S16)**
Perforation Type A(E/I)

| Cyl. No. | No dot | Dot |
|---|---|---|
| 4 | 5·00 | 5·00 |
| 5 | 5·00 | 5·00 |

Perforation Type B (I/P no dot) and C (E/P dot)

| Cyl. No. | No dot | Dot |
|---|---|---|
| 4 | 5·50 | 5·50 |

**B. Whiter Paper (No. S17)**
Perforation Type A(E/I)

| Cyl. No. | No dot | Dot |
|---|---|---|
| 4 | 5·00 | 5·00 |
| 5 | 5·00 | 5·00 |

### Minor Constant Sheet Flaws

| Cyl. 4 | 11/9 | Blue spot on "E" of "POSTAGE" |
|---|---|---|
| | 19/8 | White flaw between thistle stem and lower right rose (Th. E6) |
| Cyl. 4. | 14/11 | White spur to bottom leaf of shamrock above diadem (Th. A3) |
| Cyl. 5 | 3/5 | Dark patch below bottom right rose (Th. E5) |
| | 19/8 | White flaw between thistle stem and lower right rose (Th. E6) |
| Cyl. 5. | 1/12 | Small white flaw on top of top left daffodil (Th. A2) |

### Coils

Double pane cylinder B1 was used for cream paper printings and cylinder B3 was used for both cream and whiter paper issues with the watermark always upright.

**Vertical delivery printed in continuous reels.**
**Cream or whiter paper**

| Code No. | Number in roll | Face value |
|---|---|---|
| AB | 240 | £1 |
| E | 480 | £2 |
| B | 960 | £4 |
| X | 960 | £4 |
| Z | 1920 | £8 |

**Sideways delivery made up from sheets with sheet margin**

joins. Cream or whiter paper

| O | 480 | £2 |
|---|---|---|

**Imprimaturs from the National Postal Museum Archives**
Imperforate, watermark Type W.24. Cream or whiter paper

| Watermark upright | £2000 |
|---|---|
| Watermark inverted | £2000 |
| *Tête-bêche* pair | £8000 |

## 1958 (18 December). 1d. With graphite lines, Type S8. Watermark Crowns

**S18** (=SG 588)

| | | | Mint | Used |
|---|---|---|---|---|
| 1d. | (1) Ultramarine (coils) | | 2·00 | 1·50 |
| | (2) Bright ultramarine (booklets) | | 3·00 | 2·00 |
| a. | Watermark inverted (4.8.59) | | 1·25 | 2·00 |
| b | Two lines at left or right (7.61) | | 80 | 1·25 |
| c. | One line at left or right | | 80 | 1·25 |
| d. | Three lines | | 20·00 | 18·00 |
| i. | Flaw on thistle head (Coil, Roll 1) | | 22·00 | |

No. S18 was only issued in booklets and coils. For panes see Section SB, Nos. SB39/a.

The misplaced graphite lines (varieties b/d) came from Z coils. They were printed after the graphite line experiment had ended to use up residual stock of graphite-lined paper which had been prepared for booklets.

For illustration of No. S18i, see No. S15a.

**Coils**

Double pane cylinder B3 was used only for the Z coils with misplaced lines (issued July 1961); other coils were from cylinder B4. The watermark is always upright.

Vertical delivery printed in continuous reels

| Code No. | Number in roll | Face value |
|---|---|---|
| E | 480 | £2 |
| X | 960 | £4 |
| Z | 1920 | £8 |

**Imprimaturs from the National Postal Museum Archives**
Imperforate, watermark Type W.24

| Watermark upright | £2000 |
|---|---|
| Watermark inverted | £2000 |
| *Tête-bêche* pair | £8000 |

**Quantity Issued:** 12,428,880 including 3,400 Z coils with misplaced lines

## 1959 (18 November). 1d. Phosphor-graphite issue. Wmk. St. Edward's Crown

**S19** (=SG 600)

| | | Mint | Used |
|---|---|---|---|
| 1d. | Ultramarine | 11·00 | 11·00 |
| a. | One 6 mm. band at left or right (stamp with vert. margin) | 20·00 | |
| b. | Flaw on thistle head (Cyl. 8, R. 6/1) | 40·00 | |
| c. | Daffodil stem flaw (Cyl. 8, R. 15/2) | 40·00 | |

This has two graphite lines, Type S8, on the back and two phosphor bands on the front, (applied typo.), which react green under the lamp.

For illustrations of Nos. S19b/c, see Nos. S15a/b.

**Cylinder Numbers** (Blocks of Six)

**Single pane cylinder**

| Cyl. No. | Perf type | Dot |
|---|---|---|
| 8 | B(I/P) | 75·00 |
| 8 | C(E/P) | 75·00 |

**Imprimatur from the National Postal Museum Archives**
Perf. 15×14, watermark Type W.23

| Watermark upright | £2000 |
|---|---|

**Quantity Issued:** 709,680

*Last*

## 1960 (June 22). 1d. Two phosphor bands reacting green. Wmk. Crowns

**S20**

| | | Mint | Used |
|---|---|---|---|
| 1d. | Ultramarine | 1·50 | 1·50 |
| a. | Watermark inverted (14.8.60) | 5·50 | 5·50 |
| b. | Single 8 mm. band (wmk. upright or inverted) | 30·00 | |
| ba. | As b but 6 mm. band | 40·00 | |
| c. | Daffodil flaw (Cyl. 5 No dot, R. 10/11 | 20·00 | |
| g. | Flaw on thistle head (Coil, Roll i) | 20·00 | |

The bands were applied in Gravure.
For illustrations of No. S20c, see No. S16h and for No. S20g, see No. S15a.

**Cylinder Numbers** (Blocks of Six)
Perforation Type B (I/P no dot) and C (E/P dot)

| Cyl. No. | No dot | Dot |
|---|---|---|
| 5 | 11·00 | 11·00 |

**Minor Constant Sheet Flaws**

| Cyl. 5 | 3/5 | Dark patch below bottom right rose (Th. E5) |
|---|---|---|
| | 19/8 | White flaw between thistle stem and lower right rose (Th. E6) |
| Cyl. 5. | 1/12 | Small white flaw on top of top left daffodil (Th. A2) |

**Coils**
Double pane cylinder B3 was used with the watermark always upright.

**Vertical delivery printed in continuous reels**

| Code No. | Number in roll | Face value |
|---|---|---|
| E | 480 | £2 |
| X | 960 | £4 |
| Z | 1920 | £8 |

**Imprimatur from the National Postal Museum Archives**
Imperforate, watermark Type W.24

| Watermark upright | £2000 |
|---|---|

## 1961 (5 June)†. 1d. Two phosphor bands reacting blue. Wmk. Crowns

**S21**

### A. Cream Paper

| | | Mint | Used |
|---|---|---|---|
| 1d. | Ultramarine | 90 | 90 |
| a. | Watermark inverted (3.61) | 90 | 90 |
| b. | Watermark Crown to left (14.7.61) | 3·00 | 3·00 |
| c. | Watermark Crown to right | 3·00 | 3·00 |
| d. | One band (wmk. sideways) | 20·00 | |
| e. | Daffodil flaw (Cyl. 5 No dot, R. 10/11) | 20·00 | |
| g. | Flaw on thistle head (Coil, Roll i) | 22·00 | |

### B. Whiter Paper (21 June 1965) †
**S22**

| | | | |
|---|---|---|---|
| 1d. | Ultramarine | 80 | 80 |
| a. | Watermark Crown to left (15.8.62) | 3·00 | 3·00 |
| b. | Watermark Crown to right | 2·75 | 2·75 |
| c. | Watermark inverted (3.6.63) | 90 | 90 |
| d. | One band (wmk. sideways) | 35·00 | |
| da. | One band (wmk. upright or inverted) | 45·00 | |

The bands were applied in Gravure on the stamps with upright and inverted watermark and by Typography on those with watermark sideways.

For illustrations of No. S21e, see No. S16h and for No. S21g, see No. S15a.

### Cylinder Numbers (Blocks of Six)

**A. Cream paper (No. S21)**
Perforation Type B (I/P no dot) and C (E/P dot)

| Cyl. No. | No dot | Dot |
|---|---|---|
| 5 | 8·00 | 8·00 |

**B. Whiter paper (No. S22)**
Perforation Type A(E/I)

| Cyl. No. | No dot | Dot |
|---|---|---|
| 4 | 6·00 | 6·00 |

### Minor Constant Sheet Flaws

| Cyl. 4 | 11/9 | Blue spot on "E" of "POSTAGE" |
|---|---|---|
| | 19/8 | White flaw between thistle stem and lower right rose (Th. E6) |
| Cyl. 5 | 3/5 | Dark patch below bottom right rose (Th. E5) |
| | 19/8 | As for Cyl. 4 |
| Cyl. 5. | 1/12 | Small white flaw on top of top left daffodil (Th. A2) |

### Coils
Double pane cylinder B3 was used with the watermark always upright.

### Vertical delivery printed in continuous reels. Cream or whiter paper

| Code No. | Number in roll | Face value |
|---|---|---|
| E | 480 | £2 |
| X | 960 | £4 |
| Z | 1920 | £8 |

### Imprimaturs from the National Postal Museum Archives
Imperforate, watermark Type W.24. Cream or whiter paper

| | |
|---|---|
| Watermark upright | £2000 |
| Watermark inverted | £2000 |
| Tête-bêche pair | £8000 |

## 1965 (13 August). 1d. Two 8mm. Phosphor bands reacting violet. Wmk. Crowns

**S23**

| | | Mint | Used |
|---|---|---|---|
| 1d. | Ultramarine | 22·00 | 12·00 |
| a. | One 6 mm. band at left or right (stamp with vert. margin) | £100 | |
| b. | Bands applied photo. (1966) | 50 | 50 |
| c. | Watermark inverted (9.65) | 25 | 30 |
| ca. | One 8 mm. band (wmk. inverted) | | |
| d. | Watermark Crown to left (10.65) | 1·50 | 1·50 |
| e. | Watermark Crown to right | 1·50 | 1·50 |
| f. | One band (wmk. sideways) | 20·00 | |

The bands were originally applied by Typography on sheets and 2s. Booklets with sideways watermark and later in Gravure on sheets, coils and booklets.

### Cylinder Numbers (Blocks of Six)
Perforation Type A(E/I)

**Bands typo (No. S23)**

| Cyl. No. | No dot | Dot |
|---|---|---|
| 5 | £325 | £400 |

**Bands photo (No. S23b)**

| Cyl. No. | No dot | Dot |
|---|---|---|
| 5 | 5·50 | 5·50 |

### Minor Constant Sheet Flaws

| Cyl. 5 | 3/5 | Dark patch below bottom right rose (Th. E5) |
|---|---|---|
| | 19/8 | White flaw between thistle stem and lower right rose (Th. E6) |
| Cyl. 5. | 1/12 | Small white flaw on top of top left daffodil (Th. A2) |

### Coils
Double pane cylinder B3 was used with the watermark always upright. Bands photo.

### Vertical delivery printed in continuous reels

| Code No. | Number in roll | Face value |
|---|---|---|
| E | 480 | £2 |
| X | 960 | £4 |
| Z | 1920 | £8 |

## 1967 (Early). 1d. Two 9·5mm. Phosphor bands reacting violet. Wmk. Crowns

**S24** (=SG 611)

| | | Mint | Used |
|---|---|---|---|
| 1d. | Ultramarine | 10 | 10 |
| a. | Watermark inverted (2.67) | 85 | 85 |
| b. | Watermark Crown to left (4.67) | 90 | 90 |
| c. | Watermark Crown to right | 90 | 90 |
| e. | One 9·5 mm. band (wmk. sideways) | 10·00 | |

The bands were applied in Gravure, but the 2s. Booklets with sideways watermark had the bands applied by Typography.

### Cylinder Numbers (Blocks of Six)
Perforation Type F (L)*

| Cyl. No. | No dot (I/E) | Dot (P/E) |
|---|---|---|
| 4 | 5·00 | 5·00 |

Perforation Type A(E/I)

| Cyl. No. | No dot | Dot |
|---|---|---|
| 5 | 5·00 | 5·00 |

**Minor Constant Sheet Flaws**

| Cyl. 4 | 11/9 | Blue spot on "E" of "POSTAGE" |
|---|---|---|
|  | 19/8 | White flaw between thistle stem and lower right rose (Th. E6) |
| Cyl. 5 | 3/5 | Dark patch below bottom right rose (Th. E5) |
|  | 19/8 | As for Cyl. 4 |
| Cyl. 5. | 1/12 | Small white flaw on top of top left daffodil (Th. A2) |

**Coils**

Double pane cylinder B3 was used with the watermark always upright.

Vertical delivery printed in continuous reels

| Code No. | Number in roll | Face value |
|---|---|---|
| E | 480 | £2 |
| X | 960 | £4 |
| Z | 1920 | £8 |

## ◼ 1952–65 1½d. Green, Type S1

### 1952 (5 December). 1½d. Watermark Tudor Crown, Type W.22

**S25** (=SG 517)

|  |  |  | Mint | Used |
|---|---|---|---|---|
| 1½d. | (1) Green |  | 10 | 20 |
|  | (2) Deep green |  | 90 | 50 |
|  | b. | Imperf. between stamp and top margin | £450 |  |
|  | c. | Watermark inverted (5.53) | 1·00 | 70 |
|  | d. | Watermark sideways (15.10.54) | 50 | 70 |
|  | e. | Butterfly flaw (Cyl. 6 Dot, R. 19/1) (Cyl. block of 6) | £650 |  |
|  | f. | Flaw on daffodil stem (Cyl. 9 Dot, R. 18/1) | 20·00 |  |
|  | g. | Extra dot (Cyl. 13 Dot, R. 17/10) | 22·00 |  |
|  | h. | Rose and thistle joined at right (Cyl. 13 Dot, R. 19/1) | 22·00 |  |
|  | i. | Scratch on neck (Cyl. 13 Dot, R. 20/3) | 20·00 |  |
|  | m. | Flaw over "O" of "POSTAGE" (Sideways coil, Roll 2) | 22·00 |  |
|  | n. | Dot over rose (Sideways coil, Roll 10) | 22·00 |  |
|  | o. | Daffodil flaw (Sideways coil, Roll 8) | 22·00 |  |

Stamps with sideways watermark are from N coils with sideways delivery.

S25e (Cyl. 6)    S26g (Cyl. 14)    S26i (Cyl. 15)

The first and later states of the butterfly flaw. All on dot panes only.

Of the first thirteen cylinders used, numbered 1 to 15 (with the exception of Nos. 3 and 7 which were not used), the following is a record of the development of the above illustrated flaws:

| Cyl. 1. | No flaws |
|---|---|
| Cyls. 2, 4 and 5. | Disturbed background |
| Cyls. 6. | This is found in two states. One with disturbed background and the other with a short white flaw as illustrated, the latter being the first of the clear defects in this position |
| Cyls. 8 to 13. | Disturbed background |
| Cyl. 14. | Found in two states, one with disturbed background and the other with a long white flaw as illustrated |
| Cyl. 15. | Also found in two states, one with disturbed background and the other with a larger white flaw as illustrated, the latter only occurring on the St. Edward's Crown watermark |

The most plausible explanation of the development of this flaw is that prior to the making of cylinder 2, the multipositive was damaged and imperfectly retouched with the result that cylinders 2, 4 and 5 show an uneven background. Before the making of cylinder 6 the opaque retouching medium appears to have partly peeled off from the multipositive leaving a transparent area which produced the small white flaw on the stamp. This was evidently discovered during the run and the cylinder retouched with the result that we have cylinder 6 with uneven background.

The multipositive was again retouched and this time continued to be used uneventfully for cylinders 8 to 13. After this the retouching medium appears to have peeled off again before making cylinders 14 and 15, each time being discovered and retouched during the printing run. Cylinder 22 is normal, showing no trace of the flaw or a retouch, possibly being from a new multipositive.

*Prices are for cylinder blocks of six.* The cylinder blocks showing the disturbed background are priced without an asterisk.

S25f, SB61a

S25g, S26d Later retouched on St. Edward's Crown watermark

S25h, S26e

S25i, S26f White vertical line from ear to shoulder

S25m, S26q

S25n, S26r From sideways delivery N Coils

S25o, S26s

**Cylinder Numbers** (Blocks of Six)
Perforation Type A(E/I)

| Cyl. No. | No dot | Dot |
|---|---|---|
| 1 | 5·00 | 5·00 |
| 2 | 5·00 | 5·00 |
| 4 | 5·00 | 5·00 |
| 5 | 5·00 | 5·00 |
| 6 | 5·00 | 5·00 |
| 8 | 5·00 | 5·00 |
| 9 | 5·00 | 25·00* |
| 10 | 5·00 | 5·00 |
| 11 | 5·00 | 5·00 |

| Cyl. No. | No dot | Dot |
|---|---|---|
| 12 | 5·00 | 5·00 |
| 13 | 5·00 | 30·00* |

Perforation Type B (I/P no dot) and C (E/P dot)

| Cyl. No. | No dot | Dot |
|---|---|---|
| 1 | 5·00 | 5·00 |
| 2 | 8·00 | 8·00 |
| 6 | 5·00 | 5·00 |
| 9 | 5·00 | 30·00* |

**Coils**
Printed in continuous reels
Double pane cylinders C1 or C2 were used for the vertical delivery coils and single pane cylinder number C3 for the sideways delivery coils.

**(a) Vertical delivery. Watermark upright**

| Code No. | Number in roll | Face value |
|---|---|---|
| L | 480 | £3 |
| K | 960 | £6 |

**(b) Sideways delivery. Watermark sideways**

| | | |
|---|---|---|
| N | 480 | £3 |

**Imprimaturs from the National Postal Museum Archives**
Imperforate, watermark Type W.22

| Watermark upright | £2000 |
|---|---|
| Watermark inverted | £2000 |
| *Tête-bêche* pair | £8000 |

**1955 (11 October)†. 1½d. Watermark St. Edward's Crown, Type W.23**

S26 (=SG 542)

| | | Mint | Used |
|---|---|---|---|
| 1½d. | (1) Green | 25 | 30 |
| | (2) Deep green | 40 | 20 |
| a. | *Tête-bêche* (horiz. pair) | £3750 | |
| b. | Watermark inverted (8.55) | 65 | 60 |
| c. | Watermark sideways (7.3.56) | 35 | 70 |
| d. | Extra dot (Cyl. 13 Dot, R. 17/10) | 22·00 | |
| e. | Rose and thistle joined at right (Cyl. 13 Dot, R. 19/1) | 20·00 | |
| f. | Scratch on neck (Cyl. 13 No dot, R. 20/3) | 20·00 | |
| g. | Butterfly flaw (Cyl. 14 Dot, R. 19/1) (cyl. block of 6) | 70·00 | |
| h. | Bud on shamrock stem (Cyl. 14) No dot, R. 8/6) | 25·00 | |
| i. | Butterfly flaw (Cyl. 15 Dot, R. 19/1) (cyl. block of 6) | 55·00 | |
| j. | Spot between rose and shamrock (Cyl. 15 No dot, R. 20/3) | 20·00 | |
| q. | Flaw over "O" of "POSTAGE" (Sideways coil, Roll 2) | 22·00 | |
| r. | Dot over rose (Sideways coil, Roll 10) | 22·00 | |
| s. | Daffodil flaw (Sideways coil, Roll 8) | 22·00 | |

Stamps with sideways watermark are from N coils with sideways delivery.

For illustrations of Nos. S26d/f see Nos. S25g/i; for Nos. S26g and S26i see No. S25e; and for Nos. S26q/s see Nos. S25m/o.

S26h

S26j, S28e, S32b Later retouched on whiter paper with Crowns watermark

**Cylinder Numbers** (Blocks of Six)
Perforation Type A(E/I)

| Cyl. No. | No dot | Dot |
|---|---|---|
| 11 | 5·00 | 3·00 |
| 13 | 5·00 | 25·00* |
| 14 | 5·00 | 5·00 |
| 15 | 5·00 | 5·00 |

See note below No. S25 on the butterfly flaw which occurs on some examples of cylinders 14 and 15 dot. Prices are for normals with disturbed background.

**Minor Constant Sheet Flaws**

| | | |
|---|---|---|
| Cyl. 15 | 17/9 | Nick in frame bottom right (Th. G6) |
| | 20/9 | Speck opposite left "1" (Th. G1) |
| Cyl. 15. | 1/4 | Green dot in lower half of "1" of left "½" (Th. G1) |

**Coils**
Printed in continuous reels
Double pane cylinders C1 or C2 were again used for the vertical delivery coils and single pane
cylinder number C3 for the sideways delivery coil.

**(a) Vertical delivery. Watermark upright**

| Code No. | Number in roll | Face value |
|---|---|---|
| L | 480 | £3 |
| K | 960 | £6 |

**(b) Sideways delivery. Watermark sideways**

| | | |
|---|---|---|
| N | 480 | £3 |

**Imprimaturs from the National Postal Museum Archives**
Imperforate, watermark Type W.23

| | |
|---|---|
| Watermark upright | £2000 |
| Watermark inverted | £2000 |
| *Tête-bêche* pair | £8000 |

---

**1957 (19 November). 1½d. With graphite lines, Type S8. Wmk. St. Edward's Crown**

S27 (=SG 563)

| | | Mint | Used |
|---|---|---|---|
| 1½d. | Green | 1·20 | 1·40 |
| | a. Both lines at left | £1500 | £600 |
| | b. Horiz. pair, one stamp with only one line pair | £1250 | |
| | c. Coil join (horiz. pair) | 15·00 | |
| | d. Green stroke below "E" (Cyl. 21 No dot, R. 13/8) | 25·00 | |

Nos. S27a/b result from a misplacement of the graphite lines.

S27d, S31b
Diagonal green stroke below middle
"E" of "REVENUE" in bottom margin of stamp

**Cylinder Numbers** (Blocks of Six)
Single pane cylinder

| Cyl. No. | Perf. Type | No dot |
|---|---|---|
| 21 | B (I/P) | 10·00 |
| 21 | C (E/P) | 10·00 |

**Coil**
Sideways delivery made up from sheets with sheet margin joins

| Code No. | Number in roll | Face value |
|---|---|---|
| N | 480 | £3 |

**Quantity Issued:** 10,506,720

**Imprimatur from the National Postal Museum Archives**
Imperforate, watermark Type W.23

| | |
|---|---|
| Watermark upright | £2000 |

---

**1960 (30 August)†. 1½d. Watermark Crowns, Type W.24**

S28

| A. Cream Paper | | Mint | Used |
|---|---|---|---|
| 1½d. (1) Green | | 40 | 25 |
| (2) Deep green | | 90 | 70 |
| a. Watermark inverted (12.58) | | 1·50 | 80 |
| b. Watermark Crown to left (26.5.61) | | 9·00 | 5·00 |
| c. Watermark Crown to right | | 9·00 | 5·00 |
| d. Coil join (vert. pair) | | 6·00 | |
| e. Spot between rose and shamrock (Cyl. 15 No dot, R. 20/3) | | 20·00 | |

**B. Whiter Paper (7 May 1962)**
S29 (=SG 572)

| | Mint | Used |
|---|---|---|
| 1½d. (1) Green | 10 | 15 |
| (2) Deep green | 60 | 60 |
| a. Imperf. three sides (horiz, strip of 3) | £7500 | |
| b. Watermark Crown to left (5.6.62) | 9·00 | 6·00 |
| c. Watermark Crown to right | 9·00 | 6·00 |
| d. Watermark inverted (18.9.62) | 4·00 | 4·00 |
| e. Coil join (horiz. pair) | 5·00 | |
| g. Thistle flaws (Cyl. 22 Dot, R. 12/1) | 22·00 | |
| h. Daffodil flaw (Cyl. 22 Dot, R. 1/12) | 22·00 | |
| i. *Tete-bêche* (horiz. pair) | — | |

For illustration of No. S28e see No. S26j.

S29g, S34f White flaws in and around thistle at upper left

S29h, S34g White spot by upper left daffodil

**Cylinder Numbers** (Blocks of Six)

**A. Cream paper (No. S28)**
Perforation Type A(E/I)

| Cyl. No. | No dot | Dot |
|---|---|---|
| 15 | 5·00 | 5·00 |

**B. Whiter paper (No. S29)**
Perforation Type A(E/I)

| Cyl. No. | No dot | Dot |
|---|---|---|
| 15 | 5·00 | 5·00 |
| 22 | 5·00 | 5·00 |

Marginal arrows: Cylinder 15 "V" shaped, hand-engraved, Cylinder 22 "W" shaped, hand-engraved at top and bottom; "W" engraved, at top; "W" shaped, photo-etched, at shaped, photo-etched at both sides bottom and at both sides

Marginal rule: Cylinder 15 At bottom of sheet (1½ mm. wide)
Cylinder 22 At bottom of sheet (2 mm. wide)

**Minor Constant Sheet Flaws**
Cyl. 15  13/9   White spur on top left daffodil stem (Th. A2)
Cyl. 15.  1/4   Green dot in lower half of "1" of left "½" (Th. G1)

**Coils**
Made up from sheets with sheet margin joins. Watermark upright

| Code No. | Number in roll | Face value | |
|---|---|---|---|
| L | 480 | £3 | Vertical delivery (Cream paper) |
| N | 480 | £3 | Sideways delivery (Whiter paper) |

**Imprimaturs from the National Postal Museum Archives**
Imperforate, watermark Type W.24. Cream or whiter paper

| Watermark upright | £2000 |
|---|---|
| Watermark inverted | £2000 |
| Tête-bêche pair | £8000 |

**1959 (4 August). 1½d. With graphite lines, Type S8. Watermark Crowns**

S30 (=SG 589)

| | | Mint | Used |
|---|---|---|---|
| 1½d. | Green | 90·00 | 80·00 |
| a. | Watermark inverted (4.8.59) | 75·00 | 60·00 |

This was only issued in 3s. Booklets. See Section SB, Nos. SB70/a.

**Imprimaturs from the National Postal Museum Archives**
Imperforate, watermark Type W.24

| Watermark upright | £2000 |
|---|---|
| Watermark inverted | £2000 |
| Tête-bêche pair | £8000 |

**Quantity Issued:** 1,862,400

**1959 (18 November). 1½d. Phosphor-graphite issue. Wmk. St. Edward's Crown**

S31 (=SG 601)

| | | Mint | Used |
|---|---|---|---|
| 1½d. | Green | 4·00 | 4·00 |
| a. | One 6 mm. band at left or right (stamp with vert. margin) | 10·00 | |
| b. | Green stroke below "E" (Cyl. 21 No dot, R. 13/8) | 25·00 | |

No. S31 has two graphite lines, Type S8, on the back and two phosphor bands on the front, applied typo., which react green under the lamp.
For illustration of No. S31b see No. S27d.

**Cylinder Numbers** (Blocks of Six)
Single pane cylinder

| Cyl. No. | Perf Type | No Dot |
|---|---|---|
| 21 | B (I/P) | 30·00 |
| 21 | C (E/P) | 30·00 |

**Imprimatur from the National Postal Museum Archives**
Perf. 15 × 14, watermark Type W.23

| Watermark inverted | £2000 |
|---|---|

**Quantity Issued:** 704,160

**1960 (22 June). 1½d. Two phosphor bands reacting green. Wmk. Crowns**

S32

| | | Mint | Used |
|---|---|---|---|
| 1½d. | Green | 2·00 | 1·50 |
| a. | Watermark inverted (14.8.60) | 12·00 | 9·50 |
| b. | Spot between rose and shamrock (Cyl. 15 No dot, R. 20/3) | 20·00 | |

The bands were applied in Gravure.
For illustration of No. S32b see No. S26j.

**Cylinder Numbers** (Blocks of Six)
Perforation Type B (I/P no dot) and C (E/P dot)

| Cyl. No. | No dot | Dot |
|---|---|---|
| 15 | 14·00 | 14·00 |

**Minor Constant Sheet Flaws**
Cyl. 15  13/9   White spur on top left daffodil stem (Th. A2)
Cyl. 15.  1/4   Green dot in lower half of "1" of left "½" (Th. G1)

**Imprimaturs from the National Postal Museum Archives**
Imperforate, watermark Type W.24

| Watermark upright | £2000 |
|---|---|
| Watermark inverted | £2000 |
| Tête-bêche pair | £8000 |

## 1961 (5 June)†. 1½d. Two phosphor bands reacting blue. Wmk. Crowns

**S33**

| A. Cream Paper | | *Mint* | *Used* |
|---|---|---|---|
| 1½d. | Green | 85 | 85 |
| | a. Watermark inverted (4.61) | 12·00 | 10·00 |
| | b. Watermark Crown to left (14.7.61) | 10·00 | 10·00 |
| | c. Watermark Crown to right | 10·00 | 10·00 |
| | d. One broad band (wmk. sideways) | 25·00 | |
| | da. One broad band (wmk. upright or inverted) | 40·00 | |

**B. Whiter Paper (Sept. 1964)†**
**S34** (=SG 612)

| | | | |
|---|---|---|---|
| 1½d. | Green | 15 | 15 |
| | a. Watermark Crown to left (15.8.62) | 12·00 | 12·00 |
| | b. Watermark Crown to right | 12·00 | 12·00 |
| | c. Watermark inverted (7.64) | 22·00 | 15·00 |
| | d. One broad band (wmk. upright or inverted) | 75·00 | |
| | f. Thistle flaws (Cyl. 22 Dot, R. 12/1) | 25·00 | |
| | g. Daffodil flaw (Cyl. 22 Dot, R. 1/12) | 25·00 | |
| | h. White bulge on clover (Cyl. 22 No dot, R. 7/2) | 25·00 | |

The bands were applied in Gravure on the stamps with upright and inverted watermark and by Typography on those with watermark sideways.
For illustrations of Nos. S34f/g, see Nos. S29g/h.

S34h

**Cylinder Numbers** (Blocks of Six)

**A. Cream paper (No. S33)**
Perforation Type B (I/P no dot) and C (E/P dot)

| Cyl. No. | No dot | Dot |
|---|---|---|
| 15 | 8·00 | 8·00 |

**B. Whiter paper (No. S34)**
Perforation Type A(E/I)

| Cyl. No. | No dot | Dot |
|---|---|---|
| 15 | 5·00 | 5·00 |
| 22 | 5·00 | 5·00 |

The notes on the marginal arrows below No. S29 also apply here.

**Minor Constant Sheet Flaws**

Cyl. 15   13/9   White spur on top left daffodil stem (Th. A2)
Cyl. 15.   1/4   Green dot on lower half of "1" of left "½" (Th. G1)

**Imprimaturs from the National Postal Museum Archives**
Imperforate, watermark Type W.24. Cream or whiter paper

| Watermark upright | £2000 |
|---|---|
| Watermark inverted | £2000 |
| *Tête-bêche* pair | £8000 |

## 1965 (13 August). 1½d. Two 8mm. Phosphor bands reacting violet. Wmk. Crowns

**S35**

| | | *Mint* | *Used* |
|---|---|---|---|
| 1½d. | Green | 1·50 | 1·50 |
| | a. One 6 mm. band at left or right (stamp with vert. margin) | 5·00 | |
| | b. One 8 mm. band | 10·00 | |
| | ba. As b but 6 mm. band | 15·00 | |

The bands were applied by Typography.

**Cylinder Numbers** (Blocks of Six)
Perforation Type A(E/I)

| Cyl. No. | No dot | Dot |
|---|---|---|
| 15 | 11·00 | 11·00 |

Marginal arrows as for Cylinder 15 under Nos. S28/9.

■ **1953–67 2d. Red-brown, Type S1**

**1953 (31 August). 2d. Watermark Tudor Crown, Type W.22**

**S36** (=SG 518)

|   |   | Mint | Used |
|---|---|---|---|
| ✓ | 2d. Red-brown | 20 | 20 |
| ✓ | a. Watermark inverted (3.54) | 30·00 | 18·00 |
| ✓ | b. Watermark sideways (8.10.54) | 1·25 | 2·00 |
|   | c. Rose petal flaw (Cyl. 3 No dot, R. 4/8) | 30·00 | |
|   | d. Tadpole flaw (Cyl. 4 Dot, R. 17/6) | 40·00 | |
|   | e. Retouched (Cyl. 3 Dot, R. 17/6) | 35·00 | |
|   | g. Extra leg to "R" (Sideways coil, Roll 2) | 22·00 | |
|   | h. Retouched left "2" (Sideways coil, Roll 5) | 22·00 | |
|   | i. Dot on rose (Sideways coil, Roll 1) | 22·00 | |

Stamps with sideways watermark are from T coils with sideways delivery.

S36c, S37e

S36d, S37f, S38f White flaw resembles a tadpole below thistle

S36e, S37g, S38g, S40d
Later retouched state of the tadpole flaw

Normal          S36h, S37m, S38t,

S36g, S37l, S38s, S40i, S41b, S49c

S36i, S37k, S38w S40j, S41c, S49d

From sideways delivery T Coils

**Cylinder Numbers** (Blocks of Six)
Perforation Type A(E/I)

| Cyl. No. | No dot | Dot |
|---|---|---|
| 1 | 7·00 | 7·00 |
| 2 | 7·00 | 7·00 |
| 3 | 5·00 | 5·00 |
| 4 | 5·00 | 5·00 |

Sheets from cylinder 2 No dot are known with the marginal arrows omitted from top and bottom selvedge.

**Coils**
Double pane cylinder number D1 was used for vertical delivery coils and single pane cylinder D3 for sideways delivery coils. Printed in continuous reels

**(a) Vertical delivery. Watermark upright**

| Code No. | Number in roll | Face value |
|---|---|---|
| R | 480 | £4 |
| Q | 960 | £8 |
| V | 960 | £8 |

**(b) Sideways delivery. Watermark sideways**

| | | |
|---|---|---|
| T | 480 | £4 |

**Imprimaturs from the National Postal Museum Archives**
Imperforate, watermark Type W.22

| Watermark upright | £2000 |
|---|---|
| Watermark inverted | £2000 |
| *Tête-bêche* pair | £8000 |

**1955 (6 September). 2d. Watermark St. Edward's Crown, Type W.23**

**S37** (=SG 543)

| A. Red-brown |   | Mint | Used |
|---|---|---|---|
| ✓ | 2d. Red-brown | 25 | 35 |
|   | a. Imperf. between pair (from vert. coil) | £4250 | |
|   | aa. Imperf. between pair (from sdwys. wmk. horiz. coil) | £4250 | |
|   | ad. Imperf. between vert. pair (from sheet) | | |
| ✓ | c. Watermark inverted (9.55) | 11·00 | 9·00 |
| ✓ | d. Watermark sideways (31.7.56) | 55 | 70 |
|   | e. Rose petal flaw (Cyl. 3 No dot, R. 4/8) | 25·00 | |
|   | f. Tadpole flaw (Cyl. 4 No Dot, R. 17/6) | 30·00 | |
|   | g. Retouched (R. 17/6 on Cyls. 3, 6, 7 all Dot. Vertical coil, Roll 6) | 25·00 | |
|   | h. Tadpole flaw with shamrock flaw (Cyl. 9 Dot, R. 17/6) | 25·00 | |
|   | i. Flaw between shamrock and diadem (Cyl. 7 Dot, R. 1/6) | 22·00 | |

| A. Red-brown | | *Mint* | *Used* |
|---|---|---|---|
| j. | White spot by daffodil (Cyl. 9 Dot, R. 18/8) | 22·00 | |
| k. | Dot on rose (Sideways coil, Roll 1) | 22·00 | |
| l. | Extra leg to "R" (Sideways coil, Roll 2) | 22·00 | |
| m. | Retouched left "2" (Sideways coil, Roll 5) | 22·00 | |
| n. | Extended stem on daffodil (Sideways coil, Roll 9) | 22·00 | |

Stamps with sideways watermark are from T coils with sideways delivery.

No. S37ad came from the second vertical row of a sheet affected by a paper fold. One pair exists from this source being in a perforated block of 18 (6 × 3) with left sheet margin. Perforations at left and right of the vertical rows were severed during perforating when several stamps were folded under the sheet.

For illustrations of Nos. S37e/g, see Nos. S36c/e and for Nos. S37k/m, see Nos. S36g/i. No. S37h comprises the variety shown for No. S36d but in addition there is a white flaw to the left of the adjoining shamrock; see also Nos. S40f, S41e and S49e.

S37i, S38j This was a multipositive flaw which was retouched on other cylinders    S37n, S38u, S40k, S41d    S37j, S38k

### S38 (=SG 543b)

| B. Light red-brown (17 October 1956) | | *Mint* | *Used* |
|---|---|---|---|
| 2d. | Light red-brown | 20 | 20 |
| a. | *Tête-bêche* (horiz pair) | £3200 | |
| c. | Imperf. between stamp and top margin | £450 | |
| ✓ d. | Watermark inverted (1.57) | 9·00 | 7·00 |
| ✓ e. | Watermark sideways (5.3.57) | 8·00 | 7·00 |
| f. | Tadpole flaw (R. 17/6 on Cyls. 8, 10 and 11 Dot) | 25·00 | |
| g. | Retouched (R. 17/6 on Cyls. 6, 7, 8, 11, 12, 13 & 15 all dot, Vertical coil, Row 6) | 20·00 | |
| h. | Tadpole and shamrock flaws (R. 17/6 on Cyls. 9 & 12 Dot) | 22·00 | |
| i. | Tadpole flaw retouched with shamrock flaw (R. 17/6 on Cyls. 14 and 16 Dot) | 22·00 | |
| j. | Flaw between shamrock and diadem (Cyl. 7 dot, R. 1/6) | 22·00 | |
| k. | White spot by daffodil (Cyl. 9 Dot, R. 18/8) | 22·00 | |
| l. | Extended leaf on shamrock (Cyl. 10 No dot, R. 8/6) | 22·00 | |
| m. | Double trumpet flaw (Cyl. 10 No dot, R. 11/1) | 22·00 | |
| n. | Dot on shamrock (Cyl. 10 No dot, R. 20/1) | 20·00 | |

| B. Light red-brown (17 October 1956) | | *Mint* | *Used* |
|---|---|---|---|
| o. | White flaw on crown (Cyl. 11 No dot, R. 9/11) | 22·00 | |
| p. | White flaw on shamrock (Cyl. 12 dot, R. 20/3) | 20·00 | |
| q. | White spot by right thistle (Cyl. 14 Dot, R. 11/10) | 22·00 | |
| r. | Dot over rose stem (Cyl. 14 No dot, R. 1/1) | 20·00 | |
| s. | Extra leg to "R" (Sideways coil, Roll 2) | 22·00 | |
| t. | Retouched left "2" (Sideways coil, Roll 5) | 22·00 | |
| u. | Extended stem on daffodil (Sideways coil, Roll 9) | 22·00 | |
| w. | Dot on rose (Sideways coil, Roll 1) | 22·00 | |

Stamps with sideways watermark are from T coils with sideways delivery.

In December 1956 a completely imperforate sheet was noticed by clerks in a Kent post office, one of whom purchased it against P.O. regulations. In view of this irregularity we do not consider it properly issued. (*Price £375 pair.*)

Tadpole flaws: Nos. S38f/h are as Nos. S37f/h. The first printings from Cylinder 12 show No. S38h larger, but on later printings both flaws appear to have been retouched. No. S38i is a fourth state which combines the shamrock flaw (small on Cyl. 14, larger on Cyl. 16) with the retouched state of the tadpole flaw.

For illustrations of Nos. S38j/k, see Nos. S37i/j, and for Nos. S38s/w, see Nos. S36g/i and S37n.

S38l                                S38m

S38n                                S38o Later retouched

S38p Later retouched    S38q                S38r

**Cylinder Numbers** (Blocks of Six)

**A. Red-brown (No. S37)**
Perforation Type A(E/I)

| Cyl. No. | No dot | Dot |
|---|---|---|
| 3 | 5·00 | 5·00 |
| 4 | 5·00 | 5·00 |
| 6 | 5·00 | 5·00 |
| 7 | 5·00 | 5·00 |
| 9 | 17·00 | 17·00 |

**B. Light red-brown (No. S38)**
Perforation Type A(E/I)

| Cyl. No. | No dot | Dot |
|---|---|---|
| 6 | 5·00 | 5·00 |
| 7 | 5·00 | 5·00 |
| 8 | 5·00 | 5·00 |
| 9 | 5·00 | 5·00 |
| 10 | 25·00 | 5·00 |
| 11 | 5·00 | 5·00 |
| 12 | 5·00 | 5·00 |
| 13 | 5·00 | 5·00 |
| 14 | 5·00 | 5·00 |
| 15 | 5·00 | 5·00 |
| 16 | 5·00 | 5·00 |

Perforation Type E

| Cyl. No. | No dot (AE/I) | Dot (E/I) |
|---|---|---|
| 7 | 27·00 | 5·00** |
| 9 | 27·00 | 5·00** |

**Both light red-brown of same appearance and same prices
as perforation type A with extension holes in left margin.

**Minor Constant Sheet Flaws**

| | |
|---|---|
| Cyl. 7 | 14/8 White dot above "T" of "POSTAGE" |
| Cyl. 9 | 20/1 White spur on lower daffodil (Th. G3) |
| Cyl. 10 | 14/12 Nick in "R" of "REVENUE" |
| Cyl. 10. | 9/6 Dark spot on necklace (Th. E–F3) |
| Cyl. 16. | 20/12 "REVENUE" retouched (Th. G2–5) |

**Coils**
Double pane cylinder number D1 was used for vertical delivery
coils of No. S37, cylinder D2 for No. S38; single pane cylinder
D3 was used for the sideways delivery coils of No. S37d and
cylinders D3 or D4 for No. S38e.
Printed in continuous reels

**(a) Vertical delivery. Watermark upright**

| Code No. | Cat. No. | Number in roll | Face value |
|---|---|---|---|
| R | S37 | 480 | £4 |
| Q | S37 | 960 | £8 |
| V | S37 | 960 | £8 |
| R | S38 | 480 | £4 |
| Q | S38 | 960 | £8 |
| V | S38 | 960 | £8 |

**(b) Sideways delivery. Watermark sideways**

| | | | |
|---|---|---|---|
| T | S37d | 480 | £4 |
| T | S38e | 480 | £4 |

**Imprimaturs from the National Postal Museum Archives**
**A. Red-brown. Imperforate, watermark Type W.23**

| | |
|---|---|
| Watermark upright | £2000 |
| Watermark inverted | £2000 |
| *Tête-bêche* pair | £8000 |

**B. Light red-brown. Imperforate, watermark Type W.23**

| | |
|---|---|
| Watermark upright | £2000 |
| Watermark inverted | £2000 |
| *Tête-bêche* pair | £8000 |

**Graphite-lined Issues**

S9

On the 2d. value, Nos. S39, S42/3
the single graphite line normally
appeared at the right when
viewed from the back. It was
printed in black under the gum.

**1957 (19 November). 2d. With graphite line,
Type S9. Wmk. St. Edward's Crown**

S39 (=SG 564)

| | | Mint | Used |
|---|---|---|---|
| 2d. | Light red-brown | 1·60 | 2·25 |
| a. | Line at left (as seen from back) | £700 | £300 |
| b. | Horiz. pair, one with line omitted | £1500 | |
| c. | Coil join (vert. pair) | 15·00 | |
| d. | Coil join (horiz. pair) | 15·00 | |

Nos. S39a/b result from a misplacement of the line.

**Cylinder Numbers** (Blocks of Six)
Single pane cylinder

| Cyl. No. | Perf Type | Dot | |
|---|---|---|---|
| 17 | B (I/P) | 18·00 ✓ | *No ✓ dot* |
| 17 | C (E/P) | 18·00 | |

**Minor Constant Sheet Flaws**

| | | |
|---|---|---|
| Cyl. 17 | 11/2 | White flaw on tail of left "d" |
| | 16/1 | White flaw in centre of upper left rose (Th. B1) |

**Coils**
Made up from sheets with sheet margin joins

| Code No. | Number in roll | Face value | |
|---|---|---|---|
| V | 960 | £8 | Vertical delivery |
| T | 480 | £4 | Sideways delivery |

**Imprimatur from the National Postal Museum Archives**
Imperforate, watermark Type W.23

| | |
|---|---|
| Watermark upright | £2000 |

**Quantity Issued:** 37,686,480

**1958 (4 December)†. 2d. Watermark Crowns,
Type W.24**

S40

| | | Mint | Used |
|---|---|---|---|
| A. Cream Paper | | | |
| 2d. | Light red-brown | 40 | 25 |
| a. | Imperf. between stamp and top margin | £600 | |
| b. | Watermark sideways (3.4.59) | 1·25 | 1·25 |
| c. | Watermark inverted (10.4.61) | £140 | 70·00 |
| d. | Tadpole retouch (R. 17/6 on Cyls. 15 Dot and others) | 20·00 | |
| e. | Swan s head flaw (Cyl. 24 Dot, R. 19/10) | 20·00 | |
| f. | Tadpole flaw retouched with sham-rock flaw (Cyl. 27 Dot, R. 17/6) | 20·00 | |

### A. Cream Paper

| | Mint | Used |
|---|---|---|
| i. Extra leg to "R" (Sideways coil, Roll 2) | 20·00 | |
| j. Retouched left "2" (Sideways coil, Roll 5) | 20·00 | |
| k. Extended stem on daffodil (Sideways coil, Roll 9) | 20·00 | |

### B. Whiter Paper (5 September 1963)†
**S41** (=SG S73)

| | Mint | Used |
|---|---|---|
| 2d. Light red-brown | 10 | 10 |
| a. Watermark sideways (27.7.62) | 50 | 1·00 |
| b. Extra leg to "R" (Sideways coil, Roll 2) | 20·00 | |
| c. Retouched left "2" (Sideways coil, Roll 5) | 20·00 | |
| d. Extended stem on daffodil (Sideways coil, Roll 9) | 20·00 | |
| e. Tadpole flaw retouched with shamrock flaw (Cyl. 27 Dot, R. 17/6) | 20·00 | |

†No. S40 was issued in November 1958 in V coils and No. S41 appeared on 20 September 1962 in V coils. Stamps with sideways watermark are from T coils with sideways delivery.

Tadpole flaw: No. S40d is as No. S38g. For illustrations of Nos. S40i/j and S41b/c, see Nos. S36g/h; for Nos. S40k and S41d, see No. S37n. For description of Nos. S40f and S41e see below No. S37.

S40e

### Cylinder Numbers (Blocks of Six)
#### A. Cream paper. (No. S40)
Perforation Type A(E/I)

| Cyl. No. | No dot | Dot |
|---|---|---|
| 15 | 5·00 | 5·00 |
| 19 | 5·00 | 5·00 |
| 20 | 5·00 | 5·00 |
| 21 | 5·00 | 5·00 |
| 22 | 5·00 | 5·00 |
| 23 | 5·00 | 5·00 |
| 24 | 5·00 | 5·00 |
| 25 | 5·00 | 5·00 |
| 27 | 5·00 | 5·00 |
| 29 | 5·00 | 5·00 |
| 30 | 5·00 | 5·00 |

#### B. Whiter paper. (No. S41)
Perforation Type A(E/I)

| Cyl. No. | No dot | Dot |
|---|---|---|
| 23 | 5·00 | 5·00 |
| 25 | 5·00 | 5·00 |
| 27 | 5·00 | 5·00 |
| 30 | 5·00 | 5·00 |

### Coils
Double cylinder D2 was used for vertical delivery coils and cylinders D3 and D4 (single pane) for sideways delivery coils.
Printed in continuous reels. Cream or whiter paper

### (a) Vertical delivery. Watermark upright

| Code No. | Number in roll | Face value |
|---|---|---|
| R | 480 | £4 |
| Q | 960 | £8 |
| V | 960 | £8 |

### (b) Sideways delivery. Watermark sideways

| | | |
|---|---|---|
| T | 480 | £4 |

### Imprimaturs from the National Postal Museum Archives
Imperforate, watermark Type W.24. Cream or whiter paper

| | |
|---|---|
| Watermark upright | £2000 |
| Watermark inverted | £2000 |
| *Tête-bêche* pair | £8000 |

---

### 1958 (24 November). 2d. With graphite line, Type S9. Watermark Crowns
**S42** (=SG 590)

| | Mint | Used |
|---|---|---|
| 2d. Light red-brown | 9·00 | 3·50 |
| a. Line at extreme left (as seen from back) | £950 | |
| ab. Horizontal pair, one stamp as S42a and one without line | £2500 | |
| b. Coil join (vert. pair) | 30·00 | |

### Cylinder Numbers (Blocks of Six)
**Single pane cylinder**

| Cyl. No. | Perf type | No Dot |
|---|---|---|
| 17 | B(I/P) | 65·00 |
| 17 | C(E/P) | 65·00 |

### Minor Constant Sheet Flaw
Cyl. 17    1/2 1 White flaw on tail of left "d"

### Coil
Vertical delivery. Made up from sheets with sheet margin joins

| Code No. | Number in roll | Face value |
|---|---|---|
| V | 960 | £8 |

### Imprimatur from the National Postal Museum Archives
Imperforate, watermark Type W.24

| | |
|---|---|
| Watermark upright | £2000 |

**Quantity Issued:** 48,419,520

---

### 1959 (18 November). 2d. Phosphor-graphite issue. Watermark Crowns
**S43** (=SG 605)

| | Mint | Used |
|---|---|---|
| 2d. Light red-brown | 5·00 | 4·25 |
| a. Error. Watermark St. Edward's Crown Type W.23 (3.60) | £180 | £150 |

This has one graphite line (Type S9), on the back and one phosphor band on the front, applied typo., which reacts green under the lamp.

### Cylinder Numbers (Blocks of Six)
**Single pane cylinder**
Watermark Crowns (No. S43)

| Cyl. No. | Perf type | Dot |
|---|---|---|
| 17 | B (I/P) | 45·00 |
| 17 | C (E/P) | 45·00 |

Watermark St Edward's Crown (No. S43a)

| Cyl. No. | Perf type | Dot |
|----------|-----------|-----|
| 17 | B (I/P) | £1250 |
| 17 | C (E/P) | £1250 |

**Minor Constant Sheet Flaws**

Cyl. 17   11/2   White flaw on tail of left "d"
          16/1   White flaw in centre of upper left rose (Th.
                 B1) (on St. Edward's Crown wmk. only)

**Imprimatur from the National Postal Museum Archives**
Perf. 15 × 14, watermark Type W.24

| Watermark upright | £2000 |
|-------------------|-------|

**Quantity Issued:** 4,509,120 (including both watermarks)

**1960. (22 June). 2d. One phosphor band at left reacting green. Wmk. Crowns**

S44 (=SG 613)

| | | Mint | Used |
|--|--|------|------|
| 2d. | Light red-brown | 16·00 | 18·00 |
| a. | Coil join (vert. pair) | 45·00 | |

The band was applied in Gravure.

**Cylinder Numbers** (Blocks of Six)

**Single pane cylinder**

| Cyl. No. | Perf Type | No Dot |
|----------|-----------|--------|
| 17 | B (I/P) | £130 |
| 17 | C (E/P) | £150 |

**Minor Constant Sheet Flaw**
Cyl. 17   1/2 1 White flaw on tail of left "d"

**Coil**
Vertical delivery. Made up from sheets with sheet margin joins

| Code No. | Number in roll | Face value |
|----------|----------------|------------|
| V | 960 | £8 |

**Imprimatur from the National Postal Museum Archives**
Imperforate, watermark Type W.24

| Watermark upright | £2000 |
|-------------------|-------|

**1961 (5 June). 2d. One phosphor band at left reacting blue. Wmk. Crowns**

S45

| | | Mint | Used |
|--|--|------|------|
| 2d. | Light red-brown | 35·00 | 28·00 |

This exists on cream paper only and the phosphor band was applied in Gravure or Flexo. See General Notes Application of Phosphor Bands.

**Cylinder Numbers** (Blocks of Six)
Perforation Type A(E/I)

| Cyl. No. | No dot | Dot |
|----------|--------|-----|
| 29 | £250 | £250 |

Perforation Type B (I/P no dot) and C (E/P dot)

| Cyl. No. | No dot | Dot |
|----------|--------|-----|
| 29 | £250 | £250 |

**Minor Constant Sheet Flaw**
Cyl. 29.  17/6   There is only a slight shading to the background where the tadpole and shamrock flaws were

**Coil**
Double pane cylinder D2 was used.
Printed in continuous reels. Vertical delivery with watermark upright

| Code No. | Number in roll | Face value |
|----------|----------------|------------|
| V | 960 | £8 |

**1961 (4 October). 2d. Two phosphor bands reacting blue. Wmk Crowns**

S46

| | A. Cream Paper Bands Typographed | Mint | Used |
|--|----------------------------------|------|------|
| 2d. | Light red-brown | 10·00 | 7·00 |
| a. | Imperf. three sides* | £4500 | |
| b. | One 6 mm. band at left or right (stamp with vert. margin) | 16·00 | |
| c. | Error. One 8 mm. band (typo) | 20·00 | |
| ca. | As c. but 6 mm. band | 25·00 | |
| d. | Bands applied photo. (3.4.62) | 2·00 | 2·00 |
| da. | Error. One 8 mm. band (photo) | 25·00 | |

*This comes from the bottom row of a sheet which is imperf. at bottom and both sides. From Cyl. 29 no dot with bands applied photo.

S47

**B. Whiter Paper (5 November 1964)†**
**Bands applied in Gravure**

| | | Mint | Used |
|--|--|------|------|
| 2d. | Light red-brown | 7·00 | 7·00 |
| a. | Error. Single 8 mm. band | £110 | |

†No. S47 appeared earlier from V coils on 21 January 1963.

**Cylinder Numbers** (Blocks of Six)

**Cream paper**
Two bands applied typo (No. S46)
Perforation Type A(E/I)

| Cyl. No. | No dot | Dot |
|----------|--------|-----|
| 25 | 70·00 | † |
| 27 | † | 70·00 |
| 29 | 70·00 | 70·00 |
| 30 | 70·00 | 70·00 |

Two bands applied photo (No. S46d)
Perforation Type B (I/P no dot) and C (E/P dot)

| Cyl. No. | No dot | Dot |
|----------|--------|-----|
| 29 | 18·00 | 18·00 |

**Whiter paper**
Two bands applied photo (No. S47)
Perforation Type A(E/I)

| Cyl. No. | No dot | Dot |
|----------|--------|-----|
| 25 | 50·00 | 50·00 |

As the typographed bands were applied on individual sheets and not in the reel, it is possible that the items marked with a dagger may exist.

**Minor Constant Sheet Flaw**

Dot cyls.  17/6   There remains only a slight disturbance to the background where the tadpole and shamrock flaws were

**Coil**
Double pane cylinder D2 was used.
Printed in continuous reels. Vertical delivery with watermark upright. Cream or whiter paper.

| Code No. | Number in roll | Face value |
|----------|----------------|------------|

| V | 960 | £8 |
|---|---|---|

**Imprimatur from the National Postal Museum Archives**
Imperforate, watermark Type W.24. Cream or whiter paper

| Watermark upright | £2000 |
|---|---|

●────────────

## 1965 (17 August). 2d. Two 8mm. Phosphor bands reacting violet. Wmk. Crowns

**S48**

| | Mint | Used |
|---|---|---|
| 2d.  Light red-brown | 90 | 60 |

The bands were applied in Gravure only.

**Cylinder Numbers** (Blocks of Six)
Perforation Type A(E/I)

| Cyl. No. | No dot | Dot |
|---|---|---|
| 27 | † | £1500 |
| 30 | 8·50 | 8·50 |

**Minor Constant Sheet Flaw**

Cyl. 30.  17/6   There remains only a slight disturbance under the thistle of the original tadpole and shamrock flaws

**Coil**
Double pane cylinder D2 was used.
Printed in continuous reels. Vertical delivery with watermark upright

| Code No. | Number in roll | Face value |
|---|---|---|
| V | 960 | £8 |

●────────────

## 1967 (September). 2d. Two 9·5 mm. Phosphor bands reacting violet. Wmk. Crowns

**S49** (=SG 613a)

| | Mint | Used |
|---|---|---|
| 2d.  Light red-brown | 10 | 15 |
| a.  Watermark Crown to left (6.4.67) | 30 | 60 |
| b.  One band (wmk. sideways ex. T coil) | 15·00 | |
| c.  Extra leg to "R" (Sideways coil, Roll 2) | 20·00 | |
| d.  Retouched left "2" (Sideways coil, Roll 5) | 20·00 | |
| e.  Tadpole flaw retouched with shamrock flaw (Cyl. 27 Dot, R. 17/6) | 20·00 | |

The bands were applied in Gravure only.
  Stamps with sideways watermark are from T coils with sideways delivery.
  For illustrations of Nos. S49c/d, see Nos. S36g/h. No. S49e is described below No. S37.

**Cylinder Numbers** (Blocks of Six)
Perforation Type F (L) *

| Cyl. No. | No dot (I/E) | Dot (P/E) |
|---|---|---|
| 25 | 5·00 | 5·00 |

Perforation Type A(E/I)

| Cyl. No. | No dot | Dot |
|---|---|---|
| 27 | 5·00 | 5·00 |

**Minor Constant Sheet Flaw**

Dot panes.  17/6   There remains only a slight disturbance to the background where the tadpole and shamrock flaws were

**Coils**
Double pane cylinder D2 was used for the vertical delivery coils and cylinder D3 (single pane) for sideways delivery coils. Printed in continuous reels

**(a) Vertical delivery. Watermark upright**

| Code No. | Number in roll | Face value |
|---|---|---|
| R | 480 | £4 |
| V | 960 | £8 |

**(b) Sideways delivery. Watermark sideways**

| T | 480 | £4 |
|---|---|---|

●────────────

## ■ 1952–65 2½d. Carmine-red, Type S2

Two Types

Type I — In the frontal cross of the diadem, the top line is only half the width of the cross.

Type II — The top line extends to the full width of the cross and there are signs of strengthening in other parts of the diadem.

I        II

**Variations in the Multipositives**

The original multipositive became damaged and had to be replaced. The original negative consisted of two negatives placed in contact against each other, one for the frame and one for the Queen's head and oval setting. When these two pieces of glass were placed together the position of the two was not exactly the same as when the first multipositive was made, resulting in a slight tilting of the portrait.

The second multipositive (Type B) was used for making cylinder 46 which was employed for No. S53 and the third multipositive (Type C) was used for all later cylinder numbers, i.e. Nos. 49 onwards.

Multipositive A was used for the booklets listed under Nos. S53, S55, S57, S59, S61/2 and S65 and, in consequence, stamps from these sections showing multipositive A and upright watermark are worth the same as inverted watermark varieties from booklets

A               B

C

Type A. At the shoulder lines above "E" of "POSTAGE" the line dividing the light from the dark material of the dress, if projected, runs level with the top of the two diagonal lines of the ribbon on the wreath.

Type B. The line runs between the first and second diagonal line of the ribbon.

Type C. The line runs level with the first diagonal line of the ribbon.

These are not listed as separate varieties because the stamps printed from the cylinders made from the three variations in the multipositives differed in other respects. It was, however, a most interesting development which also applied to the 3d. value.

---

## 1952 (5 December). 2½d. Watermark Tudor Crown, Type W.22. Type i

**S50** (=SG 519)

| | | Mint | Used |
|---|---|---|---|
| ✓ 2½d. | Carmine-red | 15 | 15 |
| ✓ | a. Watermark sideways (15.11.54) | 7·00 | 8·00 |
| | b. Broken value circle (Cyl. 8 No dot, R. 20/2) | 20·00 | |
| | c. Extended broken top of diadem (Cyl. 16 Dot, R. 20/5) | 20·00 | |
| | d. Frame retouch (Sideways coil, Roll 7) | 30·00 | |

Stamps with sideways watermark are from M coils with sideways delivery.

S50b             S50c

S50d, S52e, S56ba, S56da

**Cylinder Numbers** (Blocks of Six)
Perforation Type A(E/I)

| Cyl. No. | No dot | Dot |
|---|---|---|
| 2 | 5·00 | 5·00 |
| 4 | 5·00 | 5·00 |
| 5 | 5·00 | 5·00 |
| 6 | 5·00 | 5·00 |
| 7 | 5·00 | 5·00 |
| 8 | 25·00* | 5·00 |
| 9 | 5·00 | 5·00 |
| 10 | 5·00 | 5·00 |
| 11 | 5·00 | 5·00 |
| 12 | 5·00 | 5·00 |
| 13 | 4·00 | 4·00 |
| 14 | 5·00 | 5·00 |
| 15 | 5·00 | 5·00 |
| 16 | 5·00 | 5·00 |
| 17 | 5·00 | 5·00 |
| 18 | 5·00 | 5·00 |
| 19 | 5·00 | 5·00 |
| 22 | 5·00 | 5·00 |
| 23 | 5·00 | 5·00 |
| 24 | 5·00 | 5·00 |
| 25 | 5·00 | 5·00 |
| 27 | 5·00 | 5·00 |

Perforation Type B (I/P no dot) and C (E/P dot)

| Cyl. No. | No dot | Dot |
|---|---|---|
| 14 | 11·00 | 11·00 |
| 24 | 11·00 | 11·00 |

## Minor Constant Sheet Flaws

### Multipositive flaws

| No dot | 1/4 | Red dot over left of crown (Th. A3) |
|--------|------|--------------------------------------|
|        | 12/4 | Red spot in leaf of shamrock (Th. G1) |
|        | 18/1 | Diagonal scratch from chin to neck (Th. E3–F4) |
| Dot    | 11/9 | White spot in "R" of "E R" (Cyls. 23, onwards) |

### Cylinder flaws

| Cyl. 2.  | 16/1 | Smudge line across top of "REVENUE" |
|----------|------|--------------------------------------|
| Cyl. 8.  | 19/1 | Red spot in "1" of fraction |
| Cyl. 10. | 20/1 | Extended top of "2" in value |

### Coils

Single pane cylinder L1 was used for the vertical delivery coils and L3 for the sideways delivery coils.
Printed in continuous reels

**(a) Vertical delivery. Watermark upright**

| Code No. | Number in roll | Face value |
|----------|----------------|------------|
| F | 960 | £10 |
| U | 1920 | £20 |

**(b) Sideways delivery. Watermark sideways**

| M | 480 | £5 |
|---|-----|-----|

### Imprimatur from the National Postal Museum Archives

Imperforate, watermark Type W.22

| Watermark upright | £2000 |
|-------------------|-------|

---

## 1953 (May). 2½d. Watermark Tudor Crown, Type W.22. Type II

**S51** (=SG 519b)

|  |  | Mint | Used |
|--|--|------|------|
| 2½d. | Carmine-red | 1·25 | 1·25 |
|  | a. Watermark inverted (5.53) | 60 | 75 |

This issue appeared from booklets only. See Section SB, Nos. SB80/a.

---

## 1955 (28 September). 2½d. Watermark St. Edward's Crown, Type W.23. Type I

**S52** (=SG 544)

|  |  | Mint | Used |
|--|--|------|------|
| 2½d. | Carmine-red | 20 | 25 |
|  | a. Imperf. between stamp and top margin | £850 |  |
|  | b. Watermark sideways (23.3.56) | 1·50 | 1·75 |
|  | c. "b" for "D" in value (Cyl. 30 Dot, R. 19/11) | 25·00 |  |
|  | d. White flaw below oval (Cyl. 44 Dot, R. 1/4) | 20·00 |  |
|  | e. Frame retouch (sideways coil, Roll 7) | 22·00 |  |

Stamps with sideways watermark are from M coils with sideways delivery.

S52c

S53d

For illustration of No. S52e, see No. S50d

## Cylinder Numbers (Blocks of Six)
Perforation Type A(E/I)

| Cyl. No. | No dot | Dot |
|----------|--------|-----|
| 22 | 5·00 | 5·00 |
| 24 | 5·00 | £900 |
| 25 | 5·00 | 5·00 |
| 27 | 5·00 | 5·00 |
| 30 | 5·00 | 5·00 |
| 32 | 5·00 | 5·00 |
| 33 | 5·00 | 5·00 |
| 34 | † | 18·00 |
| 37 | 5·00 | 5·00 |
| 38 | 5·00 | 5·00 |
| 39 | 5·00 | 5·00 |
| 40 | 5·00 | 5·00 |
| 42 | 5·00 | 5·00 |
| 43 | 5·00 | 5·00 |
| 44 | 5·00 | 5·00 |
| 45 | 60·00 | 60·00 |

Perforation Type E

| Cyl. No. | No dot (AE/1) | Dot (E/1) |
|----------|---------------|-----------|
| 32 | 17·00 | 5·00** |
| 37 | 17·00 | 5·00** |

\*\*Same price and appearance as perforation type A with extension holes in left margin.
 In Cylinder 42, both panes, the marginal arrows at the top and bottom were omitted at first, but added later.

### Minor Constant Sheet Flaws

Multipositive flaws as for No. S50
Cylinder flaw
Cyl. 43 18/5 Red spot on Queen's lip (Th. D3)

### Coils

Single pane cylinders L1 or L2 were used for the vertical delivery coils and L3 for the sideways delivery coils.
Printed in continuous reels

| Code No. | Number in roll | Face value |
|----------|----------------|------------|
| **(a) Vertical delivery. Watermark upright** |  |  |
| F | 960 | £10 |
| U | 1920 | £20 |
| **(b) Sideways delivery. Watermark sideways** |  |  |
| M | 480 | £5 |

### Imprimatur from the National Postal Museum Archives

Imperforate, watermark Type W.23

| Watermark upright | £2000 |
|-------------------|-------|

---

## 1957. 2½d. Watermark St. Edward's Crown, Type W.23. Type II

**S53** (=SG 544b)

|  |  | Mint | Used |
|--|--|------|------|
| 2½d. | Carmine-red | 45 | 45 |
|  | a. Tête-bêche (horiz. pair) | £3250 |  |
|  | d. Imperf. between stamp and top margin | £850 |  |
|  | e. Watermark inverted (9.55) | 25 | 70 |

### Cylinder Numbers (Blocks of Six)
Perforation Type A(E/I)

| Cyl. No. | No dot | Dot |
|----------|--------|-----|
| 46 | 5·00 | 5·00 |

**Imprimaturs from the National Postal Museum Archives**
Imperforate, watermark Type W.23

| | |
|---|---|
| Watermark upright | £2000 |
| Watermark inverted | £2000 |
| *Tête-bêche* pair | £8000 |

## 1957 (19 November). 2½d. With graphite lines, Type S8. Wmk. St. Edward's Crown. Type II

**S54** (=SG 565)

| | | Mint | Used |
|---|---|---|---|
| 2½d. Carmine-red | | 8·50 | 7·00 |
| a. Coil join (horiz. pr.) | | 30·00 | |

**Cylinder Numbers** (Blocks of Six)
Single pane cylinder

| Cyl. No. | Perf Type | No Dot |
|---|---|---|
| ✓ 49 | B (I/P) | 60·00 |
| 49 | C (E/P) | 60·00 |

**Coil**
Made up from sheets with sheet margin joins. Sideways delivery

| Code No. | Number in roll | Face value |
|---|---|---|
| M | 480 | £5 |

**Imprimatur from the National Postal Museum Archives**
Imperforate, watermark Type W.23

| | |
|---|---|
| Watermark upright | £2000 |

**Quantity Issued:** 20,578,800

## 1959 (15 September)†. 2½d. Watermark Crowns, Type W.24

**S55**

| A. Type II Cream Paper | Mint | Used |
|---|---|---|
| 2½d. Carmine-red | 60 | 30 |
| a. *Tête-bêche* (horiz. pair) | £5550 | |
| b. Imperf. strip of 3 | | |
| c. Imperf. between stamp and bottom margin | | |
| d. Watermark inverted (11.58) | 4·50 | 3·00 |
| e. State 1. Leaf and extra rose stem flaws (Cyl. 50 Dot, R. 9/4) | 25·00 | |
| ea. State 2. Extra rose stem. Leaf flaw retouched (Cyl 50 Dot, R. 9/4) | 25·00 | |
| f. White emblems (Cyl. 52 No dot, R. 12/4) | 25·00 | |

**S56**

| B. Type I. Cream Paper (4 October 1961) | Mint | Used |
|---|---|---|
| 2½d. Carmine-red | 3·50 | 2·00 |
| b. Watermark sideways (10.11.60) | 1·25 | 70 |
| ba. Imperf, strip of 6 | | |
| bb. Frame retouch (Sideways coil, Roll 7) | 25·00 | |

**S56C** (=SG 574e)

| C. Type I. Whiter Paper (30 October 1963) | Mint | Used |
|---|---|---|
| 2½d. Carmine-red | 70 | 70 |
| d. Watermark sideways (3.8.62) | 25 | 40 |
| da. Frame retouch (Sideways coil, Roll 7) | 25·00 | |

**S57** (=SG 574)

| D. Type II. Whiter Paper (7 May 1962) | 10 | 20 |
|---|---|---|
| 2½d. Carmine-red | 10 | 20 |
| a. Watermark inverted (29.7.62) | 4·50 | 3·00 |
| b. Imperf. between stamp and top margin | | |
| c. Watermark Crown to left (coils, 9.65 and booklets, 1.7.64) | 70 | 1·25 |
| d. Watermark Crown to right | 70 | 1·25 |
| e. State 2. Extra rose stem. Leaf flaw retouched (Cyl. 50 Dot, R. 9/4) | 25·00 | |
| f. Serif to "A" (Cyl. 55 No dot, R. 11/8) | 25·00 | |

**S58** (=SG 574k)

| E. Type II. Chalky Paper. Booklets only (15 July 1963) | | |
|---|---|---|
| 2½d. Carmine-red | 50 | 80 |
| a. Watermark inverted (15.7.63) | 75 | 1·25 |

*Imperf. stamps*, No. S55b comes from a booklet with watermark upright and No. S56ba is from an M coil with sideways watermark.

*Sideways watermark.* Nos. S56b, S56d and S57c came from M coils with sideways delivery and Nos. S57c/d are from 2s. Holiday Booklets No. NR2.

For illustration of Nos. S56bb and S56da, see No. S50d. No. S56da is known in a second state showing a vertical line adjoining the right-hand frame not filled in with colour.

State 1. Triangular white flaw adjoining left leaf and extra stem to rose.
State 2. Later printings exist with the leaf flaw retouched (Nos S55ea, S57e, S61c, S62b, S63e).
State 3. Both flaws retouched (S65d).

S55e

S55f Later retouched    Normal            S57f

**Cylinder Numbers** (Blocks of Six)
**Type II. (No. S55) Cream paper**
Perforation Type A(E/I)

| Cyl. No. | No dot | Dot |
|---|---|---|
| 50 | 5·00 | 5·00 |
| 51 | 5·00 | 5·00 |
| 52 | 5·00 | 5·00 |
| 53 | 5·00 | 5·00 |
| 54 | 5·00 | 5·00 |

Perforation Type B (I/P no dot) and C (E/P dot)

| Cyl. No. | No dot | Dot |
|---|---|---|
| 50 | 9·00 | 9·00 |
| 51 | 9·00 | 9·00 |
| 52 | 8·50 | 8·50 |

**Type I. (No. S56c). Whiter Paper**
Perforation Type A(E/I)

| Cyl. No. | No dot | Dot |
|---|---|---|
| 42 | 6·25 | 6·25 |

**Type I. (No. S56) Cream Paper.**
Perforation Type A(E/I)

| Cyl. No. | No dot | Dot |
|----------|--------|-----|
| 42 | 26·00 | 26·00 |

Perforation Type B (I/P no dot) and C (E/P dot) Cream paper

| Cyl. No. | No dot | Dot |
|----------|--------|-----|
| 42 | £750 | £750 |

**Type II. (No. S57). Whiter Paper**
Perforation Type A(E/I)

| Cyl. No. | No dot | Dot |
|----------|--------|-----|
| 50 | 5·00 | 5·00 |
| 51 | 5·00 | 5·00 |
| 52 | 5·00 | 5·00 |
| 53 | 5·00 | 5·00 |
| 54 | 5·00 | 5·00 |
| 55 | 5·00 | 5·00 |
| 56 | 5·00 | 5·00 |
| 57 | 5·00 | 5·00 |
| 58 | 5·00 | 5·00 |
| 59 | 5·00 | 5·00 |

Perforation Type B (I/P no dot) and C (E/P dot)

| Cyl. No. | No dot | Dot |
|----------|--------|-----|
| 51 | 8·00 | 8·00 |
| 52 | 8·00 | 8·00 |

Marginal arrows. In Type II these exist hand-engraved at left as well as photo-etched. Also sheets are known with the arrows omitted at bottom. On cylinder 55 the faint outline of the "V" shaped arrow is below rows 8/9 in addition to the etched arrow below vertical rows 6/7.

**Minor Constant Sheet Flaws**

| | | |
|--|--|--|
| Cyl. 42 | 1/4 | Red spot over left of crown (Th. A3) |
| | 12/4 | Red spot in leaf of shamrock (Th. G1) |
| Cyl. 42. | 4/1 | Red and white dots in oval (Th. B2) |
| | 5/8 | Red dot in thistle (Th. G2) |
| | 11/9 | White spot in "R" of "E R" |
| | 14/5 | Slight retouch in forehead above Queen's right eye (Th. C2) |
| | 16/3 | White dot between thistle and leaf (Th. G2) |
| | 17/2 | Small white flaw on tail of "R" of "E R" |
| | 18/10 | Red dot between Queen's lip and nose (Th. D3). Later partially removed |
| | 20/10 | White flaw by oval at left (Th. D1–2) |
| Cyl. 50. | 6/10 | Background retouched behind "P" of "POSTAGE" and "R" of "REVENUE" |
| Cyl. 51. | 7/5 | Retouch to left of hair (Th. C2) |
| | 9/6 | White dot at bottom left of "R" of "REVENUE" |
| Cyl. 55. | 11/8 | Spur on "A" of "POSTAGE" (Th. G4) |

**Coils**
Single pane cylinder L2 was used for the vertical delivery coils and cylinders L3 for sideways delivery Type I coils and L5 for Type II coils.
Printed in continuous reels

| Code No. | Number in roll | Face value | |
|----------|----------------|------------|--|

(a) Vertical delivery. Watermark upright

| F | 960 | £10 | Type I. Cream or whiter paper |
|---|-----|-----|-------------------------------|

(b) Sideways delivery. Watermark sideways

| M | 480 | £5 | Type I. Cream or whiter paper |
|---|-----|-----|------------------------------|
| M | 480 | £5 | Type II. Whiter paper |

**Imprimaturs from the National Postal Museum Archives**
Type II. Imperforate, watermark Type W.24. Cream or whiter paper

| Watermark upright | £2000 |
|-------------------|-------|

| Watermark inverted | £2000 |
|--------------------|-------|
| Tête-bêche pair | £8000 |

---

## 1959. (9 June). 2½d. With graphite lines, Type S8. Watermark Crowns. Type II

S59 (=SG 591)

| | Mint | Used |
|--|------|------|
| 2½d. Carmine-red | 10·00 | 10·00 |
| a. Watermark inverted (21.8.59) | 65·00 | 50·00 |

**Cylinder Numbers** (Blocks of Six)
Single pane cylinder

| Cyl. No. | Perf Type | Dot |
|----------|-----------|-----|
| 49 | B (I/P) | 75·00 |
| 49 | C (E/P) | 75·00 |

**Imprimaturs from the National Postal Museum Archives**
Imperforate, watermark Type W.24

| Watermark upright | £2000 |
|-------------------|-------|
| Watermark inverted | £2000 |
| Tête-bêche pair | £8000 |

**Quantity Issued:** 10,012,800

---

## 1959 (18 November). 2½d. Phosphor-graphite issue. Watermark Crowns. Type II

S60 (=SG 606)

| | Mint | Used |
|--|------|------|
| 2½d. Carmine-red | 22·00 | 18·00 |
| a. One 6 mm. band at left or right (stamp with vert. margin) | 30·00 | |
| b. One 8 mm. band | £180 | |
| ba. As b but 6 mm. band | | |

No. S60 has two graphite lines (Type S9), on the back and two phosphor bands on the front, applied typo., which react green under the lamp.

This phosphor-graphite value is known with St. Edward's Crown watermark Type W.23, but this was not officially issued.

**Cylinder Numbers** (Blocks of Six)
Single pane cylinder

| Cyl. No. | Perf Type | Dot |
|----------|-----------|-----|
| 49 | B (I/P) | £160 |
| 49 | C (E/P) | £160 |

**Imprimatur from the National Postal Museum Archives**
Perf. 15 × 14, watermark Type W.24

| Watermark upright | £2000 |
|-------------------|-------|

**Quantity Issued:** 689,280

---

## 1960 (22 June). 2½d. Two phosphor bands reacting green. Wmk. Crowns. Type II

S61

| | Mint | Used |
|--|------|------|
| 2½d. Carmine-red | 1·75 | 1·40 |
| a. Watermark inverted (14.8.60) | £170 | £140 |
| b. One broad band (wmk. upright) | 45·00 | |
| c. State 2. Extra rose stem. Leaf flaw retouched (Cyl. 50 Dot, R. 9/4) | 25·00 | |

The bands were applied in Gravure.
For illustration of No. S61c, see No. S55e.

**Cylinder Numbers** (Blocks of Six)
Perforation Type B (I/P no dot) and C (E/P dot)

| Cyl. No. | No dot | Dot |
|---|---|---|
| 50 | 15·00 | 15·00 |

**Minor Constant Sheet Flaw**
Cyl. 50. 6/10 Background retouch behind "P" of "POSTAGE" and
"R" of "REVENUE"

**Imprimaturs from the National Postal Museum Archives**
Imperforate, watermark Type W.24

| | |
|---|---|
| Watermark upright | £2000 |
| Watermark inverted | £2000 |
| *Tête-bêche* pair | £8000 |

---

## 1961 (5 June). 2½d. Phosphor bands reacting blue. Watermark Crowns.

**A. Two 8 mm. Bands (applied photo.). Type II. Cream Paper**
S62

| | | Mint | Used |
|---|---|---|---|
| 2½d. | Carmine-red | 6·00 | 3·00 |
| | a. Watermark inverted (3.61) | £170 | £140 |
| | b. State 2. Extra rose stem. Leaf flaw retouched (Cyl. 50 Dot, R. 9/4) | 25·00 | |

**B. One Band at left (applied typo.).**
**Type II. Cream Paper (4 October 1961)**
S63

| | | | |
|---|---|---|---|
| 2½d. | Carmine-red | 4·00 | 4.00 |
| | a. Band applied photo. (3.11.61) | 12·00 | 12·00 |
| | b. Watermark inverted (photo.) (3.62) | 40·00 | 38·00 |
| | c. Error. Two bands (photo.)* | 95·00 | |
| | ca. Error. Band (photo.) omitted in pair with one band at right | £170 | |
| | d. Error. Band (typo.) omitted in pair with one band at right | £200 | |
| | e. State 2. Extra rose stem. Leaf flaw retouched (Cyl. 50 Dot, R.9/4) | 25·00 | |

**C. One Band at left (applied typo.).**
**Type I. Cream Paper (4 October 1961)**
S64 (=SG 614b)

| | | | |
|---|---|---|---|
| 2½d. | Carmine-red | 45·00 | 40·00 |
| | b. Error. Band omitted, in pair with one band at right | £200 | |
| | c. Error. Two bands (typo.)* | £110 | |

**D. One Band at left (applied photo.).**
**Type II. Whiter Paper (22 June 1962)**
S65 (=SG 614a)

| | | | |
|---|---|---|---|
| 2½d. | Carmine-red | 60 | 75 |
| | a. Band applied typo. | £225 | 90·00 |
| | b. Watermark inverted (3.6.63) | 40·00 | 38·00 |
| | c. Error. Two bands (Gravure) | | |
| | d. State 3. Rose stem and leaf flaws retouched (Cyl. 50 Dot, R, 9/4) | 20·00 | |
| | e. Horiz. pair ex. pane. Band at right and one stamp missing phosphor | | |

*Two Band Errors. These can be identified by the distance between the bands. This is 12 mm. on No. S62, but 16 mm. on the two band errors, Nos. S63c, S64c, and S65c. These three varieties have the 4 mm. left band applied in error over the vertical perforations at each side of the stamp.

**E. Two Bands (applied photo.).**
**Type II. Whiter Paper (20 September 1964)**
S66 (=SG 614)

| | | | |
|---|---|---|---|
| 2½d. | Carmine-red | 40 | 30 |
| | a. Bands applied typo. | | |
| | b. One 8 mm. band (photo.) | 15·00 | |

No. S66 was a reissue of No. S62 but from cylinder 57 and on whiter paper. The shade is slightly more carmine. It was first released in error in the S.E. London area in September 1964 and then put on sale in Birmingham in December 1964 as electronic sorting machines were not in use there at that time. To prepare for the alteration in postal rates on 17 May 1965 when the 2½d. ceased to be the printed paper rate, it was released in the phosphor areas on 3 May 1965 in place of the single band stamps. However, as there was no longer a postal need for this value it was not reprinted.

For description of Nos. S62b, S63e and S65d, see illustration No S55e.

**Cylinder Numbers** (Blocks of Six)
Two bands (No. S62). Type II Cream paper.
Perforation Type A (E/I)

| Cyl. No. | No dot | Dot |
|---|---|---|
| 50 | 40·00 | 40·00 |

One band at left. Type II. Cream paper
Perforation Type A (E/I). Applied typo. (No. S63)

| Cyl. No. | No dot | Dot |
|---|---|---|
| 50 | 28·00 | 28·00 |

Perforation Type B (I/P no dot) or C (E/P dot)
Applied photo. (No. S63a)

| Cyl. No. | No dot | Dot |
|---|---|---|
| 50 | 85·00 | 85·00 |
| 53 | 85·00 | 85·00 |

One band at left. Type I. Cream paper.
Perforation Type A (E/I)
Applied typo. (No. S64)

| | | |
|---|---|---|
| 42 | £300 | £300 |

Type II. Whiter paper,
Perforation Type A (E/I)
One band. Applied photo. (No. S65)

| Cyl. No. | No dot | Dot |
|---|---|---|
| 51 | 5·00 | 5·00 |
| 52 | 5·00 | 5·00 |
| 54 | 5·00 | 5·00 |
| 56 | 5·00 | 5·00 |
| 57 | 5·00 | 5·00 |

One band. applied typo. (No. S65a)
Two bands. Applied photo. (No. S66)

| | | |
|---|---|---|
| 57 | 5·00 | 5·00 |

One band. Applied typo. (No. S65a)

| | | |
|---|---|---|
| 50 | – | – |

**Minor Constant Sheet Flaws**
As recorded for Nos. S55/7

**Imprimaturs from the National Postal Museum Archives**
One band at left. Type II. Imperforate, watermark Type W.24.
Cream or whiter paper

| | |
|---|---|
| Watermark upright | £2000 |
| Watermark inverted | £2000 |
| *Tête-bêche* pair | £8000 |

---

## ■ 1954–67 3d. Deep lilac, Type S2

### Variations in the Multipositives

There are similar variations in the tilt of the portrait in the multipositives used as occurred in the 2½d. value (see notes and illustration at the beginning of the 2½d. list).

The second multipositive, corresponding to Type B, was used for cylinders 25 to 33 and the third multipositive, corresponding to Type C, was employed for cylinders 36 and 37. A fourth multipositive, also Type C, was introduced for cylinders 41 onwards.

---

### 1954 (18 January). 3d. Watermark Tudor Crown, Type W.22

S67 (=SG 520)

|  | Mint | Used |
|---|---|---|
| 3d.  Deep lilac | 1·50 | 90 |
| a.  Imperf. between stamp and top margin | £850 | |
| b.  Coil join (horiz. pair) | 4·00 | |
| c.  Coil join (vert. pair) | 12·00 | |

See General Notes under Paper – this stamp exists on very thick paper for this issue. (*Price £75 mint*)

**Cylinder Numbers** (Blocks of Six)
Perforation Type A(E/I)

| Cyl. No. | No dot | Dot |
|---|---|---|
| 3 | 9·00 | 9·00 |

Perforation Type B (I/P no dot) and C (E/P dot)

| Cyl. No. | No dot | Dot |
|---|---|---|
| 3 | 9·00 | 9·00 |

**Minor Constant Sheet Flaws**
Multipositive flaws

| No dot | 1/3 White scratch to bottom right of "R" of large "E R" (Th. A–B6) |
|---|---|
| Dot | 9/8 Dark patch to left of central cross of tiara (Th. B3) |

**Coils**
Made up from sheets with sheet margin joins. Watermark upright

| Code No. | Number in roll | Face value | |
|---|---|---|---|
| C | 960 | £12 | Vertical delivery |
| S | 480 | £6 | Sideways delivery |

**Imprimatur from the National Postal Museum Archives**
Imperforate, watermark Type W.22

| Watermark upright | £2000 |
|---|---|

---

### 1956 (17 July). 3d. Watermark St. Edward's Crown, Type W.23

S68 (=SG 545)

|  | Mint | Used |
|---|---|---|
| 3d.  Deep lilac | 25 | 25 |
| a.  *Tête-bêche* (horiz. pair) | £3000 | |
| b.  Imperf. three sides (pair) | £2500 | |
| c.  Imperf. between stamp and bottom margin | £850 | |
| √ d.  Watermark inverted (1.10.57) | 1·00 | 1·00 |
| √ e.  Watermark sideways (22.11.57) | 18·00 | 17·00 |
| f.  Coil join (horiz. pair) | 7·00 | |
| g.  Coil join (vert. pair) | 14·00 | |

| | Mint | Used |
|---|---|---|
| h.  White flaw over Queen's eye (Cyl. 2 Dot, R. 13/7) | | 25·00 |

Stamps with sideways watermark are from S coils with sideways delivery.

No. S68b comes from a partly perforated booklet pane of six. No complete panes showing this error have been recorded.

S68h

**Cylinder Numbers** (Blocks of Six)
Perforation Type A(E/I)

| Cyl. No. | No dot | Dot |
|---|---|---|
| 2 | 5·00 | 5·00 |
| 3 | 5·00 | 5·00 |
| 4 | 5·00 | 5·00 |
| 5 | 5·00 | 5·00 |
| 9 | 5·00 | 5·00 |
| 10 | 5·00 | 5·00 |
| 15 | 5·00 | 5·00 |
| 16 | 5·00 | 5·00 |
| 17 | 5·00 | 5·00 |

Perforation Type B (I/P no dot) and C (E/P dot)

| Cyl. No. | No dot | Dot |
|---|---|---|
| 2 | 9·00 | 9·00 |
| 3 | 9·00 | 9·00 |

Perforation : Type F (L) (I/E)

| 5 | 70·00 | † |
|---|---|---|

Marginal arrows:
"V" shaped, hand engraved at top and bottom
"W" shaped, photo-etched at both sides
Early printings from cylinder 2 had the "V" shaped arrow omitted from the bottom of the sheet on no dot and dot panes (*Price for positional block showing arrow omitted £15 no dot £25 dot*)

**Minor Constant Sheet Flaws**
Multipositive flaws

| No dot | 1/3 | White scratch to bottom right of "R" of large "E R" (Th. A–B6) |
|---|---|---|
| Dot | 9/8 | Dark patch to left of central cross of tiara (Th. B3) |

| Cylinder flaw | | |
|---|---|---|
| Cyl. 17 | 17/3 | Coloured scratches through "E" of large "E R" (Th. A1) |

**Coils**
(a) Made up from sheets with sheet margin joins. Watermark upright

| Code No. | Number in roll | Face value | |
|---|---|---|---|
| C | 960 | £12 | Vertical delivery |
| S | 480 | £6 | Sideways delivery |

(b) Printed in continuous reels. Double pane cylinders M1 or M2 were used for the vertical delivery coils and cylinder M9 for the sideways delivery coil.

(a) Vertical delivery. Watermark upright

| Code No. | Number in roll | Face value |
|---|---|---|
| C | 960 | £12 |
| U | 1920 | £24 |

(b) Sideways delivery. Watermark sideways

| S | 480 | £6 |
|---|---|---|

**Imprimaturs from the National Postal Museum Archives**
Imperforate, watermark Type W.23

| | |
|---|---|
| Watermark upright | £2000 |
| Watermark inverted | £2000 |
| *Tête-bêche* pair | £8000 |

---

### 1957 (19 November). 3d. With <u>graphite lines</u>, Type S8. Wmk. <u>St. Edward's Crown</u>

**S69** (=SG 566)

| | Mint | Used |
|---|---|---|
| 3d. Deep lilac | 80 | 50 |
| a. Coil join (horiz. pair) | 2·50 | |

**Cylinder Numbers** (Blocks of Six)
Single pane cylinders

| Cyl. No. | Perf. Type | Dot |
|---|---|---|
| 7 | B (I/P) | 6·50 |
| 7 | C (E/P) | 6·50 |
| 11 | B (I/P) | 6·50 |
| 11 | C (E/P) | 6·50 |

**Coils**
Made up from sheets with sheet margin joins. Watermark upright

| Code No. | Number in roll | Face value | |
|---|---|---|---|
| S | 480 | £6 | Sideways delivery |

**Imprimatur from the National Postal Museum Archives**
Imperforate, watermark Type W.23

| | |
|---|---|
| Watermark upright | £2000 |

**Quantities Issued:** 91,466,400

---

### 1958 (8 December)†. 3d. Watermark <u>Crowns</u>, Type W.24

**S70**

| A. Cream Paper | Mint | Used |
|---|---|---|
| 3d. Deep lilac | 25 | 25 |
| c. Imperf. between stamp and top margin | £500 | |
| d. Watermark Crown <u>to left</u> (Coils, 24.10.58 and booklets, 26.5.61) | 1·25 | 75 |
| e. Watermark inverted (11.58) | 25 | 40 |
| f. Watermark Crown <u>to right</u> (Booklets, 26.5.61) | 1·25 | 65 |
| g. Spot on "T" of "POSTAGE" (Cyl. 37 No dot, R. 19/11) | 22·00 | |
| h. Phantom "R" (Cyl. 37 No dot, below R. 20/12) | 50·00 | |
| i. Do. Retouch | 15·00 | |
| j. Phantom "R" (Cyl. 41 No dot, below R. 20/12) | £350 | |
| k. Do. First retouch | 25·00 | |
| l. Do.Second or third retouch | 25·00 | |

**S71** (=SG 575)

| B. Whiter Paper (30 April 1962) | | |
|---|---|---|
| 3d. Deep lilac | 10 | 20 |
| a. Watermark Crown <u>to left</u> (Coils, 30.4.62 and booklets, 5.6.62) | 25 | 35 |
| b. Watermark Crown <u>to right</u> (Booklets, 5.6.62) | 25 | 35 |

| | | |
|---|---|---|
| c. Watermark inverted (16.7.62) | 20 | 20 |
| d. Experimental T watermark* (marginal block of 6) | 22·00 | 22·00 |
| e. Serif on "E" (Cyl. 68 Dot, R. 16/5) | 22·00 | |
| f. Flaw on "E" (R. 14/11 on Cyls. 60 No dot and others)5750 | 25·00 | |
| g. White spur on thistle left of "P" (Cyl. 70 No dot, "R". 4/2) | 22·00 | |

*In 1964 No. S71 was printed from Cylinder 70 no dot and dot on an experimental paper which is distinguished by an additional watermark letter "T" lying on its side, which occurs about four times in the sheet, usually in the side margins where it is easiest to see. It is difficult to see when it occurs on the stamps themselves. 48,000 sheets were issued.

**Variations in the Multipositives.** See the notes at the beginning of the 3d. list about the variations in the tilt of the portrait on the different multipositives used.

**Tête-bêche.** No. S70 exists *tête-bêche*, also separated by gutters. These are from booklet sheets which were not issued. (£25 *per pair*)

**Imperforate.** Examples of No. S71 are known imperforate; these come from uncut booklet sheets which were not issued.

S70g                                      S70h

S70j, S74c                                S70k

S71f

S71e, S77g                               S71g

An incomplete masking of the stamp image beneath the marginal rule revealed an "R" on Cyls. 37 and 41 no dot. It is more noticeable on the latter because of the wider marginal rule. The retouch on Cyl. 37 is not easily identified. There is no trace of the "R" but the general appearance of that part of the marginal rule is uneven. However, the retouch can be confirmed in a positional block by the presence of the Spot on "T" variety on R. 19/11, No. S70g.

The "R" on Cyl. 41 was retouched three times, the first being as illustrated here (No. S70k) and traces of the "R" can still be seen in the others.

**Cylinder Numbers** (Blocks of Six)

**A. Cream Paper. (No. S70)**
Perforation Type A(E/I)

| Cyl. No. | No dot | Dot |
|---|---|---|
| 15 | 5·00 | 5·00 |
| 16 | 45·00 | 45·00 |
| 22 | 5·00 | 5·00 |
| 25 | 5·00 | 5·00 |
| 26 | 5·00 | 5·00 |
| 28 | 5·00 | 5·00 |
| 29 | 5·00 | 5·00 |
| 30 | 5·00 | 5·00 |
| 31 | 5·00 | 5·00 |
| 33 | 5·00 | 5·00 |
| 36 | 5·00 | 5·00 |
| 37 | 5·00 | 5·00 |
| 41 | 5·00 | 5·00 |
| 46 | 5·00 | 5·00 |
| 47 | 5·00 | 5·00 |
| 49 | 5·00 | 5·00 |
| 51 | 5·00 | 5·00 |
| 52 | 5·00 | 5·00 |
| 53 | 5·00 | 5·00 |
| 54 | 5·00 | 5·00 |
| 55 | 5·00 | 5·00 |
| 58 | 5·00 | 5·00 |
| 60 | 5·00 | 5·00 |
| 61 | 5·00 | 5·00 |
| 62 | 5·00 | 5·00 |
| 64 | 5·00 | 5·00 |

Perforation Type B (I/P no dot) and C (E/P dot)

| Cyl. No. | No dot | Dot |
|---|---|---|
| 28 | 5·50 | 5·50 |
| 41* | 30·00 | † |
| 51 | 5·50 | 5·50 |
| 52 | 6·50 | 6·50 |
| 54 | 6·50 | 6·50 |

*This has been seen Perf. Type B (I/P no dot) and may be an example of No. S74 with phosphor bands omitted.
Perforation Type H

| Cyl. No. | (E/I) | (P/I) |
|---|---|---|
| 31 | 5·00** | 32·00 |
| 36 | 5·00** | 32·00 |
| 37 | 5·00** | 35·00 |
| 41 | 5·00** | 35·00 |

**Same price and appearance as perforation type A with extension holes in left margin.

**B. Whiter Paper. (No. S71)**
Perforation Type A(E/I)

| Cyl. No. | No dot | Dot |
|---|---|---|
| 51 | 5·00 | – |
| 52 | 5·00 | 5·00 |
| 54 | 5·00 | 5·00 |
| 58 | 5·00 | 5·00 |
| 60 | 5·00 | 5·00 |
| 61 | 5·00 | 5·00 |
| 62 | 5·00 | 5·00 |

| Cyl. No. | No dot | Dot |
|---|---|---|
| 63 | 5·00 | 5·00 |
| 64 | 5·00 | 5·00 |
| 66 | 5·00 | 5·00 |
| 67 | 5·00 | 5·00 |
| 68 | 5·00 | 5·00 |
| 69 | 5·00 | 5·00 |
| 70 | 5·00 | 5·00 |
| 71 | 5·00 | 5·00 |
| 72 | 5·00 | 5·00 |
| 73 | 5·00 | 5·00 |
| 75 | 5·00 | 5·00 |
| 78 | 5·00 | 5·00 |
| 79 | 5·00 | 5·00 |
| 80 | 5·00 | 5·00 |
| 81 | 5·00 | 5·00 |
| 82 | 5·00 | 5·00 |

**Marginal arrows:** These vary from cylinder to cylinder. The following combinations are known:
(a) All hand engraved. "V" shaped at top and bottom; "W" shaped at both sides
(b) "V" shaped, hand engraved at top and bottom; "W" shaped, photo-etched at both sides
(c) All photo-etched. "W" shaped at top and bottom and at both sides

**Minor Constant Sheet Flaws**
Multipositive flaws (Cyls. 15, 16 and 22 only)

| No dot | 1/3 | White scratch to bottom right of R of large E R (Th. A-B6) |
|---|---|---|
| Dot | 9/8 | Dark patch to left of central cross of tiara (Th. B3) |

Cylinder flaws

| Cyl. 46. | 20/2 | White flaw on leaves of oval at left (Th. E-F1) |
|---|---|---|
| Cyl. 52 | 17/9 | White spur to circle around 3d. by "D" (Th. G6) |
| Cyl. 52 | 18/2 | Coloured line from Queen's hair to top of oval (Th. B2) |
| Cyl. 60. | 4/11 | Coloured flaw on thistle leaf (Th. G2) |
| Cyl. 63. | 4/11 | White flaw on leaf (Th. G2) |
| Cyl. 69 | 5/10 | White flaw on wreath (Th. F6) |
| Cyl. 70. | 10/4 | White flaw above "PO" of "POSTAGE" (Th. G3) |
| | 10/11 | White flaw on daffodil stem giving appearance of thick stalk (Th. G-H2) |
| | 19/8 | Coloured scratch from tiara to oval (Th. C5) |

**Coils**
Printed in continuous reels. Double pane cylinders M1 or M2 were used for the vertical delivery coils and cylinders M9, M10 and M11 for the sideways delivery coils. Cylinders M9 and M10 were used on cream paper and M10 and M11 on the whiter paper.

**(a) Vertical delivery. Watermark upright. Cream or whiter paper**

| Code No. | Number in roll | Face value |
|---|---|---|
| C | 960 | £12 |
| U | 1920 | £24 |
| AC | 480 | £6 |
| AD | 960 | £12 |

**(b) Sideways delivery. Watermark sideways. Cream or whiter paper**

| | | |
|---|---|---|
| S | 480 | £6 |

**Imprimaturs from the National Postal Museum Archives**
Imperforate, watermark Type W.24. Cream or whiter paper

| Watermark upright | £2000 |
|---|---|
| Watermark inverted | £2000 |
| *Tête-bêche* pair | £8000 |

Lwd-

## 1958 (24 November). 3d. With graphite lines, Type S8. Watermark Crowns

S72 (=SG 592)

|  |  | Mint | Used |
|---|---|---|---|
| 3d. | Deep lilac | 50 | 65 |
| a. | Watermark inverted (4.8.59) | 45 | 75 |
| b. | Two lines at left (5.61) | £480 | £380 |
| c. | Three lines | 32·00 | 22·00 |
| d. | One line | £700 | £300 |
| e. | Coil join (horiz. pair) | 12·00 | |

The misplaced graphite lines (varieties b/d) came from sheets from Cyls. 51 no dot and dot printed after the graphite line experiment had ended to use up residual stock of graphite-lined paper. (*Price for cylinder block of 6, from £250.*)

Examples of No. S72b have both graphite lines printed clear of the perforations. Stamps showing lines cutting the perforations are common and worth a fraction of the price of the genuine variety. This applies particularly to cylinder blocks.

**Cylinder Numbers** (Blocks of Six)
Single pane cylinder

| Cyl. No. | Perf. Type | No Dot |
|---|---|---|
| 11 | B (I/P) | 6·50 |
| 11 | C (E/P) | 6·50 |

**Coils**
Printed in continuous reels. Double-pane cylinders M1 or M2 were used. Watermark upright.

| Code No. | Number in roll | Face value | |
|---|---|---|---|
| C | 960 | £12 | Vertical delivery |

Made up from sheets with sheet margin joins. Watermark upright.

| | | | |
|---|---|---|---|
| S | 480 | £6 | Sideways delivery |

**Imprimaturs from the National Postal Museum Archives**
Imperforate, watermark Type W.24

| Watermark upright | £2000 |
|---|---|
| Watermark inverted | £2000 |
| *Tête-bêche* pair | £8000 |

**Quantity Issued**: 57,222,960

## 1959 (18 November). 3d. Phosphor-graphite issue. Watermark Crowns

S73 (=SG 607)

|  |  | Mint | Used |
|---|---|---|---|
| 3d. | Deep lilac | 10·00 | 8·00 |
| a. | One 6 mm. band at left or right (stamp with vert. margin) | 22·00 | |

No. S73 has two graphite lines, Type S8, on the back and two phosphor bands on the front, applied typo., which react green under the lamp.

**Cylinder Numbers** (Blocks of Six)
Single pane cylinder

| Cyl. No. | Perf Type | No Dot |
|---|---|---|
| 11 | B (I/P) | 70·00 |
| 11 | C (E/P) | 70·00 |

**Imprimatur from the National Postal Museum Archives**
Perf. 15 × 14, watermark Type W.24

| Watermark upright | £2000 |
|---|---|

**Quantity Issued**: 4,625,040

## 1960 (22 June). 3d. Two phosphor bands reacting green. Wmk. Crowns

S74

|  |  | Mint | Used |
|---|---|---|---|
| 3d. | Deep lilac | 1·75 | 1·75 |
| a. | Watermark inverted (14.8.60) | 1·75 | 1·75 |
| b. | One 8mm band (wmk. upright) | 40·00 | |
| c. | Phantom "R" (Cyl. 41 No dot, below R. 20/12) | 40·00 | |
| ca. | As c but one 8 mm band | | |
| d. | One 8 mm. band (wmk. inverted) | | |
| da. | As d but 6 mm. band | | |

The bands were applied in Gravure. No. S74b is from sheets and booklet panes.
For illustrations of No. S74c, see No S70j.

**Cylinder Numbers** (Blocks of Six)
Perforation Type B (I/P no dot) and C (E/P dot)

| Cyl. No. | No dot | Dot |
|---|---|---|
| 41 | 16·00 | 16·00 |

## 1961 (5 June). 3d. Phosphor bands reacting blue. Watermark Crowns

S75

| A. Two Bands. Cream Paper |  | Mint | Used |
|---|---|---|---|
| 3d. | Deep lilac | 1·25 | 1·25 |
| a. | Watermark inverted (3.61) | 1·25 | 1·25 |
| b. | Watermark Crown to left (14.7.61) | 3·00 | 3·00 |
| c. | Watermark Crown to right | 3·00 | 3·00 |
| d. | One 8 mm. band (wmk. sideways) | 28·00 | |

S76 (=SG 615)

| B. Two Bands. Whiter Paper (24 October 1962) |  | | |
|---|---|---|---|
| 3d. | Deep lilac | 60 | 55 |
| a. | Watermark Crown to left (15.8.62) | 1·75 | 1·75 |
| b. | Watermark Crown to right | 1·75 | 1·75 |
| c. | Watermark inverted (25.9.62) | 50 | 90 |
| d. | Error. One band on each stamp (horiz. pair) | £100 | |

The 8 mm. bands on both stamps of No. S76d prove that the bands were displaced for this issue in addition to No. S77 (see No. S77fa). *Price for single with one 8 mm. band, £45 mint.*

S77

| C. One Side Band*. Whiter Paper (29 April 1965) |  | | |
|---|---|---|---|
| 3d. | Deep lilac (side band at left) | 2·75 | 2·50 |
| a. | Side band at right | 2·75 | 2·50 |
| ab. | Nos. S77/a (horiz. pair) | 7·00 | 5·00 |
| b. | Watermark Crown to left, band at left (16.8.65) | 25·00 | 15·00 |
| c. | Watermark Crown to left, band at right | 25·00 | 15·00 |
| d. | Watermark Crown to right, band at left | 30·00 | 20·00 |
| e. | Watermark Crown to right, band at right | 30·00 | 20·00 |
| f. | Error. Pair, left-hand stamp with phosphor omitted, right-hand stamp with one 8 mm. band | 90·00 | |
| g. | Serif on "E" (Cyl. 68 Dot, R. 16/5) | 22·00 | |

The bands were all applied in Gravure on the stamps with upright and inverted watermark and by Typography on those with watermark sideways.
*The one side band stamps were produced by an 8 mm. band

applied down alternate vertical rows of the sheet over the perforations so that alternate stamps have the band at left (No. S77) or right (No. S77a). In theory the width of the band on a single stamp should be 4 mm. but this will vary if the bands have not been perfectly positioned.

For illustration of No. S77g see No. S71e.

**Cylinder Numbers** (Blocks of Six)

**Two bands (No. S75). Cream paper.**
Perforation Type B (I/P no dot) and C (E/P dot)

| Cyl. No. | No dot | Dot |
|---|---|---|
| 52 | 80·00 | 80·00 |
| 60 | 80·00 | 80·00 |

**Two bands. (No. S76) Whiter paper.**
Perforation Type A(E/I)

| Cyl. No. | No dot | Dot |
|---|---|---|
| 60 | 5·50 | 5·50 |
| 61 | 5·50 | 5·50 |
| 62 | 5·50 | 5·50 |
| 64 | 5·50 | 5·50 |
| 67 | 5·50 | 5·50 |
| 71 | 5·50 | 5·50 |

**One side band. (No. S77)**

| | No dot | Dot |
|---|---|---|
| 67 | 26·00 | 26·00 |
| 68 | 26·00 | 26·00 |
| 71 | 26·00 | 26·00 |
| 72 | 26·00 | 26·00 |

**Minor Constant Sheet Flaws**

| | | |
|---|---|---|
| Cyl. 52 | 17/9 | White spur to circle around 3d. by "D" (Th. G6) |
| Cyl. 52. | 18/2 | Coloured line from Queen's hair to top of oval (Th. B2) |
| Cyl. 60. | 4/11 | Coloured flaw on thistle leaf (Th. G2) |

**Coils**
Double pane cylinders M1 or M2 were used. Watermark upright.
Two bands. Vertical delivery in continuous reels. Cream or whiter paper

| Code No. | Number in roll | Face value |
|---|---|---|
| AC | 480 | £6 |
| AD | 960 | £12 |
| U | 1920 | £24 |

One side band (left or right). Vertical delivery in continuous reels. Whiter paper

| | | |
|---|---|---|
| AC | 480 | £6 |
| AD | 960 | £12 |
| U | 1920 | £24 |

**Imprimaturs from the National Postal Museum Archives**
Two Bands. Imperforate, watermark Type W.24. Cream or whiter paper

| | |
|---|---|
| Watermark upright | £2000 |
| Watermark inverted | £2000 |
| *Tête-bêche* pair | £8000 |

One Side Band. Imperforate, watermark Type W.24. Whiter paper

| | |
|---|---|
| Watermark sideways | £2000 |
| Vertical *Tête-bêche* pair with sideways watermark | £8000 |

**1965 (13 August). 3d. Phosphor bands reacting violet. Watermark crowns**

**S78** (=SG 615c)

| A. One Side Band* | Mint | Used |
|---|---|---|
| 3d.  Deep lilac (side band at left) | 60 | 70 |
| a.  Side band at right | 60 | 55 |
| ab.  Nos. S78/a (horiz. pair) | 1·25 | 1·25 |
| b.  One 8 mm. band (wmk. sideways) | 10·00 | |
| ba.  Pair, left-hand stamp with phosphor omitted, right- hand stamp with one band (wmk. upright) (pair) | 45·00 | |
| bb.  One 8 mm. band (wmk. upright) | 15·00 | |
| c.  Watermark Crown to left, band at left (10.65) | 5·50 | 5·00 |
| d.  Watermark Crown to left, band at right | 5·50 | 5·00 |
| e.  Watermark Crown to right, band at left | 5·50 | 5·00 |
| f.  Watermark Crown to right, band at right | 5·50 | 5·00 |
| g.  Watermark inverted (band at left) (2.67) | 50·00 | 45·00 |
| h.  Watermark inverted (band at right) | 2·25 | 2·25 |
| ha.  Nos. S78g/h (horiz. pair) | 60·00 | |

**S79** (=SG 615e)

| B. One 4 mm. Centre Band (8 December 1966) | Mint | Used |
|---|---|---|
| 3d.  Deep Lilac | 40 | 45 |
| a.  Watermark sideways (19.6.67) | 70 | 50 |
| b.  Watermark inverted (8.67) | 2·25 | 2·25 |

**S80** (=SG 615b)

| C. Two 9·5 mm. Bands. Se-tenant 2s. Booklets only (November 1967) | | |
|---|---|---|
| 3d.  Deep lilac (Watermark Crown to left) | 1·75 | 1·75 |
| a.  Watermark Crown to right | 1·75 | 1·75 |
| b.  One 9·5 mm. band (wmk. sideways) | 20·00 | |

The bands applied in Gravure, except for stamps with sideways watermark where they were applied by Typography.

*The one side band stamps were produced by an 8 mm. band applied down alternate vertical rows of the sheet over the perforations so that alternate stamps have the band at left (No. S78) or right (No. S78a). In theory the width of the band on a single stamp should be 4 mm. but this will vary if the bands have not been perfectly positioned. In addition, one side band stamps with sideways watermark were produced by applying a 9·5 mm. band over the perforations but these only came in the April 1967 and October 1967 2s. Booklets (N28p(b) and N30p(b)) *se-tenant* with the 1d. value. As it is not possible to distinguish these from the 8 mm. bands (Nos. S78c/f) in singles, the complete panes only are listed under No. SB55 to SB58.

†**Inverted watermark.** Nos. S78g/h only come from the 10s. Booklet of February 1967 (X15p(a/b)). Each pane, No. SB103a comprises two stamps with band at left and four stamps with band at right.

**Sideways watermark.** Nos. S78c/f come from 2s. Booklets N22p(b), N23p(b), N24p/28p(a), N29p/30p(a), N31p(c) and N32p(c). No. S79a comes from S coils with sideways delivery and Nos. S80/a come from 2s. Booklets N31p(a/b) and N32p(a/b).

**Cylinder Numbers** (Blocks of Six)
Perforation Type A (E/I)
One side band. (No. S78)

| Cyl. No. | No dot | Dot |
|---|---|---|
| 67 | 5·00 | 5·00 |
| 71 | 5·00 | 5·00 |

| Cyl. No. | No dot | Dot |
|---|---|---|
| 72 | ✓ 5·00 | 5·00 |
| 81 | 5·00 | 5·00 |
| 82 | 5·00 | 5·00 |

Perforation Type A(E/I)
One centre band. (No. S7a)

| Cyl. No. | No dot | Dot |
|---|---|---|
| 78 | 5·00 | 5·00 |
| 79 | 5·00 | 5·00 |
| 81 | 5·00 | 5·00 |
| 82 | 5·00 | 5·00 |

**Coils**

Double pane cylinder M12 was used for the vertical delivery coils and cylinder M11 for the sideways delivery coils.

(a) One side band. Vertical delivery printed in continuous reels with the watermark upright

| Code No. | Number in roll | Face value |
|---|---|---|
| AC | 480 | £6 |
| AD | 960 | £12 |
| U | 1920 | £24 |

(b) One centre band. Printed in continuous reels

**(a) Vertical delivery. Watermark upright**

| Code No. | Number in roll | Face value |
|---|---|---|
| AC | 480 | £6 |
| AD | 960 | £12 |

**(b) Sideways delivery. Watermark sideways**

| | | |
|---|---|---|
| S | 480 | £6 |

---

## ■ 1953-67 4d. Ultramarine, Type S3

### 1953 (2 November). 4d. Watermark Tudor Crown, Type W.22

**S81** (=SG 521)

| | Mint | Used |
|---|---|---|
| 4d. Ultramarine | 3·25 | 1·25 |
| a. Coil join (horiz. pair) | 14·00 | |
| b. Dotted "R" (Cyl. 1 No dot, R. 10/8 | 30·00 | |

S81b, S82c

The blue dot is of varying size and was eventually touched out on the St. Edward's Crown watermark.

**Cylinder Numbers** (Blocks of Six)
Perforation Type A(E/I)

| Cyl. No. | No dot | Dot |
|---|---|---|
| 1 | 25·00 | 25·00 |

Perforation Type B (I/P no dot) and C (E/P dot)

| Cyl. No. | No dot | Dot |
|---|---|---|
| 1 | 28·00 | 28·00 |

**Minor Constant Sheet Flaws**

| Cyl.1 | 1/4 | Retouch on cheek left of ear (Th. D4) |
|---|---|---|
| | 16/9 | Scar on neck. This was later the object of a major retouch (see No. S82d) but the original flaw is not available for illustrating and listing here |

**Coil**

Made up from sheets with sheet margin joins. Sideways delivery with the watermark upright

| Code No. | Number in roll | Face value |
|---|---|---|
| H | 480 | £8 |

**Imprimatur from the National Postal Museum Archives**
Imperforate, watermark Type W.22

| Watermark upright | £2000 |
|---|---|

---

### 1955 (14 November). 4d. Watermark St. Edward's Crown, Type W.23

**S82** (=SG 546)

| | Mint | Used |
|---|---|---|
| 4d. Ultramarine | 1·25 | 45 |
| a. Coil join (vert. pair) | 12·00 | |
| b. Coil join (horiz. pair) | 10·00 | |
| c. Dotted "R (Cyl. 1 No dot, R. 10/8) | 28·00 | |
| d. Retouched neck (Cyl. 1 No dot, R. 16/9) | 25·00 | |

For illustration of No. S82c, see No. S81b.

This is the major retouch of the flaw described in this position on No. S81 under Minor Constant Sheet Flaws. The blue line joining the Queen's neck to the frame is also constant.

S82d, S83c

**Cylinder Numbers** (Blocks of Six)
Perforation Type A(E/I)

| Cyl. No. | No dot | Dot |
|---|---|---|
| 1 | 17·00 | 17·00 |
| 3 | 19·00 | 19·00 |

Perforation Type B (I/P no dot) and C (E/P dot)

| Cyl. No. | No dot | Dot |
|---|---|---|
| 1 | 11·00 | 11·00 |

**Minor Constant Sheet Flaws**

| | | |
|---|---|---|
| Cyl. 1 | 1/4 | Retouch on cheek left of ear (Th. D4) |
| | 16/9 | Scar on neck before retouch as No. S82d |

**Coils**
Made up from sheets with sheet margin joins with the watermark always upright

| Code No. | Number in roll | Face value | |
|---|---|---|---|
| A | 960 | £16 | Vertical delivery |
| H | 480 | £8 | Sideways delivery |

**Imprimatur from the National Postal Museum Archives**
Imperforate, watermark Type W.23

| | |
|---|---|
| Watermark upright | £2000 |

---

**1958 (29 October). 4d. Watermark Crowns, Type W.24**

**S83**

**A. Ultramarine. Cream Paper**

| | Mint | Used |
|---|---|---|
| 4d. Ultramarine | 1·60 | 90 |
| a. Coil join (vert. pair) | 10·00 | |
| b. Coil join (horiz. pair) | 10·00 | |
| c. Retouched neck (Cyl 1 No dot, R. 16/9) | 25·00 | |
| d. Imperf. between stamp and top margin | £650 | |

**S84** (=SG 576)

**B. Ultramarine. Whiter Paper** (18 October 1962)

| | | |
|---|---|---|
| 4d. Ultramarine | 45 | 35 |
| a. Coil join (vert. pair) | 9·00 | |
| b. Coil join (horiz. pair) | 9·00 | |

**S85** (=SG 576a)

**C. Deep Ultramarine†. Whiter Paper** (28 April 1965)

| | | |
|---|---|---|
| 4d. Deep ultramarine | 15 | 15 |
| b. Double impression | £3000 | |
| c. Imperf. between stamp and top margin | £350 | |
| d. Wmk. Crown to left (Coils, 31.5.65 and booklets, 16.8.65) | 70 | 55 |
| e. Watermark inverted (21.6.65) | 60 | 50 |

| | | |
|---|---|---|
| f. Watermark Crown to right (Booklets only, 16.8.65) | 70 | 55 |

†This "shade" was brought about by making more deeply etched cylinders from a new multipositive, resulting in apparent depth of colour in parts of the design but there is no difference in the colour of the ink. The change was made deliberately and coincided with the change in the letter rate from 3d. to 4d. on 17 May 1965.

Examples of No. S85b were the result of slight paper movement during printing rather than the sheet actually being presented twice in the press.

For illustration of No. S83c, see No. S82d.

**Cylinder Numbers** (Blocks of Six)
Perforation Type A(E/I)

**(a) Ultramarine, Cream paper (No S83)**

| Cyl. No. | No dot | Dot |
|---|---|---|
| 1 | 13·00 | 13·00 |
| 6 | 13·00 | 13·00 |
| 8 | 13·00 | 13·00 |

**Whiter paper (No S84)**

| Cyl. No. | No dot | Dot |
|---|---|---|
| 8 | 5·50 | 5·50 |

**(b) Deep Ultramarine, Whiter paper (No S85)**

| Cyl. No. | No dot | Dot |
|---|---|---|
| 12 | 5·00 | 5·00 |
| 13 | 5·00 | 5·00 |
| 16 | 5·00 | 5·00 |
| 18 | 5·00 | 5·00 |
| 20 | 5·00 | 5·00 |
| 23 | 5·00 | 5·00 |
| 25 | 5·00 | 5·00 |
| 26 | 5·00 | 5·00 |
| 27 | 5·00 | 5·00 |

**Minor Constant Sheet Flaws**

| | | |
|---|---|---|
| Cyl. 1 | 1/4 | Retouch on cheek left of ear (Th. D4) |
| | 10/8 | Darker shading to right of and below large R caused by retouching the dot variety |
| Cyl. 18 | 18/11 | Two patches of retouching by frame at left (Th. C1) |

**Coils**

**(a) Ultramarine. Cream or whiter paper**
Made up from sheets with sheet margin joins. Watermark upright

| Code No. | Number in roll | Face value | |
|---|---|---|---|
| A | 960 | £16 | Vertical delivery |
| H | 480 | £8 | Sideways delivery |

**(b) Deep ultramarine**
Printed in continuous reels. It is believed that cylinder P1 was used for the vertical delivery coil and that it was a double pane cylinder but that cylinder P2 was used for the sideways delivery coil and that this was a single pane cylinder.

**(a) Vertical delivery. Watermark upright**

| A | 960 | £16 |
|---|---|---|

**(b) Sideways delivery. Watermark sideways**

| H | 480 | £8 |
|---|---|---|

**Imprimatur from the National Postal Museum Archives**
Imperforate, watermark Type W.24. Cream or white paper

| | |
|---|---|
| Watermark upright | £2000 |

## 1959 (29 April). 4d. With graphite lines, Type S8. Watermark Crowns

**S86** (=SG 593)

|  | Mint | Used |
|---|---|---|
| 4d.  Ultramarine | 5·50 | 5·00 |
| a.  Two lines at left | £2200 | |

The misplaced graphite lines listed as No. S86a result in two lines at left (with the left line down the perforations) and traces of a third line down the opposite perforations.

**Cylinder Numbers** (Blocks of Six)
Perforation Type A(E/I)

| Cyl. No. | No dot | Dot |
|---|---|---|
| 6 | 45·00 | 45·00 |

**Imprimatur from the National Postal Museum Archives**
Imperforate, watermark Type W.24

| Watermark upright | £2000 |
|---|---|

**Quantity Issued:** 6,891,600

## 1959 (18 November). 4d. Phosphor-graphite issue. Watermark Crowns

**S87** (=SG 608)

|  | Mint | Used |
|---|---|---|
| 4d.  Ultramarine | 20·00 | 16·00 |
| a.  One 6 mm. band at left or right (stamp with vert.margin) | | 15·00 |

No. S87 has two graphite lines (Type S8) on the back and two phosphor bands on the front, applied typo., which react green under the lamp.

**Cylinder Numbers** (Blocks of Six)
Perforation Type A(E/I)

| Cyl. No. | No dot | Dot |
|---|---|---|
| 6 | £140 | £120 |

**Imprimatur from the National Postal Museum Archives**
Perf. 15 × 14, watermark Type W.24

| Watermark upright | £2000 |
|---|---|

**Quantity Issued:** 490,560

## 1960 (22 June). 4d. Two phosphor bands reacting green. Watermark Crowns

**S88**

|  | Mint | Used |
|---|---|---|
| 4d.  Ultramarine | 9·00 | 8·00 |

The bands were applied in Gravure.

**Cylinder Numbers** (Blocks of Six)
Perforation Type B (I/P no dot) and C (E/P dot)

| Cyl. No. | No dot | Dot |
|---|---|---|
| 8 | 70·00 | 70·00 |

**Imprimatur from the National Postal Museum Archives**
Imperforate, watermark Type W.24

| Watermark upright | £2000 |
|---|---|

## 1961 (5 June). 4d. Two phosphor bands reacting blue. Watermark Crowns

**S89** (=SG 616)

| A. Ultramarine. Cream Paper | Mint | Used |
|---|---|---|
| 4d.  Ultramarine | 3·50 | 3·50 |
| a.  Error. One 8 mm. band | £150 | |

**S90**

| B. Deep Ultramarine †. Whiter Paper (28 April 1965) | | |
|---|---|---|
| 4d.  Deep ultramarine | 70 | 60 |
| b.  Watermark inverted (21.6.65) | 1·40 | 1·00 |
| c.  Watermark Crown to left (16.8.65) | 2·00 | 2·00 |
| d.  Watermark Crown to right (16.8.65) | 2·00 | 2·00 |
| e.  One broad band (wmk. sideways) | 50·00 | |

The bands were applied in Gravure on the stamps with upright and inverted watermark and by Typography on those with watermark sideways.

†The note below No. S85 concerning deep ultramarine applies here.

**Cylinder Numbers** (Blocks of Six)

**(a) Ultramarine. (No. S89)**
Perforation Type B (I/P no dot) and C (E/P dot)

| Cyl. No. | No dot | Dot |
|---|---|---|
| 8 | 32·00 | 32·00 |

**(b) Deep ultramarine. (No. S90)**
Perforation Type A(E/I)

| Cyl. No. | No dot | Dot |
|---|---|---|
| 12 | 6·50 | 6·50 |
| 13 | 6·50 | 6·50 |
| 18 | 6·50 | 6·50 |
| 20 | 6·50 | 6·50 |

**Minor Constant Sheet Flaw**

| Cyl. 18 | 18/11 | Two patches of retouching by frame at left (Th. C1) |
|---|---|---|

## 1965 (13 August). 4d. Two 8 mm. Phosphor bands reacting violet. Wmk. Crowns

**S91**

|  | Mint | Used |
|---|---|---|
| 4d.  Deep ultramarine | 60 | 60 |
| a.  Watermark inverted (9.65) | 45 | 45 |
| b.  Wmk. Crown to left (photo.) (1.67) | 60 | 60 |
| c.  Wmk. Crown to right (photo.) (1.67) | 60 | 60 |
| d.  One 8 mm. band (photo.) (wmk. sideways) | 10·00 | |
| e.  Wmk. Crown to left (typo.) (10.65) | 15·00 | |
| f.  Wmk. Crown to right (typo.) (10.65) | 15·00 | |

The bands were applied in Gravure, except for the sideways watermark stamps from 2s. Booklets N22p (b) and N23p (b) which also had them applied by Typography.

No. S91 is known with a very wide "phantom" band in addition to the normal two bands. This was probably due to a weak mixture of the phosphor ink, which leaked under the doctor blade. This occurred in the first and second vertical rows in a sheet.

**Cylinder Numbers** (Blocks of Six)
Perforation Type A(E/I)

| Cyl. No. | No dot | Dot |
|---|---|---|
| 18 | 5·50 | 5·50 |

| Cyl. No. | No dot | Dot |
|---|---|---|
| ✓20 | 5·50 | 5·50 |

**Minor Constant Sheet Flaw**

Cyl. 18   18/11   Two patches of retouching by frame at left (Th. C1)

### 1967 (Early). 4d. Two 9·5 mm. Phosphor bands reacting violet. Wmk. Crowns

S92 (=SG 616a)

|  | Mint | Used |
|---|---|---|
| 4d.   Deep ultramarine | 25 | 25 |
| a.   Watermark inverted (2.67) | 40 | 40 |
| b.   Wmk. Crown to left (Booklets, 4.67 and Coils, 24.4.67) | 35 | 50 |
| c.   Wmk. Crown to right (Booklets, 4.67) | 35 | 50 |
| e.   One 9·5 mm. band (wmk. sideways) | 12·00 | |

The bands were applied in Gravure.

**Cylinder Numbers** (Blocks of Six)
Perforation Type A(E/I)

| Cyl. No. | No dot | Dot |
|---|---|---|
| 16 | 5·00 | 5·00 |
| 18 | 5·00 | 5·00 |
| 23 | 5·00 | 5·00 |
| 26 | 5·00 | 5·00 |
| 27 | 5·00 | 5·00 |

**Minor Constant Sheet Flaw**

Cyl. 18   18/11   Two patches of retouching by frame at left (Th. C1)

**Coil**

Printed in continuous reels. It is believed that cylinder P2 was used and that it was a single pane cylinder.
Sideways delivery. Watermark sideways

| Code No. | Number in roll | Face value |
|---|---|---|
| H | 480 | £8 |

### ■ 1959–66 4½d. Chestnut, Type S3

### 1959 (9 February). 4½d. Watermark Crowns, Type W.24

S93

| A. Cream Paper | Mint | Used |
|---|---|---|
| 4½d.   Chestnut | 55 | 55 |

S94 (=SG 577)

| B. Whiter Paper (29 May 1962) | | |
|---|---|---|
| 4½d.   Chestnut | 10 | 25 |
| a.   Phantom frame (Cyl. 8 No dot below R. 20/12) | 18·00 | |

An incomplete marginal rule revealed a right-angled shaped frame-line on cylinder 8 no dot below R. 20/12. Later retouched on No. S98.

S94a, S98c

**Cylinder Numbers** (Blocks of Six)
Perforation Type A(E/I)

Cream paper (No. S93)

| Cyl. No. | No dot | Dot |
|---|---|---|
| 2 | 8·50 | 8·50 |
| 6 | 5·50 | 5·50 |
| 7 | 5·50 | 5·50 |

| Whiter paper. (No. S94) | | |
|---|---|---|
| 7 | 5·00 | 5·00 |
| 8 | 5·00 | 5·00 |

**Minor Constant Sheet Flaws**
Multipositive flaw:

No dot   5/6 Pale top half of rose in bottom left corner (Th. F1–2)

Cylinder flaws

| Cyl. 2 | 1/9 | White spot on cheek level with mouth (Th. D3) |
|---|---|---|
| | 1/11 | Break in bottom frame line at left corner |
| | 5/5 | Three dots to right of curve in "S" of "POSTAGE" |
| | 10/8 | White dot in laurel oval (Th. E6) |
| | 16/2 | Dotted line in bottom right corner (Th. H6) |
| | 19/10 | White dot on tail of "R" of "E R" |
| Cyl. 6 | 5/5 | Nick in laurel oval at left (Th. D1) |
| | 16/9 | Extra jewel on dress above "O" of "POSTAGE" |
| Cyl. 7 | 18/6 | White flaw in thistle flower (Th. G2) |

**Imprimatur from the National Postal Museum Archives**
Imperforate, watermark Type W.24. Cream or whiter paper

| Watermark upright | £2000 |
|---|---|

## 1959 (3 June). 4½d. With Graphite Lines, Type S8. Watermark Crowns

**S95** (=SG 594)

| | Mint | Used |
|---|---|---|
| 4½d. Chestnut | 6·50 | 5·00 |

**Cylinder Numbers** (Blocks of Six)
Perforation Type A(E/I)

| Cyl. No. | No dot | Dot |
|---|---|---|
| 6 | 50·00 | 50·00 |

**Minor Constant Sheet Flaw**
Cyl. 6 5/6 Pale top half of rose in bottom left corner (Th. F1–2)

**Imprimatur from the National Postal Museum Archives**
Imperforate, watermark Type W.24

| Watermark upright | £2000 |
|---|---|

**Quantity Issued:** 5,388,480

## 1959 (18 November). 4½d. Phosphor-graphite issue. Watermark Crowns

**S96** (=SG 609)

| | Mint | Used |
|---|---|---|
| 4½d. Chestnut | 30·00 | 20·00 |
| a. One 6 mm. band at left or right (stamp with vert. margin) | 42·00 | |
| b. One 9·5 mm. band | | |

This has two graphite lines (Type S8), on the back and two phosphor bands on the front, applied typo., which react green under the lamp. No. S96 is known with the phosphor bands additionally printed on the back of the stamp.

**Cylinder Numbers** (Blocks of Six)
Perforation Type A(E/I)

| Cyl. No. | No dot | Dot |
|---|---|---|
| 6 | £210 | £210 |

**Minor Constant Sheet Flaw**
Cyl. 6 5/6 Pale top half of rose in bottom left corner (Th. F1–2)

**Imprimatur from the National Postal Museum Archives**
Perf. 15 × 14, watermark Type W.24

| Watermark upright | £2000 |
|---|---|

**Quantity Issued:** 696,000

## 1961 (13 September). 4½d. Two phosphor bands reacting blue. Watermark Crowns

**S97**

| A. Cream Paper. Bands by Typography | Mint | Used |
|---|---|---|
| 4½d. Chestnut | 3·50 | 2·50 |
| a. One 6 mm. band at left or right (stamp with vert. margin) | 10·00 | |
| b. One 8 mm. band | 15·00 | |
| ba. As b but 6 mm. band | 20·00 | |
| c. Bands applied photo. (3.4.62) | 22·00 | 15·00 |

**S98** (=SG 616b)

| B. Whiter Paper. Bands applied in Gravure (24 January 1963) | | |
|---|---|---|
| 4½d. Chestnut | 25 | 30 |
| a. Bands applied typo. (6.65) | 2·00 | 2·00 |

| B. Whiter Paper. Bands applied in Gravure (24 January 1963) | | |
|---|---|---|
| ab. One 6 mm. band at left or right (stamp with vert. margin) | 10·00 | |
| b. One 8 mm. band (typo.) | 15·00 | |
| ba. As b but 6 mm. band | 20·00 | |
| c. Phantom frame (Cyl. 8, below R. 20/12) | 22·00 | |

For illustration of No. S98c., see No. S94a.

**Cylinder Numbers** (Blocks of Six)

**A. Cream Paper**
Applied typo. (No. S97)
Perforation Type A(E/I)

| Cyl. No. | No dot | Dot |
|---|---|---|
| 7 | 32·00 | 32·00 |

Applied photo. (No. S97c)
Perforation Type B (I/P no dot) and C (E/P dot)

| Cyl. No. | No dot | Dot |
|---|---|---|
| 7 | 45·00 | £140 |

**B. Whiter Paper**
Applied photo. (No. S98)
Perforation Type A(E/I)

| Cyl. No. | No dot | Dot |
|---|---|---|
| 7 | 5·00 | 5·00 |
| 8 | 5·00 | 5·00 |

Applied typo. (No. S98a)
Perforation Type A(E/I)

| Cyl. No. | No dot | Dot |
|---|---|---|
| 8 | 22·00 | 22·00 |

**Minor Constant Sheet Flaws**

| Cyls. 7/8 | 5/6 | Pale top half of rose in bottom left corner (Th. F1–2) |
|---|---|---|
| Cyl. 7 | 18/6 | White flaw in thistle flower (Th. G2). Later retouched |

**Imprimatur from the National Postal Museum Archives**
Imperforate, watermark Type W.24. Cream or whiter paper

| Watermark upright | £2000 |
|---|---|

## ■ 1953-67 5d. Brown, Type S4

### 1953 (6 July). 5d. Watermark Tudor Crown, Type W.22

**S99** (=SG 522)

| | | Mint | Used |
|---|---|---|---|
| 5d. | Brown | 75 | 3·50 |
| a. | Spot by "E" of "POSTAGE" (No dot, R. 4/8) | 28·00 | |
| b. | Spot on daffodil (No dot, R. 10/12) | 22·00 | |
| c. | Neck retouch (Cyl. 1 Dot, R. 2/12) | 22·00 | |

S99/103a

S99/103b                    S99/103c

These two varieties occur on the multipositive

**Cylinder Numbers** (Blocks of Six)

Perforation Type A(E/I)

| Cyl. No. | No dot | Dot |
|---|---|---|
| 1 | 8·50 | 8·50 |

**Imprimatur from the National Postal Museum Archives**
Imperforate, watermark Type W.22

| Watermark upright | £2000 |
|---|---|

### 1955 (21 September). 5d. Watermark St. Edward's Crown, Type W.23

**S100** (=SG 547)

| | | Mint | Used |
|---|---|---|---|
| 5d. | Brown | 6·00 | 6·00 |
| a. | Spot by "E" of "POSTAGE" (No dot, R. 4/8) | 30·00 | |
| b. | Spot on daffodil (No dot, R. 10/12) | 25·00 | |
| c. | Neck retouch (Cyl. 1 Dot, R. 2/12) | 25·00 | |

For illustrations of Nos. S100a/c, see Nos. S99a/c.

**Cylinder Numbers** (Blocks of Six)
Perforation Type A(E/I)

| Cyl. No. | No dot | Dot |
|---|---|---|
| 1 | 50·00 | 50·00 |

**Imprimatur from the National Postal Museum Archives**
Imperforate, watermark Type W.23

| Watermark upright | £2000 |
|---|---|

### 1958 (10 November). 5d. Watermark Crowns, Type W.24

**S101**

| A. Cream Paper | | Mint | Used |
|---|---|---|---|
| 5d. | Brown | 3·00 | 1·50 |
| a. | Spot by "E" of "POSTAGE" (No dot, R. 4/8) | 28·00 | |
| b. | Spot on daffodil (No dot, R. 10/12) | 22·00 | |
| c. | Neck retouch (Cyl. 1 Dot, R. 2/12) | 22·00 | |

**S102** (=SG 578)

| B. Whiter Paper (1 May 1963) | | Mint | Used |
|---|---|---|---|
| 5d. | Brown | 40 | 30 |
| a. | Spot by "E" of "POSTAGE" (No dot, R. 4/8) | 28·00 | |
| b. | Spot on daffodil (No dot, R. 10/12) | 22·00 | |
| c. | Neck retouch (Cyl. 1 Dot, R. 2/12) | 22·00 | |

For illustrations of Nos. S101/2a, S101/2b and S101/2c, see Nos. S99a, S99b and S99c respectively.

**Cylinder Numbers** (Blocks of Six)

**Cream Paper. (No. S101)**
Perforation Type A(E/I)

| Cyl. No. | No dot | Dot |
|---|---|---|
| 1 | 22·00 | 22·00 |
| 2 | 22·00 | 22·00 |

**Whiter Paper. (No. S102)**
Perforation Type A(E/I)

| Cyl. No. | No dot | Dot |
|---|---|---|
| 1 | 5·00 | 5·00 |

Perforation Type F(L)* (I/E no dot and P/E dot) 1*
*This is probably No. S103 but with phosphor omitted.

**Imprimatur from the National Postal Museum Archives**
Imperforate, watermark Type W.24. Cream or whiter paper

| Watermark upright | £2000 |
|---|---|

### 1967 (9 June). 5d. Two 9·5 mm. Phosphor bands reacting violet. Wmk. Crowns

**S103** (=SG 616c)

| | | Mint | Used |
|---|---|---|---|
| 5d. | Brown | 25 | 35 |
| a. | Spot by "E" of "POSTAGE" (No dot, R. 4/8) | 25·00 | |
| b. | Spot on daffodil (No dot, R. 10/12) | 20·00 | |
| c. | Neck retouch (Cyl. 1 Dot, R. 2/12) | 20·00 | |

The bands were applied in Gravure.
For illustrations of Nos. S103a/c, see Nos S99a/c.

**Cylinder Numbers** (Blocks of Six)
Perforation Type A(E/I)

| Cyl. No. | No dot | Dot (P/E) |
|---|---|---|
| ✓1 | 5·00 | 5·00 |

Perforation Type F (L)*

| Cyl. No. | No dot (I/E) | Dot (P/E) |
|---|---|---|
| 1 | 5·00 | 5·00 |

## ■ 1954-67 6d. Purple, Type S4

### 1954 (18 January). 6d. Watermark Tudor Crown, Type W.22

**S104** (=SG 523)

|  | Mint | Used |
|---|---|---|
| 6d. Reddish purple | 4·00 | 1·00 |
| a. Imperforate at top and sides (pair) | £3000 | |
| b. Imperf. between stamp and bottom margin | £850 | |
| c. Coil join (vert. pair) | 15·00 | |

**Cylinder Numbers** (Blocks of Six)
Single pane cylinder
Perforation Type B

| Cyl. No. | No dot (I/P) |
|---|---|
| 1 | 35·00 |

Perforation Type C

| Cyl. No. | No dot (E/P) |
|---|---|
| 1 | 35·00 |

Perforation Type F(L)

| Cyl. No. | No dot (I/E) |
|---|---|
| 1 | 35·00 |

**Minor Constant Sheet Flaws**
Multipositive flaws used for cylinders 1, 2 and 3
8/8 Small purple flaw joining "C" of "PENCE" to inner frame line
19/6 Small dark flaw on daffodil stem (Th. G2)
20/3 Coloured dot in top leaf of thistle (Th. A6)

**Coil**
Made up from sheets with sheet margin joins. Vertical delivery with the watermark upright

| Code No. | Number in roll | Face value |
|---|---|---|
| J | 480 | £12 |

**Imprimatur from the National Postal Museum Archives**
Imperforate, watermark Type W.22

| Watermark upright | £2000 |
|---|---|

### 1955 (20 December). 6d. Watermark St. Edward's Crown, Type W.23

**S105** (=SG 548)

**A. Reddish Purple**

|  | Mint | Used |
|---|---|---|
| 6d. Reddish purple | 4·50 | 1·25 |
| a. Imperforate three sides (pair) | £4700 | |
| b. Imperf. between stamp and left margin | | |
| c. Coil join (vert. pair) | 24·00 | |
| d. Pink tinted paper†† | 75·00 | |

**S106** (=SG 548a)

**B. Deep Claret† (8 May 1958)**

|  | Mint | Used |
|---|---|---|
| 6d. Deep claret | 4·50 | 1·40 |
| a. Imperforate three sides (pair) | £4700 | |
| b. Coil join (vert. pair) | 15·00 | |

†This was a deliberate change of colour although shade variations exist. See footnote after No. S108.
  ††This is known from cylinder 1 perforation Type C (E/P).

**Cylinder Numbers** (Blocks of Six)
Single pane cylinders

**Reddish purple (No. S105)**
Perforation Type B (I/P )

| Cyl. No. | No dot |
|---|---|
| 1 | 38·00 |
| 2 | 38·00 |

Perforation Type C (E/P)

| Cyl. No. | No dot |
|---|---|
| 1 | 35·00 |
| 2 | 35·00 |

**Deep claret (No. S106)**
Perforation Type B (I/P)

| Cyl. No. | No dot |
|---|---|
| 2 | 38·00 |
| 3 | 38·00 |

Perforation Type C (E/P)

| Cyl. No. | No dot |
|---|---|
| 2 | 35·00 |
| 3 | 35·00 |

Perforation Type F (L) (I/E)

| Cyl. No. | No dot |
|---|---|
| 3 | 50·00 |

**Minor Constant Sheet Flaws**
Multipositive flaws as shown for No. S104

**Coils**
Made up from sheets with sheet margin joins. Vertical delivery with the watermark upright

| Code No. | Number in roll | Face value | |
|---|---|---|---|
| J | 480 | £12 | Reddish purple |
| J | 480 | £12 | Deep claret |

**Imprimatur from the National Postal Museum Archives**
A. Reddish Purple. Imperforate, watermark Type W.23

| Watermark upright | £2000 |
|---|---|

B. Deep Claret. Imperforate, watermark Type W.23

| Watermark upright | £2000 |
|---|---|

### 1958 (23 December). 6d. Watermark Crowns, Type W.24

**S107**

**A. Cream Paper**

|  | Mint | Used |
|---|---|---|
| 6d. Deep claret* | 1·25 | 70 |
| a. Imperforate three sides (pair) | £3000 | |
| b. Imperf. (pair) | £3500 | |
| c. Coil join (vert. pair) | 15·00 | |

**S108** (=SG 579)

**B. White Paper** (29 June 1962)

|  | Mint | Used |
|---|---|---|
| 6d. Deep claret* | 30 | 25 |
| a. Coil join (vert. pair) | 12·00 | |
| b. Spur to frame (Cyl. 10 No dot. R. 17/2) | 22·00 | |

*This colour is unstable and a range of shades exists which also vary according to the colour of the paper. One of the more marked variations is a purple-claret on the cream paper from cylinder 8.

S108b

**Cylinder Numbers** (Blocks of Six)

**A. Cream Paper (No. S107)**
Single pane cylinders
Perforation Type B (I/P)

| Cyl. No. | No dot |
|---|---|
| 2 | 11·00 |
| 3 | 11·00 |

Perforation Type C (E/P)

| Cyl. No. | No dot |
|---|---|
| 2 | 11·00 |
| 3 | 11·00 |

Double pane cylinders
Perforation Type B (I/P no dot) and C (E/P dot)

| Cyl. No. | No dot | Dot |
|---|---|---|
| 5 | 17·00 | 17·00 |
| 7 | 11·00 | 11·00 |

Perforation Type A(E/I)

| Cyl. No. | No dot | Dot |
|---|---|---|
| 7 | 11·00 | 11·00 |
| 8 | 11·00 | 11·00 |

**B. Whiter Paper. (No. S108)**
Perforation Type A(E/I)

| Cyl. No. | No dot | Dot |
|---|---|---|
| 8 | 5·00 | 5·00 |
| 10 | 5·00 | 5·00 |
| 11 | 35·00 | 35·00 |

Perforation Type F (L)*

| Cyl. No. | No dot (I/E) | Dot (P/E) |
|---|---|---|
| 10 | 5·50 | 5·50 |

The marginal rule is damaged in most positions on cyl. 8

**Minor Constant Sheet Flaws**
Multipositive flaws on cylinders 2 and 3 as shown for No. S104
A second multipositive was used for cylinder 5 and a third for cylinders 7 onwards.

**Coils**
(a) Made up from sheets with sheet margin joins. Vertical delivery with the watermark upright

| Code No. | Number in roll | Face value | |
|---|---|---|---|
| J | 480 | £12 | Cream paper |
| J | 480 | £12 | Whiter paper |

(b) Printed in continuous reels. Single pane cylinder Q1 was used. Vertical delivery. Watermark upright

| J | 480 | £12 | Whiter paper |
|---|---|---|---|

**Imprimatur from the National Postal Museum Archives**
Imperforate, watermark Type W.24. Cream or whiter paper

| Watermark upright | £2000 |
|---|---|

## 1960 (27 June). 6d. Two phosphor bands reacting green. Watermark Crowns

S109

| | | Mint | Used |
|---|---|---|---|
| 6d. | Deep claret | 2·75 | 2·25 |

The bands were applied in Gravure.

**Cylinder Numbers** (Blocks of Six)
Single pane cylinder
Perforation Type B (I/P)

| Cyl. No. | No dot |
|---|---|
| 2 | 24·00 |

Perforation Type C (E/P)

| Cyl. No. | No dot |
|---|---|
| 2 | 24·00 |

**Minor Constant Sheet Flaws**
Multipositive flaws as shown for No. S104

**Imprimatur from the National Postal Museum Archives**
Imperforate, watermark Type W.24

| Watermark upright | £2000 |
|---|---|

## 1961 (5 June). 6d. Two phosphor bands reacting blue. Watermark Crowns

S110

| A. Cream Paper. Bands applied in Gravure | Mint | Used |
|---|---|---|
| 6d.  Deep claret | 4·50 | 3·50 |
| a.  Bands applied typo. | | |

S111

| B. White Paper. Bands applied in Gravure (3 October 1963) | | |
|---|---|---|
| 6d.  Deep claret | 1·00 | 80 |
| a.  Bands applied typo. | £450 | |
| ab.  Narrow band at left or right (stamp with vert. margin) | £500 | |

**Cylinder Numbers** (Blocks of Six)

**Cream paper (No. S110)**
Perforation Type A(E/I)
Bands applied photo.

| Cyl. No. | No dot | Dot |
|---|---|---|
| 7 | 38·00 | 38·00 |

**Cream paper (No. S110a)**
Perforation Type A(E/I)
Bands applied photo.

| Cyl. No. | No dot | Dot |
|---|---|---|
| 8 | † | |

**Whiter paper (No. S111)**
Perforation Type A(E/I)
Bands applied photo.

| Cyl. No. | No dot | Dot |
|---|---|---|
| 8 | 10·00 | 10·00 |
| 10 | 10·00 | 10·00 |

**Whiter paper (No. S111a)**
Perforation Type A(E/I)
Bands applied typo.

| Cyl. No. | No dot | Dot |
|---|---|---|
| 8 | | |

The marginal rule is damaged in most positions on cyl. 8

---

**1965 (13 August). 6d. Two 8 mm. Phosphor bands reacting violet. Wmk. Crowns**

S112

| | | Mint | Used |
|---|---|---|---|
| 6d. | Deep claret | 12·00 | 9·00 |
| a. | One 6 mm. band at left or right (stamp with vert. margin) | 20·00 | |
| b. | One 8 mm. band | 25·00 | |

The bands were applied by Typography.

**Cylinder Numbers** (Blocks of Six)
Perforation Type A(E/I)
Applied typo.

| Cyl. No. | No dot | Dot |
|---|---|---|
| 8 | 75·00 | 75·00 |

---

**1967 (Early). 6d. Two 9·5 mm. Phosphor bands reacting violet. Wmk. Crowns**

S113 (=SG 617)

| | | Mint | Used |
|---|---|---|---|
| 6d. | Deep claret | 30 | 30 |

The bands were applied in Gravure only.

**Cylinder Numbers** (Blocks of Six)
Perforation Type A(E/I)

| Cyl. No. | No dot | Dot |
|---|---|---|
| 10 | 11·00 | 11·00 |
| 11 | 5·50 | 5·50 |

Perforation Type F (L)*

| Cyl. No. | No dot (I/E) | Dot (P/E) |
|---|---|---|
| 10 | 5·00 | 5·00 |

**Coils**
Printed in continuous reels. It is believed that cylinder Q1 was used and that it was a single pane cylinder.
Vertical delivery. Watermark upright

| Code No. | Number in roll | Face value |
|---|---|---|
| J | 480 | £12 |

---

## 1954-67 7d. Bright green, Type S4

**1954 (18 January). 7d. Watermark Tudor Crown, Type W.22-**

S114 (=SG 524)

| | Mint | Used |
|---|---|---|
| | | |
| 7d.  Bright green | 9·50 | 5·50 |

**Cylinder Numbers** (Blocks of Six)
Perforation Type A(E/I)

| Cyl. No. | No dot | Dot |
|---|---|---|
| 2 | 70·00 | 70·00 |

Perforation Type B (I/P no dot) and C (E/P dot)

| Cyl. No. | No dot | Dot |
|---|---|---|
| 2 | 70·00 | 70·00 |

**Imprimatur from the National Postal Museum Archives**
Imperforate, watermark Type W.22

| Watermark upright | £2000 |
|---|---|

---

**1956 (23 April). 7d. Watermark St. Edward's Crown, Type W.23**

S115 (=SG 549)

| | Mint | Used |
|---|---|---|
| 7d.  Bright green | 50·00 | 10·00 |

**Cylinder Numbers** (Blocks of Six)
Perforation Type A(E/I)

| Cyl. No. | No dot | Dot |
|---|---|---|
| 2 | £350 | £350 |

**Imprimatur from the National Postal Museum Archives**
Imperforate, watermark Type W.23

| Watermark upright | £2000 |
|---|---|

---

**1958 (26 November). 7d. Watermark Crowns, Type W.24**

S116

| A. Cream Paper | Mint | Used |
|---|---|---|
| 7d.  Bright green | 2·50 | 70 |

S117 (=SG 580)

| B. Whiter Paper (3 July 1962) | | |
|---|---|---|
| 7d.  Bright green | 50 | 45 |

**Cylinder Numbers** (Blocks of Six)

**Cream Paper (No. S116)**
Perforation Type A(E/I)

| Cyl. No. | No dot | Dot |
|---|---|---|
| 1 | 20·00 | 20·00 |
| 2 | 20·00 | 20·00 |

Perforation Type B (I/P no dot) and C (E/P dot)

| Cyl. No. | No dot | Dot |
|---|---|---|
| 2 | 18·00 | 18·00 |

## Whiter Paper (No. S117)
Perforation Type A(E/I)

| Cyl. No. | No dot | Dot |
|----------|--------|-----|
| 1 | 5·00 | 5·00 |
| 2 | 5·00 | 5·00 |

Perforation Type F (L)*

| Cyl. No. | No dot | Dot |
|----------|--------|-----|
| 1* | £400 | £400 |

*This is probably No. S118 but with phosphor omitted.

**Imprimatur from the National Postal Museum Archives**
Imperforate, watermark Type W.24. Cream or whiter paper

| Watermark upright | £2000 |
|-------------------|-------|

---

## 1967 (15 February). 7d. Two 9·5 mm. Phosphor bands reacting violet. Wmk. Crowns

S118 (=SG 617a)

| | | Mint | Used |
|---|---|------|------|
| 7d. | Bright green | 55 | 50 |
| a. | Imperf. between stamp and top margin | £3000 | |

The bands were applied in Gravure.
No. S118a came from the top row of twelve examples of which six were defective.

**Cylinder Numbers** (Blocks of Six)
Perforation Type F (L)*

| Cyl. No. | No dot | Dot |
|----------|--------|-----|
| 1 | 9·00 | 9·00 |

Perforation Type A(E/I)

| Cyl. No. | No dot | Dot |
|----------|--------|-----|
| 2 | 5·50 | 5·50 |

**Imprimatur from the National Postal Museum Archives**
Imperforate, watermark Type W.24

| Watermark upright | £2000 |
|-------------------|-------|

---

## ■ 1953-67 8d. Magenta, Type S5

### 1953 (6 July). 8d. Watermark Tudor Crown, Type W.22

S119 (=SG 525)

| | | Mint | Used |
|---|---|------|------|
| 8d. | Magenta | 75 | 85 |

**Cylinder Numbers** (Blocks of Six)
Perforation Type A(E/I)

| Cyl. No. | No dot | Dot |
|----------|--------|-----|
| 3 | 8·25 | 8·25 |

Perforation Type B (I/P no dot) and C (E/P dot)

| Cyl. No. | No dot | Dot |
|----------|--------|-----|
| 3 | 8·25 | 8·25 |

**Minor Constant Sheet Flaw**

Cyl. 3   20/1   Coloured dot between rose at top left and "A" of "POSTAGE" (Th. B2)

**Imprimatur from the National Postal Museum Archives**
Imperforate, watermark Type W.22

| Watermark upright | £2000 |
|-------------------|-------|

---

### 1955 (21 December). 8d. Watermark St. Edward's Crown, Type W.23

S120 (=SG 550)

| | | Mint | Used |
|---|---|------|------|
| 8d. | Magenta | 7·00 | 1·25 |

**Cylinder Numbers** (Blocks of Six)
Perforation Type A(E/I)

| Cyl. No. | No dot | Dot |
|----------|--------|-----|
| 3 | 50·00 | 50·00 |

**Minor Constant Sheet Flaw**

Cyl. 3   20/1   Coloured dot between rose at top left and "A" of "POSTAGE" (Th. B2). Later retouched

**Imprimatur from the National Postal Museum Archives**
Imperforate, watermark Type W.23

| Watermark upright | £2000 |
|-------------------|-------|

---

### 1960 (24 February). 8d. Watermark Crowns, Type W.24

S121

| A. Cream Paper | | Mint | Used |
|----------------|---|------|------|
| 8d. | Magenta | 4·00 | 1·00 |

S122 (=SG 581)

| B. Whiter Paper (6 July 1962) | | | |
|-------------------------------|---|------|----|
| 8d. | Magenta | 60 | 40 |
| a. | Diadem flaw (Cyls. 4 No dot, R. 18/2) | 22·00 | |
| b. | Extra pearl (Cyl. 4 Dot, R. 16/2) | 25·00 | |

S122a, S123a Multipositive white flaw on diadem, lower left of "E" of "POSTAGE" Exists as a minor flaw on Cyl. 3

S122b, S123b

**Cylinder Numbers** (Blocks of Six)

**Cream Paper (No. S121)**
Perforation Type A(E/I)

| Cyl. No. | No dot | Dot |
|---|---|---|
| 3 | 30·00 | 30·00 |

**Whiter Paper (No. S122)**
Perforation Type A(E/I)

| Cyl. No. | No dot | Dot |
|---|---|---|
| 3 | 25·00* | 6·00 |
| 4 | 28·00* | 6·00 |

Perforation Type F (L)*( I/E no dot) and C (P/E dot)

| Cyl. No. | No dot | Dot |
|---|---|---|
| 4** | | |

** This is probably No. S123 but with phosphor omitted.

**Marginal arrows:**
"V" shaped, hand engraved at top and bottom of sheet (Cyls. 3 and 4)
"W" shaped, photo-etched at both sides (Cyl. 3) or photo-etched at left and hand engraved at right (Cyl. 4)

**Imprimatur from the National Postal Museum Archives**
Imperforate, watermark Type W.24. Cream or whiter paper

| Watermark upright | £2000 |
|---|---|

**Cylinder Numbers** (Blocks of Six)
Perforation Type A(E/I)

| Cyl. No. | No dot | Dot |
|---|---|---|
| 4 | 25·00* | 5·00 |

Perforation Type F (L) *

| Cyl. No. | No dot (I/E) | Dot (P/E) |
|---|---|---|
| 4 | 25·00* | 5·00 |

**Marginal arrows:**
"V" shaped, hand engraved at top and bottom of sheet
"W" shaped, photo-etched at left and hand engraved at right

**Imprimatur from the National Postal Museum Archives**
Imperforate, watermark Type W.24

| Watermark upright | £2000 |
|---|---|

**1967 (28 June). 8d. Two 9·5 mm. Phosphor bands reacting violet. Wmk. Crowns**

S123 (=SG 617b)

| | | Mint | Used |
|---|---|---|---|
| 8d. | Magenta | 40 | 45 |
| a. | Diadem flaw (Cyl. 4 No dot, R. 18/2) | 22·00 | |
| b. | Extra pearl (Cyl. 4 Dot, R. 16/2) | 25·00 | |
| c. | Petal joined to frame (Cyl. 4 Dot, R. 13/11) | 25·00 | |

The bands were applied in Gravure.
For illustrations of Nos. S123a/b, see Nos. S122a/b.

S123c

## ■ 1954-66 9d. Bronze-green, Type S5

### 1954 (8 February). 9d. Watermark <u>Tudor Crown</u>, Type W.22

**S124** (=SG 526)

| | Mint | Used |
|---|---|---|
| 9d. Bronze-green | 23·00 | 4·75 |
| a. Frame break at upper right (Cyl. 1 No dot, R. 8/6) | 35·00 | |
| b. Imperf. between stamp and top margin* | £3000 | |

*No. S124b was caused by a paper fold.

 Frame broken at upper right and shading below it missing. Later retouched on Crowns watermark. A very similar variety occurs on Cyl. 2, R. 11/11; see Nos. S126c. etc

S124a, S125a, S126a

**Cylinder Numbers** (Blocks of Six)
Perforation Type A(E/I)

| Cyl. No. | No dot | Dot |
|---|---|---|
| 1 | £145 | £145 |

Perforation Type B (I/P no dot) and C (E/P dot)

| Cyl. No. | No dot | Dot |
|---|---|---|
| 1 | £145 | £145 |

**Imprimatur from the National Postal Museum Archives**
Imperforate, watermark Type W.22

| Watermark upright | £2000 |
|---|---|

### 1955 (15 December). 9d. Watermark St. Edward's Crown, W.23

**S125** (=SG 551)

| | Mint | Used |
|---|---|---|
| 9d. Bronze-green | 20·00 | 2·75 |
| a. Frame break at upper right (Cyl. 1 No dot, R. 8/6) | 35·00 | |

For illustration of No. S125a, see No. S124a.

**Cylinder Numbers** (Blocks of Six)
Perforation Type A(E/I)

| Cyl. No. | No dot | Dot |
|---|---|---|
| 1 | £140 | £140 |

Perforation Type B (I/P no dot) and C (E/P dot)

| Cyl. No. | No dot | Dot |
|---|---|---|
| 1 | £140 | £140 |

**Imprimatur from the National Postal Museum Archives**
Imperforate, watermark Type W.23

| Watermark upright | £2000 |
|---|---|

### 1959 (24 March). 9d. Watermark Crowns, Type W.24

**S126**

| A. Cream Paper | Mint | Used |
|---|---|---|
| 9d. Bronze-green | 4·00 | 1·00 |
| a. Frame break at upper right (Cyl. 1 No dot, R. 8/6) | 25·00 | |
| b. Broken daffodil (Cyl. 2 No dot, R. 7/2) | 25·00 | |
| c. Frame break at upper right (Cyl. 2 No dot, R. 11/11) | 25·00 | |
| d. Frame flaw (Cyl. 2 Dot, R. 12/5) | 25·00 | |

**S127** (=SG 582)

| B. Whiter Paper (4 June 1962) | | |
|---|---|---|
| 9d. Bronze-green | 60 | 40 |
| a. Broken daffodil (Cyl. 2 No dot, R. 7/2) | 25·00 | |
| b. Frame break at upper right (Cyl. 2 No dot, R. 11/11) | 25·00 | |
| c. Frame flaw (Cyl. 2 Dot, R. 12/5) | 25·00 | |

For illustration of No. S126a, see No. S124a.

S126b, S127a, S128b Stem of daffodil is broken

S126c, S127b, S128c A very similar variety to the one on Cyl. 1, R. 8/6 but more pronounced

S126d, S127c, S128d
Flaw on frame at lower left

**Cylinder Numbers** (Blocks of Six)

**Cream paper (No. S126)**
Perforation Type A(E/I)

| Cyl. No. | No dot | Dot |
|---|---|---|
| 1 | 30·00 | 30·00 |
| 2 | 30·00 | 30·00 |

**Whiter paper (No. S127)**
Perforation Type A(E/I)

| Cyl. No. | No dot | Dot |
|---|---|---|
| 2 | 5·25 | 5·25 |

**Imprimatur from the National Postal Museum Archives**
Imperforate, watermark Type W.24. Cream or whiter paper

| Watermark upright | £2000 |
|---|---|

**1966 (29 December). 9d. Two 9·5 mm. Phosphor bands reacting violet. Wmk. Crowns**

S128 (=SG 617c)

|  |  | Mint | Used |
|---|---|---|---|
| 9d. | Bronze-green | 60 | 55 |
| a. | Imperf. between stamp and top margin | £1200 | |
| b. | Broken daffodil (Cyl. 2 No dot, R. 7/2) | 25·00 | |
| c. | Frame break at upper right (Cyl. 2 No dot, R. 11/11) | 25·00 | |
| d. | Frame flaw (Cyl. 2 Dot, R. 12/5) | 25·00 | |

The bands were applied in Gravure.
For illustrations of Nos. S128b/d, see Nos. S126b/d.

**Cylinder Numbers** (Blocks of Six)
Perforation Type A(E/I)

| Cyl. No. | No dot | Dot |
|---|---|---|
| 2 | 5·50 | 5·50 |

**Imprimatur from the National Postal Museum Archives**
Imperforate, watermark Type W.24

| Watermark upright | £2000 |
|---|---|

---

■ **1954-66 10d. Prussian blue, Type S5**

**1954 (8 February). 10d. Watermark Tudor Crown, Type W.22**

S129 (=SG 527)

|  | Mint | Used |
|---|---|---|
| 10d. Prussian blue | 18·00 | 4·75 |

**Cylinder Numbers** (Blocks of Six)
Perforation Type A(E/I)

| Cyl. No. | No dot | Dot |
|---|---|---|
| 1 | £120 | £120 |

Perforation Type B (I/P no dot) and C (E/P dot)

| Cyl. No. | No dot | Dot |
|---|---|---|
| 1 | £120 | £120 |

**Minor Constant Sheet Flaws**

| Cyl. 1 | 3/3 | White spur on right fork of "V" of "REVENUE" |
|---|---|---|
| | 10/12 | White flaw on thistle shows as a cut into the left-hand side of the flower (Th. A6) |
| | 13/10 | White flaw on rim of diadem below emblems (Th. B4) |

**Imprimatur from the National Postal Museum Archives**
Imperforate, watermark Type W.22

| Watermark upright | £2000 |
|---|---|

---

**1955 (22 September). 10d. Watermark St. Edward's Crown, Type W.23**

S130 (=SG 552)

|  | Mint | Used |
|---|---|---|
| 10d. Prussian blue | 20·00 | 2·75 |

**Cylinder Numbers** (Blocks of Six)
Perforation Type A(E/I)

| Cyl. No. | No dot | Dot |
|---|---|---|
| 1 | £150 | £150 |

**Minor Constant Sheet Flaws**

| Cyl. 1 | 3/3 | White spur on right fork of "V" of "REVENUE" |
|---|---|---|
| | 10/12 | White flaw on thistle shows as a cut into the left-hand side of the flower (Th. A6) |
| | 13/10 | White flaw on rim of diadem below emblems (Th. B4) |

**Imprimatur from the National Postal Museum Archives**
Imperforate, watermark Type W.23

| Watermark upright | £2000 |
|---|---|

---

**1958 (18 November). 10d. Watermark Crowns, Type W.24**

S131

| A. Cream Paper | Mint | Used |
|---|---|---|
| 10d. Prussian blue | 3·75 | 1·00 |

S132 (=SG 583)

| B. Whiter Paper (13 November 1962) | Mint | Used |
|---|---|---|
| 10d. Prussian blue | 1·00 | 50 |

**Cylinder Numbers** (Blocks of Six)

**Cream paper (No. S131)**
Perforation Type A(E/I)

| Cyl. No. | No dot | Dot |
|---|---|---|
| 1 | 30·00 | 30·00 |

Perforation Type B (I/P no dot) and C (E/P dot)

| Cyl. No. | No dot | Dot |
|---|---|---|
| 1 | 30·00 | 30·00 |

**Whiter Paper (No. S132)**
Perforation Type A(E/I)

| Cyl. No. | No dot | Dot |
|---|---|---|
| 1** | 8·25 | 8·25 |

Perforation Type F (L)* (I/E no dot) and P/E dot)

| Cyl. No. | No dot | Dot |
|---|---|---|
| 1** | £2250 | |

**This is probably No. S133 but with the phosphor omitted.

**Minor Constant Sheet Flaws**

| Cyl. 1 | 3/3 | White spur on right fork of "V" of "REVENUE". Later retouched |
|---|---|---|
| | 10/12 | White flaw on thistle shows as a cut into the left-hand side of the flower (Th. A6). Later retouched |
| | 13/10 | White flaw on rim of diadem below emblems (Th. B4). Later retouched |
| | 14/3 | Retouch on Queen's nose (Th. D3) |

**Imprimatur from the National Postal Museum Archives**
Imperforate, watermark Type W.24. Cream or whiter paper

| Watermark upright | £2000 |
|---|---|

---

**1966 (30 December). 10d. Two 9·5 mm. Phosphor bands reacting violet. Wmk. Crowns**

S133 (=SG 617d)

| | | Mint | Used |
|---|---|---|---|
| 10d. | Prussian blue | 70 | 60 |
| a. | One 9·5 mm. band | £200 | |

The bands were applied in Gravure.

**Cylinder Numbers** (Blocks of Six)
Perforation Type A(E/I)

| Cyl. No. | No dot | Dot |
|---|---|---|
| 1 | 6·00 | 6·00 |

Perforation Type F (L) *

| Cyl. No. | No dot (I/E) | Dot (P/E) |
|---|---|---|
| 1 | 6·00 | 6·00 |

**Minor Constant Sheet Flaws**

| Cyl. 1 | 3/3 | White spur on right fork of "V" of "REVENUE". Later retouched |
|---|---|---|
| | 14/3 | Retouch on Queen's nose (Th. D3) |

**Imprimatur from the National Postal Museum Archives**
Imperforate, watermark Type W.24

| Watermark upright | £2000 |
|---|---|

---

## ▉ 1954-65 11d. Brown-purple, Type S5

**1954 (8 February). 11d. Watermark Tudor Crown, Type W.22**

S134 (=SG 528)

| | | Mint | Used |
|---|---|---|---|
| 11d. | Brown-purple | 35·00 | 15·00 |

**Cylinder Numbers** (Blocks of Six)
Perforation Type B (I/P no dot) and C (E/P dot)

| Cyl. No. | No dot | Dot |
|---|---|---|
| 1 | £240 | £240 |

**Minor Constant Sheet Flaw**

| Cyl. 1 | 19/3 | White flaw in frame pattern at left by "O" of "POSTAGE" (Th. D1) |
|---|---|---|

**Imprimatur from the National Postal Museum Archives**
Imperforate, watermark Type W.22

| Watermark upright | £2000 |
|---|---|

---

**1955 (28 October). 11d. Watermark St. Edward's Crown, Type W.23**

S135 (=SG 553)

| | | Mint | Used |
|---|---|---|---|
| 11d. | Brown-purple | 50 | 1·10 |

**Cylinder Numbers** (Blocks of Six)
Perforation Type A(E/I)

| Cyl. No. | No dot | Dot |
|---|---|---|
| 1 | 5·00 | 5·00 |

Perforation Type B (I/P no dot) and C (E/P dot)

| Cyl. No. | No dot | Dot |
|---|---|---|
| 1 | 5·00 | 5·00 |

**Minor Constant Sheet Flaw**

| Cyl. 1 | 19/3 | White flaw in frame pattern at left by "O" of "POSTAGE" (Th. D1) |
|---|---|---|

**Imprimatur from the National Postal Museum Archives**
Imperforate, watermark Type W.23

| Watermark upright | £2000 |
|---|---|

---

### ■ 1953–67 1s. Bistre-brown, Type S6

#### 1953 (6 July). 1s. Watermark Tudor Crown, Type W.22

S136 (=SG 529)

|  | Mint | Used |
|---|---|---|
| 1s.  Bistre-brown | 80 | 50 |

**Cylinder Numbers** (Blocks of Six)
Perforation Type A(E/I)

| Cyl. No. | No dot | Dot |
|---|---|---|
| 1 | 9·00 | 9·00 |
| 2 | 24·00 | 24·00 |

Perforation Type B (I/P no dot) and C (E/P dot)

| Cyl. No. | No dot | Dot |
|---|---|---|
| 1 | 13·00 | 13·00 |

**Minor Constant Sheet Flaws**

| Cyl. 1. | 3/10 | Coloured flaw between left-hand leaves of thistle (Th. B6) |
|---|---|---|
|  | 5/10 | Coloured spur to top of lacing at right of value (Th. G5) |
| Cyl. 2. | 3/10 | As on Cyl. 1. (multipositive flaw) |

**Imprimatur from the National Postal Museum Archives**
Imperforate, watermark Type W.22

| Watermark upright | £2000 |
|---|---|

●————————

#### 1955 (3 November). 1s. Watermark St. Edward's Crown, Type W.23

S137 (=SG 554)

|  | Mint | Used |
|---|---|---|
| 1s.  Bistre-brown | 22·00 | 65 |
| a.  Thistle flaw (Cyl. 3 Dot, R. 4/5) | 40·00 |  |

S137a, S138b, S139a

**Cylinder Numbers** (Blocks of Six)
Perforation Type A(E/I)

| Cyl. No. | No dot | Dot |
|---|---|---|
| 2 | £150 | £150 |
| 3 | £150 | £150 |

Perforation Type B (I/P no dot) and C (E/P dot)

| Cyl. No. | No dot | Dot |
|---|---|---|
| 4 | £160 | £180 |

**Minor Constant Sheet Flaws**

| Cyl. 2. | 3/10 | Coloured flaw between left-hand leaves of thistle (Th. B6). Later retouched leaving a pale mark |
|---|---|---|
| Cyl. 3. | 3/10 | As on Cyl. 2, but flaw is retouched and appears much smaller (multipositive flaw) |

| Cyl. 4. | 3/10 | As for Cyl. 3. |
|---|---|---|
|  | 11/12 | Coloured spur to foot of first "E" of "REVENUE" |

**Imprimatur from the National Postal Museum Archives**
Imperforate, watermark Type W.23

| Watermark upright | £2000 |
|---|---|

●————————

#### 1958 (30 October). 1s. Watermark Crowns, Type W.24

S138

| A. Cream Paper |  | Mint | Used |
|---|---|---|---|
| 1s.  Bistre-brown |  | 3·75 | 80 |
| a.  Double impression |  | £275 |  |
| b.  Thistle flaw (Cyl. 3 Dot, R. 4/5) |  | 25·00 |  |

S139 (=SG 584)

| B. Whiter Paper (22 July 1962) |  | Mint | Used |
|---|---|---|---|
| 1s.  Bistre-brown |  | 45 | 30 |
| a.  Thistle flaw (Cyl. 3 Dot, R. 4/5) |  | 25·00 |  |

The note below No. S85 4d. deep ultramarine concerning paper movement applies to No. S138a.
For illustration of Nos. S138b and S139a, see No. S137a.

**Cylinder Numbers** (Blocks of Six)

Cream paper (No. S138)
Perforation Type A(E/I)

| Cyl. No. | No dot | Dot |
|---|---|---|
| 2 | 29·00 | 29·00 |
| 3 | 29·00 | 29·00 |
| 4 | 29·00 | 29·00 |

Whiter paper (No. S139)
Perforation Type A(E/I)

| Cyl. No. | No dot | Dot |
|---|---|---|
| 2 | 5·00 | 5·00 |
| 3 | 5·00 | 5·00 |
| 4 | 5·00 | 5·00 |

**Minor Constant Sheet Flaws**
Multipositive flaw

| Dot | 3/10 | Coloured flaw between left-hand leaves of thistle (Th. B6) now only exists retouched. Cyls. 2. and 3. show as a smudge and Cyl. 4. as a much smaller flaw |
|---|---|---|
| Cyl. 4. | 11/12 | Coloured spur to foot of first "E" of "REVENUE" |

**Imprimatur from the National Postal Museum Archives**
Imperforate, watermark Type W.24. Cream or whiter paper

| Watermark upright | £2000 |
|---|---|

●————————

**1967 (28 June). 1s. Two 9·5 mm. Phosphor bands reacting violet. Wmk. Crowns**

S140 (=SG 617e)

| | | Mint | Used |
|---|---|---|---|
| 1s. | Bistre-brown | 40 | 35 |

The bands were applied in Gravure.

**Cylinder Numbers** (Blocks of Six)
Perforation Type F (L)*

| Cyl. No. | No dot (I/E) | Dot (P/E) |
|---|---|---|
| 1 | 5·00 | 5·00 |

**Minor Constant Sheet Flaws**

| Cyl. 4. | 3/10 | Coloured flaw between left-hand leaves of thistle (Th. B6) is now retouched leaving a much smaller flaw |
|---|---|---|
| | 11/12 | Coloured spur to foot of first "E" of "REVENUE" |

**Imprimatur from the National Postal Museum Archives**
Imperforate, watermark Type W.24

| Watermark upright | £2000 |
|---|---|

---

## ■ 1953-67 1s.3d. Green, Type S7

**1953 (2 November). 1s.3d. Watermark Tudor Crown, Type W.22**

S141 (=SG 530)

| | | Mint | Used |
|---|---|---|---|
| 1s.3d. | Green | 4·75 | 3·25 |
| | a. White flaw in Queen's hair (Dot, R. 2/9) | 25·00 | |
| | b. "P" flaw (Dot, R. 6/10) | 25·00 | |

S141a, S142a, S143a, S144a, S145a, S146a, S147b    S141b, S142b, S143b, S144b, S145b, S146b, S147c

**Cylinder Numbers** (Blocks of Six)
Perforation Type A(E/I)

| Cyl. No. | No dot | Dot |
|---|---|---|
| 1 | 38·00 | 38·00 |

Perforation Type B (I/P no dot) and C (E/P dot)

| Cyl. No. | No dot | Dot |
|---|---|---|
| 1 | 38·00 | 38·00 |

**Imprimatur from the National Postal Museum Archives**
Imperforate, watermark Type W.22

| Watermark upright | £2000 |
|---|---|

---

**1956 (27 March). 1s.3d. Watermark St. Edward's Crown, Type W.23**

S142 (=SG 555)

| | | Mint | Used |
|---|---|---|---|
| 1s.3d. | Green | 30·00 | 1·60 |
| | a. White flaw in Queen's hair (Dot, R. 2/9) | 50·00 | |
| | b. "P" flaw (Dot, R. 6/10) | 50·00 | |

For illustrations of Nos. S142a/b, see Nos. S141a/b.

**Cylinder Numbers** (Blocks of Six)
Perforation Type B (I/P no dot) and C (E/P dot)

| Cyl. No. | No dot | Dot |
|---|---|---|
| 1 | £200 | £200 |

**Imprimatur from the National Postal Museum Archives**
Imperforate, watermark Type W.23

| Watermark upright | £2000 |
|---|---|

## 1959 (17 June). 1s.3d. Watermark Crowns, Type W.24

**S143**

| A. Cream Paper | Mint | Used |
|---|---|---|
| 1s.3d. Green | 3·00 | 1·25 |
|   a. White flaw in Queen's hair (Cyl. 1 Dot, R. 2/9) | 28·00 | |
|   b. "P" flaw (Cyl, 1, Dot, R. 6/10) | 28·00 | |

**S144 (=SG 585)**

| B. Whiter Paper (29 August 1962) | | |
|---|---|---|
| 1s.3d. Green | 45 | 30 |
|   a. White flaw in Queen's hair (Cyl. 1 Dot, R. 2/9) | 25·00 | |
|   b. "P" flaw (Cyl. 1 Dot, R. 6/10) | 25·00 | |

For illustrations of Nos. S143a/b and S144a/b, see Nos. S141a/b.

**Cylinder Numbers** (Blocks of Six)

**Cream Paper No (S143)**
Perforation Type A(E/I)

| Cyl. No. | No dot | Dot |
|---|---|---|
| 1 | 23·00 | 23·00 |

**Whiter Paper No (S144)**
Perforation Type A(E/I)

| Cyl. No. | No dot | Dot |
|---|---|---|
| 1 | 5·00 | 5·00 |
| 2 | 5·00 | 5·00 |

**Imprimatur from the National Postal Museum Archives**
Imperforate, watermark Type W.24. Cream or whiter paper

| Watermark upright | £2000 |
|---|---|

## 1960 (22 June). 1s.3d. Two phosphor bands reacting green. Wmk Crowns

**S145**

| | Mint | Used |
|---|---|---|
| 1s.3d. Green | 7·00 | 4·50 |
|   a. White flaw in Queen's hair (Dot, R. 2/9) | 28·00 | |
|   b. "P" flaw (Dot, R. 6/10) | 28·00 | |

The bands were applied in Gravure.
For illustrations of Nos. S145a/b, See Nos. S141a/b.

**Cylinder Numbers** (Blocks of Six)
Perforation Type B (I/P no dot) and C (E/P dot)

| Cyl. No. | No dot | Dot |
|---|---|---|
| 1 | 50·00 | 50·00 |

**Imprimatur from the National Postal Museum Archives**
Imperforate, watermark Type W.24

| Watermark upright | £2000 |
|---|---|

## 1961 (5 June). 1s.3d. Two phosphor bands reacting blue. Wmk Crowns

**S146**

| A. Cream Paper | Mint | Used |
|---|---|---|
| 1s.3d. Green | 22·00 | 10·00 |
|   a. White flaw in Queen's hair (Cyl. 1 Dot, R. 2/9) | 40·00 | |

| A. Cream Paper | Mint | Used |
|---|---|---|
|   b. "P" flaw (Cyl. 1 Dot, R. 6/10) | 40·00 | |

The bands were applied in Gravure.

**S147 (=SG 618)**

| B. Whiter Paper (21 January 1963) | | |
|---|---|---|
| 1s.3d. Green | 1·90 | 2·50 |
|   a. One 8 mm. band | 10·00 | |
|   b. White flaw in Queen's hair (Cyl. 1 Dot, R. 2/9) | 25·00 | |
|   c. "P" flaw (Cyl. 1 Dot, R. 6/10) | 25·00 | |

For illustrations of Nos. S146a/b and S147b/c, see Nos. S141a/b.

**Cylinder Numbers** (Blocks of Six)

**Cream Paper (No. S146)**
Perforation Type A(E/I)

| Cyl. No. | No dot | Dot |
|---|---|---|
| 1 | £140 | £140 |

**Whiter Paper (No. S147)**
Perforation Type A(E/I)

| Cyl. No. | No dot | Dot |
|---|---|---|
| 1 | 17·00 | 17·00 |
| 2 | 17·00 | 17·00 |

**Imprimatur from the National Postal Museum Archives**
Imperforate, watermark Type W.24. Cream or whiter paper

| Watermark upright | £2000 |
|---|---|

## 1965 (13 August). 1s.3d. Two 8 mm. Phosphor bands reacting violet. Wmk. Crowns

**S148**

| | Mint | Used |
|---|---|---|
| 1s.3d. Green | 18·00 | 4·50 |
|   a. One 6 mm. band at left or right (stamp with vert. margin) | 27·00 | |
|   b. Bands applied photo. (1966) | 7·50 | 3·50 |
|   c. Error. One 8 mm. band (photo.) | 30·00 | |
|   d. Error. One 8 mm. band (typo.) | 25·00 | |
|   da. Error. As d but 6 mm. band (typo.) | 40·00 | |

The bands were originally applied by Typography.

**Cylinder Numbers** (Blocks of Six)
Perforation Type A(E/I)
Applied typo (No. S148)

| Cyl. No. | No dot | Dot |
|---|---|---|
| 2 | £150 | £150 |

Perforation Type B (I/P no dot) and C (E/P dot)
Applied photo (No. S148b)

| Cyl. No. | No dot | Dot |
|---|---|---|
| 2 | 50·00 | 50·00 |

**1967  (Early). 1s.3d. Two 9·5 mm. Phosphor bands reacting violet. Wmk. Crowns**

S149

| | Mint | Used |
|---|---|---|
| 1s.3d.  Green | 9·00 | 5·00 |

The bands were applied in Gravure only.

**Cylinder Numbers** (Blocks of Six)
Perforation Type A(E/I)

| Cyl. No. | No dot | Dot |
|---|---|---|
| 2 | 65·00 | 65·00 |

---

■ **1953-66 1s.6d. Grey-blue, Type S6**

**1953  (2 November). 1s.6d. Watermark Tudor Crown, Type W.22**

S150 (=SG 531)

| | Mint | Used |
|---|---|---|
| 1s.6d.  Grey-blue | 14·00 | 3·75 |
| a. White flaw in Queen's hair below diadem (Dot, R. 20/1) | 30·00 | |
| b. White flaw in Queen's hair opposite "N" of "REVENUE" (Dot, R. 20/2) | 30·00 | |

| S150a, S151a, S152a, S153a, S154a | S150b, S151b, S152b Later retouched on Crowns watermark |
|---|---|

**Cylinder Numbers** (Blocks of Six)
Perforation Type A(E/I)

| Cyl. No. | No dot | Dot |
|---|---|---|
| 1 | 95·00 | £120* |

Perforation Type B (I/P no dot) and C (E/P dot)

| Cyl. No. | No dot | Dot |
|---|---|---|
| 1 | 95·00 | £120* |

**Imprimatur from the National Postal Museum Archives**
Imperforate, watermark Type W.22

| Watermark upright | £2000 |
|---|---|

---

**1956  (27 March). 1s.6d. Watermark St. Edward's Crown, Type W.23**

S151 (=SG 556)

| | Mint | Used |
|---|---|---|
| 1s.6d.  Grey-blue | 23·00 | 1·60 |
| a. White flaw in Queen's hair below diadem (Dot, R. 20/1) | 40·00 | |
| b. White flaw in Queen's hair opposite "N" of "REVENUE" (Dot, R. 20/2) | 40·00 | |

For illustrations of Nos. S151a/b, see Nos. S150a/b.

**Cylinder Numbers** (Blocks of Six)
Perforation Type A(E/I)

| Cyl. No. | No dot | Dot |
|---|---|---|
| 1 | £140 | £175* |

Perforation Type B (I/P no dot) and C (E/P dot)

| Cyl. No. | No dot | Dot |
|---|---|---|
| 1 | £140 | £175* |

**Imprimatur from the National Postal Museum Archives**
Imperforate, watermark Type W.23

| Watermark upright | £2000 |
|---|---|

## 1958 (16 December). 1s.6d. Watermark Crowns, Type W.24

### S152

**A. Cream Paper**

| | Mint | Used |
|---|---|---|
| 1s.6d. Grey-blue | 15·00 | 4·00 |
| a. White flaw in Queen's hair below diadem (Cyl. 1 Dot, R. 20/1) | 30·00 | |
| b. White flaw in Queen's hair opposite "N" of "REVENUE" (Cyl. 1 Dot, R. 20/2) | 30·00 | |

### S153 (=SG 586)

**B. Whiter Paper** (14 November 1962)

| | Mint | Used |
|---|---|---|
| 1s.6d. Grey-blue | 4·00 | 40 |
| a. White flaw in Queen's hair below diadem (Cyl. 1 Dot, R. 20/1) | 25·00 | |

For illustrations of Nos. S152a/b and S153a, see Nos. S150a/b.

**Cylinder Numbers** (Blocks of Six)

**Cream paper (No. S152)**
Perforation Type A (E/I)

| Cyl. No. | No dot | Dot |
|---|---|---|
| 1 | 90·00 | £120* |
| 3 | 90·00 | 90·00 |

Perforation Type B (I/P no dot) and C (E/P dot)

| Cyl. No. | No dot | Dot |
|---|---|---|
| 1 | 90·00 | £120* |
| 3 | 90·00 | 90·00 |

**Whiter paper (No. S153)**
Perforation Type A(E/I)

| Cyl. No. | No dot | Dot |
|---|---|---|
| 1 | 32·00 | 38·00 |

**Imprimatur from the National Postal Museum Archives**
Imperforate, watermark Type W.24. Cream or whiter paper

| Watermark upright | £2000 |
|---|---|

## 1966 (12 December). 1s.6d. Two 9·5 mm. Phosphor bands reacting violet. Wmk. Crowns

### S154 (=SG 618a)

| | Mint | Used |
|---|---|---|
| 1s.6d. Grey-blue | 2·00 | 2·00 |
| a. White flaw in Queen's hair below diadem (Cyl. 1 Dot, R. 20/1) | 25·00 | |

The bands were applied in Gravure.
For illustration of No. S154a, see No. S150a.

**Cylinder Numbers** (Blocks of Six)
Perforation Type A (E/I)

| Cyl. No. | No dot | Dot |
|---|---|---|
| 1 | 16·00 | 35·00* |

Perforation Type F(L)

| Cyl. No. | No dot (I/E) | Dot (P/E) |
|---|---|---|
| 8 | 22·00 | 22·00 |

**Imprimatur from the National Postal Museum Archives**
Imperforate, watermark Type W.24

| Watermark upright | £2000 |
|---|---|

## Presentation Packs

| SPP1 (issued 1960) Eighteen values | £275 |
|---|---|

The issued pack contained one of each value. The 1½d. and 11d. were with St. Edward's Crown watermark (Nos. S26 and S135) and the remainder were Crowns watermark all on cream paper, ½d. (No. S4), 1d (S16), 2d. (S40), 2½d. (S55), 3d. (S70), 4d. (S83), 4½d. (S93), 5d. (S101), 6d. (S107), 7d. (S116), 8d. (S121), 9d. (S126), 10d. (S131), 1s. (S138), 1s.3d. (S144), 1s.6d. (S152).
Two forms of the pack exist:
(a) Inscribed 10s 6d for sale in the U.K. and
(b) Inscribed $1·80 for sale in the U.S.A.

| SPP2 (issued 1960) Sixteen values | £300 |
|---|---|

The issued pack contained two of each value of the Phosphor-Graphite experimental issue, ½d. (No. S8), 1d. (S19), 1½d. (S31), 2d. (S43), 2½d. (S60), 3d. (S73), 4d. (S87), 4½d. (S96). The ½d., 1d. and 1½d. were with St. Edward's Crown watermark and the remainder with Crowns watermark. Although the details printed on the pack erroneously describe the stamps as all having Crowns watermark, the packs usually bear a sticker inscribed "CORRECTION. The ½d., 1d., & 1½d. stamps bear the St. Edward Crown Royal Cypher watermark."
Two forms of the pack exist:
(a) Inscribed 3s 8d for sale in the U.K. and
(b) Inscribed 50c for sale in the U.S.A. ˙

## "Dollis Hill" Phosphor Trials

This is a listing of unused trial stamps except for the used ½d. and 2½d. values on cover, the subject of notes 1 and 7 below. The majority of extant trial stamps are 2d. values. There is a significant proportion of 3d. values and a very few ½d. and 2½d. values. Substantially, the colours of the trial stamps are similar to issued stamps and the same colours are used in this list. However, it should be noted that the 2d. Red-brown trials are a much less deep shade than the stamps issued in 1953 and 1955 but are a deeper shade than the issued and trial stamps in the Light red-brown shade. Thus, the trials may be subject to lack of colour consistency (which would not be important to the phosphor experiments) if printed specially for the Post Office laboratory. All watermarked stamps are Watermark Crowns, Type W.24 except ST6 (1) 2½d. trial which has Watermark St Edward's Crown, Type W.23. Prices are for unused trial stamps.

### ST1 ½d. Orange-red

(1) Green phosphor, three 3mm bands (note 1)
To date, no unused ½d. trial stamps have been found.

### ST4 2d. Red-brown

| | |
|---|---|
| (1) No phosphor bands | |
| a. No watermark | £450 |
| b. Watermark sideways right | £700 |
| (2) Green phosphor within the paper, no watermark, imperforate (note 2) | £1250 |
| (3) Green all-over phosphor (note 3) | |
| a. No watermark | £400 |
| b. Watermark sideways left | £550 |
| c. Watermark sideways right | £500 |
| (4) Green phosphor bands, Watermark sideways left | |
| a. Two side 1.5mm bands | £700 |
| b. As (a) and one, two or five additional 1.5mm bands | £700 |
| c. As (a) and a circular band | £1200 |

### ST5 2d. Light red-brown

| | |
|---|---|
| (1) No phosphor bands, no watermark | £300 |
| (2) Green phosphor within the paper, no watermark | |
| a. Imperforate | £1200 |
| (b) Perforated | £1000 |
| (3) Green all-over phosphor (note 4) | |
| a. No watermark, variable printing, gummed or not gummed | £200 |
| b. Watermark upright | £120 |
| c. Watermark sideways left | £375 |
| d. Watermark sideways right | £450 |
| e. Watermark sideways right, phosphor front and back | £800 |
| (4) Yellow all-over phosphor no watermark (note 5) | £550 |
| (5) Green phosphor bands | |
| a. No watermark, one wide central band | £500 |
| b. No watermark, two side bands | £700 |
| c. Watermark upright, 3mm band at left | 150 |
| (6) Green honey comb,(mainly 5 rows of 5 dots) (note 6) | £550 |

There is considerable variation in the print and paper quality of these 2d. Light red-brown trial stamps ranging from mottled and powdery to high quality.

### ST6 2½d. Carmine-red

| | |
|---|---|
| (1) Yellow phosphor, one band at left, watermark St Edward's Crown upright | – |
| (2) Imperforate, Green all-over phosphor (note 7) | |
| (3) Yellow phosphor bands | |
| a. Watermark upright, two typo 8mm bands | – |
| b. Watermark upright, typo 6mm band at left with selvedge and 8mm band at right (see Section S Notes) | – |

### ST7 3d. Deep lilac

| | |
|---|---|
| (1) No phosphor bands, watermark upright, with imperforate selvedge at left | £175 |
| (2) Blue all-over phosphor | |
| (a) No watermark (note 8) | £350 |
| b. Watermark upright | £125 |
| c. Watermark sideways right | £225 |
| (3) Blue phosphor bands, over the ink | |
| a. Watermark upright, one 2mm central band (note 9) | £225 |
| b. Watermark upright, one 2mm band at left or right | £350 |
| c. Watermark upright, two 3mm side bands | 95·00 |
| d. Watermark sideways left, two 3mm side bands | £275 |
| e. Watermark upright, one 4mm central band (note 10) | £450 |
| f. Watermark sideways right, one 4mm band at left | £500 |
| (4) Blue phosphor bands, under the ink | |
| a. Watermark upright, one 1½mm band at right | £300 |
| b. Watermark upright, two 1½mm side bands | £300 |
| c. Watermark upright, one 2mm central band | £300 |
| d. Watermark upright, one 4mm central band | £400 |

The blue phosphor on these trials is a greenish-blue, which is more blue than the green phosphor on the trials but less blue than on the blue phosphor issued stamps.

Generally, some of the paper, particularly for the 2d. trial stamps, was susceptible to tearing. Torn paper was mended with repair tape prior to printing and this produced varieties such as printed on double paper, printed part on paper and tape and phosphor on stamp but not on tape.

**Notes**
The following is a brief list of trial usages.
1. On blank postcard with slogan postmark Norwich 29 February 1972
2. On blank cover with slogan postmark Norwich 14 February 1972
3. On blank postcard with slogan postmark Norwich 14 February 1972
4. On addressed covers to P O Research Station with slogan postmarks Harrow 15 December 1958, 16 December 1958 and 29 December 1958
5. On addressed cover to P O Research Station with postmark Gloucester 22 December 1971
6. On blank postcard with slogan postmark Norwich 24 February 1972
7. On blank postcard with slogan postmark Norwich 29 February 1972
8. On addressed cover to P O Research Station with slogan

postmark Norwich 29 February 1972
9.  On blank postcard with slogan postmark Norwich
    29 February 1972
10. On blank postcard with slogan postmark Norwich
    29 February 1972

Examples exist of other dates of trial usage on cover or postcard. Also, many of the trial stamps are known with postmarks but off cover. These used stamps show considerable variation in phosphor after-glow, possibly due to the stamps having been soaked to remove them from their original trial cover.

●────────────────

# SECTION SB

## Dorothy Wilding Issues
## 1953–68. Booklet Panes in Photogravure

## General Notes

**Introduction.** All panes were printed in photogravure by Harrison & Sons. As for counter sheets described in section SA, panes of six were printed in the reel in double-panes of 480 stamps, consisting of two panes (no dot and dot), each of 240 stamps arranged in 20 rows of 12. From 1957 most cylinders were engraved every 21 rows resulting in cylinder numbers appearing on either the top or bottom rows when guillotined into double panes of 20 rows. Panes of four for 2s. booklets with sideways watermark were printed in the Reel as above, but being printed sideways, the double pane of 480 stamps comprised 24 rows of 20. Panes of four for 1s. and 2s. booklets with upright/inverted watermark were printed from single-pane cylinders on sheet-fed machines, all being 18 rows of 12 stamps; except for the 1963 Holiday Booklet (NRI) which was 20 rows of 12. See the detailed notes under Section S for information on printing, paper, gum and phosphor application.

**Arrangement.** The panes are listed in face value order of the stamps they include (for *se-tenant* panes under the lowest denomination). The main listing is followed by errors and varieties.

**Perforation.** Wilding booklet stamps exist in panes of two, four and six and details together with illustrations of the perforation types will be found in Appendix G, section 4. The type abbreviations found above the pane prices refer to the appearance of the binding margin, i.e. I = imperforate, AP = alternate perf., P = perforated, E = extension hole and AP(2E)=alternate perf with two extension holes only.

**Booklet errors.** Those listed as "Imperf. pane" show one row of perforations either at top or bottom of booklet pane. Those listed as "part perf." pane have one row of three stamps imperforate on three sides. The *tête-bêche* errors derive from booklets but these are listed in Section SA.

**Booklet cylinder numbers.** These are listed for panes where the prefix letter and/or the number is visible. Some panes of four had the number engraved wide of the stamps so that they never showed on panes, but information on the cylinders used is given in most cases. Phosphor cylinder numbers have not been found on Wilding panes. The cylinder numbers being hand-engraved varied slightly as to their position in relation to the stamp so that some were invariably trimmed. A pane showing a complete cylinder number placed away from the stamp will only exist with trimmed perforations on the opposite side.

**Booklet cylinder flaws.** Cylinder flaws on booklet stamps are listed under the panes in which they occur. Prices are for the variety in a complete pane with its binding margin intact. In cases where a 21-row cylinder has been used both possible positions in the pane are given. Where a cylinder pane contains a variety, that variety, is listed additionally as a pane and the cylinder listing bears an asterix to identify that it contains a variety. Where a listed pane contains a variety, a description of it follows the listing.

When quoting the position on booklet panes no attention is paid to the labels. In a pane of six with the binding margin at the left, stamp 3 would be the third stamp in the row counting from left to right. Again "R. 1/3" refers to row one, third stamp from the left margin. Panes of four from 1s. and 2s. booklets contain panes with a top binding margin and "R. 2/2" refers to row two second stamp – viewing the pane with stamps upright.

**Phosphor band widths and misplacement.** See notes in Section S; the booklet stamps being similar to those printed in Post Office counter sheets. The 4 mm and 5·5 mm bands were printed on both sides of booklet sheets in typo on panes of four, but these can only be identified when the bands are slightly misplaced. Normally, panes of six showing 8 mm. bands have the 4 mm. band printed *over the first vertical row of perforations at the left*. Major shifts result in stamps from the first column having one 6 mm. wide band and the other four stamps a misplaced band of 8 mm. This, in effect, changes the number of bands on a single stamp and these have always been popular with collectors. In order to be treated as a wide band variety, each band must be printed wholly on the stamp and not overlap any part of the adjacent stamp or the binding margin. Partial shifts of phosphor bands are common and command much reduced prices. A different kind of variety exists where 9·5 mm phosphor bands were printed one band on 3d. stamps instead of two but this only occurred in a small printing of the 1d./3d. *se-tenant* panes in 2s. booklets listed as varieties of SB55 and SB58.

See Section SA for phosphor bands misplaced on singles derived from panes. Although complete panes with full perforations showing listable band shifts are included some remain unpriced due to their scarcity. It is possible that such panes were split up later especially if the perforations were no better than average. *Prices quoted in this Section are for good perfs all round*.

**Phosphor application.** Refer to the notes in Section S under "Phosphor Issues" for information on the types of phosphor employed.

**Stamps overprinted "Specimen".** Panes exist with a handstamped overprint in two sizes. These derive from the National Postal Museum archive sales mentioned in the Introductory Notes. The handstamp can be found inverted or overlapping the perforations but these are not listed as varieties.

> **BOOKLET PANE PRICES.** The prices quoted are for panes with good perforations all round and with binding margin attached. Panes showing some degree of trimming will be worth less than the published prices in this Catalogue. It should be appreciated that some panes are scarce with full perforations and the prices shown in the Catalogue reflect this. Panes from the 2s. booklets are particularly difficult to find with full perforations on the three sides.

> **BOOKLET PANE VARIETIES.** Panes of six with listed varieties have been placed in the I perf column for typographic convenience. However, the variety will occur on a pane with I perf or Ie perf, depending on its location in the booklet sheet. It will not occur on a pane with the other perf selvedge.

**Index to Booklet panes**

| SB No. | Face Value | Watermark | Size of Pane | Further description | Page |
|---|---|---|---|---|---|
| 1 | ½d. | Tudor Crown | 6 | | 62 |
| 2 | ½d. | Tudor Crown | 4 | | 62 |
| 3 | ½d. | Tudor Crown | 2 | | 62 |
| 4 | ½d. | St. Edward's Crown | 6 | | 62 |
| 5 | ½d. | St. Edward's Crown | 4 | | 63 |
| 6 | ½d. | St. Edward's Crown | 2 | | 63 |
| 7 | ½d. | Crowns | 6 | Cream paper | 63 |
| 8 | ½d. | Crowns | 6 | Whiter paper | 63 |
| 9 | ½d. | Crowns | 4 | Cream paper | 63 |
| 10 | ½d. | Crowns, sideways | 4 | Cream paper | 64 |
| 11 | ½d. | Crowns, sideways | 4 | Whiter paper | 64 |
| 12 | 3× ½d.+2½d. | Crowns | 4 | Chalky paper | 64 |
| 13 | 2×½d. +2×2½d. | Crowns, sideways | 4 | Whiter paper | 65 |
| 14 | ½d. | Crowns | 6 | Graphite lines | 65 |
| 15 | ½d. | Crowns | 6 | Green phosphor | 65 |
| 16 | ½d. | Crowns | 6 | Blue phosphor, cream paper | 66 |
| 17 | ½d. | Crowns | 6 | Blue phosphor, whiter paper | 66 |
| 18 | ½d. | Crowns, sideways | 4 | Blue phosphor, cream paper | 66 |
| 19 | ½d. | Crowns, sideways | 4 | Blue phosphor, whiter paper | 66 |
| 20 | 1d. | Tudor Crown | 6 | | 66 |
| 21 | 1d. | Tudor Crown | 4 | | 67 |
| 22 | 1d. | Tudor Crown | 2 | | 67 |
| 23 | 1d. | Tudor Crown | 6 | Including 3 labels: "MINIMUM INLAND PRINTED PAPER RATE 1½d." | 67 |
| 24 | 1d. | Tudor Crown | 6 | Including 3 labels: "PLEASE POST EARLY IN THE DAY" | 68 |
| 25 | 1d. | Tudor Crown | 6 | Including 3 different labels | 68 |
| 26 | 1d. | St. Edward's Crown | 6 | | 69 |
| 27 | 1d. | St. Edward's Crown | 4 | | 69 |
| 28 | 1d. | St. Edward's Crown | 2 | | 69 |
| 29 | 1d. | St. Edward's Crown | 6 | Including 3 different labels | 69 |
| 30 | 1d. | Crowns | 6 | Cream paper | 70 |
| 31 | 1d. | Crowns | 6 | Whiter paper | 70 |
| 32 | 1d. | Crowns | 4 | Cream paper | 70 |
| 33 | 1d. | Crowns, sideways | 4 | Cream paper | 70 |
| 34 | 1d. | Crowns, sideways | 4 | Whiter paper | 70 |
| 35/8 | 2 × 1d. +2 × 3d. | Crowns, sideways | 4 | Whiter paper | 71 |
| 39 | 1d. | Crowns | 6 | Graphite lines | 71 |
| 40 | 1d. | Crowns | 6 | Green phosphor | 72 |
| 41 | 1d. | Crowns | 6 | Blue phosphor, cream paper | 72 |
| 42 | 1d. | Crowns | 6 | Blue phosphor, whiter paper | 72 |
| 43 | 1d. | Crowns, sideways | 4 | Blue phosphor, cream paper | 72 |
| 44 | 1d. | Crowns, sideways | 4 | Blue phosphor, whiter paper | 72 |
| 45/8 | 2 × 1d. +2 × 3d. | Crowns, sideways | 4 | Blue phosphor, whiter paper | 73 |
| 49 | 1d. | Crowns | 6 | Violet phosphor, 8 mm. | 73 |
| 50/3 | 2 × 1d. +2 × 3d. | Crowns, sideways | 4 | 3d. with 1 side violet 8 mm. band | 73 |
| 54 | 1d. | Crowns | 6 | Violet phosphor, 9·5 mm. | 74 |
| 55/58 | 2 × 1d.+2 × 3d. | Crowns | 4 | 3d. with 2 violet 9·5 mm. bands | 74 |
| 59 | 1½d. | Tudor Crown | 6 | | 74 |
| 60 | 1½d. | Tudor Crown | 4 | | 75 |
| 61 | 1½d. | Tudor Crown | 2 | | 75 |
| 62 | 1½d. | St. Edward's Crown | 6 | | 75 |
| 63 | 1½d. | St. Edward's Crown | 4 | | 76 |
| 64 | 1½d. | St. Edward's Crown | 2 | | 76 |
| 65 | 1½d. | Crowns | 6 | Cream paper | 76 |
| 66 | 1½d. | Crowns | 6 | Whiter paper | 76 |
| 67 | 1½d. | Crowns | 4 | Cream paper | 76 |
| 68 | 1½d. | Crowns, sideways | 4 | Cream paper | 77 |
| 69 | 1½d. | Crowns, sideways | 4 | Whiter paper | 77 |
| 70 | 1½d. | Crowns | 6 | Graphite lines | 77 |
| 71 | 1½d. | Crowns | 6 | Green phosphor | 77 |
| 72 | 1½d. | Crowns | 6 | Blue phosphor, cream paper | 77 |

| SB No. | Face Value | Watermark | Size of Pane | Further description | Page |
|---|---|---|---|---|---|
| 73 | 1½d. | Crowns | 6 | Blue phosphor, whiter paper | 77 |
| 74 | 1½d. | Crowns, sideways | 4 | Blue phosphor, cream paper | 78 |
| 75 | 1½d. | Crowns, sideways | 4 | Blue phosphor, whiter paper | 78 |
| 76 | 2d. | Tudor Crown | 6 | | 78 |
| 77 | 2d. | St. Edward's Crown | 6 | Red-brown | 78 |
| 78 | 2d. | St. Edward's Crown | 6 | Light red-brown | 78 |
| 79 | 2d. | Crowns | 6 | Cream paper | 79 |
| 80 | 2½d. | Tudor Crown | 6 | Type II | 79 |
| 81 | 2½d. | St. Edward's Crown | 6 | Type II | 80 |
| 82 | 2½d. | Crowns | 6 | Type II. Cream paper | 80 |
| 83 | 2½d. | Crowns | 6 | Type II. Whiter paper | 80 |
| 84 | 2½d. | Crowns | 4 | Type II. Chalky paper | 81 |
| 85 | 2½d. | Crowns | 6 | Type II. Graphite lines | 81 |
| 86 | 2½d. | Crowns | 6 | Type II. Green phosphor | 81 |
| 87 | 2½d. | Crowns | 6 | Type II. Blue phosphor, 2 bands, cream paper | 81 |
| 88 | 2½d. | Crowns | 6 | Type II. Blue phosphor, 1 band, cream paper | 82 |
| 89 | 2½d. | Crowns | 6 | Type II. Blue phosphor, 1 band, whiter paper | 82 |
| 90 | 3d. | St. Edward's Crown | 6 | | 82 |
| 91 | 3d. | St. Edward's Crown | 4 | | 82 |
| 92 | 3d. | Crowns | 6 | Cream paper | 83 |
| 93 | 3d. | Crowns | 6 | Whiter paper | 83 |
| 94 | 3d. | Crowns | 4 | Cream paper | 83 |
| 95 | 3d. | Crowns, sideways | 4 | Cream paper | 83 |
| 96 | 3d. | Crowns, sideways | 4 | Whiter paper | 83 |
| 97 | 3d. | Crowns | 6 | Graphite lines | 84 |
| 98 | 3d. | Crowns | 6 | Green phosphor | 84 |
| 99 | 3d. | Crowns | 6 | Blue phosphor, cream paper | 84 |
| 100 | 3d. | Crowns | 6 | Blue phosphor, whiter paper | 84 |
| 101 | 3d. | Crowns, sideways | 4 | Blue phosphor, cream paper | 85 |
| 102 | 3d. | Crowns, sideways | 4 | Blue phosphor, whiter paper | 85 |
| 103 | 3d. | Crowns | 6 | Violet phosphor, 1 side band | 85 |
| 104 | 3d. | Crowns | 6 | Violet phosphor, 1 centre band | 85 |
| 105 | 4d. | Crowns | 6 | Deep ultramarine | 85 |
| 106 | 4d. | Crowns, sideways | 4 | Deep ultramarine | 86 |
| 107 | 4d. | Crowns | 6 | Deep ultramarine. Blue phosphor | 86 |
| 108 | 4d. | Crowns, sideways | 4 | Deep ultramarine. Blue phosphor | 86 |
| 109 | 4d. | Crowns | 6 | Violet phosphor, 8 mm. | 87 |
| 110 | 4d. | Crowns, sideways | 4 | Violet phosphor, 8 mm. | 87 |
| 111 | 4d. | Crowns | 6 | Violet phosphor, 9·5 mm. | 87 |
| 112 | 4d. | Crowns, sideways | 4 | Violet phosphor, 9·5 mm. | 88 |

## ½d. Panes of six, Tudor Crown

From 2s.6d. Booklets F14/38 and F42/43 and 5s. Booklets H6/19 and H21.
**A. Watermark upright**

|  |  | Perf. Type | |
|---|---|---|---|
|  |  | I | Ie |
| SB1 | Pane of 6 × ½d. (containing No. S1×6) (3.54) | 3·75 | 4·50 |

**B. Watermark inverted**

|  |  | Perf. Type | |
|---|---|---|---|
|  |  | I | Ie |
| SB1a | Pane of 6 × ½d. (containing No. S1a×6) (3.54) | 6·00 | 7·50 |

**Booklet Cylinder Numbers**
Panes of six (20-row cylinders)

| Cylinder No. | No Dot | Dot |
|---|---|---|
| E1 | 40·00 | 25·00 |
| E2 | 30·00 | 30·00 |
| E4* | 35·00 | 35·00 |

*The no dot pane of cylinder E4 originally had a dot inserted in error. This can be distinguished from the true dot cylinder in which the "4" is broader and further from the "E", and the dot is more circular than the erroneous dot.

The erroneous dot was not noticed until the Crowns watermark which exists in three states: I with the erroneous dot; II with dot removed leaving a smudge; and III with smudge removed. These are shown in the following illustration:

True dot       I       II       III

## ½d. Panes of four, Tudor Crown

From 1s. Booklet K1/a for use in "E" slot machines.
**A. Watermark upright**

|  |  | Perf. Type P |
|---|---|---|
| SB2 | Pane of 4 × ½d. (containing No. S1×4) (22.7.54) | 8·00 |

**B. Watermark inverted**

| SB2a | Pane of 4 × ½d. (containing No. S1a×4) (22.7.54) | 10·00 |
|---|---|---|

**Booklet Cylinder Number**
Cylinder No. E3 was used, but it does not appear in the finished booklets.

**Imprimatur from the National Postal Museum Archives**
Booklet pane of four. Imperforate, watermark Type W.22

| Two panes arranged vertically *tête-bêche* with a 12 mm. horizontal gutter margin between | £20,000 |
|---|---|

## ½d. Panes of two, Tudor Crown

From 1s. Booklet E1 for use in experimental "D" slot machines.
**Watermark upright**

|  |  | Perf. Type | |
|---|---|---|---|
|  |  | E | E(½v) |
| SB3 | Pane of 2 × ½d. (containing No. S1×2) (2.9.53) | 5·00 | 10·00 |

Made up from vertical columns 1 and 2 from sheets.

**Booklet Cylinder Numbers**
Panes of two (from sheets). *Perf. Type E*

| Cylinder No. | No Dot | Dot |
|---|---|---|
| 1 | 60·00 | 80·00 |
| 3 | 50·00 | 40·00 |

## ½d. Panes of six, St. Edward's Crown

From 2s.6d. Booklets F34/61, 3s. Booklets M1/10 and 5s. Booklets H17/37

|  |  | Perf. Type | |
|---|---|---|---|
|  |  | I | Ie |
| **A. Watermark upright** | | | |
| SB4 | Pane of 6 × ½d. (containing No. S2×6) (9.55) | 2·50 | 3·00 |
| b. | Part perf. pane* | £4750 | |
| c. | White flaw in Queen's hair (R. 1/3 or 2/3) | 30·00 | |

|  |  | Perf. Type | |
|---|---|---|---|
|  |  | I | Ie |
| **B. Watermark inverted** | | | |
| SB4a | Pane of 6 × ½d. (containing No. S2b×6) (9.55) | 4·00 | 5·00 |
| ab. | Part perf pane | £4750 | |

*Booklet error see General Notes.

SB4c, SB7e, SB14b
(Cyl. E4 dot)

**Booklet Cylinder Numbers**
Panes of six (20/21-row cylinders)

| Cylinder No. | No Dot | Dot |
|---|---|---|
| E4* | 30·00 | 30·00 |
| E4 T* | 40·00 | 40·00 |

*See notes after booklet panes of No. SB1.

The ½d. double pane cylinders E1, E2 and E4 contained 20 rows and the cylinder number always occurred opposite row 18 so that it always appears next to the bottom row of the pane.

Cylinder E4 was later modified by adding another row of 24. In this and later 21-row cylinders, which are printed continuously on the web, the perforated web is cut at every 20th row to make sheets of 480. Consequently on successive sheets the cylinder number appears one row lower and thus a pane can have it adjoining the top or bottom row. Where the cylinder number adjoins the top row of the pane it is designated by the letter "T".

## ½d. Panes of four, St. Edward's Crown

From 1s. Booklets K2/b for use in "E" slot machines and 2s. Booklet N1

| A. Watermark upright | Perf. Type | |
|---|---|---|
| | AP | P |
| SB5    Pane of 4 × ½d. (containing No. S2×4) (5.7.56) | 10·00 | 10·00 |
| B. Watermark inverted | | |
| SB5a    Pane of 4 × ½d. (containing No. S2b×4) (5.7.56) | 10·00 | 10·00 |

**Booklet Cylinder Number**
Cylinder No. E3 was used, but it does not appear in the finished booklets.

**Imprimatur from the National Postal Museum Archives**
Booklet pane of four. Imperforate, watermark Type W.23

| Two panes arranged vertically *tête-bêche* with a 12 mm. horizontal gutter margin between | £20,000 |
|---|---|

---

## ½d. Panes of two, St. Edward's Crown

From 1s. Booklet E2 for use in experimental "D" slot machines.

**Watermark upright**

| | Perf. Type | |
|---|---|---|
| | E | E(½v) |
| SB6    Pane of 2 × ½d. (containing No. S2×2) (11.57) | 25·00 | 40·00 |

Made up from vertical rows 1 and 2 from sheets.

**Booklet Cylinder Numbers**
Panes of two (from sheets). *Perf. Type* E

| Cylinder No. | No Dot | Dot |
|---|---|---|
| 3 | 95·00 | £150 |

---

## ½d. Panes of six, Crowns Wmk

Cream or whiter paper
From 3s. Booklets M9(a)/74, 5s. Booklets H35(a) and H37/74 and 10s. Booklets X1/2

| Cream Paper | Perf. Type | |
|---|---|---|
| A. Watermark upright | I | Ie |
| SB7    Pane of 6 × ½d. (containing No. S4×6) (11.58) | 5·50 | 6·50 |
|    b. Part perf. pane* | £3000 | |
|    c. Dot on left fraction bar (R. 1/1 or R. 2/1) | 35·00 | |
|    d. Extended right fraction bar (R. 1/1 or R. 2/1) | 35·00 | |
|    e. White flaw in Queen s hair (R. 1/3 or R. 2/3) | 35·00 | |
| B. Watermark inverted | | |
| SB7a    Pane of 6 × ½d. (containing No. S4c×6) (11.58) | 5·50 | 6·50 |

**Whiter Paper**

| A. Watermark upright | | |
|---|---|---|
| SB8    Pane of 6 × ½d. (containing No. S5×6) (6.62) | 7·50 | 12·00 |
|    b. Dot on left fraction bar (R. 1/1 or R. 2/1) | 40·00 | |
|    c. Extended right fraction bar (R. 1/1 or R. 2/1) | 40·00 | |
| B. Watermark inverted | | |
| SB8a    Pane of 6 × ½d. (containing No. S5c×6) (6.62) | 5·50 | 12·00 |

*Booklet error. See General Notes.
For illustration of No. SB7e see No. SB4c.

| SB7c, SB8b, SB16c, SB17c | SB7d, SB8c, SB16b, SB17b |
|---|---|
| (Cyl. E12 no dot) | (Cyl. E12 no dot) |

**Booklet Cylinder Numbers**
Panes of six (21-row cylinders)

**Cream paper**

| Cylinder No. | | No Dot | Dot |
|---|---|---|---|
| E4* | With erroneous dot | 40·00 | 40·00 |
| E4* | No dot with smudge | 60·00 | † |
| E4* | Smudge removed | 50·00 | † |
| E4 T* | With erroneous dot | 50·00 | 50·00 |
| E4 T* | No dot with smudge | 50·00 | † |
| E4 T* | Smudge removed | 40·00 | † |
| E11 | | 40·00 | 50·00 |
| E11T | | 40·00 | 50·00 |
| E12 | | 60·00 | 50·00 |
| E12T | | 60·00 | 50·00 |

*For explanation see notes below No. SB1.

**Whiter paper**

| | No Dot | Dot |
|---|---|---|
| E11 | 70·00 | 70·00 |
| E11T | 70·00 | 70·00 |
| E12 | 70·00 | 70·00 |
| E12T | 70·00 | 70·00 |

**Specimen overprints from the National Postal Museum Archives**
Booklet pane of six. Perf. 15 × 14, watermark Type W.24 inverted
Each stamp handstamped Specimen (15 × 2½ mm.)

---

## ½d. Panes of four, Crowns Wmk

Cream paper
From 1s. Booklets K3/a for use in "E" slot machines and 2s. Booklets N2/3.

| | Perf. Type |
|---|---|
| | AP |
| A. Watermark upright | |
| SB9    Pane of 4 × ½d. (containing No. S4×4) (13.8.59) | 6·00 |
| B. Watermark inverted | |
| SB9a    Pane of 4 × ½d. (containing No. S4c×4) (13.8.59) | 6·00 |

**Booklet Cylinder Numbers**
Cylinder No. E3 was used, but it does not appear in the finished booklets.

**Imprimaturs from the National Postal Museum Archives**
Booklet pane of four. Imperforate, watermark Type W.24

Two panes arranged vertically *tête-bêche* with a
12 mm. horizontal gutter margin between            £20,000

**Specimen overprints from
the National Postal Museum Archives**
Booklet pane of four. Perf. 15×14, watermark Type W.24
inverted
Each stamp handstamped "Specimen" (13×2 mm.)

## ■ ½d. Panes of four, Crowns Wmk sideways

Cream or whiter paper
From 2s. Booklets N4/20

**Cream Paper**

| A. Watermark Crown to left | Perf. Type | | | |
|---|---|---|---|---|
| | *I* | *I(½v)* | *AP* | *AP(2E)* |
| SB10    Pane of 4 × ½d. (containing No. S4d × 4) (26.5.61) | 20·00 | 50·00 | 10·00 | 30·00 |
| B. Watermark Crown to right | | | | |
| SB10a   Pane of 4 × ½d. (containing No. S4e × 4) (26.5.61) | † | 20·00 | 50·00 | |

**Whiter Paper**

| A. Watermark Crown to left | | | | |
|---|---|---|---|---|
| SB11    Pane of 4 × ½d. (containing No. S5a × 4) (5.6.62) | 20·00 | 50·00 | 10·00 | 30·00 |
| B. Watermark Crown to right | | | | |
| SB11a   Pane of 4 × ½d. (containing No. S5b × 4) (5.6.62) | † | 20·00 | 50·00 | 10·00 |

**Booklet Cylinder Number**
Pane of four

| | Perf Type I |
|---|---|
| Cylinder No. | No Dot |
| E13 (wk crown to left) | 85·00 |

Due to the width of the selvedge, the "3" was normally
trimmed off.

**Specimen overprints from
the National Postal Museum Archives**
Booklet pane of four. Perf. 15×14, watermark Type W.24
Each stamp handstamped "Specimen" (13×2 mm.)

SB12

SB13

## ■ *Se-tenant* panes of four from Holiday Booklets, Crowns Wmk

Chalk-surfaced paper. 3×½d. with 2½d. from 2s. Booklet
NR1/1a

| A. Watermark upright | Perf. Type | | |
|---|---|---|---|
| | *I* | *I(½v)* | *AP* |
| SB12    Pane of ½d./2½d. (containing No. S6×3, S58) (15.7.63) | 15·00 | 25·00 | 9·00 |
| b.        Screen damage on 2½d. (R. 2/2) | † | † | 50·00 |
| **B. Watermark inverted** | | | |
| SB12a   Pane of ½d./2½d. (containing No. S6a×3, S58a) (15.7.63) | 15·00 | 25·00 | 9·00 |
| ab.      Daffodil flaw on ½d. (R. 2/1) | † | † | 55·00 |
| ac.      Daffodil trumpet flaw on ½d (R. 1/2) | † | † | 55·00 |

SB12b

SB12ab Bottom
left stamp of pane
(2½d. to right)

SB12ac
Upper right  stamp
of pane

Whiter paper. Crowns sideways watermark
Pair of ½d. with pair of 2½d. from 2s. Booklet NR2

### A. Watermark Crown to left

| | | Perf. Type | |
| --- | --- | :---: | :---: |
| | | I | I(½v) | AP |
| SB13 | Pane of 2× ½d./2½d. (containing Nos. S5a×2, S57c×2) (1.7.64) | 12·00 | 20·00 | ✓2·00 |
| b. | Comma flaw (R. 1/2) | 35·00 | † | † |
| c. | Spot to right of d (R. 1/1) | 30·00 | † | † |
| d. | Rose flaw (R. 1/2) | † | † | 25·00 |
| e. | "P" for "D" (R. 2/1) | † | † | 30·00 |
| f. | Wreath flaw (R. 2/1) | † | † | 25·00 |
| g. | White spot above "2" (R. 2/2) | † | † | 25·00 |

### B. Watermark Crown to right

| | | | | |
| --- | --- | :---: | :---: | :---: |
| SB13a | Pane of 2× ½d./2 ½d. (containing Nos. S5b×2, S57d×2) (1.7.64) | 12·00 | 20·00 | 2·00 |
| ab. | Rose stem flaw (R. 1/2) | † | † | 25·00 |
| ac. | Frame flaw (R. 1/2) | † | † | 35·00 |
| ad. | White spot by daffodil (R. 1/1) | † | † | 35·00 |

SB13b
Upper right stamp of pane

SB13c
Upper left stamp of pane

SB13d
Upper right stamp of pane

SB13e
Lower left stamp of pane

SB13f
Lower left stamp of pane

SB13g
Lowwer left stamp of pane

SB13ab
Upper right stamp of pane

SB13ac
Upper right stamp of pane

SB13ad
Upper left stamp of pane

**Booklet Cylinder Numbers**
Panes of four Perf. Type I.
Cylinder numbers did not appear in the finished booklets NR1/1a but the following exists from the Holiday Booklet NR2 on whiter paper, Perf. Type I, watermark crowns to right.

| Cylinder No. | No Dot |
| --- | --- |
| E14 (½d.), J15 (2½d. | 45·00 |

Due to the width of the selvedge "E" and "I were normally trimmed off.

**Imprimaturs from the National Postal Museum Archives**
Se-tenant booklet panes of four.
Imperforate, watermark Type W.24

| | |
| --- | --- |
| Two panes as No. SB12 arranged vertically *tête-bêche* with binding margin at top and bottom | £20,000 |
| Two panes as No. SB13 arranged sideways *tête-bêche* with binding margin at top and bottom | £20,000 |

---

## ■ ½d. Panes of six with graphite lines, Crowns Wmk

Graphite lines as Type S8, shown above No. S3 on page 12.
From 3s. Booklets M13g/15g, M19g/21g and 5s. Booklets H39g, H43g and H46g

| | | Perf. Type | |
| --- | --- | :---: | :---: |
| | | I | Ie |
| **A. Watermark upright** | | | |
| SB14 | Pane of 6 × ½d. (containing No. S7×6) (4.8.59) | 65·00 | 75·00 |
| b. | White flaw in Queen's hair (R. 1/3 or 2/3) | £100 | |
| **B. Watermark inverted** | | | |
| SB14a | Pane of 6 × ½d. (containing No. S7a×6) (4.8.59) | 25·00 | 30·00 |

For illustration of No. SB14b, see No. SB4c.

**Booklet Cylinder Numbers**
Panes of six (21-row cylinder)

| Cylinder No. | No Dot | Dot |
| --- | --- | --- |
| E4 | £150 | £150 |
| E4 T | £150 | £150 |

---

## ■ ½d. Panes of six, phosphor bands

Two phosphor bands reacting green applied in photogravure From 3s. Booklets M25p, M28p/29p and M37p(a) and 5s. Booklet H46p

| | | | |
| --- | --- | :---: | :---: |
| **A. Watermark upright** | | | |
| SB15 | Pane of 6 × ½d. (containing No. S9×6) (14.8.60) | 25·00 | 30·00 |
| **B. Watermark inverted** | | | |
| SB15a | Pane of 6 × ½d. (containing No. S9a×6) (14.8.60) | 85·00 | 95·00 |

**Booklet Cylinder Numbers**

Panes of six (21-row cylinder)

| Cylinder No. | No Dot | Dot |
|---|---|---|
| E11 | £120 | £120 |
| E11 T | £120 | £120 |

**Specimen overprints from the National Postal Museum Archives**

Booklet pane of six, perf. 15 × 14, watermark type W.24 upright. Each stamp handstamped "Specimen" (13 × 2 mm).

●━━━━━━━━━━━━

## ■ ½d. panes of six, phosphor bands

Two phosphor bands reacting blue applied in photogravure. Cream or whiter paper

From 3s. Booklets M33p, M36p, M37p(b), M38p/39p, M43p/47p, M49p/53p, M55p/61p, M64p/74p, and 5s. Booklets H49p, H51p/52p and H54p/74p

| Cream Paper | | Perf. Type | |
|---|---|---|---|
| **A. Watermark upright** | | *I* | *Ie* |
| SB16 | Pane of 6 × ½d. (containing No. S10×6) (3.61) | 5·00 | 6·00 |
| | b. Extended right fraction bar (R. 1/1 or 2/1) | 40·00 | |
| | c. Dot on left fraction bar (R. 1/1 or 2/1) | 40·00 | |
| | d. One band on each stamp | £450 | |
| **B. Watermark inverted** | | | |
| SB16a | Pane of 6 × ½d. (containing No. S10a×6) (3.61) | 8·00 | 9·50 |

| Whiter Paper | | | |
|---|---|---|---|
| **A. Watermark upright** | | | |
| SB17 | Pane of 6 × ½d. (containing No. S11×6) (3.6.63) | 20·00 | 25·00 |
| | b. Extended right fraction bar (R. 1/1 or 2/1) | 70·00 | |
| | c. Dot on left fraction bar (R. 1/1 or 2/1) | 70·00 | |
| **B. Watermark inverted** | | | |
| SB17a | Pane of 6 × ½d. (containing No. S11c×6) (3.6.63) | 25·00 | 30·00 |

For illustrations of Nos. SB16b/c and SB17b/c, see Nos. SB7c/d.

**Booklet Cylinder Numbers**

Panes of six (21-row cylinder)

**Cream paper**

| Cylinder No. | No Dot | Dot |
|---|---|---|
| E12 | 65·00 | 65·00 |
| E12 T | 65·00 | 65·00 |

**Whiter paper**

| | | |
|---|---|---|
| E12 | 85·00 | 85·00 |
| E12 T | 85·00 | 85·00 |

**Specimen overprints from the National Postal Museum Archives**

Booklet pane of six. Perf. 15 × 14, watermark Type W.24 upright Each stamp handstamped "Specimen" (15 × 2½ mm.)

●━━━━━━━━━━━━

## ■ ½d. Panes of four, phosphor bands

Sideways watermark. Two phosphor bands reacting blue applied by Typography. Cream or whiter paper
From 2s. Booklets N4p, N8p/10p, N12p/20p

**Cream Paper**

| A. Watermark Crown to left | | Perf. Type | | | |
|---|---|---|---|---|---|
| | | *I* | *I(½v)* | *AP* | *AP(2E)* |
| SB18 | Pane of 4 × ½d. (containing No. S10b×4) (14.7.61) | 70·00 | 85·00 | 40·00 | † |
| | b. One 8 mm band on each stamp | £200 | — | £120 | 70·00 |
| **B. Watermark Crown to right** | | | | | |
| SB18a | Pane of 4 × ½d. (containing No. S10c×4) (14.7.61) | 70·00 | 85·00 | 40·00 | † |
| | ab. One 8 mm band on each stamp | — | — | £100 | † |

| Whiter Paper | | Perf. Type | | | |
|---|---|---|---|---|---|
| A. Watermark Crown to left | | *I* | *I(½v)* | *AP* | *A(2E)* |
| SB19 | Pane of 4 × ½d. (containing No. S11a×4) (15.8.62) | 85·00 | £120 | 60·00 | 75·00 |
| **B. Watermark Crown to right** | | | | | |
| SB19a | Pane of 4 × ½d. (containing No. S11b×4) (15.8.62) | 85·00 | £120 | 60·00 | † |

**Booklet Cylinder Number**

Pane of four Perf. Type I

| Cylinder No. | |
|---|---|
| E13 (wmk Crown to left) | £175 |

Due to the width of the selvedge, the "3" was usually trimmed off.

**Imprimaturs from the National Postal Museum Archives**

Booklet pane of four. Imperforate, watermark Type W.24 Two panes arranged sideways *tête-bêche*

**Specimen overprints from the National Postal Museum Archives**

| Booklet pane of four. Perf. 15 × 14, watermark Type W.24 Crown to right, perf Type A.P. | £20,000 |
|---|---|

Each stamp handstamped "Specimen" (13 × 2 mm.)

●━━━━━━━━━━━━

## ■ 1d. Panes of six, Tudor Crown

From 5s. Booklets H7/19 and H21

| | | Perf. Type | |
|---|---|---|---|
| | | *I* | *Ie* |
| **A. Watermark upright** | | | |
| SB20 | Pane of 6 × 1d. (containing No. S13×6) (3.54) | 30·00 | 35·00 |
| | b. Hair flaw (R. 1/1) | 55·00 | |
| **B. Watermark inverted** | | | |
| SB20a | Pane of 6 × 1d. (containing No. S13a×6) (3.54) | 60·00 | 70·00 |
| | ab. Extended leaf on shamrock (R. 2/1) | 90·00 | |

SB20b, SB26d
(Cyl. F4 no dot)

SB20ab, SB26ad, SB30ac,
SB31ad, SB39ac, SB40ac,
SB41ab, SB42ab, SB49ab, SB54ab

This is a multipositive flaw from booklet panes.
All watermarks and phosphors (Cyls. F3, F4 and F10 from the
dot pane)

**Booklet Cylinder Numbers**
Panes of six from 5s. Booklets

| Cylinder No. | No Dot | Dot |
|---|---|---|
| F4 | 90·00 | 50·00* |

*Contains the dot in serif flaw (R. 1/3).

## ■ 1d. Panes of four, Tudor Crown

From 1s. Booklet K1/a for use in "E" slot machines.

|  |  | Perf. Type P |
|---|---|---|
| **A. Watermark upright** | | |
| SB21 | Pane of 4 × 1d. (containing No. S13 × 4) (22.7.54) | 10·00 |
| **B. Watermark inverted** | | |
| SB21a | Pane of 4 × 1d. (containing No. S13a × 4) (22.7.54) | 45·00 |

**Booklet Cylinder Number**
Cylinder No. F7 was used, but it does not appear in the finished
booklets.

**Imprimatur from the National Postal Museum Archives**
Booklet pane of four. Imperforate, watermark Type W.22

| Two panes arranged vertically *tête-bêche* with a 12 mm. horizontal gutter margin between | £20,000 |
|---|---|

## ■ 1d. Panes of two, Tudor Crown

From 1s. Booklet E1 for use in experimental "D" slot machines.
Watermark upright

|  |  | Perf. Type | | | |
|---|---|---|---|---|---|
|  |  | I | I(½v) | E | E(½v) |
| SB22 | Pane of 2 × 1d. (containing No. S13 × 2) (2.9.53) | 5·00 | £125 | 5·00 | 10·00 |
| a. | Shamrock flaw on cyl. 2 No dot pane (as on No. S13c) | † | † | 40·00 | † |

Made up from columns 1 and 2 from sheets.

**Booklet Cylinder Numbers**
Panes of two (from sheets)

|  | Perf. Type | |
|---|---|---|
|  | I | E |
| Cylinder No. | No Dot | Dot |
| 1 | 40·00 | 40·00 |

|  | Perf. Type | |
|---|---|---|
|  |  | E |
| 2 | 40·00* | £100 |

SB23

## ■ 1d. *Se-tenant* with printed labels, Tudor Crown

"MINIMUM INLAND PRINTED PAPER RATE 1½d."
3 × 1d. Tudor Crown
From 2s.6d. Booklet F15

|  |  | Perf. Type | |
|---|---|---|---|
|  |  | I | IE |
| **A. Watermark upright** | | | |
| SB23 | Pane of 3 × 1d. (containing S13 × 3) (3.54) | £350 | £350 |
| | b. Height of label print 16 mm. (on cyl. F6 £475 pane) | £475 | |
| | c. Dot in serif (R. 1/3) | £400 | |
| **B. Watermark inverted** | | | |
| SB23a | Pane of 3 × 1d. (containing S13a × 3) (3.54) | £350 | £350 |

In the label inscription the height from "MINIMUM" TO "1½d." is
usually 15 mm. However, on the cylinder pane of No. SB23, F5
dot and F6 no dot and dot only, the right-hand label shows a
height of 16 mm. due to a larger 2mm. space between "RATE"
and "1½". All issues of label panes were printed on 20-row
cylinders to accommodate the format of stamps and labels on
alternate rows.

SB23c, SB24ba, SB24c, SB25b, SB26b, SB29b,
SB30e, SB31b, SB41b, SB42b, SB49b, SB54b

**Dot in serif of "1". Right-hand stamp**
This is a multipositive flaw which is found only in booklet
panes, stamp 3 in either the first or second horizontal rows; all
watermarks and phosphors on the dot cylinder panes F3, F4
and F10 also on the ordinary panes from cylinders F3, F5, F6, F9
and F10. On cylinder F3 dot the flaw exists as a retouched state
leaving the dot as a blemish and later the mark was removed.
The later state occurs only in the position R. 2/3 and is not listed
separately. Note that the flaw is present on all panes of six (R.
1/3) with cylinder number in bottom position.

**Booklet Cylinder Numbers**
Panes with printed labels from 2s.6d. Booklet F15

| Cylinder No. | No Dot | Dot |
|---|---|---|
| F5 | † | £1500 |
| F6 Spacing error | £475* | £475* |
| F6 Spacing corrected | — | † |

SB24

SB25, SB29

## ■ 1d. *Se-tenant* with printed labels, Tudor Crown

"PLEASE POST EARLY IN THE DAY"
3 × 1d. Tudor Crown
From 2s.6d. Booklets F16/25

| | | Perf. Type | |
|---|---|---|---|
| | | *I* | *Ie* |
| **A. Watermark upright** | | | |
| SB24 | Pane of 3 × 1d. (containing S13 × 3) (4.54) | 40·00 | 50·00 |
| b. | Modified setting | 85·00 | |
| ba. | Do. Dot in serif (R. 1/3) | £110 | |
| c. | Dot in serif (R. 1/3) | 65·00 | |
| **B. Watermark inverted** | | | |
| SB24a | Pane of 3 × 1d. (containing S13a × 3) (4.54) | 35·00 | 50·00 |
| ab. | Modified setting | 85·00 | |

In the modified setting the distance between "IN THE" is 1 mm. and this is only found on the majority of the Jan. 1955 edition (Booklet F25). The normal spacing is 1½ mm.

**Booklet Cylinder Numbers**
Panes with printed labels from 2s.6d. Booklets F16/25

| Cylinder No. | No Dot | Dot |
|---|---|---|
| F6 | 95·00 | 75·00 |
| F6 (modified setting) | £250 | £250 |

On panes SB25 and SB29, the labels were printed in Gravure instead of Typography.

## ■ 1d. *Se-tenant* with printed labels, Tudor Crown

"PACK YOUR PARCELS SECURELY" (1st LABEL)
"ADDRESS YOUR LETTERS CORRECTLY" (2nd label)
"AND POST EARLY IN THE DAY" (3rd label)
3 × 1d. Tudor Crown
From 2s.6d. Booklets F26/36

| | | Perf. Type | |
|---|---|---|---|
| | | *I* | *Ie* |
| **A. Watermark upright** | | | |
| SB25 | Pane of 3 × 1d. (containing No. S13 × 3) (1.55) | 50·00 | 60·00 |
| b. | Dot in serif (R. 1/3) | 80·00 | |
| c. | Daffodil flaw (R. 1/1) | 80·00 | |
| **B. Watermark inverted** | | | |
| SB25a | Pane of 3 × 1d. (containing No. S13a × 3) (1.55) | | 55·00 |

SB25c, SB29c
(Cyl. F6 no dot)

**Booklet Cylinder Numbers**
Panes with printed labels from 2s.6d. Booklets F26/36

| Cylinder No. | No Dot | Dot |
|---|---|---|
| F6 | 95·00 | 95·00 |

**Imprimatur from the National Postal Museum Archives**
Booklet pane with printed labels. Imperforate, watermark Type W.22

| Two panes as No. SB25 arranged *tête-bêche* | £20,000 |
|---|---|

## ■ 1d. Panes of six, St. Edward's Crown

From 3s. Booklets M1/10 and 5s. Booklets H17/37

| | Perf. Type | |
|---|---|---|
| | I | Ie |
| **A. Watermark upright** | | |
| SB26 Pane of 6 × 1d. (containing No. S14×6) (8.55) | 5·00 | 6·00 |
| b. Dot in serif (R. 2/3, F3 dot)) | 45·00 | |
| c. Dew drop (R. 1/1 or 2/1) | 35·00 | |
| d. Hair flaw (R. 1/1) | 40·00 | |
| **B. Watermark inverted** | | |
| SB26a Pane of 6 × 1d. (containing No. S14b×6) (8.55) | 8·00 | 7·00 |
| ab. Spot on "d" (R. 1/1 or 2/1) | 35·00 | |
| ac. White flaw by rose (R. 1/2 or 2/2) | 35·00 | |
| ad. Extended leaf on shamrock (R. 1/1 or 2/1) | 35·00 | |
| ae. Rose flaw (R. 1/1 or 2/1) | 35·00 | |

For illustrations of No. SB26b, see No. SB23c, for No. SB26d, see No. SB20b and for No. SB26ad, see No. SB20ab.

SB26c, SB30d, SB39b Later retouched on Crowns and phosphor (Cyl. F3 dot)

SB26ab, SB30ab, SB31ac SB39ab, SB40ab (Cyl. F3 dot)

SB26ac (Cyl. F3 dot)

SB26ae, SB30ad, SB39ad, SB40ad (Cyl. F3 no dot)

**Booklet Cylinder Numbers**
Panes of six

| Cylinder No. | Cat No. | No Dot | Dot |
|---|---|---|---|
| F3 | SB26 | 40·00 | 40·00* |
| F3 | SB26 | 40·00 | 40·00 |
| F4 | SB26 | 50·00 | 45·00* |

Cylinder F3 contained 21 rows so that cylinder numbers adjoin either the top (T) or the bottom row. It was used in all 5s. Booklets H31/37. Cylinder F4 was a 20-row cylinder and used for the 5s. Booklets H17/30.

## ■ 1d. Panes of four, St. Edward's Crown

From 1s. Booklets K2/b for use in "E" slot machines and 2s. Booklet N1

| | Perf. Type | |
|---|---|---|
| | AP | P |
| **A. Watermark upright** | | |
| SB27 Pane of 4 × 1d. (containing No. S14×4) (5.7.56) | 10·00 | 8·00 |
| b. Spur to shamrock (R. 2/1) | 40.00 | † |
| **B. Watermark inverted** | | |
| SB27a Pane of 4 × 1d. (containing No. S14b×4) (5.7.56) | 10·00 | 10·00 |

SB27b, SB32b Later retouched on Crowns wmk.

**Booklet Cylinder Numbers**
Cylinder Nos. F7 and F8 were used, but they do not appear in the finished booklets.

**Imprimaturs from the National Postal Museum Archives**
Booklet pane of four. Imperforate, watermark Type W.23

| Two panes arranged vertically *tête-bêche* with a 12 mm. horizontal gutter margin between | £20,000 |
|---|---|

## ■ 1d. Panes of two, St. Edward's Crown

From 1s. Booklet E2 for use in experimental "D" slot machines. Watermark upright

| | Perf.Type | |
|---|---|---|
| | E | E(½v) |
| SB28 Pane of 2 × 1d. (containing No. S14×2) (11757) | 25·00 | 40·00 |

Made up from columns 1 and 2 from sheets.

**Booklet Cylinder Numbers**
Panes of two (from sheets). *Perf. Type* E

| Cylinder No. | No Dot | Dot |
|---|---|---|
| 1 | £150 | £150 |

## ■ 1d. *Se-tenant* with printed labels, St. Edward's Crown

"PACK YOUR PARCELS SECURELY" (1st label),
"ADDRESS YOUR LETTERS CORRECTLY" (2nd label)
"AND POST EARLY IN THE DAY" (3rd label)
From 2s.6d. Booklets F33/52

| | Perf. Type | |
|---|---|---|
| | I | Ie |
| **A. Watermark upright** | | |
| SB29 Pane of 3 × 1d. (containing No. S14×3) (8.55) | 16·00 | 19·00 |
| b. Dot in serif (R. 1/3) | 35·00 | |
| c. Daffodil flaw (R. 1/1) | 45·00 | |
| **B. Watermark inverted** | | |
| SB29a Pane of 3 × 1d. (containing No. S14b×3) (8.55) | 16·00 | 19·00 |

For illustration of No. SB29b see No. SB23c and for No. SB29c see No. SB25c.

**Booklet Cylinder Numbers**
Panes with printed labels from 2s.6d. Booklets F33/52

| Cylinder No. | No Dot | Dot |
|---|---|---|
| F6 | 50·00 | 50·00 |
| F9 | 95·00 | 95·00 |

Cylinder F6 was used for the 2s.6d. Booklets F33/40 and part of F41/52 and F9 for 2s.6d. Booklets F41/52.

**Imprimatur from the National Postal Museum Archives**
Booklet pane with printed labels. Imperforate, watermark Type W.23

| Two panes as No. SB29 arranged *tête-bêche* | £20,000 |
|---|---|

## ■ 1d. Panes of six, Crowns Wmk

Cream or whiter paper
From 3s. Booklets M9(b)/(e), M10/74, 4s.6d. Booklets L59/65, 5s. Booklets H35(b)/(c), H36(a) and H37/74 and 10s. Booklets X1/14

| Cream Paper | | | Perf. Type | |
|---|---|---|---|---|
| A. Watermark upright | | | *I* | *Ie* |
| SB30 | Pane of 6 × 1d. (containing No. | | | |
| | S16×6) (11.58) | | 7·00 | 9·00 |
| b. | Imperf. pane* | | £5500 | |
| c. | Part perf. pane* | | £4250 | |
| d. | Dew drop (R. 1/1 or 2/1) | | 35·00 | |
| e. | Dot in serif (R. 2/3) | | 30·00 | |
| B. Watermark inverted | | | | |
| SB30a | Pane of 6 × 1d. (containing No. | | | |
| | S16d×6) (11.58) | | 7·00 | 9·00 |
| ab. | Spot on "d" (R. 1/1 or 2/1) | | 35·00 | |
| ac. | Extended leaf on shamrock (R. 1/1 | | | |
| | or 2/1) | | 35·00 | |
| ad. | Rose flaw (R. 1/1 or 2/1) | | 25·00 | |

| Whiter Paper | | | Perf. Type | |
|---|---|---|---|---|
| A. Watermark upright | | | *I* | *Ie* |
| LSB31 | Pane of 6 × 1d. (containing No. | | | |
| | S17×6) (29.7.62) | | 10·00 | 12·00 |
| b. | Dot in serif (R. 2/3) | | 35·00 | |
| B. Watermark inverted | | | | |
| SB31a | Pane of 6 × 1d. (containing No. | | | |
| | S17c×6) (29.7.62) | | 10·00 | 12·00 |
| ab. | Part perf. pane* | | £4250 | |
| ac. | Spot on "d" (R. 1/1 or 2/1) | | 45·00 | |
| ad. | Extended leaf on shamrock (R. 1/1 | | | |
| | or 2/1) | | 45·00 | |
| ae. | Imperf pane* | | £5500 | |

*Booklet errors See General Notes.
For illustrations of No. SB30d see No. SB26c; for Nos. SB30ab and SB31ac see No. SB26ab; for Nos. SB30ac and SB31ad see No. SB20ab and for No. SB30ad see No. SB26ae.
　　On the cream paper the dot in serif flaw (Cyl. F3 dot) was removed by retouching but a smudged state exists. For illustration of No. SB30e, see No SB23c. On white paper the flaw exists from Cyl. F10 dot.

**Booklet Cylinder Numbers**
Panes of six (21-row cylinders)

**Cream paper**

| Cylinder No. | No Dot | Dot |
|---|---|---|
| F3 | 40·00 | 35·00* |
| F3 T | 40·00 | 40·00 |
| F10 | 50·00 | 40·00* |
| F10 T | 50·00 | 40·00 |

**Whiter paper**

| | | |
|---|---|---|
| F3 | 60·00 | 60·00 |
| F3 T | 60·00 | 60·00 |
| F10 | 60·00 | 45·00* |
| F10 T | 60·00 | 45·00 |

**Specimen overprints from
the National Postal Museum Archives**
Booklet pane of six. Perf. 15×14, watermark Type W.24
Each stamp handstamped "Specimen" (13×2 mm.) wmk. upright
Each stamp handstamped "Specimen" (15×2½ mm.) wmk. inverted

## ■ 1d. Panes of four, Crowns Wmk

Cream paper
From 1s. Booklets K3/a for use in "E" slot machines and 2s. Booklets N2/3.

| A. Watermark upright | | Perf. Type AP |
|---|---|---|
| SB32 | Pane of 4 × 1d. (containing No. | |
| | S16×4) (13.8.59) | 5·00 |
| b. | Spur to shamrock (R. 2/1) | 35·00 |
| B. Watermark inverted | | |
| SB32a | Pane of 4 × 1d. (containing No. | |
| | S16d×4) (13.8.59) | 5·00 |

For illustration of No. SB32b see No. SB27b.

**Booklet Cylinder Number**
Cylinder No. F8 was used, but it does not appear in the finished booklets.

**Imprimatur from the National Postal Museum Archives**
Booklet pane of four. Imperforate, watermark Type W.24

| Two panes arranged vertically *tête-bêche* with a 12 mm. horizontal gutter margin between | £20,000 |
|---|---|

**Specimen overprints from
the National Postal Museum Archives**
Booklet pane of four. Perf. 15×14, watermark Type W.24 upright
Each stamp handstamped "Specimen" (13×2 mm.)

## ■ 1d. Panes of four, Crowns Wmk sideways

Cream or whiter paper
From 2s. Booklets N4/20

**Cream paper**

| A. Watermark Crown to left | | Perf. Type | | | |
|---|---|---|---|---|---|
| | | *I* | *I(½v)* | *AP* | *AP(2E)* |
| SB33 | Pane of 4 × 1d. (containing No. | | | | |
| | S16e×4) (26.5.61) | 20·00 | 70·00 | 10·00 | 30·00 |
| B. Watermark Crown to right | | | | | |
| SB33a | Pane of 4 × 1d. (containing No. | | | | |
| | S16f×4) (26.5.61) | 20·00 | 70·00 | 10·00 | † |

**Whiter Paper**

| A. Watermark Crown to left | | | | | |
|---|---|---|---|---|---|
| SB34 | Pane of 4 × 1d. (containing No. | | | | |
| | S17a×4) (5.6.62) | 30·00 | 85·00 | 12·00 | 40·00 |
| B. Watermark Crown to right | | | | | |
| SB34a | Pane of 4 × 1d. (containing No. | | | | |
| | S17b×4) (5.6.62) | 30·00 | 85·00 | 12·00 | † |

**Booklet Cylinder Numbers**
Pane of four, Perf Type I
Cyl. No F12 9wmk Crown to left) £150
Due to the width of the selvedge, the "2" was normally trimmed off.

**Specimen overprints from
the National Postal Museum Archives**
Booklet pane of four. Perf. 15×14, watermark Type W.24 Perf. Type AP
Each stamp handstamped "Specimen" (13×2 mm.), .

SB35, SB37, SB45, SB47, SB50, SB52, SB55, SB57 (1d. values at left)

SB36, SB38, SB46, SB48, SB51, SB53, SB56, SB58 (1d. values at right)

## ◼ 1d. and 3d. *Se-tenant* panes of four, Crowns Wmk sideways.

Pair of 1d. with pair of 3d. Crowns, Whiter paper
From 2s. Booklets N21/27

**Panes SB35 and SB37**   Panes of four with 1d. at left
**Panes SB36 and SB38**   Panes of four with 1d. at right

**A. Watermark Crown to left**

| | | I | I(½v) | AP | AP(E2) |
|---|---|---|---|---|---|
| SB35 | Pane of 2 × 1d./3d. (containing Nos. S17a×2, S71a×2) (16.8.65) | 15·00 | † | 10·00 | † |
| SB36 | Pane of 2 × 3d./1d. (containing Nos. S71a×2, S17a×2) (16.8.65) | 15·00 | 75·00 | 11·00 | † |

The 1(½v) pane has the Hustle flaw on 1d. (R.2/2)B.

**Watermark Crown to right**

| | | I | I(½v) | AP | |
|---|---|---|---|---|---|
| SB37 | Pane of 2 × 1d./3d. (containing Nos. S17b×2, S71b×2) (16.8.65) | 15·00 | 75·00 | 10·00 | — |

| | | | | |
|---|---|---|---|---|
| SB38 | Pane of 2 × 3d./1d. (containing Nos. S71b×2, S17b×2) (16.8.65) | 15·00 | — | 10·00 | — |
| | a. "R" flaw on 1d. (R. 2/2) | | | 50·00 | † |

**Perf AP (E2).** Due to the scarity of these panes, it is surmised that they are from the phosphor issue panes SB52 and SB53 or SB57 and SB58 with phosphor omitted in error as N30pa and N32f, all known with phosphor omitted on the *se-tenant* panes.

SB36a, SB46c, SB51c, SB56a, SB56ba Large white flaw to right of left thistle. Occurs on bottom right stamp of I(½v) pane with 3d. at left

SB38a, SB48c, SB53c, SB58a, SB58ba Flaw on P which appears as R and occurs on bottom right stamp of pane with 3d. at left

**Booklet Cylinder Numbers**
Panes of four (24-row single pane cylinder of 480 stamps, sideways).
From 1d./3d./ *se-tenant* pane Perf. Type I, wmk Crown to left

| Cylinder No. | No Dot | |
|---|---|---|
| F13 (1d.), K22 (3d.) | 50·00 | |

## ◼ 1d. Panes of six with graphite lines, Crowns Wmk

Graphite lines as Type **S8** (page 12)
From 3s. Booklets M13g/15g, M19g/21g and 5s. Booklets H39g, H43g and H46g

| | Perf. Type | |
|---|---|---|
| | I | Ie |
| **A. Watermark upright** | | |
| SB39 Pane of 6 × 1d. (containing No. S18×6) (4.8.59) | 30·00 | 35·00 |
| b. Dew drop (R. 1/1 or 2/1) | 65·00 | |
| **B. Watermark inverted** | | |
| SB39a Pane of 6 × 1d. (containing No. S18a×6) (4.8.59) | 20·00 | 22·00 |
| ab. Spot on "d" (R. 1/1 or 2/1) | 65·00 | |
| ac. Extended leaf on shamrock (R. 1/1 or 2/1) | 65·00 | |
| ad. Rose flaw (R. 1/1 or 2/1) | 65·00 | |

For illustrations of No. SB39b see No. SB26c; for Nos. SB39ab/ad see Nos. SB26ab, SB20ab and SB26ae.

**Booklet Cylinder Numbers**
Panes of six (21-row cylinder)

| Cylinder No. | No Dot | Dot |
|---|---|---|
| F3 | £100 | £100 |
| F3 T | £100 | £100 |

## ■ **1d. Panes of six with phosphor bands, Crowns Wmk**

6 × 1d. Crowns. Two phosphor bands reacting green applied in photogravure
From 3s. Booklets M25p, M28p/29p and M37p(a) and 5s. Booklet H46p

|  |  | Perf. Type | |
|---|---|---|---|
|  |  | *I* | *Ie* |
| **A. Watermark upright** |  |  |  |
| SB40 | Pane of 6 × 1d. (containing No. S20×6) (14.8.60) | 30·00 | 35·00 |
| b. | One 8mm. band on each stamp | £200 | |
| **B. Watermark inverted** |  |  |  |
| SB40a | Pane of 6 × 1d. (containing No. S20a×6) (14.8.60) | 45·00 | 50·00 |
| ab. | Spot on d (R. 1/1 or 2/1) | 95·00 | |
| ac. | Extended leaf on shamrock (R. 1/1 or 2/1) | 95·00 | |
| ad. | Rose flaw (R. 1/1 or 2/1) | 95·00 | |
| ae. | One 8mm. band on each stamp | £200 | |
| af. | Stamps 1 and 4 with one 6mm. band, others with one 8mm band | £200 | |

For illustrations of Nos. SB40ab/ad see Nos. SB26ab, SB20ab and SB26ae.

**Booklet Cylinder Numbers**
Panes of six (21-row cylinder)

| Cylinder No. | No Dot | Dot |
|---|---|---|
| F3 | £135 | £135 |
| F3 T | £135 | £135 |

**Specimen overprints from
the National Postal Museum Archives**
Booklet pane of six. Perf. 15 × 14, watermark Type W.24 inverted
Each stamp handstamped "Specimen" (13 × 2 mm.)

## ■ **1d. Panes of six with phosphor bands, Crowns Wmk**

Two phosphor bands reacting blue applied in photogravure.
Cream or whiter paper
From 3s. Booklets M33p, M36p, M37p(b), M38p/9p, M43p/7p, M49p/53p, M55p/61p, M64p/74p, 4s.6d. Booklets L59p/60p(a), L61p(a), L62p(a) and 5s. Booklets H49p, H51p/2p, H54p/74p

**Cream Paper**

**A. Watermark upright**

| SB41 | Pane of 6 × 1d. (containing No. S21×6) (3.61) | 7·00 |
|---|---|---|
| b. | Dot in serif (R. 2/3) | 45·00 |

**B. Watermark inverted**

| SB41a | Pane of 6 × 1d. (containing No. S21a×6) (3.61) | 8·00 |
|---|---|---|
| ab. | Extended leaf on shamrock (R. 1/1 or 2/1) | 55·00 |

**Whiter Paper**

**A. Watermark upright**

| SB42 | Pane of 6 × 1d. (containing No. S22×6) (3.6.63) | 12·00 |
|---|---|---|
| b. | Dot in serif (R. 2/3) | 55·00 |
| c. | One band on each stamp | |

**B. Watermark inverted**

| SB42a | Pane of 6 × 1d. (containing No. S22c×6) (3.6.63) | 15·00 |
|---|---|---|
| ab. | Extended leaf on shamrock (R. 1/1 or 2/1) | 65·00 |
| ac. | One band on each stamp | |

For illustrations of Nos. SB41b and SB42b see No. SB23c; for Nos. SB41ab and SB42ab see No. SB20ab.

**Booklet Cylinder Numbers**
Panes of six (21-row cylinders).

**Cream paper**

| Cylinder No. | No Dot | Dot |
|---|---|---|
| F10 | 75.00 | 75·00* |
| F10 T | 75·00 | 75·00 |

**Whiter paper**

| F10 | 85·00 | 85·00* |
|---|---|---|
| F10 T | 85·00 | 85·00 |

**Specimen overprints from
the National Postal Museum Archives**
Booklet pane of six. Perf. 15 × 14, watermark Type W.24 inverted
Each stamp handstamped "Specimen" (15 × 2½ mm.)

## ■ **1d. Panes of four with phosphor bands, Crowns Wmk sideways**

Two phosphor bands reacting blue. applied by Typography.
Cream or whiter paper
From 2s. Booklets N4p, N8p/10p, N12p/20p

**Cream Paper**

| **A. Watermark Crown to left** |  | Perf. Type | | | |
|---|---|---|---|---|---|
|  |  | *I* | *I(½v)* | *AP* | *AP(2E)* |
| SB43 | Pane of 4 × 1d. (containing No. S21b×4) (14.7.61) | 20·00 | 75·00 | 15·00 | 25·00 |
| b. | One 8mm. band on each stamp | — | — | 85·00 | — |
| **B. Watermark Crown to right** |  |  |  |  |  |
| SB43a | Pane of 4 × 1d. (containing No. S21c×4) (14.7.61) | 20·00 | 75·00 | 15·00 | † |
| ab. | One 8mm. band on each stamp | — | — | 85·00 | † |

**Whiter Paper**

| **A. Watermark Crown to left** |  |  |  |  |
|---|---|---|---|---|
| SB44 | Pane of 4 × 1d. (containing No. S22a×4) (15.8.62) | 30·00 | 85·00 | 20·00 |
| b. | One 8mm. band on each stamp | £200 | — | £200 |
| **B. Watermark Crown to right** |  |  |  |  |
| SB44a | Pane of 4 × 1d. (containing No. S22b×4) (15.8.62) | 30·00 | 85·00 | 20·00 |
| ab. | One 8mm band on each stamp | £200 | — | £200 |

**Booklet Cylinder Numbers**
Pane of four, Perf. Type I cyl. No. F12 (wmk. Crown to left) £150
Due to the width of the selvedge, the "2" was normally trimmed off.

**Imprimaturs from the National Postal Museums Archives**
Booklet pane of four. Imperforate, watermark Type W.24

| Two panes arranged vertically *tête-bêche* | £20,000 |
|---|---|

**Specimen overprints from
the National Postal Museum Archives**
Booklet pane of four. Perf. 15 × 14, watermark Type W.24 Crown to right, Perf Type AP. Each stamp handstamped "Specimen" (13 × 2 mm.)

## ■ 1d. and 3d. *Se-tenant* panes of four with phosphor bands

Phosphor bands reacting blue. Sideways watermark
Pair of 1d. (two bands) with pair of 3d. (1 side 8 mm. blue band) applied by Typography. Crowns.

**Whiter paper**
From 2s. Booklets N21p/22p(a) and N23p(a)

**Panes SB45 and SB47** Panes of four with 1d. (two bands) at left; 3d. side band at left
**Panes SB46 and SB48** Panes of four with 1d. (two bands) at right; 3d. side band at right

|  |  | Perf. Type | | |
|---|---|---|---|---|
| **A. Watermark Crown to left** | | *I* | *I(½v)* | *AP* |
| SB45 | Pane of 2 × 1d./3d. (containing Nos. S22a×2, S77b×2) (16.8.65) | £100 | † | 80·00 |
| SB46 | Pane of 2 × 3d./1d. (containing Nos. S77c×2, S22a×2) (16.8.65) | £100 | £150 | 80·00 |
| a. | One band on each stamp | — | — | — |
| b. | One band on 1d. and no bands on 3d. | — | — | — |

**B. Watermark Crown to right** The I(½v) pane has the thistle flaw on the 1d. (R.2/2)

| SB47 | Pane of 2 × 1d./3d. (containing Nos. S22b×2, S77d×2) (16.8.65) | £100 | £150 | 80·00 |
|---|---|---|---|---|
| a. | One band on each stamp | † | † | |
| SB48 | Pane of 2 × 3d./1d. (containing Nos. S77e×2, S22b×2) (16.8.65) | £100 | | 80·00 |
| a. | One band on each stamp | | | |
| b. | One band on 1d. and no bands on 3d. | — | † | — |
| c. | "R" flaw on 1d. (R. 2/2) | † | † | £100 |

For illustrations of Nos. SB46 and SB48c see Nos. SB36 and SB38a.

The following illustration shows how the se-tenant stamps with one phosphor band on 3d. are printed and the arrows indicate where the guillotine falls. The result gives 1d. stamps with two bands and 3d. stamps with one band, either at left or right.

3d.   1d.   1d.   3d.   3d.   1d.   1d.   3d.

The stamps were printed sideways, as indicated by the position of the watermark.

**Booklet Cylinder Numbers**
Panes of four (24-row single pane cylinder of 480 stamps sideways).
From 1d./3d. *se-tenant* Perf. Type I, wmk Crown to left

| Cylinder No. | No Dot |
|---|---|
| F13 (1d.), K22 (3d.) | £175 |

## ■ 1d. Panes of six with phosphor bands

Two 8 mm phosphor bands reacting violet applied in photogravure
From 4s.6d. Booklets L60p(b), L61p(b) and L62p(b)/65p(a) and 10s. Booklet X15p(a)

|  |  | Perf. Type | |
|---|---|---|---|
|  |  | *I* | *Ie* |
| **A. Watermark upright** | | | |
| SB49 | Pane of 6 × 1d. (containing No. S23b×6) (9.65) | 10·00 | 12·00 |
| b. | Dot in serif (R. 2/3) | 25·00 | |
| **B. Watermark inverted** | | | |
| SB49a | Pane of 6 × 1d. (containing No. S23c×6) (9.65) | 10·00 | 12·00 |
| ab. | Extended leaf on shamrock (R. 1/1 or 2/1) | 25·00 | |

For illustrations of Nos. SB49b and SB49ab see Nos. SB23c and SB20ab.

**Booklet Cylinder Numbers**
Panes of six (21-row cylinder). Bands photo.

| Cylinder No. | No Dot | Dot |
|---|---|---|
| F10 | 50·00 | 50·00 |
| F10 T | 50·00 | 50·00 |

## ■ 1d. and 3d. *Se-tenant* panes of four with phosphor bands

With 8 mm. Phosphor bands reacting violet. Sideways watermark
Pair of 1d. (two bands) with pair of 3d. (1 side 8 mm. violet band) applied by Typography.
Crowns.
From 2s. Booklets N22p(b), N23p(b)/28p(a), N29p, N30p(a), N31p(c) and N32p(c)

**Panes SB50 and SB52** Panes of four with 1d. (two bands) at left; 3d. side band at left
**Panes SB51 and SB53** Panes of four with 1d. (two bands) at right; 3d. side band at right

|  |  | Perf. Type | | |
|---|---|---|---|---|
| **A. Watermark Crown to left** | | *I* | *I(½v)* | *AP* |
| SB50 | Pane of 2 × 1d./3d. (containing Nos. S23d×2, S78c×2) (10.65) | 20·00 | † | 15·00 |
| SB51 | Pane of 2 × 3d./1d. (containing Nos. S78d×2, S23d×2) (10.65) | 20·00 | 65·00 | 15·00 |
| a. | One 8 mm. band on each stamp | 60·00 | — | 50·00 |
| b. | One 8 mm. band on 1d. and no bands on 3d. | 80·00 | † | 70·00 |
| c. | Thistle flaw on 1d. (R. 2/2) | † | 65·00 | † |
| **B. Watermark Crown to right** | | | | |
| SB52 | Pane of 2 × 1d./3d. (containing Nos. S23e×2, S78e×2) (10.65) | 20·00 | 65·00 | 15·00 |
| SB53 | Pane of 2 × 3d./1d. (containing Nos. S78f×2, S23e×2) (10.65) | 20·00 | † | 15·00 |
| a. | One 8 mm. band on each stamp | 80·00 | — | 70·00 |
| b. | One 8 mm. band on 1d. and no bands on 3d. | 80·00 | — | 70·00 |
| c. | "R" flaw on 1d. (R. 2/2) | † | † | 30·00 |

For illustrations of Nos. SB51c and SB53c see Nos. SB36a and SB38a.

**Booklet Cylinder Numbers**
Pane of four (24-row single pane cylinder of 480 stamps sideways). From 1d./3d. *se-tenant Perf. Type* I, Wmk crown to left.

| Cylinder No. | No Dot |
|---|---|
| F13 (1d.), K22 (3d.) | 50·00 |

## ■ 1d. Panes of six with phosphor bands

With two 9·5 mm. Phosphor bands reacting violet
6 × 1d. Crowns. Two phosphor bands applied in photogravure
From 4s.6d. Booklets L65p(b)/71p and 10s. Booklets X15p(b) and X16p/17p

| | Perf Type | |
|---|---|---|
| | I | Ie |
| **A. Watermark upright** | | |
| SB54  Pane of 6 × 1d. (containing No. S24×6) (2.67) | 6·00 | 7·50 |
| b.  Dot in serif (R. 2/3) | 30·00 | |
| **B. Watermark inverted** | | |
| SB54a  Pane of 6 × 1d. (containing No. S24a×6) (2.67) | 6·00 | 7·50 |
| ab.  Extended leaf on shamrock (R. 1/1 or 2/1) | 30·00 | |

For illustrations of Nos. SB54b and SB54ab see Nos. SB23c and SB20ab.

**Booklet Cylinder Numbers**
Panes of six (21-row cylinder)

| Cylinder No. | No Dot | Dot |
|---|---|---|
| F10 | 50·00 | 50·00* |
| F10 T | 50·00 | 50·00 |

## ■ 1d. and 3d. *Se-tenant* panes of four with phosphor bands

With 9·75 mm. Phosphor bands reacting violet. Sideways watermark
Pair of 1d. (two bands) with pair of 3d. (two bands) applied by Typography.
Crowns
From 2s. Booklets N31p(a/b) and N32p(a/b)

**Panes SB55 and SB57**  Panes of four with 1d. (two bands) at left; 3d. (two bands) at right
**Panes SB56 and SB58**  Panes of four with 1d. (two bands) at right; 3d. (two bands) at left

| A. Watermark Crown to left | Perf. Type | | |
|---|---|---|---|
| | I | I(½v) | AP |
| SB55  Pane of 2 × 1d./3d. (containing Nos. S24b×2, S80×2) (11.67) | 12·00 | † | 8·00 |
| a.  As SB55 but one side band on 3d. | £200 | — | £200 |
| SB56  Pane of 2 × 3d./1d. (containing Nos. S80×2, S24b×2) (11.67) | 12·00 | 50·00 | 8·00 |
| a.  Thistle flaw on 1d. (R. 2/2) | † | 35·00 | † |
| b.  As SB56 but one side band on 3d. | £200 | — | £200 |
| c.  One 9·5 mm. band on each stamp | £100 | £130 | 85·00 |
| d.  One 9·5 mm. band on 1d. and no bands on 3d. | £100 | — | £100 |

The I (½v) pane has the thistle flaw on 1d. (R.2/2)

**B. Watermark Crown to right**

| | | | | |
|---|---|---|---|---|
| SB57  Pane of 2 × 1d./3d. (containing Nos. S24c×2, S80a×2) (11.67) | 12·00 | 35·00 | 8·00 |
| a.  As SB57 but one side band on 3d | £200 | — | £200 |
| SB58  Pane of 2 × 3d./1d. (containing Nos. S80a×2, S24c×2) (11.67) | 12·00 | † | 8·00 |
| a.  "R" flaw on 1d. (R. 2/2) | † | † | 35·00 |
| b.  As SB58 but one band on 3d | £200 | | £200 |
| ba.  Do. with R flaw | † | † | £190 |
| c.  One 9·5 mm. band on each stamp | £100 | — | 85·00 |

Part of the October 1967 2s. Booklets (N30p(a)) had 8 mm. bands and part 9·5 mm. bands (N30p(b)) which had only a side band on the 3d. value at right or left as listed above. As these bands are applied across the perforations and are liable to shift, it is not possible to distinguish the 3d. side band 9·5 mm. bands from the 8 mm. bands of Nos. SB50, etc. in singles, and hence these are not listed as varieties under the 3d. value. Two examples of the April 1967 2s. Booklet (N28p(b)) are also known with a single 9·5 mm. band on the 3d.
For illustrations of Nos. SB56a and Sb58a/ba, see Nos. SB36a and SB38a.

**Booklet Cylinder Numbers**
Pane of four (24-row single pane cylinder of 480 stamps sideways). From 1d./3d. *se-tenant* Perf. Type I, wmk Crown to left

| Cylinder No. | No Dot |
|---|---|
| F13 (1d.), K22 (3d.) Two bands | 35·00 |
| F13(1d.), K22(3d.) Side band | — |

## ■ 1½d. Panes of six, Tudor Crown

From 2s.6d. Booklets F1/36 and 5s. Booklets H1/17

| | Perf. Type | |
|---|---|---|
| | I | Ie |
| **A. Watermark upright** | | |
| SB59  Pane of 6 × 1½d. (containing No. S25×6) (5.53) | 4·00 | 5·00 |
| b.  Extra jewel (R. 1/1) | 45·00 | |
| c.  Extra bud on daffodil stem (R. 2/1) | 45·00 | |
| **B. Watermark inverted** | | |
| SB59a  Pane of 6 × 1½d. (containing No. S25c×6) (5.53) | 4·00 | 5·00 |
| ab.  Imperf. pane* | | |

*Booklet error. This pane of six stamps is completely imperf. (cf. General Notes).

SB59b, SB62c

SB59c

Multipositive flaw on Tudor and Edward Crown watermarks

**Booklet Cylinder Numbers**
Panes of six (20-row cylinders)

| Cylinder No. | No Dot | Dot |
|---|---|---|
| G2 | 35·00 | 35·00 |

| Cylinder No. | No Dot | Dot |
|---|---|---|
| G3 | 35·00 | 35·00 |
| G6 | £100 | £100 |

## 1½d. Panes of four, Tudor Crown

From 1s. Booklet K1/a for use in "E" slot machines.

**A. Watermark upright**                                    Perf. Type P

| SB60 | Pane of 4 × 1½d. (containing No. S25 × 4) (22.7.54) | |
|---|---|---|
| | | 10·00 |
| b. | Rose petal flaw (R. 1/1) | 45·00 |

**B. Watermark inverted**

| SB60a | Pane of 4 × 1½d. (containing No. S25c × 4) (22.7.54) | |
|---|---|---|
| | | 12·00 |

SB60b, SB63b, SB67b

**Booklet Cylinder Number**
Cylinder No. G5 was used, but it does not appear in the finished booklets.

**Imprimatur from the National Postal Museum Archives**
Booklet pane of four. Imperforate, watermark Type W.22

| Two panes arranged vertically *tête-bêche* with a 12 mm. horizontal gutter margin between | £20,000 |
|---|---|

## 1½d. Panes of two, Tudor Crown

From 1s. Booklet E1 for use in experimental "D" slot machines.

| Watermark upright | Perf. Type | | | |
|---|---|---|---|---|
| | I | I(½v) | E | E(½v) |
| SB61 Pane of 2 × 1½d. (containing No. S25 × 2) (2.9.53) | 10·00 | 50·00 | 6·00 | 25·00 |
| a. Flaw on daffodil stem (as on No. S25f) | | | 65·00 | |

Made up from columns 1 and 2 from sheets.
No. SB61a was later retouched on cylinder 9 dot.

**Booklet Cylinder Numbers**
Panes of two (from sheets)

| Cylinder No. | No Dot Perf Type I | Dot Perf Type E |
|---|---|---|
| 2 | £150 | £150 |
| 4 | † | — |

| Cylinder No. | No Dot Perf Type E | Dot Perf Type E |
|---|---|---|
| 6 | £150 | £150 |
| 9 | £100 | 65·00* |
| 12 | £100 | 60·00 |

Panes purporting to have come from cylinder 1 are believed to have been forged.

## 1½d. Panes of six, St. Edward's Crown

From 2s.6d. Booklets F33(b) and F34/52, 3s. Booklets M1/11 and 5s. Booklets H17/31

| | | Perf. Type | |
|---|---|---|---|
| **A. Watermark upright** | | I | Ie |
| SB62 | Pane of 6 × 1½d. (containing No. S26 × 6) (8.55) | 3·50 | 4·00 |
| b. | Rabbit's ears (R. 2/2) | 30·00 | |
| c. | Extra jewel (R. 1/1 or 2/1) | 40·00 | |
| d. | Large dot by daffodil (R. 1/1) | 40·00 | |
| e. | Major retouch around emblems (R. 2/2) | 55·00 | |
| f. | Flaw on rose at right (R. 1/2) | 40·00 | |
| **B. Watermark inverted** | | | |
| SB62a | Pane of 6 × 1½d. (containing No. S26b × 6) (8.55) | 5·00 | 6·00 |
| ab. | Flaw on rose at top left (R. 1/2 or 2/2) | 40·00 | |

For illustration of No. SB62c see No. SB59b

SB62b
Two white dots extending upwards from shamrock at left appearing as rabbit s ears (Cyl. G7 no dot)

SB62d (Cyl. G7)

SB62e
Major retouch affecting a pair with weak shading in the emblems. (Cyl. G7 dot)

Normal

SB62f
(Cyl. G10 dot)

SB62ab
White flaw on rose at top left (Cyl. G10 dot)

**Booklet Cylinder Numbers**
Panes of six (G6 and G7 20-row cylinders, others 21-row cylinders)

| Cylinder No. | No Dot | Dot |
|---|---|---|
| G6 | 50·00 | 40·00 |
| G7 | 60·00 | 50·00 |
| G9 | 85·00 | 85·00 |
| G9 T | £100 | £100 |

| Cylinder No. | No Dot | Dot |
|---|---|---|
| G10 | £100 | 80·00 |
| G10 T | £100 | 80·00 |

## 1½d. Panes of four, St. Edward's Crown

From 1s. Booklet K2/b for use in "E" slot machines and 2s. Booklet N1

| | Perf. Type | |
|---|---|---|
| A. Watermark upright | AP | P |
| SB63 Pane of 4 × 1½d. (containing No. | | |
| S26×4) (5.7.56) | 12·00 | 12·00 |
| b. Rose petal flaw (R. 1/1) | 30·00 | 45·00 |
| B. Watermark inverted | | |
| SB63a Pane of 4 × 1½d. (containing No. | | |
| S26b×4) (5.7.56) | 12·00 | 12·00 |

For illustration of No. SB63b see No. SB60b.

**Booklet Cylinder Number**
Cylinder No. G5 was used, but it does not appear in the finished booklets.

**Imprimatur from the National Postal Museum Archives**
Booklet pane of four. Imperforate, watermark Type W.23

| Two panes arranged vertically *tête-bêche* with a 12 mm. horizontal gutter margin between | £20,000 |
|---|---|

## 1½d. Panes of two, St. Edward's Crown

From 1s. Booklet E2 for use in experimental "D" slot machines.

| | Perf. Type | |
|---|---|---|
| Watermark upright | E | E(½v) |
| SB64 Pane of 2 × 1½d. (containing No. | | |
| S26×2) (11.57) | 25·00 | 40·00 |

Made up from columns 1 and 2 from sheets

**Booklet Cylinder Numbers**
Panes of two (from sheets)

| Cylinder No. | No Dot | Dot |
|---|---|---|
| 13 | — | † |
| 14 | £150 | £125 |

## 1½d. Panes of six, Crowns Wmk

Cream or whiter paper
From 3s. Booklets M9/74 and 10s. Booklets X1/9

| Cream Paper | Perf. Type | |
|---|---|---|
| A. Watermark upright | I | Ie |
| SB65 Pane of 6 × 1½d. (containing No. | | |
| S28×6) (12.58) | 10·00 | 12·00 |
| b. Dot on thistle (R. 1/3 or 2/3) | 45·00 | |
| B. Watermark inverted | | |
| SB65a Pane of 6 × 1½d. (containing No. | | |
| S28a×6) (12.58) | 12·00 | 14·00 |

**Whiter Paper**

| A. Watermark upright | | |
|---|---|---|
| SB66 Pane of 6 × 1½d. (containing No. | | |
| S29×6) (18.9.62) | 35·00 | 40·00 |
| b. Dot on thistle (R. 1/3 or 2/3) | 55·00 | |

**B. Watermark inverted**

| SB66a Pane of 6 × 1½d. (containing No. | | |
|---|---|---|
| S29d×6) (18.9.62) | 45·00 | 50·00 |

SB65b, SB66b
Dot on thistle Retouched on cream paper (Cyl. G15 dot)

**Booklet Cylinder Numbers**
Panes of six (21-row cylinders)

**Cream paper**

| Cylinder No. | No Dot | Dot |
|---|---|---|
| G10 | 90·00 | 90·00 |
| G10 T | 90·00 | 90·00 |
| G11 | 90·00 | 90·00 |
| G11 T | 70·00 | 70·00 |
| G15 | 50·00 | 50·00 |
| G15 T | 50·00 | 50·00 |

**Whiter paper**

| Cylinder No. | No Dot | Dot |
|---|---|---|
| G15 | 90·00 | 90·00 |
| G15 T | 90·00 | 90·00 |
| G16 | £130 | £130 |
| G16 T | £130 | £130 |

**Specimen overprints from the National Postal Museum Archives**
Booklet pane of six. Perf. 15×14, watermark Type W.24 upright
Each stamp handstamped "Specimen" (13×2 mm.)

## 1½d. Panes of four, Crowns Wmk

Cream paper
From 1s. Booklet K3/a for use in "E" slot machines and 2s. Booklets N2/3. *Perf. Type AP*

| A. Watermark upright | Perf Type AP |
|---|---|
| SB67 Pane of 4 × 1½d. (containing No. | |
| S28×4) (13.8.59) | 10·00 |
| b. Rose petal flaw (R. 1/1) | 45·00 |
| B. Watermark inverted | |
| SB67a Pane of 4 × 1½d. (containing No. | |
| S28a×4) (13.8.59) | 12·00 |

For illustration of No. SB67b see No. SB60b.

**Booklet Cylinder Number**
Cylinder No. G5 was used, but it does not appear in the finished booklets.

**Imprimatur from the National Postal Museum Archives**
Booklet pane of four. Imperforate, watermark Type W.24

| Two panes arranged vertically *tête-bêche* with a 12 mm. horizontal gutter margin between | £20,000 |
|---|---|

**Specimen overprints from the National Postal Museum Archives**
Booklet pane of four. Perf. 15×14, watermark Type W.24 inverted
Each stamp handstamped "Specimen" (13×2 mm.)

## ◼ 1½d. Panes of four, Crowns Wmk sideways

With sideways watermark
Cream or white paper
From 2s. Booklets N4/20

**Cream Paper**

| A. Watermark Crown to left | *I* | *I(½v)* | *AP* | *AP(ZE)* |
|---|---|---|---|---|
| SB68 Pane of 4 × 1½d. (containing No. S28b×4) (26.5.61) | 60·00 | £120 | 50·00 | 70·00 |
| **B. Watermark Crown to right** | | | | |
| SB68a Pane of 4 × 1½d. (containing No. S28c×4) (26.5.61) | 60·00 | £120 | 50·00 | † |

*Perf. Type*

**Whiter Paper**

| A. Watermark Crown to left | | | | |
|---|---|---|---|---|
| SB69 Pane of 4 × 1½d. (containing No. S29b×4) (5.6.62) | 40·00 | 50·00 | 95·00 | 60·00 |
| **B. Watermark Crown to right** | | | | |
| SB69a Pane of 4 × 1½d. (containing No. S29c×4) (5.6.62) | 40.00 | 50·00 | 95·00 | † |

**Booklet Cylinder Number**
Pane of four, Perf. Type, I cyl. No. G.17 (wmk Crown to left),
*From* £100
Due to the width of the selvedge the "7" was usually trimmed off.

**Specimen overprints from
the National Postal Museum Archives**
Booklet pane of four. Perf. 15 × 14, watermark Type W.24 Crown to left, Perf. AP(2E)
Each stamp handstamped "Specimen" (13 × 2 mm.)

## ◼ 1½d. Panes of six with graphite lines, Crowns Wmk

Graphite lines as Type **S8**
From 3s. Booklets M13g/15g and M19g/21g

| | Perf Type | |
|---|---|---|
| A. Watermark upright | *I* | *Ie* |
| SB70 Pane of 6 × 1½d. (containing No. S30×6) (4.8.59) | £500 | £500 |
| **B. Watermark inverted** | | |
| SB70a Pane of 6 × 1½d. (containing No. S30a×6) (4.8.59) | £250 | £250 |

**Booklet Cylinder Numbers**
Panes of six (21-row cylinder)

| Cylinder No. | No Dot | Dot |
|---|---|---|
| G11 | £950 | £950 |
| G11 T | £950 | £950 |

**Imprimatur from the National Postal Museum Archives**
Booklet pane of six. Imperforate, watermark Type W.24

| Two panes as No. SB70 arranged *tête-bêche* | £25,000 |
|---|---|

## ◼ 1½d. Panes of six with phosphor bands

6 × 1½d. Crowns. Two phosphor bands reacting green applied in photogravure
From 3s. Booklets M25p, M28p/29p and M37p(a)

**A. Watermark upright**

| | Perf. Type | |
|---|---|---|
| | *I* | *Ie* |
| SB71 Pane of 6 × 1½d. (containing No. S32×6) (14.8.60) | 50·00 | 60·00 |
| **B. Watermark inverted** | | |
| SB71a Pane of 6 × 1½d. (containing No. S32a×6) (14.8.60) | £100 | £110 |

**Booklet Cylinder Numbers**
Panes of six (21-row cylinders)

| Cylinder No. | No Dot | Dot |
|---|---|---|
| G11 | £175 | £175 |
| G11 T | £175 | £175 |

## ◼ 1½d. Panes of six with phosphor bands

Applied in photogravure reacting blue. Cream or whiter paper
From 3s. Booklets M33p, M36p, M37p(b), M38p/9p, M43p/7p, M49p/53p, M55p/61p and M64p/74p

**Cream Paper**

| | Perf. Type | |
|---|---|---|
| A. Watermark upright | *I* | *Ie* |
|   b. One 8mm. band on each stamp | £400 | |
| **B. Watermark inverted** | | |
| SB72a Pane of 6 × 1½d. (containing No. S33a×6) (4.61) | 85·00 | 95·00 |
|   ab. One 8mm. band on each stamp | £400 | |

**Whiter Paper**

| A. Watermark upright | | |
|---|---|---|
| SB73 Pane of 6 × 1½d. (containing No. S34×6) (7.64) | 55·00 | 65·00 |
|   b. One 8mm. band on each stamp | £500 | |
| **B. Watermark inverted** | | |
| SB73a Pane of 6 × 1½d. (containing No. S34c×6) (7.64) | £175 | £195 |
|   ab. One 8 mm. band on each stamp | £500 | |
|   ac. Phosphor displaced with stamps 1 and 4 showing 6mm. left and centre bands, others with one 8 mm. band in centre | — | |

**Booklet Cylinder Numbers**
Pane of six (21-row cylinders)

**Cream paper**

| Cylinder No. | No Dot | Dot |
|---|---|---|
| G15 | 85·00 | 85·00 |
| G15 T | 85·00 | 85·00 |

**Whiter paper**

| Cylinder No. | No Dot | Dot |
|---|---|---|
| G16 | £150 | £150 |
| G16 T | £150 | £150 |

## 1½d. Panes of four with phosphor bands watermark sideways

Sideways watermark
Phosphor bands reacting blue, applied by Typography. Cream or whiter paper
From 2s. Booklets N4p, N8p/10p, N12p/20p

**Cream Paper**

**A. Watermark Crown to left**

| | | Perf. Type | | | |
|---|---|---|---|---|---|
| | | I | I(½v) | AP | AP(2e) |
| SB74 | Pane of 4 × 1½d. (containing No. S33b×4) (14.7.61) | 70·00 | £150 | 50·00 | 80·00 |
| b. | One 8 mm. band on each stamp | £150 | — | £125 | — |

**B. Watermark Crown to right**

| | | I | I(½v) | AP | AP(2e) |
|---|---|---|---|---|---|
| SB74a | Pane of 4 × 1½d. (containing No. S33c×4) (14.7.61) | 70·00 | £150 | 50·00 | † |
| ab. | One 8 mm. band on each stamp | £150 | — | £125 | † |

**Whiter Paper**

**A. Watermark Crown to left**

| | | I | I(½v) | AP | AP(2e) |
|---|---|---|---|---|---|
| SB75 | Pane of 4 × 1½d. (containing No. S34a×4) (15.8.62) | 80·00 | £170 | 60·00 | 90·00 |

**B. Watermark Crown to right**

| | | I | I(½v) | AP | AP(2e) |
|---|---|---|---|---|---|
| SB75a | Pane of 4 × 1½d. (containing No. S34b×4) (15.8.62) | 80·00 | £170 | 60·00 | † |

**Booklet Cylinder Numbers**
Pane of four Perf. Type I Cyl No. G.17 (wmk Crown to left) from £200
Due to the width of the selvedge the "7" was usually trimmed off..

**Imprimaturs from the National Postal Museum Archives**
Booklet pane of four. Imperforate, watermark Type W.24

| Two panes arranged vertically *tête-bêche* | £20,000 |
|---|---|

**Specimen overprints from the National Postal Museum Archives**
Booklet pane of four. Perf. 15 × 14, watermark Type W.24, Crown to right, Perf. Type AP.
Each stamp handstamped "Specimen" (13 × 2 mm.)

## 2d. Red-brown panes of six, Tudor Crown

From 5s. Booklets H8/19 and H21a

| | | Perf. Type | |
|---|---|---|---|
| | | I | Ie |
| **A. Watermark upright** | | | |
| SB76 | Pane of 6 × 2d. (containing No. S36×6) (3.54) | 50·00 | 55·00 |
| **B. Watermark inverted** | | | |
| SB76a | Pane of 6 × 2d. (containing No. S36a×6) (3.54) | £200 | £225 |

**Booklet Cylinder Numbers**
Panes of six (20-row cylinder)

| Cylinder No. | No Dot | Dot |
|---|---|---|
| H1 | £120* | £100 |

*Includes retouched face variety (R. 2/1). Two states exist showing as a small retouch to left of ear and in state two the retouched area includes the forehead and cheek. Same price for either state included in the cylinder pane with upright watermark.

## 2d. Red-brown panes of six, St. Edward's Crown

From 5s. Booklets H17/25

| | | Perf. Type | |
|---|---|---|---|
| | | I | Ie |
| **A. Watermark upright** | | | |
| SB77 | Pane of 6 × 2d. (containing No. S37×6) (9.55) | 25·00 | 28·00 |
| **B. Watermark inverted** | | | |
| SB77a | Pane of 6 × 2d. (containing No. S37c×6) (9.55) | 90·00 | £100 |

**Booklet Cylinder Numbers**
Panes of six (20-row cylinder)

| Cylinder No. | No Dot | Dot |
|---|---|---|
| H1 | £120* | £120 |

*Includes the second state of the retouched face variety (R. 2/1).

## 2d. Light red-brown panes of six, St. Edward's Crown

From 2s.6d. Booklets F53/61 and 5s. Booklets H26/31

| | | Perf. Type | |
|---|---|---|---|
| | | I | Ie |
| **A. Watermark upright** | | | |
| SB78 | Pane of 6 × 2d. (containing No. S38×6) (1.57) | 15·00 | 18·00 |
| b. | Imperf. pane* | £5250 | |
| ba. | Part perf. pane* | £5250 | |
| ✓ c. | Daffodil flaw (R. 1/3 or 2/3) | 60·00 | |
| d. | Shamrock flaw (R. 1/3 or 2/3) | 55·00 | |
| e. | Bud on thistle stem (R. 1/3 or 2/3) | 50·00 | |
| f. | White flaw on thistle (R. 1/1 or 2/1) | 50·00 | |
| g. | Daffodil stem flaw (R. 2/2) | 55·00 | |
| **B. Watermark inverted** | | | |
| SB78a | Pane of 6 × 2d. (containing No. S38d×6) (1.57) | 40·00 | 50·00 |
| ac. | "D" for "P" (R. 1/2 or 2/2) | 80·00 | |
| ad. | Spot after "2" (R. 1/2 or 2/2) | 70·00 | |
| ae. | Dew drop (R. 1/2 or 2/2) | 70·00 | |
| af. | Diadem flaw (R. 1/3 or 2/3) | 70·00 | |
| ag. | White flaw at top of thistle (R. 1/2 or 2/2) | 70·00 | |
| ah. | Accent on first "2" and spot on shamrock (R. 1/3 or 2/3) | 85·00 | |
| aha. | Retouched state. Spot on shamrock (R. 1/3 or 2/3) | 85·00 | |

*Booklet errors. See General Notes.

SB78c
Later retouched (Cyl. H6 no dot)

SB78d
Later retouched (Cyl. H6 no dot)

SB78e, SB79b
Later retouched  (Cyl. H6 dot)

SB78f, SB79c
(Cyl. H6 dot)

SB78g
Later retouched (Cyl. pane H6 and on ordinary pane)

SB78ac, SB79ab
(Cyl. H6 dot)

SB78ad, SB79ac
(Cyl. H6 no dot)

SB78ae
Later retouched
(Cyl. H6 no dot)

SB78af
Later retouched  (Cyl. H6 dot)

SB78ag
Later retouched
(Cyl. H6 no dot)

SB78ah
The flaw on value was later retouched but the spot on shamrock remained.
(Cyl. H6 no dot)

**Booklet Cylinder Numbers**
Panes of six (21-row cylinder)

| Cylinder No. | No Dot | Dot |
|---|---|---|
| H6 | £125 | 75·00 |
| H6 T | £125 | 85·00 |

Early printings of the Cyl. H6 pane show a white dot below the daffodil stem at left (R. 1/2). This was later removed by retouch. *Cylinder No.* H6 no dot *with variety price* £125.

## ◼ 2d. Light red-brown panes of six, Crowns Wmk

Cream paper
From 10s. Booklets X1/2

| | | Perf Type | |
|---|---|---|---|
| | | *I* | *Ie* |
| **A. Watermark upright** | | | |
| SB79 | Pane of 6 × 2d. (containing No. S40×6) (10.4.61) | £100 | £110 |
| b. | Bud on thistle stem (R. 1/3 or 2/3) | £150 | |
| c. | White flaw on thistle (R. 1/1 or 2/1) | £150 | |
| **B. Watermark inverted** | | | |
| SB79a | Pane of 6 × 2d. (containing No. S40c×6) (10.4.61) | £950 | £950 |
| ab. | "D" for "P" (R. 1/2 or 2/2) | £1000 | |
| ac. | Spot after "2" (R. 1/2 or 2/2) | £1000 | |

For illustration of No. SB79b, see No. SB78e and for Nos. SB79ab/ac see Nos. SB78ac/ad.

**Booklet Cylinder Numbers**
Panes of six (21-row cylinder). Cream paper

| Cylinder No. | No Dot | Dot |
|---|---|---|
| H6 | £500 | £500 |
| H6 T | £500 | £500 |

All stamps in the 2½d. panes show the frontal cross of the diadem with the top line extending the full width of the cross (Type II).

## ◼ 2½d. Panes of six, Tudor Crown

From 2s.6d. Booklets F1/36, F37a, F42b/43b, 3s.9d. Booklets G1/10 and 5s. Booklets H1/19

| | | Perf Type | |
|---|---|---|---|
| | | *I* | *Ie* |
| **A. Watermark upright** | | | |
| SB80 | Pane of 6 × 2½d. (containing No. S51×6) (5.53) | 6·00 | 7·00 |
| b. | Jewels flaw (R. 2/2) | 55·00 | |
| **B. Watermark inverted** | | | |
| SB80a | Pane of 6 × 2½d. (containing No. S51a×6) (5.53) | 4·50 | 4·00 |
| ab. | "R" flaw (R. 1/1) | 55·00 | |

SB80b
(Cyl. J1 or J3 no dot)

SB80ab, SB81ad
(Cyl. J5 no dot)

**Booklet Cylinder Numbers**
Panes of six (20-row cylinders)

| Cylinder No. | No Dot | Dot |
|---|---|---|
| J1 | 30·00 | 30·00 |

| Cylinder No. | No Dot | Dot |
|---|---|---|
| J3 | 30·00 | 30·00 |
| J5 | 35·00 | 35·00 |

## ◼ 2½d. Panes of six, St. Edward's Crown

From 2s.6d. Booklets F34(d)/36(c) and F37/61, 3s.9d. Booklets G9(a)/(c) and G10(a)/21 and 5s. Booklets H17/36

|  |  | Perf Type | |
|---|---|---|---|
| **A. Watermark upright** |  | *I* | *Ie* |
| SB81 | Pane of 6 × 2½d. (containing No. S53×6) (9.55) | 3·50 | 4·00 |
| b. | Imperf. pane* | £5000 | |
| c. | Part perf pane* | £4250 | |
| d. | Swan's head (R. 1/1 or 2/1) | 75·00 | |
| e. | Wreath flaw (R. 1/3 or 2/3) | 50·00 | |
| f. | Damaged "P" (R. 1/3 or 2/3) | 50·00 | |
| g. | Dot by shamrock (R. 1/1 or 2/1) | 50·00 | |
| h. | Forehead retouch R. 1/2 or 2/2) | 60·00 | |
| i. | White flaw below thistle (R. 1/2 or 2/2) | 50·00 | |
| **B. Watermark inverted** |  |  | |
| SB81a | Pane of 6 × 2½d. (containing No. S53e×6) (9.55) | 3·50 | 4.00 |
| ab. | Imperf pane* | £5000 | |
| ac. | Part perf. pane* | £4250 | |
| ad. | "R" flaw (R. 1/1) | 50·00 | |
| ae. | Dotted "R" (R. 1/3 or 2/3) | 50·00 | |
| af. | Spur to "1" (R. 1/1 or 2/1) | 40·00 | |

For illustration of No. SB81ad, see No. SB80ab.

SB81d, SB82d
Top of figure 2 is extended and curled (Cyl. J8 no dot)

SB81e, SB82e
(Cyl. J9 no dot)

SB81f, SB82f
Red flaw almost obliterates the loop on "P". St. Edward's and Crown wmks., (Cyl. J8 dot)

SB81g
Retouched later (Cyl. J9 dot)

SB81h, SB82g
(Cyl. J9 no dot)

SB81i, SB82h
(Cyl. J8 no dot)

SB81ae
Later retouched on Crowns wmk. (Cyl. J9 no dot)

SB81af, SB82ac, SB85ab
(Cyl. J9 dot)

### Booklet Cylinder Numbers

Panes of six (J5 20-row cylinder, others 21-row cylinders)

| Cylinder No. | No Dot | Dot |
|---|---|---|
| J5 | 35·00 | 35·00 |
| J6 | 70·00 | 70·00 |
| J6 T | 70·00 | 45·00 |
| J8 | 70·00 | 50·00 |
| J8 T | 70·00 | 50·00 |
| J9 | 90·00 | 90·00 |
| J9 T | 90·00 | 90·00 |

## ◼ 2½d. Panes of six, Crowns Wmk

Cream or whiter paper
From 5s. Booklets H36(b)/(c), (e) and H37/74 and 10s. Booklets X3/9

| **Cream Paper** |  | Perf Type | |
|---|---|---|---|
| **A. Watermark upright** |  | *I* | *Ie* |
| SB82 | Pane of 6 × 2½d. (containing No. S55×6) (11.58) | 15·00 | 17·00 |
| d. | Swan's head (R. 1/1 or 2/1) | 85·00 | |
| e. | Wreath flaw (R. 1/3 or 2/3) | 55·00 | |
| f. | Damaged "P" (R. 1/3 or 2/3) | 55·00 | |
| g. | Forehead retouch (R. 1/2 or 2/2) | 55·00 | |
| h. | White flaw below thistle (R. 1/2 or 2/2) | 55·00 | |
| **B. Watermark inverted** |  |  | |
| SB82a | Pane of 6 × 2½d. (containing No. S55d×6) (11.58) | 30·00 | 32·00 |
| ac. | Spur to "1" (R. 1/1) | 65·00 | |

**Whiter Paper**

| **A. Watermark upright** |  |  | |
|---|---|---|---|
| SB83 | Pane of 6 × 2½d. (containing No. S57×6) (29.7.62) | 25·00 | 27·00 |
| b. | Imperf. pane* | £4000 | |
| **B. Watermark inverted** |  |  | |
| SB83a | Pane of 6 × 2½d. (containing No. S57a×6) (29.7.62) | 65·00 | 70·00 |

*Booklet error. See General Notes.
For illustrations of Nos. SB82d/f, see Nos. SB81d/f, for Nos.

SB82g/h, see Nos. SB81h/i and for No. SB82ac see No. SB81af.

**Booklet Cylinder Numbers**
Panes of six (21-row cylinders)

**Cream paper**

| Cylinder No. | No Dot | Dot |
|---|---|---|
| J6 | £100 | £100 |
| J6 T | £100 | £100 |
| J8 | £120 | £120 |
| J8 T | £120 | £120 |
| J9 | £120 | £120 |
| J9 T | £120 | £120 |
| J13 | £120 | £120 |
| J13 T | £120 | £120 |

**Whiter paper**

| Cylinder No. | No Dot | Dot |
|---|---|---|
| J13 | £130 | £130 |
| J13 T | £130 | £130 |
| J14 | £150 | £150 |
| J14 T | £150 | £150 |

**Specimen overprints from
the National Postal Museum Archives**
Booklet pane of six. Perf. 15 × 14, watermark Type W.24
inverted
Each stamp handstamped "Specimen" (15 × 2½ mm.)

## ■ 2½d. Panes of four, Crowns Wmk

Chalk-surfaced paper
From 2s. Booklet NR1/1a

| | | Perf. Type | |
|---|---|---|---|
| **A. Watermark upright** | I | I(½v) | AP |
| SB84　Pane of 4 × 2½d. (containing No. S58 × 4) (15.7.63) | 5·00 | 15·00 | 2·00 |
| **B. Watermark inverted** | | | |
| SB84a　Pane of 4 × 2½d. (containing No. S58a × 4) (15.7.63) | 5·00 | 15·00 | 2·00 |

**Booklet Cylinder Numbers**
Panes of four (20-row single pane cylinder of 480 stamps).
Cylinder numbers are not known from Booklets NR1/1a.

**Imprimatur from the National Postal Museum Archives**
Booklet pane of four. Imperforate, watermark Type W.24

| Two panes arranged vertically *tête-bêche* | £20,000 |
|---|---|

## ■ 2½d. Panes of six with graphite lines, Crowns Wmk

6 × 2½d. Crowns. Graphite lines as Type **S8**
From 5s. Booklets H39g, H43g and H46g

| | Perf Type | |
|---|---|---|
| **A. Watermark upright** | I | Ie |
| SB85　Pane of 6 × 2½d. (containing No. S59 × 6) (21.8.59) | £100 | £110 |
| 　b.　Forehead retouch (R. 1/2 or 2/2) | £150 | |
| **B. Watermark inverted** | | |
| SB85a　Pane of 6 × 2½d. (containing No. S59a × 6) (21.8.59) | £400 | £400 |
| 　ab.　Spur to "1" (R. 1/1 or 2/1) | £475 | |

For illustration of No. SB85b, see No. SB81h and for No.
SB85ab, see No. SB81af.

**Booklet Cylinder Numbers**
Panes of six (21-row cylinders)

| Cylinder No. | No Dot | Dot |
|---|---|---|
| J6 | £600 | £600 |
| J6 T | £600 | £600 |
| J9 | £600 | £600 |
| J9 T | £600 | £600 |

## ■ 2½d. Panes of six with phosphor bands

Two phosphor bands reacting green applied in photogravure.
From 5s. Booklet H46p

| | | Perf Type | |
|---|---|---|---|
| **A. Watermark upright** | | I | Ie |
| SB86　Pane of 6 × 2½d. (containing No. S61 × 6) (14.8.60) | | £120 | £130 |
| 　b.　One band on each stamp | | £400 | |
| **B. Watermark inverted** | | | |
| SB86a　Pane of 6 × 2½d. (containing No. S61a × 6) (14.8.60) | | £1100 | £1100 |

**Booklet Cylinder Numbers**
Panes of six (21-row cylinder)

| Cylinder No. | No Dot | Dot |
|---|---|---|
| J13 | £500 | £500 |
| J13 T | £500 | £500 |

**Specimen overprints from
the National Postal Museum Archives**
Booklet pane of six. Perf. 15 × 14, watermark Type W.24 upright
Each stamp handstamped "Specimen" (13 × 2 mm.)

## ■ 2½d. Panes of six with phosphor bands

Two phosphor bands reacting blue applied in gravure. Cream
paper
From 5s. Booklets H49p, H51p/52p and H54p

| | | Perf Type | |
|---|---|---|---|
| **A. Watermark upright** | | I | Ie |
| SB87　Pane of 6 × 2½d. (containing No. S62 × 6) (3.61) | | £100 | £110 |
| **B. Watermark inverted** | | | |
| SB87a　Pane of 6 × 2½d. (containing No. S62a × 6) (3.61) | | £1100 | £1100 |

**Booklet Cylinder Numbers**
Panes of six (21-row cylinders)
Two bands. Cream paper

| Cylinder No. | No Dot | Dot |
|---|---|---|
| J13 | £450 | £450 |
| J13 T | £450 | £450 |

### ■ 2½d. Panes of six with one phosphor band

With one phosphor band at left reacting blue applied in photogravure.
Cream or whiter paper
From 5s. Booklets H55p/74p

| Cream Paper | | Perf Type | |
|---|---|---|---|
| **A. Watermark upright** | | *I* | *Ie* |
| SB88 | Pane of 6 × 2½d. (containing No. S63 × 6) (3.62) | 90·00 | £100 |
| **B. Watermark inverted** | | | |
| SB88a | Pane of 6 × 2½d. (containing No. S63b × 6) (3.62) | £275 | £275 |

**Whiter Paper**

| **A. Watermark upright** | | | |
|---|---|---|---|
| SB89 | Pane of 6 × 2½d. (containing No. S65 × 6) (3.6.63) | £100 | |
| | b. One 4 mm. band at right but omitted on stamps 3 and 6 | — | |
| | c. Two narrow bands over perforations | — | |
| **B. Watermark inverted** | | | |
| SB89a | Pane of 6 × 2½d. (containing No. S65b × 6) (3.6.63) | £275 | |

No. SB89b was the source of No. S65e and No. SB89c was the source of No. 565c.

**Booklet Cylinder Numbers**
Pane of six (21-row cylinders)

**One band. Cream paper**

| Cylinder No. | No Dot | Dot |
|---|---|---|
| J13 | £450 | £450 |
| J13 T | £450 | £450 |

**One band. Whiter paper**

| Cylinder No. | No Dot | Dot |
|---|---|---|
| J13 | £300 | £300 |
| J13 T | £300 | £300 |
| J14 | £300 | £300 |
| J14 T | £300 | £300 |

**Specimen overprints from the National Postal Museum Archives**
Booklet pane of six. Perf. 15 × 14, watermark Type W.24 upright
Each stamp handstamped "Specimen" (15 × 2½ mm.)

### ■ 3d. Panes of six, St. Edward's Crown

From 3s. Booklets M1/10, 4s.6d. Booklets L1/17 and 5s. Booklets H32/36

| | | Perf Type | |
|---|---|---|---|
| **A. Watermark upright** | | *I* | *Ie* |
| SB90 | Pane of 6 × 3d. (containing No. S68 × 6) (1.10.57) | 5·00 | 6·00 |
| | b. White dot on laurel leaf (R. 1/2 or 2/2) | 45·00 | |
| **B. Watermark inverted** | | | |
| SB90a | Pane of 6 × 3d. (containing No. S68d × 6) (1.10.57) | 10·00 | 11·00 |

SB90b
(Cyl. K2 no dot)

**Booklet Cylinder Numbers**
Panes of six (K8 20-row cylinder, others 21-row cylinders)

| Cylinder No. | No Dot | Dot |
|---|---|---|
| K1 | 70·00 | 70·00 |
| K1 T | 70·00 | 70·00 |
| K2 | 55·00 | 55·00 |
| K2 T | 55·00 | 55·00 |
| K7 | 45·00 | 45·00 |
| K7 T | 45·00 | 45·00 |
| K8 T | 60·00 | 45·00 |

K8 was engraved in the middle of the sheet by row 11 and only occurs at the top of the pane.

### ■ 3d. Panes of four, St. Edward's Crown

From 2s. Booklet N1.

| **A. Watermark upright** | | Perf. Type AP |
|---|---|---|
| SB91 | Pane of 4 × 3d. (containing No. S68 × 4) (22.4.59) | 40·00 |
| **B. Watermark inverted** | | |
| SB91a | Pane of 4 × 3d. (containing No. S68d × 4) (22.4.59) | 45·00 |

**Booklet Cylinder Numbers**
Cylinder numbers did not appear in the finished booklets, but it is known that K12 and one other cylinder were used.

**Imprimatur from the National Postal Museum Archives**
Booklet pane of four. Imperforate, watermark Type W.23
Two panes arranged vertically *tête-bêche* with a 12 mm. horizontal gutter margin between

## ▇ 3d. Panes of six, Crowns Wmk

Cream or whiter paper
From 3s. Booklets M9d/74, 4s.6d. Booklets L8/58, 5s. Booklets
H36(d)/(e) and H37/74 and 10s. Booklets X1/14

**Cream Paper**

| | | Perf Type | |
|---|---|---|---|
| **A. Watermark upright** | | *I* | *Ie* |
| SB92 | Pane of 6 × 3d. (containing No. | | |
| | S70×6) (11.58) | 3·50 | 4·00 |
| b. | Imperf. pane* | £3750 | |
| c. | Part perf. pane* | £3500 | |
| **B. Watermark inverted** | | | |
| SB92a | Pane of 6 × 3d. (containing No. | | |
| | S70e×6) (11.58) | 4·00 | 5·00 |
| ab. | Long tailed "R" (R. 1/1) | 45·00 | |
| ac. | Background retouch (R. 1/1) | 45·00 | |
| ad. | Part perf. pane* | £3500 | |

**Whiter Paper**

| | | | |
|---|---|---|---|
| **A. Watermark upright** | | | |
| SB93 | Pane of 6 × 3d. (containing No. | | |
| | S71×6) (16.7.62) | 3·50 | 4·00 |
| **B. Watermark inverted** | | | |
| SB93a | Pane of 6 × 3d. (containing No. | | |
| | S71c×6) (16.7.62) | 3·75 | 4·50 |
| ab. | Long tailed "R" (R. 1/1) | 45·00 | |
| ac. | Background retouch (R. 1/1) | 45·00 | |

*Booklet errors. See General Notes.

| | |
|---|---|
| SB92ab, SB93ab, SB97ab, SB99ab, SB100ab (Cyl. K15 no dot) | SB92ac, SB93ac, SB97ac, SB99ac, SB100ac Retouched area of fine dots behind Queens head (Cyl. K15 no dot) |

**Booklet Cylinder Numbers**
Panes of six (K13, K15 and K16 20-row cylinders, others 21-row cylinders)

**Cream paper**

| Cylinder No. | No Dot | Dot |
|---|---|---|
| K7 | 80·00 | 80·00 |
| K7 T | 80·00 | 80·00 |
| K13 | 35·00 | 35·00 |
| K15 | 45·00 | 45·00 |
| K17 | 50·00 | 40·00 |
| K17 T | 40·00 | 40·00 |
| K18 | 50·00 | 50·00 |
| K18 T | 50·00 | 50·00 |
| K20 | 50·00 | 50·00 |
| K20 T | 50·00 | 50·00 |

**Whiter paper**

| Cylinder No. | No Dot | Dot |
|---|---|---|
| K15 | 50·00 | 50·00 |
| K16 | £175 | £175 |
| K18 | 60·00 | 60·00 |
| K18 T | 60·00 | 60·00 |
| K20 | 60·00 | 60·00 |

| Cylinder No. | No Dot | Dot |
|---|---|---|
| K20 T | 60·00 | 60·00 |
| K21 | — | — |
| K21 T | — | — |

**Specimen overprints from
the National Postal Museum Archives**
Booklet pane of six. Perf. 15 × 14, watermark Type W.24 upright
Each stamp handstamped "Specimen" (13 × 2 mm.)
Each stamp handstamped "Specimen" (15 × 2½ mm.)
●━━━━━━

## ▇ 3d. Panes of four, Crowns Wmk

Cream paper
From 2s. Booklets N2/3. *Perf. Type* AP

| | | |
|---|---|---|
| **A. Watermark upright** | | |
| SB94 | Pane of 4 × 3d. (containing No. S70×4) | |
| | (2.11.60) | 25·00 |
| **B. Watermark inverted** | | |
| SB94a | Pane of 4 × 3d. (containing No. S70e×4) | |
| | (2.11.60) | 25·00 |
| ab. | Break in bottom ribbon (R. 1/2) | 75·00 |

SB94ab

**Booklet Cylinder Numbers**
Cylinder No. K14 was used, but it does not appear in the finished booklets.

**Specimen overprints from
the National Postal Museum Archives**
Booklet pane of four. Perf. 15×14, watermark Type W.24 inverted
Each stamp handstamped "Specimen" (13×2 mm.)
●━━━━━━

## ▇ 3d. Panes of four, Crowns Wmk sideways

Cream or whiter paper
From 2s. Booklets N4/20 and NX1

| **Cream Paper** | | Perf. Type | | | |
|---|---|---|---|---|---|
| **A. Watermark Crown to left** | | *I* | *I(½v)* | *AP* | *AP(2E)* |
| SB95 | Pane of 4 × 3d. (containing No. S70d×4) (26.5.61) | 20·00 | 60·00 | 10·00 | 25·00 |
| **B. Watermark Crown to right** | | | | | |
| SB95a | Pane of 4 × 3d. (containing No. S70f×4) (26.5.61) | 20·00 | 60·00 | 10·00 | † |

**Whiter Paper**

| **A. Watermark Crown to left** | | | | | |
|---|---|---|---|---|---|
| SB96 | Pane of 4 × 3d. (containing No. S71a×4) (5.6.62) | 18·00 | 55·00 | 9·00 | 20·00 |
| **B. Watermark Crown to right** | | | | | |
| SB96a | Pane of 4 × 3d. (containing No. S71b×4) (5.6.62) | 18·00 | 55·00 | 9·00 | † |

**Booklet Cylinder Numbers**
Pane of four, Perf. Type T Cyl. No. K19 (Wmk Crown to left)
£150
Due to the width of the selvedge, the "19" was normally
trimmed off.

**Imprimaturs from the National Postal Museum Archives**
Booklet pane of four. Imperforate, watermark Type W.24

| | |
|---|---|
| Two panes arranged vertically *tête-bêche* with a 12 mm. horizontal gutter margin between | £20,000 |

**Specimen overprints from**
**the National Postal Museum Archives**
Booklet pane of four. Perf. 15 × 14, watermark Type W.24
Crown to left, Perf. AP(2E)
Each stamp handstamped "Specimen" (13 × 2 mm.)

---

### 3d. Panes of six with graphite lines, Crowns Wmk

Graphite lines as Type **S8**
From 3s. Booklets M13g/15g, M19g/21g, 4s.6d. Booklets L11g,
L15g/16g, L18g/19g and 5s. Booklets H39g, H43g and H46g

| | | Perf Type | |
|---|---|---|---|
| | | *I* | *Ie* |
| A. **Watermark upright** | | | |
| SB97 | Pane of 6 × 3d. (containing No. S72 × 6) (4.8.59) | 6·00 | 7·50 |
| B. **Watermark inverted** | | | |
| SB97a | Pane of 6 × 3d. (containing No. S72a × 6) (4.8.59) | 7·00 | 8·50 |
| ab. | Long tailed "R" (R. 1/1) | 65·00 | |
| ac. | Background retouch (R. 1/1) | 65·00 | |

For illustrations of Nos. SB97ab/ac, see Nos. SB92ab/ac.

**Booklet Cylinder Numbers**
Panes of 6 (K7 21-row cylinder, others 20-row cylinders)

| Cylinder No. | No Dot | Dot |
|---|---|---|
| K7 | 70·00 | 70·00 |
| K7 T | 70·00 | 70·00 |
| K13 | 90·00 | 90·00 |
| K13T | 80·00 | 80·00 |

---

### 3d. Panes of six with phosphor bands

Two phosphor bands reacting green applied in photogravure
From 3s. Booklets M25p, M28p/9p and M37p(a), 4s.6d. Booklets L21p, L24p, and L27p(a) and 5s. Booklet H46p

| | | Perf Type | |
|---|---|---|---|
| | | *I* | *Ie* |
| A. **Watermark upright** | | | |
| SB98 | Pane of 6 × 3d. (containing No. S74 × 6) (14.8.60) | 16·00 | 19·00 |
| b. | One 8mm. band on each stamp | £350 | |
| B. **Watermark inverted** | | | |
| SB98a | Pane of 6 × 3d. (containing No. S74a × 6) (14.8.60) | 16·00 | |
| ab. | Stamps 1 and 4 with one 6 mm. band, others with one 8 mm. band | £400 | |

See No. S74b,d for the one 8 mm. band variety and No. S74da
for the one 6 mm. band variety.

**Booklet Cylinder Numbers**
Panes of six (21-row cylinders)

| Cylinder No. | No Dot | Dot |
|---|---|---|
| K17 | 90·00 | 90·00 |
| K17 T | 90·00 | 90·00 |

**Specimen overprints from**
**the National Postal Museum Archives**
Booklet pane of six, Perf. 15 × 14, Wmk Type W.24 upright, each
stamp handstamped "Specimen" (13 × 2 mm.).

---

### 3d. Panes of six with phosphor bands

Two phosphor bands reacting blue applied in gravure. Cream
or whiter paper
From 3s. Booklets M33p, M36p, M37p(b), M38p/9p,
M43p/7p, M49p/53p, M55p/61p, M64p/74p, 4s.6d. Booklets
L25p, L27p(b), L28p, L30p/42p, L44p/57p and 5s. Booklets
H49p, H51p/2p and H54p/74p

**Cream Paper**

| | | Perf Type | |
|---|---|---|---|
| | | *I* | *Ie* |
| A. **Watermark upright** | | | |
| SB99 | Pane of 4 × 3d. (containing No. S75 × 6) (3.61) | 7·50 | 9·00 |
| B. **Watermark inverted** | | | |
| SB99a | Pane of 4 × 3d. (containing No. S75a × 6) (3.61) | 7·50 | 9·00 |
| ab. | Long tailed "R" (R. 1/1) | 60·00 | |
| ac. | Background retouch (R. 1/1) | 60·00 | |

**Whiter Paper**

| | | Perf Type | |
|---|---|---|---|
| | | *I* | *Ie* |
| A. **Watermark upright** | | | |
| SB100 | Pane of 4 × 3d. (containing No. S76 × 6) (25.9.62) | 9·00 | 10·00 |
| B. **Watermark inverted** | | | |
| SB100a | Pane of 4 × 3d. (containing No. S76c × 6) (25.9.62) | 9·00 | 10·00 |
| ab. | Long tailed "R" (R. 1/1) | 60·00 | |
| ac. | Background retouch (R. 1/1) | 60·00 | |

For illustrations of Nos. SB99ab/ac and SB100ab/ac, see Nos.
SB92ab/ac.

**Booklet Cylinder Numbers**
Panes of six (K15 20-row cylinder, others 21-row cylinders). Two
bands.

**Cream paper**

| Cylinder No. | No Dot | Dot |
|---|---|---|
| K15 | 75·00 | 75·00 |
| K18 | 95·00 | 95·00 |
| K18 T | 95·00 | 95·00 |

**Whiter paper**

| Cylinder No. | No Dot | Dot |
|---|---|---|
| K15 | 80·00 | 80·00 |
| K18 | 80·00 | 80·00 |
| K18 T | 80·00 | 80·00 |
| K20 | 95·00 | 95·00 |
| K20 T | 95·00 | 95·00 |

**Specimen overprints from**
**the National Postal Museum Archives**
Booklet pane of six. Perf. 15 × 14, watermark Type W.24 upright
Each stamp handstamped "Specimen" (15 × 2½ mm.)

## ■ 3d. Panes of four with phosphor bands, wmk sideways

Two phosphor bands reacting blue applied by typography.
Cream or whiter paper
From 2s. Booklets N4p, N8p/10p, N12p/20p

**Cream Paper**

**A. Watermark Crown to left**

| | | | Perf. Type | | |
|---|---|---|---|---|---|
| | | *I* | *I(½v)* | *AP* | *AP(2E)* |
| SB101 | Pane of 4 × 3d. (containing No. S75b × 4) (14.7.61) | 40·00 | £100 | 25·00 | 50·00 |
| b. | One broad band on each stamp | | | £200 | — |

**B. Watermark Crown to right**

| | | | | | |
|---|---|---|---|---|---|
| SB101a | Pane of 4 × 3d. (containing No. S75c × 4) (14.7.61) | 40·00 | £100 | 25·00 | † |
| ab. | One broad band on each stamp | | | £200 | † |

**Whiter Paper**

**A. Watermark Crown to left**

| | | | | | |
|---|---|---|---|---|---|
| SB102 | Pane of 4 × 3d. (containing No. S76a × 4) (15.8.62) | 50·00 | £125 | 30·00 | 60·00 |

**B. Watermark Crown to right**

| | | | | | |
|---|---|---|---|---|---|
| SB102a | Pane of 4 × 3d. (containing No. S76b × 4) (15.8.62) | 50·00 | £125 | 30·00 | † |

**Booklet Cylinder Numbers**
Pane of four, Perf. Type I Cyl. No. K19″(Wmk Crown to left) £150
Due to the width of the selvedge, the "19" was normally trimmed off.

**Imprimaturs from the National Postal Museum Archives**
Booklet pane of four. Imperforate, watermark Type W.24

| Two panes arranged vertically *tête-bêche* | £20,000 |
|---|---|

**Specimen overprints from the National Postal Museum Archives**
Booklet pane of four. Perf. 15 × 14, watermark Type W.24.
Crown to right, Perf. Type AP
Each stamp handstamped "Specimen" (13 × 2 mm.)

SB103

## ■ 3d. Panes of six with phosphor band

With 4 mm. Phosphor band reacting violet at side
2 × 3d. (band at left) and 4 × 3d. (band at right). Crowns.
Phosphor bands applied in gravure
From 10s. Booklet X15p(a/b)

| | | Perf Type | |
|---|---|---|---|
| | | *I* | *Ie* |
| **A. Watermark upright** | | | |
| SB103 | Pane of 6 × 3d. (containing Nos. S78 × 2, S78a × 4) (2.67) | 35·00 | 40·00 |
| **B. Watermark inverted** | | | |
| SB103a | Pane of 6 × 3d. (containing Nos. S78g × 2, S78h × 4) (2.67) | £120 | £130 |

**Booklet Cylinder Numbers**
Panes of six (21-row cylinder)

| Cylinder No. | No Dot | Dot |
|---|---|---|
| K18 | £150 | £150 |
| K18 T | £150 | £150 |

## ■ 3d. Panes of six, with phosphor band

With one 4 mm. centre phosphor band reacting violet
6 × 3d. . Crowns. The centre phosphor bands were applied in
gravure using a mixed screen.
From 10s. Booklets X16p/17p

| | | Perf Type | |
|---|---|---|---|
| | | *I* | *Ie* |
| **A. Watermark upright** | | | |
| SB104 | Pane of 6 × 3d. (containing No. S79 × 6) (8.67) | 8·00 | 9·50 |
| **B. Watermark inverted** | | | |
| SB104a | Pane of 6 × 3d. (containing No. S79b × 6) (8.67) | 20·00 | 24·00 |

**Booklet Cylinder Numbers**
Panes of six (21-row cylinder)

| Cylinder No. | No Dot | Dot |
|---|---|---|
| K18 | 85·00 | 85·00 |
| K18 T | 85·00 | 85·00 |

## ■ 4d. Deep ultramarine panes of six, Crowns Wmk

From 4s.6d. Booklets L59/65, 6s. Booklets Q1/23 and 10s.
Booklets X10/14

| | | Perf Type | |
|---|---|---|---|
| | | *I* | *Ie* |
| **A. Watermark upright** | | | |
| ✓ SB105 | Pane of 6 × 4d. (containing No. S85 × 6) (21.6.65) | 6·00 | 7·50 |
| b. | Imperf. pane* | £4750 | |
| c. | Part perf. pane* | £4000 | |
| ✓ d. | Line through diadem (R. 1/1 or 2/1) | 60·00 | |
| e. | Dot below top frame (R. 1/1 or 2/1) | 55·00 | |
| f. | "Y" flaw (R. 1/2 or 2/2) | 45·00 | |
| **B. Watermark inverted** | | | |
| ✓ SB105a | Pane of 6 × 4d. (containing No. S85e × 6) (21.6.65) | 6·00 | 7·50 |
| ab. | Retouch over "4" (R. 1/1 or 2/1) | 55·00 | |

SB105d
Later retouched (Cyl. N1 no dot)

SB105e, SB107c, SB109b,
SB111c (Cyl. N1 dot)

SB105f, SB107d, SB109c, SB111d
Multipositive flaw from panes
showing N1, N2 (T), N3 also
without cylinder no.

SB105ab, SB107ab, SB109ab,
SB111ac (Cyl. N1 no dot)

### Booklet Cylinder Numbers (Deep ultramarine)

Panes of six (21-row cylinders N1/2 or 20-row cylinder N3)

| Cylinder No. | No Dot | Dot |
|---|---|---|
| N1 | 55·00* | 55·00* |
| N1 T | 60·00 | 60·00 |
| N2 | 60·00 | 60·00 |
| N2 T | 55·00* | 55·00* |
| N3 | 50·00* | 50·00 |

**Specimen overprints from
the National Postal Museum Archives**
Booklet pane of six. Perf. 15 × 14, watermark Type W.24 inverted
Each stamp handstamped "Specimen" (13 × 2 mm.)

### ■ 4d. Deep ultramarine panes of four, Crowns Wmk sideways

From 2s. Booklets N21/27

| | | Perf. Type | | |
|---|---|---|---|---|
| **A. Watermark Crown to left** | *I* | *I(½v)* | *AP* | *AP(2E)* |
| SB106   Pane of 4 × 4d. (containing No. S85d×4) (16.8.65) | 15·00 | 75·00 | 7·00 | — |
| **B. Watermark Crown to right** | | | | |
| SB106a   Pane of 4 × 4d. (containing No. S85f×4) (16.8.65) | 10·00 | 75·00 | 6·00 | † |

Perf. AP(2E). Due to the scarcity of these panes it is surmised
that they are from the phosphor pane SB112, as booklets N31p
and N32p are known with phosphor omitted on the 4d. pane.

**Booklet Cylinder Numbers**
Pane of four (24-row single pane cylinder of 480 stamps
sideways). .

| | Perf. Type I |
|---|---|
| Cylinder No. | No Dot |
| N4 (Wmk. Crown to left) | £120 |
| N4 (Wmk. Crown to right) | £120 |

On single-pane cylinders with sideways printing the number
is engraved in the right margin by row 22. As some of the
4d. value was printed with the watermark either upright or
inverted tot he direction of print, this issue and the phosphor
issues applied in gravure occur with the cylinder number on
panes with sideways watermark either to the left or to the right.

### ■ 4d. Deep ultramarine panes of six with phosphor bands

With two phosphor bands reacting blue
Applied in gravure
From 4s.6d. Booklets L59p, L60p(a)/(62p(a) excl. (b) nos. and
6s. Booklets Q1p/3p, Q4p(a)/8p(a) excl. (b) nos.

| | | Perf Type | |
|---|---|---|---|
| | | *I* | *Ie* |
| **A. Watermark upright** | | | |
| SB107   Pane of 6 × 4d. (containing No. S90×6) (21.6.65) | | 12·00 | 12·00 |
|    c.   Dot below top frame (R. 1/1 or 2/1) | | 60·00 | |
|    d.   "Y" flaw (R. 1/2 or 2/2) | | 50·00 | |
| **B. Watermark inverted** | | | |
| SB107a   Pane of 6 × 4d. (containing No. S90b×6) (21.6.65) | | 18·00 | 20·00 |
|    ab.   Retouch over "4" (R. 1/1 or 2/1) | | 60·00 | |

For illustrations of Nos. SB107c/d and SB107ab, see Nos.
SB105e/f and SB105ab.

**Booklet Cylinder Numbers**
Panes of six (21-row cylinder)

| Cylinder No. | No Dot | Dot |
|---|---|---|
| N1 | 60·00 | 60·00 |
| N1 T | 60·00 | 60·00 |

### ■ 4d. Deep ultramarine panes of four with phosphor bands, wmk sideways

With two phosphor bands reacting blue. Applied by
typography
From 2s. Booklets N21p, N22p(a) and N23p(a)

| | | Perf. Type | |
|---|---|---|---|
| | *I* | *I(½v)* | *AP* |
| **A. Watermark Crown to left** | | | |
| SB108   Pane of 4 × 4d. (containing No. S90c×4) (16.8.65) | 25·00 | 75·00 | 15·00 |
|    b.   One 8 mm. band on each stamp | | | |
| **B. Watermark Crown to right** | | | |
| SB108a   Pane of 4 × 4d. (containing No. S90d×4) (16.8.65) | 25·00 | 75·00 | 15·00 |
|    ab.   One 8 mm. band on each stamp | | | |

**Booklet Cylinder Numbers**
Pane of four (24-row single pane cylinder of 480 stamps
sideways).

| | Perf. Type I |
|---|---|
| Cylinder No. | No Dot |
| N4 (Wmk. Crown to right) | £140 |

## ■ 4d. Deep ultramarine panes of six with phosphor bands

With two 8 mm. Phosphor bands reacting violet
Applied in gravure
From 4s.6d. Booklets L60p(b), L61p(b) and L62p(b)/65p(a), 6s.
Booklets Q4p(b)/8p(b) excl.
(a) nos. and Q9p/20p and 10s. Booklet X15p(a)

| | | Perf Type | |
|---|---|---|---|
| | | *I* | *Ie* |
| **A. Watermark upright** | | | |
| SB109 | Pane of 6 × 4d. (containing No. S91 × 6) (9.65) | 5·50 | 6·50 |
| b. | Dot below top frame (R. 1/1 or 2/1) | 55·00 | |
| c. | "Y" flaw (R. 1/2 or 2/2) | 40·00 | |
| **B. Watermark inverted** | | | |
| SB109a | Pane of 6 × 4d. (containing No. S91a × 6) (9.65) | 5·50 | 6·50 |
| ab. | Retouch over "4" (R. 1/1 or 2/1) | 55·00 | |

For illustrations of Nos. SB109b/c and SB109ab, see Nos.
SB105e/f and SB105ab.

**Booklet Cylinder Numbers**
Panes of six (21-row cylinders N1 and N2 or 20-row cylinder
N3)

| Cylinder No. | No Dot | Dot |
|---|---|---|
| N1 | 60·00* | 60·00 |
| N1 T | 50·00 | 60·00 |
| N2 | 60·00 | 60·00 |
| N2 T | 60·00* | 60·00 |
| N3 | 80·00* | 80·00 |

## ■ 4d. Deep ultramarine panes of four with phosphor bands, wmk sideways

With two 8 mm. Phosphor bands reacting violet. Applied in
photogravure or typography
From 2s. Booklets N22p(b), N23p(b)/28p(a), N29p, N30p(a),
N31p(b) and N32(b)

| | | Perf. Type | | | |
|---|---|---|---|---|---|
| | | *I* | *I(½v)* | *AP* | *AP(2E)* |
| **A. Watermark Crown to left** | | | | | |
| SB110 | Pane of 4 × 4d. (containing No. S91b × 4) (1.67) | 10·00 | 75·00 | 6·00 | — |
| b. | One 8 mm. band on each stamp | — | — | — | † |
| c. | Bands typo. (10.65) | 70·00 | — | 60·00 | † |
| **B. Watermark Crown to right** | | | | | |
| SB110a | Pane of 4 × 4d. (containing No. S91c × 4) (1.67) | 10·00 | 75·00 | 6·00 | 8·50 |
| ab. | One broad band on each stamp | — | — | — | † |
| ac. | Bands typo. (10.65) | 70·00 | — | 60·00 | |

**Booklet Cylinder Numbers**
Pane of four (24-row single pane cylinder of 480 stamps
sideways).

| **Gravure bands** | Perf. Type I |
|---|---|
| Cylinder No. | No Dot |
| N4 (Wmk. Crown to left) | £110 |
| N4 (Wmk. Crown to right) | 90·00 |

**Typo bands**

| Cylinder No. | No Dot |
|---|---|
| N4 (Wmk. Crown to left) | † |
| N4 (Wmk. Crown to right) | — |

See note below SB106 cylinder numbers.

## ■ 4d. Deep ultramarine panes of six with phosphor bands

With two 9·5 mm. Phosphor bands reacting violet. Applied in
photogravure
From 4s.6d. Booklets L65p(b)/71p, 6s. Booklets Q21p/27p and
10s. Booklets X15p(b), X16p/17p

| | | Perf Type | |
|---|---|---|---|
| | | *I* | *Ie* |
| **A. Watermark upright** | | | |
| SB111 | Pane of 6 × 4d. (containing No. S92 × 6) (2.67) | 3·50 | 4·00 |
| a. | Part perf. pane* | £4750 | |
| b. | Dot below frame (R. 1/1 or 2/1) | 50·00 | |
| c. | "Y" flaw (R. 1/2 or 2/2) | 40·00 | |
| **B. Watermark inverted** | | | |
| SB111a | Pane of 6 × 4d. (containing No. S92a × 6) (2.67) | 3·50 | 4·00 |
| ab. | Part perf. pane* | £4750 | |
| ac. | Retouch over "4" (R. 1/1 or 2/1) | 50·00 | |

*Booklet error. See General Notes.
For illustrations of Nos. SB111b/c and SB111ac, see Nos.
SB105e/f and SB105ab.

**Booklet Cylinder Numbers**
Panes of six (21-row cylinders)

| Cylinder No. | No Dot | Dot |
|---|---|---|
| N1 | 45·00* | 45·00 |
| N1 T | 45·00 | 45·00 |
| N2 | 45·00 | 45·00 |
| N2 T | 45·00* | 45·00 |
| N2 (Wmk inverted) | | |
| N2 T (Wmk inverted) | £400 | £400 |

Cylinder panes showing watermark inverted (Cyl. No. N2) come
from Booklet X17p.

**Specimen overprints from
the National Postal Museum Archives**
Booklet pane of six. Perf. 15 × 14, watermark Type W.24 inverted
Each stamp handstamped "Specimen" (13 × 2 mm.)

## 4d. Deep ultramarine panes of four with phosphor bands, wmk sideways

With two 9·5 mm. Phosphor bands reacting violet. Applied by gravure
From 2s. Booklets N28p(b), N30p(b), N31p(a), N31p(c), N32p(a) and N32p(c)

| | | Perf. Type | | | |
|---|---|---|---|---|---|
| **A. Watermark Crown to left** | | *I* | *I(½v)* | *AP* | *AP(ZE)* |
| SB112 | Pane of 4 × 4d. (containing No. S92b × 4) (4.67) | 8·00 | 50·00 | 2·50 | 10·00 |
| b. | One 9·5 mm. band on each stamp | £100 | | 90·00 | — |
| **B. Watermark Crown to right** | | | | | |
| SB112a | Pane of 4 × 4d. (containing No. S92c × 4) (4.67) | 8·00 | 50·00 | 2·50 | 30·00 |
| ab. | One 9·5 mm. band on each stamp | £100 | | 90·00 | — |

**Booklet Cylinder Numbers**
Pane of four (24-row single pane cylinder of 480 stamps sideways).
Sideways watermark

| | Perf. Type I |
|---|---|
| Cylinder No. | No Dot |
| N4 (Wmk. Crown to left) | — |
| N4 (Wmk. Crown to right) | £100 |

# SECTION T

Dorothy Wilding Issues
1955–68. High Values. Recess-printed

## General Notes

### Plate preparation

The original master dies were engraved in three stages at Waterlows by HJ Bard. First the Queen's head was engraved, based on that on the 2½d. stamp. Following transfer by roller to a second die, the embrasure and word 'POSTAGE' were added, before being transferred to a third die, on to which the individual castles and values were engraved. Transfer roller impressions were taken from the finished dies for creation of the plates.

The finished dies were used by all three printers, although Waterlow and De la Rue prepared their own sets of transfer rollers for plate production. Bradbury Wilkinson initially employed the Waterlow And De la Rue trasfer rollers, but subsequently prepared their own for the 2s.6d., 10s. and £1 values.

Waterlow experimented with a new method of plate production, by preparing a 'master' plate (46936) from which a mould (60555) was taken; two plates (46959 and 46992) being taken from that mould. The plates were not used and all were subsequently destroyed, but the nickel mould is held at the BPMA.

De La Rue also used ('alto') moulds for the production of some of their printing plates.

Bradbury Wilkinson produced their printing plates direct from transfer rollers.

**Crowns Watermark.** The Crowns are slightly smaller than in the low values.

**Paper.** The stamps are all on unsurfaced paper except the 2s.6d., No. T6 which is on chalk-surfaced paper.

Bradbury, Wilkinson printings are found with a degree of fluorescence when viewed under a short-wave u.v. lamp. This is due to the use of optical brightening agents in the rags used for paper making.

Stamps printed by Waterlow and De la Rue tend to curl from top to bottom while Bradbury, Wilkinson printings curl at the sides.

**Perforation.** All stamps in this Section are comb perforated 11 × 12 and the sheet perforation is always Type A.

Bradbury Wilkinson Plate No.

**Plate Numbers.** All plates were made from the original Waterlow Die. All stamps were printed from double plates producing left and right panes which were guillotined to make Post Office sheets of 40 (4 × 10). Plate numbers were used both by Waterlow and De la Rue but they appeared between the panes and were trimmed off. The Bradbury, Wilkinson plate numbers appear below stamps 3/4 in the bottom margin, the whole numbers on the left pane and the "A" numbers on the right pane. All three printers used rotary sheet-fed machines, although Waterlow's 2s.6d. plate 47316, still held at the BPMA is flat.

a. No dot   b. One dot   c. Two dots

**De La Rue Plate Dots.** De La Rue printed on paper with St. Edward's Crown watermark and with Crowns watermark and as a control to distinguish the two papers during the changeover period, dots were inserted in the bottom margin below the first stamp in the bottom row.

In the case of the 2s.6d. the first printings on St. Edward's Crown paper were without dot, but later a single dot appeared on this paper, whilst early printings of stamps on the Crowns paper had two dots. The stamps with one dot in the bottom margin were released on 17 April 1959.

In the 10s. the dots are 7 mm. from the design and 5 mm. apart and in the other values they are 6 mm. from the design and 2½ mm. apart.

The number of sheets printed with double dots were:—

| | | | |
|---|---|---|---|
| **2s.6d.** | 93,630 | **10s.** | 37,510 |
| **5s.** | 60,158 | **£1** | 18,660 |

**Distinguishing the work of the three printers.** Waterlow printed the stamps up to 31 December 1957 and then De La Rue held the contract until 31 December 1962, after which all printings were made by Bradbury, Wilkinson. The following characteristics will help to distinguish their work:—

**Paper**

| Waterlow | De La Rue | Bradbury, Wilkinson |
|---|---|---|
| (a) Wmk. W.23 Creamy | (a) Wmk. W.23 Light cream | (a) Wmk. W.24 Whiter |
| (b) Wmk. W.23 Light cream (From Feb., '57) | (b) Wmk. W.24 Light cream | (b) Wmk. W.24 Chalk-surfaced (2s.6d. only) |
| | (c) Wmk. W.24 Whiter (From 1962) | (c) No wmk. White |

## Shades

| | Waterlow | De La Rue |
|---|---|---|
| **2s.6d.** | Blackish brown | More chocolate |
| **5s.** | Rose-carmine | Lighter red, less carmine |
| **10s.** | Ultramarine | More blue |
| **£1** | Black | Less intense |

The shade variations result in part from the differences in paper.

**Gutters.** The width of gutters between the stamps varies, particularly the horizontal, as follows:—

| Waterlow | De La Rue |
|---|---|
| 3.8 to 4.0 mm. | 3.4 to 3.8 mm. |

Later De La Rue plates were less distinguishable in this respect.

**Perforation.** The vertical perforation of the Bradbury, Wilkinson is 11.9 to 12 as against 11.8 for the De La Rue.

**Impression.** The individual lines of the De La Rue impression are cleaner and devoid of the whiskers of colour of Waterlow's, and the whole impression is lighter and softer. The Bradbury, Wilkinson stamps are generally more deeply engraved than the De La Rue, showing more of the diadem detail and heavier lines on the Queen's face.

### Waterlow Sheet Markings

*Perforation Markings.* As a check for the alignment of the perforations the following marks occur between the stamps in the Waterlow printings only:—

(a) 3 mm. cross in the centre of the sheet.
(b) 2½ mm. vertical lines in centre at top and bottom of sheet.
(c) 2½ mm. horizontal lines in centre at each side of sheet.

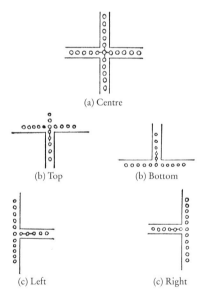

(a) Centre

(b) Top (b) Bottom

(c) Left (c) Right

*Perforation Pin-holes.* Coloured circles appear at left and right with a pin-hole through the opposite row six at left and right, although one is usually trimmed off.

Pin-hole          Corner trim mark

*Corner Trim Marks.* These occur in the corners but naturally one or both sides may be trimmed off.

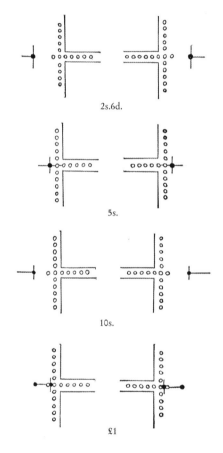

2s.6d.

5s.

10s.

£1

### De La Rue Sheet Markings

*Guide Marks.* The only markings on De La Rue sheets are the guide marks which appear in the side margins between rows 5 and 6 which also serve to distinguish the left and right panes. Their position varies with each value and also in some cases in format between the different plates used from time to time. The circles or crosses also have pin-holes.

*St. Edward's Crown Watermark*
2s.6d., 5s., 10s. Type 1. £1 Type 1a

*Multiple Crowns Watermark*
2s.6d. Types 1, 2, 2a, 2b, 2c, 4. 5s. Types 1, 2c, 2d, 3. 10s. Types 1, 2, 2d. £1 Types 1, 1b, 2, 4a.

Specialists recognise four basic types of guide marks which are described as seen from left panes. Reverse for right.

Type 1 Horizontal "T" shaped mark with spot at intersection.

a   As above but dot added to left extremity of horizontal arm.

b    As above but with "target" added between the two dots. The "target" mark is small, circular with open centre which was pierced by the perforating machine.

Type 2 This is as type 1 but with the addition of a "target" between the horizontal "T" and stamp

a    As type 2 but intersection dot to right of cross over point.

b    As type 2 but intersection dot to left of cross over point.

c    As type 2 but no dot.

d    As type 2c but "target" joined to "T".

Type 3 This is as type 1 but "target" is added first followed by "T".

Type 4 "Target" centred on "T" and without dot at intersection.

a    As type 4 but arms partly erased (south and east arms erased left pane; north and west arms for right pane).

### Bradbury, Wilkinson Sheet Markings

*Guide Holes.* These appear in a coloured circle opposite row 6, at left on left-hand panes and at right on right-hand panes.

*Lay Dots.* On the 2s.6d. plates 1/1A to 7/7A small "lay" dots appear in the top sheet margin, above the first vertical row on the left-hand pane and on the right-hand pane above the fourth vertical row. Only one copy of the 5s. is known but examples may exist on the other values. These were guide marks to check any movement of the plate.

Guide hole                    Guide cross

*Guide Crosses.* These occur in the region of rows 5 and 6 at right on left-hand panes and at left on right-hand panes. However, these do not appear on all plates, being omitted for instance on plates 8/8A, 9/9A of the 2s.6d. and 4/4A of the 5s.

**Tinted sheet margins.** Some sheets show a background wash or tint of the colour in which the stamps are printed. This is an indication of a new state of a plate or a plate that has been rechromed. The explanation for this is that in wiping off the excess ink from the surface of the plate a small amount may be left at the edge of the plate and this will continue until the plate is sufficiently smooth for the surface to be thoroughly wiped clean of ink. These marginal tints stop short of the edge of the sheet as the extremities of the plate do not come into contact with the inking roller.

All Bradbury Wilkinson plates were subsequently destroyed.

**Dates of issue.** Where a change of watermark or paper occurs the date given is generally that on which the stamps were first issued by the Suppliers Department to Postmasters.

**Post Office Training School stamps.** All values of the Waterlow printings exist over-printed with thick vertical bars and stamps from the other printings with thin vertical bars. These were supplied to Post Office Training Schools, and their issue to the public was unauthorised.

**"Cancelled" Overprint.** Nos. T5, T17 and T24 come overprinted "CANCELLED" (size 40 × 5 mm) as part of the test programme carried out by the Forensic Department of the Post Office.

The values overprinted "CANCELLED" (size 24 × 3 mm) from the De La Rue archive are listed below No. T2.

**Withdrawal dates.** It is known that the following went off sale at the Philatelic Bureau in the months shown:

| | |
|---|---|
| Mar. 1968 | £1 No. T24 |
| Nov. 1968 | 2s.6d. No. T6 |
| Nov. 1968 | 5s. No. T12 |
| Jan. 1969 | 2s.6d. No. T5 |
| Mar. 1970 | 10s. No. T18 |

The 2s.6d., 5s., 10s. and £1 no watermark, white paper (Nos. T7, T13, T19 and T25) were all withdrawn on 15 May 1970.

All 2s.6d., 5s. and 10s. stamps were invalidated as from 1 March 1972.

**T1**. Carrickfergus Castle

**T2**. Caernarvon Castle

**T3**. Edinburgh Castle

**T4**. Windsor Castle

(Des. Lynton Lamb. Portrait by Dorothy Wilding, Ltd.)

■ **1955–68. 2s.6d., Type T1**

**1955 (September 23). 2s.6d. Watermark St. Edward's Crown, Type W.23**

T1 (=S.G.536)

| (a) Waterlow Printings | Mint | Used |
|---|---|---|
| 2s.6d.  Black-brown | 13·00 | 2·00 |
| a.  Re-entry (R. 2/2) | 65·00 | |

**Quantity Issued** 47,919,460

T2 (=S.G.536a)

| (b) De La Rue Printings (17 July 1958) | | |
|---|---|---|
| 2s.6d.  Black-brown | 30·00 | 2·50 |
| a.  Watermark inverted | † | £3000 |
| b.  With one plate dot in bottom margin (R. 10/1) (released 17.4.59) | 80·00 | |

No T2a: three used examples are known
**Quantity Issued** 21,350,400

**Imprimatur from the National Postal Museum Archives**
No. T1 imperforate, watermark Type W.23
Watermark upright

**Cancelled Overprints from the De La Rue Archives**
Nos. T2, T9, T15 and T21 overprinted "CANCELLED" (24×3 mm)
*Set of four* £900.
The overprint was handstamped in violet and impressions vary slightly in position.
  The above were from surplus registration sheets used by the printer for colour matching. They were placed on the market in 1990.

**Plates.** Plates numbered 46725, 46936, 47001, 47145 and 47316, each double pane, are known to have been used by Waterlow. The first two plates were later destroyed but the remaining three are all held at the BPMA. Oddly, plate 47316 is flat (although stamps printed from it are known). All other printing plates are curved for the rotary press. The De La Rue plates were made using the original Waterlow dies. No plate numbers were found on the issued sheets, but it is now known that they were numbered 47320, 47321 and 47322. 47321 was issued as a "master" plate from which seven further printing plates were produced designated N1, N2 (the "one dot" printing), N3 (the "two dot" and "no dot" printings), N8, N9, N10 and N12.

T1a
The doubling occurs down the left-hand margin

T5b
Lines of shading weak or omitted at base of collar, on dress, and at foot of background. Occurs on R.5/4 and 6/4 (the illustration is of R.6/4

T5c, T6a
Re-entry shows in the form of brown dots over battlements. The re-entry on Nos. T5d and T6b occurs in the same place but is less marked

## 1959 (July 22). 2s.6d. Watermark Crowns, Type W.24

T3

### (a) De La Rue Printings

**A. Light Cream Paper**

| | Mint | Used |
|---|---|---|
| 2s.6d.  Black-brown | 15·00 | 1·00 |
| a. With two plate dots in bottom margin (R. 10/1) | 40·00 | |

T4 (=S.G.595)

**B. Whiter Paper (13 July 1962)**

| | | |
|---|---|---|
| 2s.6d.  Black-brown | 10·00 | 75 |
| a. Watermark inverted | — | £2200 |

No. T4a. Probably no more than five used examples exist.

**Quantity Issued** (both papers) 95, 999, 880

### (b) Bradbury, Wilkinson Printings
T5 (=S.G.595a)

**A. Whiter Paper (1 July 1963)**

| | | |
|---|---|---|
| 2s.6d.  Black-brown | 35 | 40 |
| a. Watermark inverted | £2750 | £250 |
| b. Weak entry (Pl. 5A, R. 5/4 or 6/4) | 20·00 | |
| c. Re-entry (Pl. 9A, R. 8/4) | 25·00 | |
| d. Re-entry (Pl. 9, R. 10/2) | 25·00 | |

T6 (=S.G.595k)

**B. Chalk-surfaced Paper (30 May 1968)**

| | | |
|---|---|---|
| 2s.6d.  Black-brown | 50 | 1·50 |
| a. Re-entry (Pl. 9A, R. 8/4) | 25·00 | |
| b. Re-entry (Pl. 9, R. 10/2) | 25·00 | |

**Imprimatur from the National Postal Museum Archives**
No. T6 imperforate, watermark Type W.24
Watermark upright

**Plates Numbers** (Blocks of Four)
Bradbury, Wilkinson Printings
Whiter Paper. (No. T5)

| Plate No. | | Plate No | |
|---|---|---|---|
| 1 | 22·00 | 1A | 22·00 |
| 2 | 22·00 | 2A | 22·00 |
| 3 | 22·00 | 3A | 22·00 |
| 4 | £300 | 4A | £500 |
| 5 | 9·00 | 5A | 9·00 |
| 6 | 5·50 | 6A | 5·50 |
| 7 | 5·50 | 7A | 5·50 |
| 8 | 5·00 | 8A | 5·00 |
| 9 | 4·00 | ✓ 9A | 4·00 |

Chalk-surfaced Paper. (No. T6)

| | | | |
|---|---|---|---|
| 9 | 6·00 | 9A | 6·00 |

A perforation variety exists on plates 5 and 6, of which 21,000 sheets were reported to come with double extension holes in the side margins. It is now known that this was an error, rather than a "trial", as previously thought.

**Minor Constant Flaws**
On Plate 9 there are a number of faint scratch marks in the top and bottom margins and these are particularly noticeable on the chalky paper. They occur in the top margin on R. 10/3 and in the bottom margin on R. 1/1, 1/2, 2/1, 3/3, 3/4, 7/2, 7/4 and 8/2.
Plates 8A, 10 and 10A all show evidence of progressive wear around the guide hole. On plates 10 and 10A this takes the form of a crack extending from the guide hole towards the stamps.
Plate 13A R. 1/2 shows a 2 cm. long scratch on the left-hand side of the bottom margin.

### 1968 (July 1). 2s.6d. No Watermark. White paper

**T7** (=S.G.759)

| Bradbury, Wilkinson Printings | Mint | Used |
|---|---|---|
| 2s.6d.   Black-brown | 30 | 45 |

**Plates Numbers** (Blocks of Four)

| Plate No. | | Plate No | |
|---|---|---|---|
| 10 | 4·00 | ✓ 10A | 4·00 |
| 11 | 4·00 | 11A | 4·00 |
| 12 | 3·00 | 12A | 3·00 |
| 13 | 3·00 | 13A | £500 |

**Imprimatur from the National Postal Museum Archives**
No. T7 imperforate
No watermark

●——————————

### ■ 1955–68. 5s., Type T2

### 1955 (September 23). 5s. Watermark St. Edward's Crown, Type W.23

**T8** (=S.G.537)

| (a) Waterlow Printings | Mint | Used |
|---|---|---|
| 5s.  Rose-carmine | 35·00 | 4·00 |
| a.  Re-entry (R. 8/1) | £110 | |

**Quantity Issued** 16, 571, 120

**T9** (=S.G.537a)

| (b) De La Rue Printings (30 April 1958) | | |
|---|---|---|
| 5s.  Rose-carmine | 65·00 | 10·00 |

**Quantity Issued** 7, 466, 880

T8a

**Quantity Issued** 16, 571, 120
Major re-entry showing doubling of vertical lines of background above the diadem, and in the diadem along the left edge of the frontal cross, both sides of the side cross and the diagonals

**Imprimatur from the National Postal Museum Archives**
No. T8 imperforate, watermark Type W.23
Watermark upright

**Plates.** It is known that a double pane plate numbered 46726 was used by Waterlow. De La Rue created further plates, all double pane. Plate numbers did not occur on the issued sheets although it is now known that they were numbered 47317, 47323 and 47325. 47325 was used as a master plate to produce three printing plates; N1, N2 and N3.

●——————————

## 1959 (June 15). 5s. Watermark Crowns, Type W.24

### (a) De La Rue Printings
**T10**

| A. Light Cream Paper | Mint | Used |
|---|---|---|
| 5s.  Scarlet-vermilion | 65·00 | 3·00 |
| a.  Watermark inverted | £7500 | £450 |
| b.  With two plate dots in bottom margin (R. 10/1) | £100 | |

Some sheets of No. T10 are known perforated through the bottom margin and imperf in the top margin having been fed into the perforator the wrong way up (see Appendix G)

**T11** (=S.G.596)

| B. Whiter Paper (7 May 1962) | | |
|---|---|---|
| 5s.  Scarlet-vermilion | 45·00 | 2·00 |

**Quantity issued (both papers)** 30, 200, 320

### (b) Bradbury, Wilkinson Printings
**T12** (=S.G.596a)

| Whiter Paper (3 September 1963) | | |
|---|---|---|
| 5s.  (1) Red | 2·50 | 70 |
| (2) Brownish red (Plates 3, 4) | 1·20 | 50 |
| a.  Watermark inverted | £375 | £200 |
| b.  Printed on the gummed side | £1500 | |

**Plates Numbers** (Blocks of Four)
Bradbury, Wilkinson Printings. (No. T12)

| Plate No. | | Plate No | |
|---|---|---|---|
| 1 | 45·00 | 1A | 45·00 |
| 2 | 45·00 | 2A | 45·00 |
| 3 | 6·00 | 3A | 6·00 |
| 4 | 8·50 | 4A | 8·50 |

## 1968 (April 10). 5s. No Watermark. White paper

**T13** (=S.G.760)

| Bradbury, Wilkinson Printings | Mint | Used |
|---|---|---|
| 5s.  Brownish red | 70 | 75 |

**Plate Numbers** (Blocks of Four)

| Plate No. | | Plate No | |
|---|---|---|---|
| 4 | 7·00 | 4A | 7·00 |
| 5 | 7·00 | 5A ✓ | 7·00 |
| 6 | 9·00 | 6A | 9·00 |

**Imprimatur from the National Postal Museum Archives**
No. T13 imperforate
No watermark

## ■ 1955–68. 10s., Type T3

## 1955 (September 1). 10s. Watermark St. Edward's Crown, Type W.23

**T14** (=S.G.538)

| (a) Waterlow Printings | Mint | Used |
|---|---|---|
| 10s.  (1) Ultramarine | 85·00 | 14·00 |
| (2) Pale ultramarine | 85·00 | 14·00 |
| a.  Weak entry (R. 1/2) | £175 | 40·00 |

**Quantity Issued** 7, 967, 800

**T15** (=S.G.538a)

| (b) De La Rue Printings (25 April 1958) | | |
|---|---|---|
| 10s.  Dull ultramarine | £225 | 22·00 |
| a.  Weak frame (R. 4/1) | £300 | |

A used example of No. T15 with inverted watermark has been reported.

**Quantity Issued** 3, 680, 240

T14a
Weak entry to right of lower panel gives ragged appearance

T15a, T17a

**Minor Sheet Flaws**
In rows 8, 9 and 10 there are blue marks on the extremity of the white letters and figures of "POSTAGE" and value which are more marked on the bottom two rows. These may not be fully constant but could be helpful for purposes of identification.

**Imprimatur from the National Postal Museum Archives**
No. T14 imperforate, watermark Type W.23
Watermark upright

**Plates.** It is known that Waterlow used a double pane plate numbered 46728. De La Rue plates are now known to have been numbered 47318, 47324 and 47326. 47326 was used as a master plate to produce two printing plates; N1 and N2.

## 1959 (July 21). 10s. Watermark Crowns, Type W.24

**T16**

### (a) De La Rue Printings

| A. Light Cream Paper | Mint | Used |
|---|---|---|
| 10s.  Blue | 70·00 | 8·00 |
| a.  With two plate dots in bottom margin (R. 10/1) | £150 | |

**T17** (=S.G.597)

| B. Whiter Paper (30 April 1962) | | |
|---|---|---|
| 10s.  Blue | 55·00 | 5·00 |
| a.  Weak frame (R. 4/1) | £110 | |

**Quantity Issued (both papers)** 12, 704, 720

**(b) Bradbury, Wilkinson Printings**
**Whiter Paper (16 October 1963)**
**T18** (=S.G.597a)

| | | | |
|---|---|---|---|
| 10s. Bright ultramarine | | 4·50 | 4·50 |
| a. Watermark inverted | | — | £2200 |

No. T18a. Three used examples have been confirmed.

**Plate Numbers** (Blocks of Four)
Bradbury, Wilkinson Printings. (No. T18)

| Plate No. | | Plate No | |
|---|---|---|---|
| 1 | 65·00 | 1A | 65·00 |
| 2 | 23·00 | 2A | 23·00 |

---

### 1968 (April 10). 10s. No Watermark. White paper

**T19** (=S.G.761)

| Bradbury, Wilkinson Printings | | Mint | Used |
|---|---|---|---|
| 10s. Bright ultramarine | | 7·75 | 4·00 |

**Plate Numbers** (Blocks of Four)

| Plate No. | | Plate No | |
|---|---|---|---|
| 2 | 30·00 | 2A | 30·00 |

**Imprimatur from the National Postal Museum Archives**
No. T19 imperforate
No watermark

---

## 1955–67. £1, Type T4

### 1955 (September 1). £1 Watermark St. Edward's Crown, Type W.23

**T20** (=S.G.539)

| (a) Waterlow Printings | Mint | Used |
|---|---|---|
| £1 Black | £130 | 35·00 |

**Quantity Issued** 2, 769, 780

**T21** (=S.G.539a)

| (b) De La Rue Printings (28 April 1958) | | |
|---|---|---|
| £1 Black | £350 | 65·00 |

**Quantity Issued** 1, 521, 960

**Minor Re-entries**

**Waterlow Printings**
1/2 Slight doubling (Th. B1 and D–F1)
4/4 Slight doubling (Th. B1)
5/2 Slight doubling (Th. B1 and D–E1)
6/1 Slight doubling (Th. A–C13)
7/1 Slight doubling (Th. A–C13)
Other minute signs of doubling of left frame line occur on R. 7/2 and of right frame line on R. 1/1, 2/1, 3/3, 4/1, 4/2 and 9/2.

**Imprimatur from the National Postal Museum Archives**
No. T20 imperforate, watermark Type W.23
Watermark upright

**Plates.** It is known that the double pane plate used by Waterlow was numbered 46727. A further two plates were created by De La Rue, which are now known to be numbered 47319 and 47327. 47327 was used as a master plate to produce two printing plates; N1 and N2.

---

### 1959 (June 30). £1 Watermark Crowns, Type W.24

**T22**

**(a) De La Rue Printings**

| A. Light Cream Paper | Mint | Used |
|---|---|---|
| £1 Black | £130 | 15·00 |
| a. With two plate dots in bottom margin (R. 10/1) | £200 | |
| b. Watermark inverted | — | £2500 |

**B. Whiter Paper (30 April 1962)**
**T23** (=S.G.598)

| £1 Black | £120 | 12·00 |
|---|---|---|
| a. Watermark inverted | £2500 | |

No. T23a. No more than three or four examples, all used, have been reported.

**Quantity Issued** 6, 281, 120

**(b) Bradbury, Wilkinson Printings**
**T24** (=S.G.598a)

**Whiter Paper (14 November 1963)**

| £1 Black | 13·00 | 8·00 |
|---|---|---|
| a. Watermark inverted | £12000 | £3500 |

10,000 sheets of the £1 were printed on chalk-surfaced paper (as 2s.6d., No. T6) but they were never issued. Nevertheless, examples exist in private hands.
Die proofs of tht £1 value on gummed, unwatermarked paper were taken from the original die by Bradbury, Wilkinson, probably in 1963. Two examples are known in private hands,

both from the Goaman archive.

**Plate Numbers** (Blocks of Four)
Bradbury, Wilkinson Printings. (No. T24)

| Plate No. | | Plate No | |
|---|---|---|---|
| 1 | 60·00 | 1A | 60·00 |

## 1967 (December 4). £1 No Watermark. White Paper

**T25** (=S.G.762)

| Bradbury, Wilkinson Printings | | Mint | Used |
|---|---|---|---|
| £1  Black | | 7·50 | 4·50 |

**Plate Numbers** (Blocks of Four)

| Plate No. | | Plate No | |
|---|---|---|---|
| 1 | 25·00 | 1A | 25·00 |

**Imprimatur from the National Postal Museum Archives**
No. T25 perf. 11 × 12
No watermark

## Presentation Pack

| TPP1 (issued 1960) Four values | £1250 |
|---|---|

The issued pack contained one of each value in the De La Rue printing with Crowns watermark on the light cream paper (Nos. T3, T10, T16 and T22).

Three forms of the pack exist:

(a) Inscribed "$6·50" for sale in the U.S.A. (Price £750)

(b) Without price for sale in the U.K.

(c) With "£1.18s." for sale at 1960 Festival Hall, Int. Stamp Exhibition

# SECTION U

## Machin £.s.d. Issues
### 1967-70. Sheet and Coil Stamps in Gravure

## General Notes

**Introduction.** In February 1965, after twelve years of the Wilding portrait issue, the Queen granted permission for the preparation of studies for a new definitive series. Designs from several artists were submitted and Arnold Machin was eventually selected. His preferred approach, with the aim of emulating the simplicity of the Penny Black of 1840, was to present the Queen's head in profile by the medium of a plaster cast or plaque. He progressively worked upon this cast through most of 1966, for instance by adding a corsage at the Queen's request, until he was satisfied that his aim had been fulfilled.

Photographs were taken of the cast in various conditions of light, of which one was finally approved. The first version came to be used for values with a solid background, but it was found to be unsatisfactory for other values with a light or gradated background. Accordingly an earlier version of the cast was also selected which gave an improved sculptured appearance to the image. There were small differences between these two casts, which, as is explained above the check-list of Machin heads and phosphor screens, led to two different series of Head Types.

Of the original casts used by Arnold Machin, one is in the National Postal Museum and the other is said to have been lost.

The first three values, 4d., deep sepia, 1s. and 1s.9d., of the sterling Machin definitives appeared on 5 June 1967. The remaining values were issued in stages during the following thirteen months and the low value series was completed on 1 July 1968, although subsequent changes of stamp colours and variations in the number of phosphor bands on some values introduced further additions to the basic series. Uniquely this was the first definitive issue to be printed on paper without watermark, thus eliminating some of the factors which complicated the listing for previous issues.

**Printers.** All the low value £.s.d. Machin issues were printed in Gravure by Harrison & Sons. They were printed on continuous reels of paper on the web generally in double pane width, i.e. 480 stamps consisting of two panes (no dot and dot) each of 240 stamps arranged in twenty rows of twelve stamps, the panes being guillotined before issue. The 10d., 1s.6d., 1s.9d. and part of the 1s. printings were made from single cylinders printing sheets of 240 stamps (i.e. no dot panes only). The bulk of the £.s.d Machin series were printed on Timson presses. The 4d. (both colours) from cylinders 14, 15, 16 and 17 and the 5d. from cylinders 11 and 13 were printed variously on the Halley or Thrissell presses as were the 1s.6d. and 1s.9d. values. The 1s. multi-value coils were printed on the five colour Thrissell press. The panes for the £1 'Stamps for Cooks' booklet were sheet fed printed on the L & M No. 4 press.

Single colour booklet panes of six were printed on the Timson press while booklet panes of four and *se-tenant* panes (both panes of four and six) were printed on the Halley press.

The phosphor bands were applied at the same operation. The bi-coloured 1s.6d. and 1s.9d. were printed by the three-colour (including the phosphor cylinder) Halley machine and the remainder by the two-colour Timson machine. The multi-value coils and se-tenant panes from the £1 Stamps for Cooks booklet were printed by the five-colour Thrissell machine.

**Master negatives and multipositives.** The process of preparing a new Machin definitive Gravure cylinder started with a master negative from photographs (sometimes referred to as master positives) of one of the two casts of the Queen's head in profile. Further master negatives are taken as needed and there is evidence that these can be retouched. The next step is the transfer of the image on this master negative by means of a step-and-repeat camera onto a photographic plate known as a multipositive. This is normally rather larger than the pane size of 240 or double pane size of 480. This multipositive of the head and background is then combined with a second multipositive for the face value, added to the previously screened carbon tissue. The relative positioning of these two multipositives is not always uniformly precise and can result in tiny variations of distance between head and value digits described under Machin Heads in these notes. Finally this carbon tissue forms the medium by means of which each new cylinder is etched. After an application of a thin layer of chrome the cylinder is ready for use.

**Paper.** Unwatermarked chalk-surfaced paper was used for all values. Exceptionally, examples of all four panes from the £1 Stamps for Cooks booklet and the 3d. and 10d. from sheets exist on uncoated paper. It does not respond to the chalky test (that is applying silver to see if it will produce a black line) and may be further distinguished from the normal chalk-surfaced paper by the fibres which clearly show on the surface, resulting in the printing impression being rougher, and by the screening dots which are not so evident.

**Paper Thickness and Fluorescence.** Variation in the thickness of paper sometimes occurs in the making and is undetected where the finished reel conforms to the prescribed weight. Within the reel there may be sections where the paper is unusually thick or thin. A particular example is the 2s. booklet of March 1970 which is known with panes UB15 and UB18 on very thick paper. This has an effect on the thickness of the booklet and could cause jamming in the vending machine. Such varieties are not listed. Certain coil issues were on translucent paper, the design showing clearly on the back of the stamps.

On some printings the fluorescent reaction varies. This is best seen on marginal examples, but the difference is not sufficient or consistent to warrant separate listing and indeed, the brighter paper can be made to appear dull by exposure to sunlight. Stamps cannot be made to appear brighter, however, and none of the pre-decimal paper is as bright under u.v. as the fluorescent coated paper which was introduced in 1971.

**Gum.** Polyvinyl alchohol (PVA) was introduced by Harrison & Sons in place of gum arabic in 1968. It is almost invisible except that a small amount of pale yellowish colouring matter was introduced to make it possible to see that the stamps had been gummed. Although this can be distinguished from gum arabic in unused stamps there is, of course, no means of detecting it in used examples. Where the two forms of gum exist on the same value they are listed separately.

It should be further noted that gum arabic is normally shiny in appearance, and that, normally, PVA has a matt appearance. However, depending upon the qualities of the paper ingredients and the resultant absorption of the gum, occasionally, PVA has a slightly shiny appearance, and in cases of severe under-gumming gum arabic may appear matt. In such cases it is sometimes impossible to be absolutely sure which gum has been used except by testing the stamps with a very expensive infra-red spectrometer. Chemical tests unfortunately destroy the stamps. Therefore, whilst very shiny gum is gum arabic it does not follow that all matt gum is PVA. A few late printings of stamps originally issued on PVA were made on gum arabic paper, either in error or to use up stocks.

Paper treated with gum arabic is passed over a fracture bar before printing to reduce its tendency to curl. This results in a crazy paving appearance, often visible under magnification, not present on PVA.

The term PVA is used because it is generally accepted, but the official abbreviation is PVAl to distinguish it from PVAc, polyvinyl acetate, another adhesive which has not so far been used for stamps, although it does occur on postal stationery. De La Rue use the term PVOH, polyvinyl hydroxyl, to describe the same adhesive.

**Machin Heads.** Basically two master negatives were used for preparing the multipositive for each value comprising (a) head with background and (b) value. The portrait negative used for the initial releases had a three-dimensional effect only in the 10d. and 1s. values where a light background was used. On the other values, for which a different portrait master negative was used, the darker background merged with the outline and much of the relief effect was lost.

Beginning with coils and booklets in March 1968 a modified portrait negative was used giving greater contrast at those points where it had been lost. Thus there are three clearly different portraits; the original Head A with a flatter base to the bust, Head B with a curved shadow beneath the bust and Head C the three-dimensional version from the light background stamps.

These differences are listed and, for ease of reference, appear in tabulated form, together with details of the phosphor screens, at the beginning of the catalogue list.

As a result of the combination of two master negatives described above the position of the value in relation to the frame varies from one multipositive to another. The 2d. Types I and II show an extreme case of this, where the change was made deliberately. Taking the 4d. for example the distance to the left frame varies from 0·9 mm. on the early sheet cylinders to 1·2 mm. on the multi-value coils, while the spacing to the bottom is normally 0·9 mm. but decreases to 0·6 mm. in the £1 Stamps for Cooks booklet.

**Phosphor bands.** See the General Notes for Section S for a detailed description of these. The Machin definitives were normally issued with violet phosphor bands only. Most values have appeared with the phosphor omitted in error and these are listed separately.

The 1s.6d. (No. U29) was issued as an experiment in 1969 with violet phosphor incorporated into the coating.

**Phosphor screens.** The phosphor bands were applied in Gravure, some of the cylinders having a 150-line screen and others a 250-line screen. The absence of a screen on parts of a printing is due to the cylinder becoming clogged.

The phosphor screen used for the single centre band on the 3d., 4d. sepia and 4d. vermilion booklet panes of six is unique in having a mixed screen. Continuous 21-row cylinders are normally produced from two pieces of carbon tissue, thus giving two joins. On this particular phosphor cylinder, the pieces of carbon tissue had different screens. Thus four types of booklet panes can be found (1) 150 screen; (2) screen join 150/250; (3) 250 screens; (4) screen join 250/150. It is calculated that out of 100 panes the proportions are 67 150 screen, 14 250 screen and 19 screen joins.

It is not easy to distinguish the different screens but we include them in the following check list of the Machin Head Types.

**Perforation.** Harrisons used the same 15×14 comb perforation as for the previous Wilding definitives. A number of different perforators were used for both sheets and booklets and these are described and illustrated in Appendix G. The cylinder numbers are listed and priced according to the type of perforator used. The 1s. multi-value coils, for the first time, used a new rotary perforator - the Swedish 'Lawnmower'

**Booklet panes.** In Section UB we list separately the booklet

panes and the varieties on them and priced according to perforator types. See General Notes to that Section.

**Coil varieties.** See General Notes for Section S for detailed notes on these.

**Shades.** There are numerous shades in these issues and we have restricted our listing to the most marked ones and related them to the cylinder number blocks where possible.

**Dates of issue.** The dates given are those announced by the Post Office, except in the case of dates for changes of gum or in the number of phosphor bands when we have quoted either the dates of release by the Philatelic Bureau or the earliest dates known. As in Section S the dates given in bold type in the headings are those on which stamps first appeared in sheet form. Where a date is followed by a dagger it means that the stamp appeared earlier in coils or booklets as indicated in footnotes.

**First Day Covers.** They are listed after the Presentation Pack but we only quote for official covers, prepared and issued by the Post Office, cancelled by FIRST DAY OF ISSUE circular postmarks.

**Presentation Packs.** See General Notes under Section W.

**"Unprinted stamps".** Widely trimmed sheet margins may produce the effect of unprinted stamps as illustrated above. The blank paper has the phosphor bands printed as on the normal stamps. In the Machin and Regional issues they come from either the left or right-hand margins; in the special issues they are known from the top of the sheet.

**Invalidation.** All £.s.d. Machin definitives were withdrawn from sale on 25 November 1971, and were, with the exception of the £1 value, invalidated as from 1 March 1972. They ceased to be valid in Guernsey and Jersey from 1 October 1969 when these islands each established their own independent postal administrations and introduced their own stamps.

**Sheet Markings.** Reference should be made to the descriptions of Sheet Markings given in the General Notes for Section S, as most of these apply to this Section and the information given there is not repeated here. In the case of the 1s.6d. and 1s.9d. bicoloured Machin definitives reference should be made to the descriptions of Sheet Markings given in Section W as many of them also apply to these two values. Additional information to that provided in Sections S and W is given here.

**Cylinder Numbers.** In the Machin definitives ½d. to 1s. values they appear in the left-hand margin opposite Row 18 No. 1 in the style as illustrated in Section S. In the case of the 1s.6d. and 1s.9d. values the cylinder numbers appear boxed in the left-hand margin opposite Row 19 No. 1 in the style as illustrated in Section W.

**Phosphor Cylinder Numbers.** As with the 1970 General Anniversaries, special issue in Section W, phosphor cylinder numbers were introduced during 1970, "Ph 1" appearing on the Machin issues. It only occurs on the dot panes and appears in the right-hand margin and therefore not on the cylinder block. Moreover it is not synchronised with the ink cylinders and so can appear anywhere in the margin, and the "1" is often trimmed off. Its existence is recorded under the Sheet Markings.

**Varieties in Cylinder Blocks.** Where a cylinder block contains a listed variety the price is adjusted accordingly and bears an asterisk.

**Marginal Arrows.** In the Machin definitives these are "W" shaped (photo-etched) at top, bottom and sides, unless otherwise stated.

**Perforation Guide Holes.** A number of different styles of guide hole box have been used for the Machin definitives and these are fully illustrated as for Sections S and W.

In addition to guide hole boxes of one type or another opposite rows 14/15 (used for perforation Type A), the earlier cylinders of nearly all the values from ½d. to 1s. also show a single traffic light type box above and below the eighth vertical row in the no dot panes. This latter type would only be used in conjunction with perforation Type F (L)* and it is illustrated here to explain its presence on the sheets. When Type F (L)* is used the circular central part of the box is either partly or completely removed.

**Colour trials.** In preparation for the decimal currency Machin stamps, colour trials were prepared by Harrisons, using three values from the pre-decimal series. It is believed that as many as 40 different colours may have been tested in the trials which were conducted to determine which would be the most suitable for sorting mail under different lighting conditions.

It is probable that a small hand press would have been used to print the trials which were on ordinary coated paper with PVA gum and did not have phosphor bands. Due to the size of the press it is believed that a maximum of four stamps were printed in wach colour, a;though in some cases as few as two examples have been recorded.

The 8d. value was used to trial stamps with solid backgrounds, the 1s. for light and gradated backgrounds and the 1s.6d. for bi-coloured stamps. Those which are known to exist are listed under the relevant values. All have been hinged and most have a letter and/or number annotated in pencil on the gummed side.

**CHECK LIST OF MACHIN HEADS AND PHOSPHOR SCREENS**
For fuller explanations see General Notes.

Head A Flatter base to the bust

Head B Curved shadow beneath the bust

Head C Three-dimensional effect with light background

**Abbreviations**
Phosphor bands: 1C = one centre; 1L = one left side; 1R = one right side
Booklet panes: s/t = stamps se-tenant; s/t labels = stamps se-tenant with labels
Coils:    MV    =    multi-value;    S    =    sideways    delivery;
V = vertical delivery

| Face Value | Cat. No. | Description | Phosphor Bands | Gum | Head | Screen | Sheet Cylinders | Sources Booklet Panes | Coils |
|---|---|---|---|---|---|---|---|---|---|
| ½d. | U 1 | | 2 | PVA | A | 150 | 2, 3 | — | — |
| 1d. | U 2 | | 2 | PVA | A | 150 | 2 | — | — |
| | U 2 | | 2 | PVA | B | 150 | 4, 6 | 6 | V |
| | U 2 | | 2 | PVA | B | 250 | — | s/t, 6 s/t 15 s/t | — |
| | U 3 | | 1C | PVA | B | 250 | — | 6 s/t | — |
| | U 4 | | 1C | GA | B | 250 | — | — | MV |
| 2d. | U 5 | Type I | 2 | PVA | A | 150 | 1 | — | — |
| | U 6 | Type II | 2 | PVA | B | 150 | 5, 6 | — | V |
| | U 6 | Type II | 2 | PVA | B | 250 | — | — | V, S |
| | U 7 | Type II | 1C | GA | B | 250 | — | — | MV |
| 3d. | U 8 | | 1C | GA | A | 150 | 1 | — | V |
| | U 8 | | 1C | GA | A | 250 | — | — | S |
| | U 8 | | 1C | GA | B | 250 | — | — | MV |
| | U 9 | | 1C | PVA | A | 150 | 1, 3, 4 | — | — |
| | U 9 | | 1C | PVA | A | 250 | — | — | S |
| | U 9 | | 1C | PVA | B | 150 | — | 6 | — |
| | U 9 | | 1C | PVA | B | Join | — | 6 | — |
| | U 9 | | 1C | PVA | B | 250 | — | 6 | — |
| | U10 | | 2 | PVA | A | 150 | 3, 4 | — | V |
| | U10 | | 2 | PVA | B | 150 | — | — | V |
| | U10 | | 2 | PVA | B | 250 | — | 4 s/t | — |
| 4d. | U11 | Sepia | 2 | GA | A | 150 | 4, 8 | 6 | V |
| | U11 | Sepia | 2 | GA | A | 250 | — | — | S |
| | U11 | Sepia | 2 | GA | B | 250 | 14 | — | — |
| | U12 | Sepia | 2 | PVA | A | 150 | 4, 10, 12, 13 | 6 | — |
| | U12 | Sepia | 2 | PVA | B | 250 | 14, 15 | 4 | — |
| | U13 | Sepia | 1C | PVA | A | 150 | 4, 12, 13 | 6 | V |
| | U13 | Sepia | 1C | PVA | A | Join | — | 6 | — |
| | U13 | Sepia | 1C | PVA | A | 250 | — | 6 | S |
| | U13 | Sepia | 1C | PVA | B | 250 | 14, 15 | 4, 4 s/t labels 6 s/t | — |
| 4d. | | | | | | | | | |
| | U14 | Vermilion | 1C | PVA | A | 150 | 4, 10, 13 | 6 | V |
| | U14 | Vermilion | 1C | PVA | A | Join | — | 6 | — |
| | U14 | Vermilion | 1C | PVA | A | 250 | — | 6 | S |

| Face Value | Cat. No. | Description | Phosphor Bands | Gum | Head | Screen | Sheet Cylinders | Sources Booklet Panes | Coils |
|---|---|---|---|---|---|---|---|---|---|
| | U14 | Vermilion | 1C | PVA | B | 150 | — | 6 | — |
| | U14 | Vermilion | 1C | PVA | B | Join | — | 6 | — |
| | U14 | Vermilion | 1C | PVA | B | 250 | 15, 16, 17 | 4, 4 s/t labels 6, 15 | S |
| | U15 | Vermilion | 1C | GA | B | 250 | — | — | MV |
| | U15 | Vermilion Feb/Mar | 1C | 1C | GA | A | 150 | — | 6 |
| | U15 | Vermilion '69 6s. & | 1C | 1C | GA | A | Join | — | 6 |
| | U15 | Vermilion May '69 10s | 1C | 1C | GA | A | 250 | — | 6 |
| | U16 | Vermilion | 1L | PVA | B | 250 | — | 6 s/t, 15 s/t | — |
| | U16A | Vermilion | 1R | PVA | B | 250 | — | 15 s/t | — |
| 5d. | U17 | | 2 | PVA | A | 150 | 1 | — | — |
| | U17 | | 2 | PVA | B | 150 | 7, 10, 15 | 6 | V |
| | U17 | | 2 | PVA | B | 250 | 11, 13 | 15, 15 s/t | S |
| 6d. | U18 | | 2 | PVA | A | 150 | 2, 3, 4, 5 | — | — |
| | U18 | | 2 | PVA | B | 150 | — | — | V |
| | U18 | | 2 | PVA | B | 250 | — | — | V |
| 7d. | U19 | | 2 | PVA | B | 150 | 3, 4 | — | — |
| 8d. | U20 | Vermilion | 2 | PVA | A | 150 | 2 | — | — |
| | U21 | Turquoise-blue | 2 | PVA | B | 150 | 3 | — | — |
| 9d. | U22 | | 2 | GA | A | 150 | 2 | — | — |
| | U23 | | 2 | PVA | A | 150 | 2 | — | — |
| 10d. | U24 | | 2 | PVA | C | 150 | 1 | — | — |
| | U24 | | 2 | PVA | C | 250 | 1 | — | — |
| 1s. | U25 | | 2 | GA | C | 150 | 3, 11 | — | — |
| | U26 | | 2 | PVA | C | 150 | 11 | — | — |
| | U26 | | 2 | PVA | C | 250 | 11 | — | — |
| 1s.6d. | U27 | | 2 | GA | A | 150 | 2A–2B, 3A–2B | — | — |
| | U27 | (3) Phosphor omitted | — | GA | A | — | 5A–2B | — | — |
| | U28 | | 2 | PVA | A | 150 | 3A–2B, 5A–2B | — | — |
| | U28 | | 2 | PVA | A | 250 | 3A–1B | — | — |
| | U29 | "All-over" phos. | — | PVA | A | — | 5A–2B | — | — |
| 1s.9d. | U30 | | 2 | GA | A | 150 | 1A–1B | — | — |
| | U31 | | 2 | PVA | A | 250 | 1A–1B | — | — |

**INDEX TO COIL STAMPS**

| Face Value | Phosphor Bands | Gum | Head | Further description | Delivery | | See stamp No. |
|---|---|---|---|---|---|---|---|
| 1d. | 2 | PVA | B | | V | | U2 |
| 2d. | 2 | PVA | B | Type II | V | S | U6 |
| 3d. | 1C | GA | A | | V | S | U8 |
| 3d. | 1C | PVA | A | | | S | U9 |
| 3d. | 2 | PVA | A | | V | | U10 |
| 3d. | 2 | PVA | B | | V | | U10 |
| 4d. | 2 | GA | A | Deep olive-brown | V | S | U11 |
| 4d. | 1C | PVA | A | Deep olive-brown | V | S | U13 |
| 4d. | 1C | PVA | A | Bright vermilion | V | S | U14 |
| 4d. | 1C | PVA | B | Bright vermilion | | S | U14 |
| 5d. | 2 | PVA | B | | V | S | U17 |
| 6d. | 2 | PVA | B | | V | | U18 |
| 2×2d. | 1C | GA | B | Multi-value coil. 4d. Bright vermilion | | S | U32 |
| +3d. | 1C | GA | B | Multi-value coil. 4d. Bright vermilion | | S | U32 |
| +1d. | 1C | GA | B | Multi-value coil. 4d. Bright vermilion | | S | U32 |
| +4d. | 1C | GA | B | Multi-value coil. 4d. Bright vermilion | | S | U32 |

**U1**
Value at left
Queen Elizabeth II

**U2**
Value at right

(Des. after plaster cast by Arnold Machin)

## ½d. Type U1 (1968)

**1968 (5 February). ½d. Two 9·5 mm. Phosphor bands. PVA gum. Head A**

**U1** (=SG 723)

|  |  | Mint | Used |
|---|---|---|---|
| ½d. | Orange-brown | 10 | 20 |
| a. | Phosphor omitted | 30·00 | |
| b. | Dot in "1" of "½" (Cyl. 3 No dot, R. 20/2) | 10·00 | |

U1b

**Cylinder Numbers (Blocks of Six)**
Perforation Type A

| Cylinder No. | No dot | Dot |
|---|---|---|
| 2 | 2·00 | 2·00 |
| 3 | 6·00 | 5·00 |

*Includes variety U1b.

**Minor Constant Sheet Flaws**

| Cyl. 2. | 5/12 | Small retouch at base of Queen's hair (Th. E4–5) |
|---|---|---|
| | 9/5 | Dark horizontal strip of shading behind Queen's neck (Th. F5–6) |
| Cyl. 3 | 12/9 | Dark patch below Queen's chin (Th. E2–3) |

A number of stamps from cylinder 2 dot display irregularities of the background in the form of dark patches and lines. This is most prominent on R. 9/5 recorded above; others occur on R. 2/2, 7/6, 8/6, 9/11, 10/1, 13/25, 14/5, 17/4–5 and 18/1.

**Sheet Markings**
**Guide holes**: In double "SON" box opposite rows 14/15, at left (no dot) or right (dot). In addition a single traffic light type box appears above and below the eighth vertical row in the no dot pane only. (These would only be used in conjunction with perforation Type F (L)*).
**Others**: As given in General Notes

**Sold Out**: 10.2.70.

## ■ 1d. Type U1 (1968-70)

### 1968 (5 February). 1d. Yellowish olive

U2 (=SG 724)

#### A. Two 9·5 mm. Phosphor bands. PVA Gum.

| | | Mint | Used |
|---|---|---|---|
| 1d. (1) Light olive (A) Head A | | 60 | 15 |
| (2) Yellowish olive (B) Head B | | 10 | 10 |
| (3) Greenish olive | | 20 | 15 |
| a. Imperf. (coil strip)* | | £2200 | |
| b. Uncoated paper (1970)** | | 90·00 | |
| c. Phosphor omitted | | 1·00 | |
| d. Phosphor omitted on front but printed on the gummed side | | £280 | |
| e. Error. One 9·5 mm. phosphor band | | 5·00 | |
| g. Neck retouches (Cyl. 4 No dot, R. 20/3) | | 10·00 | |
| h. Flaw by Queen's chin (Vertical coil) | | 10·00 | |
| i. Thick "1 D" (Vertical coil) | | 15·00 | |
| j. Flaw by Queen's chin (Vertical coil) | | 10·00 | |
| k. Imperforate at bottom (Vertical coil) | | — | £300 |
| s. Optd. "Specimen" (14 mm.) | | £250 | |

#### B. One 4 mm. Centre Phosphor band. PVA Gum.
Se-tenant Booklet pane only (16 September 1968)
U3 (=SG 725)

| | Mint | Used |
|---|---|---|
| 1d. Yellowish olive (Head B) | 30 | 35 |

#### C. One 4 mm. Centre Phosphor band. Gum Arabic.
Multi-value coil only (27 August 1969)
U4 (=SG 725Eg)

| | Mint |
|---|---|
| 1d. Yellowish olive (Head B) | 30 |
| a. Dark vert. line (Roll 7 etc) | 3·00 |

*No. U2a occurs in a vertical strip of four, top stamp perforated on three sides, bottom stamp imperf. three sides and the two middle stamps completely imperf.

**Uncoated paper. No. U2b comes from the se-tenant pane of 15 in the £1 Stamps for Cooks Booklet (see No. UB2ab); see also General Notes.

No. U3 only comes from the 10s. Booklet of September 1968 (XP6). It also occurs with the phosphor omitted but since a single stamp would be difficult to distinguish from No. U2c it is only listed when in a complete se-tenant booklet pane (see No. UB3a).

No. U4 only comes from the multi-value coil strip which is listed as No. U32.

A single used example is known of No. U2k.

U2g

U2h

Normal

U2

### Cylinder Numbers (Blocks of Six)
Two bands. Perforation Type A

| Cylinder No. | No dot | Dot |
|---|---|---|
| 2 (Shade 1)(Head A) | 7·00 | 7·00 |
| 4 (Shade 1)(Head A) | 2·00 | 2·00 |
| 4 (shade 1)(Head A) | 2·00 | 2·00 |

### Minor Constant Sheet Flaws

| Cyl. 2. | 5/11 | Small flaw at back of Queen's collar (Th. F5) |
|---|---|---|
| Cyl. 4 | 6/9 | White flaw at top of Queen's hair (Th. B3) |
| Cyl. 6. | 11/7 | Horizontal line of coloured dots across Queen's shoulder (Th. F3–5) |
| | 12/10 | Vertical lines of coloured dots through Queen's forehead and cheek (Th. B2, C2 3 and D2) |

### Coils
Two bands. Vertical delivery printed in continuous reels from double pane cylinders B1 or B2
Head B

| Code No. | Number in roll | Face value |
|---|---|---|
| E | 480 | £2 |
| X | 960 | £4 |
| Z | 1920 | £8 |

One centre band. Multi-value coil, see No. U32.

### Sheet Markings
**Guide holes:** Cyl. 4, in single "SN" box opposite rows 14/15, at left (no dot) or right (dot)
Cyls. 2 and 6, in double "SON" box opposite rows 14/15, at left (no dot) or right (dot)
**Marginal arrows:**
Cyls. 2 and 6, "W" shaped, photo-etched at top, bottom and sides
Cyl. 4, "W" shaped, hand engraved at top, bottom and sides
**Marginal rule:**
Cyl. 2, at bottom of sheet, 2 mm. wide
Cyls. 4 and 6, at bottom of sheet, 2 ½ mm. wide
**Others:** As given in General Notes

## ■ 2d. Type U1 (1968–69)

Two Types

I

II

Type I. Value spaced away from left side of stamp (Cyls. 1 no dot and dot)

Type II. Value closer to left side from new multipositive (Cyls. 5 no dot and dot onwards). The portrait apperas in the centre, thus conforming to the other values.

● ————————————————

### 1968 (5 February). 2d. Type I. Two 9·5 mm. Phosphor bands. PVA gum. Head A

**U5** (=SG 726)

|  |  | Mint | Used |
|---|---|---|---|
| 2d. | Lake-brown | 10 | 15 |
| a. | Phosphor omitted | 30·00 | |

**Cylinder Numbers (Blocks of Six)**
Perforation Type A

| Cylinder No. | No dot | Dot |
|---|---|---|
| 1 | 1·75 | 1·75 |

**Minor Constant Sheet Flaws**

| Cyl. 1 | 3/11 | Small white spot in band of diadem (Th. C5) |
|---|---|---|
| | 8/8 | Dark spot by emblems at rear of diadem (Th. B5) |
| | 12/9 | Retouching in Queen's hair just by ear (Th. C–D4) |

**Sheet Markings**
**Guide holes:** In double "SON" box opposite rows 14/15, at left (no dot) or right (dot)
**Others:** As given in General Notes

● ————————————————

### 1969 (February)†. 2d. Change to Type II. Head B

**A. Two 9·5 mm. Phosphor bands. PVA Gum**
**U6** (=SG 727)

|  |  | Mint | Used |
|---|---|---|---|
| 2d. | Lake-brown | 15 | 20 |
| a. | Phosphor omitted | 1·00 | |
| b. | Error. One 9·5 mm. phosphor band | 55·00 | |

**B. One 4 mm. Centre Phosphor band. Gum Arabic.**
Multi-value coil only (27 August 1969)
**U7** (=SG 728)

|  |  | Mint | Used |
|---|---|---|---|
| 2d. | Lake-brown | 70 | 90 |

†No. U6 was issued on 4 April 1968 in sideways delivery coils, and on 19 March 1969 in vertical delivery coils.
   No. U7 only comes from the multi-value coil strip which is listed as No. U32.

**Cylinder Numbers (Blocks of Six)**
Two bands. Perforation Type A

| Cylinder No. | No dot | Dot |
|---|---|---|
| 5 | 4·50 | 4·00 |
| | 4·00 | 4·00 |

**Minor Constant Sheet Flaws**

| Cyl. 5. | 6/8 | Dark area above 2 (Th. F1) |
|---|---|---|

| 8/1 | Small flaw on Queen's shoulder (Th. F3) |
|---|---|
| 10/1 | Coloured line through Queen's nose and upper lip (Th. C–D2) |
| 10/3 | Dark spot below Queen's chin (Th. E2) |
| 19/5 | Retouch to background to left of diadem (Th. A2–3). There are two states of this |

| Cyl. 6. | 18/4 | Small retouch at top of Queen's neck and vertical scratch extending to her dress (Th. E3–G3). Several states exist |
|---|---|---|

**Coils**
Two bands. Printed in continuous reels from double pane cylinders D2 (vertical) or single pane D1 (sideways)

| Code No. | Number in roll | Face value | |
|---|---|---|---|
| T | 480 | £4 | Sideways delivery |
| V | 960 | £8 | Vertical delivery |

One centre band. Multi-value coil, see No. U32

**Sheet Markings**
**Phosphor cylinder number:** "Ph 1" found on a later printing of cyl. 6 dot, right margin (price £25 in block of 6).
**Guide holes:** In double "SON" box opposite rows 14/15, at left (no dot) or right (dot). In addition a single traffic light type box appears above and below the eighth vertical row in the no dot pane only (These would only be used in conjunction with perforation Type F (L)*).
**Others:** As given in General Notes

● ————————————————

## ■ 3d. Type U1 (1967-69)

### 1967 (8 August). 3d. One 4 mm. Centre Phosphor band

U8 (=SG 729)

| | | Mint | Used |
|---|---|---|---|
| 3d. | (1) Violet (A) Head A | 15 | 10 |
| | (2) Bluish violet (sideways coils) | 2·50 | 50 |
| | (1) Violet (multi-value coils) (B) Head B | 60 | 15 |
| a. | Imperf (vertical pair) | £850 | |
| b. | Phosphor omitted | 1·25 | |
| c. | Spot on nose (Sideways coil, Roll 10) | 10·00 | |
| d. | Gash on diadem (Multi-value coil, Roll 1) | 10·00 | |

U9 (=SG 729Ev)

**B. PVA Gum (12 March 1968)**

| | | Mint | Used |
|---|---|---|---|
| 3d. | (1) Violet (A) Head A | 15 | |
| | (2) Bluish violet (sideways coils) | 45·00 | |
| | (1) Violet (booklets) (B) Head B | 5·00 | |
| a. | Phosphor omitted | 2·00 | |
| b. | Spot on nose (Sideways coil, Roll 10) | 10·00 | |

No. U8 is known pre-released on 7 August at Bournemouth, Hyde (Cheshire), in South London and at Torquay.

U8c, U9b
From sideways delivery coils

U8d
Occurs in sideways delivery multi-value GS and GL coils on every fifth 3d. stamp

### Cylinder Numbers (Blocks of Six)

**Gum Arabic**
Perforation Type A

| Cylinder No. | No dot | Dot |
|---|---|---|
| 1 | 25·00 | 28·00 |

Perforation Type F (L:)

| | | |
|---|---|---|
| 1 | 2·50 | 2·50 |

**PVA Gum**
Perforation Type A

| Cylinder No. | No dot | Dot |
|---|---|---|
| 1 | 2·50 | 2·50 |
| 3 | 2·50 | 2·50 |
| 4 | 8·00 | 8·00 |

Perforation Type F (L:)

| | | |
|---|---|---|
| 1 | † | — |

There are two states of cyl. 1 no dot: (a) 1 is hatched, the bottom part lacks colour and the serifs are short (gum arabic printings); (b) 1 is solid and the serifs are long (gum arabic perf. type F(L)* and PVA).

Cylinder blocks from the no dot pane of Cylinder 3 show a phantom "3", slightly smaller and just below and to the right of the normal cylinder number. This occurred on part of the printing.

### Minor Constant Sheet Flaws

| Cyl. 1 | 1/9 | Vertical scratch on Queen's neck (Th. E3–4) |
|---|---|---|
| | 3/9 | Pale patch in background around "D" of value |
| | 7/1 | Small white flaw inside cross of diadem (Th. B5) |
| Cyl. 1. | 1/4 | Small retouch on Queen's neck below ear (Th. D4). PVA only |
| | 1/7 | White scratch in Queen's hair below diadem at right (Th. C5). PVA only |
| | 4/11 | Small retouch on Queen's neck (Th. E3). |
| | 12/4 | Retouch at front of Queen's collar (Th. G3) |
| | 19/6 | Small retouch by Queen's mouth (Th. D3) |
| Cyl. 3. | 8/3 | Scratch on Queen's temple (Th. C3) |
| | 12/7 | Retouch on Queen's neck below necklace (Th. F4) |
| | 16/4 | Flaw on Queen's shoulder (Th. F4). Later retouched |

### Coils
Printed in continuous reels from double pane cylinder M1 (vertical) or single pane M2 (sideways). Head A

**Gum Arabic.**

| Code No. | Number in roll | Face value | |
|---|---|---|---|
| S | 480 | £6 | Sideways delivery |
| AC | 480 | £6 | Vertical delivery |
| AD | 960 | £12 | do. |
| U | 1920 | £24 | do. |
| **PVA Gum** | | | |
| S* | 480 | £6 | Sideways delivery |

*Stamps from this coil can be distinguished from all other PVA centre-band stamps in singles. The coil stamps have Machin Head Type A and 250-line phosphor screen. The sheet stamps have Head Type A and 150-line screen, whilst the booklet stamps have Head Type B.
One centre band. Multi-value coil, see No. U32

### Sheet Markings
**Guide holes**: Perf. Type A, in double "SON" box opposite rows 14/15, at left (no dot) or right (dot). In addition a single traffic light type box appears above and below the eighth vertical row in the no dot pane from cyl. 1 (latter only used in conjunction with perforation Type F (L)*).
Perf. Type F (L)*, boxed above and below the eighth vertical row in the no dot pane only. The usual "SON" boxes opposite rows 14/15 remain.
**Others**: As given in General Notes

●———————

### 1969 (20 August)†. 3d. Change to Two 9·5 mm. Phosphor bands. PVA Gum

U10 (=SG 730)

| | | Mint | Used |
|---|---|---|---|
| 3d. | Violet (A) Head A | 30 | 35 |
| | (B) Head B | 50 | 40 |
| a. | Uncoated paper* (A) Head A | £2200 | |
| b. | Error. One 9·5 mm. phosphor band | 2·50 | |

*Uncoated paper see General Notes.
†Issued on 6.4.68 in 2s. Booklets dated May 1968, on 26 September 1968 in vertical delivery coils.

### Cylinder Numbers (Blocks of Six)
Perforation Type A

| Cylinder No. | No dot | Dot |
|---|---|---|
| 3 (Head A) | 3·75 | 3·75 |
| 4 (Head A) | 6·50 | 6·50 |

The note about the phantom "3" mentioned under No. U9 also applies here and the whole of the printing was affected.

## Minor Constant Sheet Flaws

| Cyl. 3. | 8/3 | Scratch on Queen's temple (Th. C3) |
|---|---|---|
| | 12/7 | Retouch on Queen's neck below necklace (Th. F4) |

## Coil
Vertical delivery printed in continuous reels from double pane cylinders M1 (Head A) or M4

### (Head B)

| Code No. | Number in roll | Face value |
|---|---|---|
| AD | 960 | £12 |

## Sheet Markings
**Guide holes:** In double "SON" box opposite rows 14/15, at left (no dot) or right (dot)
**Others:** As given in General Notes

---

## ■ 4d. Deep sepia, Type U1 (1967-68)

### 1967 (5 June). 4d. Two 9.5 mm. Phosphor bands

**U11** (=SG 731/Ea)

**A. Gum Arabic**

| | | Mint | Used |
|---|---|---|---|
| 4d. | (1) Deep sepia (A) Head A | 10 | 10 |
| | (2) Deep olive-brown | 10 | 15 |
| | (2) Deep olive-brown (B) Head B | £1400 | |
| a. | Phosphor omitted. Shade (1) | 1·00 | |
| ab. | Phosphor omitted. Shade (2) | 2·00 | |
| b. | Error. One 9·5 mm. phosphor band | 50·00 | |

**U12** (=SG 731Eav)

**B. PVA Gum (22 January 1968)**

| | | | |
|---|---|---|---|
| 4d. | (2) Deep olive-brown (A) Head A | 10 | |
| | (3) Deep olive-sepia | 10 | 10 |
| | (2) Deep olive-brown (B) Head B | 25 | 10 |
| | (3) Deep olive-sepia | 25 | 10 |
| a. | Error. One 9·5 mm. phosphor band | 5·00 | |
| b. | Phosphor omitted | 2·00 | |
| c. | White patch (Cyl. 13 No dot, R. 20/12) | 10·00 | |
| d. | Nick in hair (Cyl. 15 Dot, R. 16/5) | 10·00 | |

No. U11 (1) in shades of washed out grey are colour change-lings which we understand are caused by the concentrated solvents used in modern dry-cleaning methods.
No. U11 (1) is known pre-released on 25 May at Gravesend.

U12c, U13b, U14e White patch over eye and hair    U12d, U13c, U14f Reported as being later retouched

### Cylinder Numbers (Blocks of Six)

**Gum Arabic**
Perforation Type A

| Cylinder No. | No dot | Dot |
|---|---|---|
| **(a) Shade (1) Deep sepia** | | |
| 4 | 5·50 | 5·50 |
| 8 | 6·75 | 6·75 |
| **(b) Shade (1) Deep olive-brown** | | |
| 4 | 12·00 | 12·00 |
| 8 | 12·00 | 12·00 |
| Perforation Type F (L) | | |
| 14 | — | — |

**PVA Gum**
Perforation Type F (L)*

| Cylinder No. | No dot | Dot |
|---|---|---|
| **(a) Shade (1) Deep olive-brown** | | |
| 4 (Head A) | 24·00 | 20·00 |
| Perforation Type A | | |
| 4 | 12·00 | 12·00 |
| 10 | 4·00 | 4·00 |
| 12 | 12·00 | 12·00 |

| Cylinder No. | No dot | Dot |
|---|---|---|
| 13 | 20·00 | 20·00 |
| 14 | 3·00 | 3·00 |
| 15 | 70·00 | 70·00 |

**(b) Shade (3) Deep olive-sepia**
Perforation Type A

| | | |
|---|---|---|
| 14 | 3·00 | 3·00 |
| 15 | 70·00 | 70·00 |

Stamps from cylinder 12 show traces of screening dots within the white area of the face value. Cylinder 15 has the number close to the stamp resulting in the dot often being removed by the perforations. The dot pane has a tiny dot on the horizontal rule below R. 20/1 whilst in the no dot pane the marginal rule below R. 20/1 is damaged and there is a line in the margin below R. 20/2.

**Minor Constant Sheet Flaws**

| Cyl. 4. | 1/1 | Nick in neck (Th. F5) |
|---|---|---|
| | 1/13 | Nick in neck (Th. F5) |
| | 2/9 | Dark flaw in Queen's hair (Th. C4) |
| | 20/8 | Scar on Queen's forehead (Th. C2–3) |
| Cyl. 8 | 18/12 | Diagonal line through back of Queen's hair (Th. C5) |
| Cyl. 8. | 9/9 | White spot in band of diadem (Th. B3–4) |
| | 15/3 | Diagonal coloured line on Queen's shoulder and dress (Th. F–G4) |
| | 15/5 | Prominent retouch on Queen's neck just below jawline (Th. E3–4) |
| Cyl. 10 | 18/12 | As Cyl. 8 |
| Cyl. 10. | 3/4 | Coloured flaw on Queen's shoulder (Th. F3) |
| | 3/6 | Two coloured flaws on Queen's shoulder (Th. F3) |
| | 10/8 | Pale patch in background to left of Queen's throat (Th. E2) |
| | 11/7 | Dark flaw at back of Queen's neck, just above necklace (Th. E4) |
| | 12/5 | Dark flaw on Queen's shoulder, just below necklace (Th. F3) |
| | 15/3 | As Cyl. 8 |
| | 15/5 | As Cyl. 8 |
| | 19/2 | Dark coloured vertical line in lower right-hand stamp margin (Th. G7) |
| Cyl. 12 | 18/12 | As Cyl. 8. |
| Cyl. 12. | 15/3 | As Cyl. 8 |
| | 15/5 | As Cyl. 8 |
| Cyl. 13 | 9/12 | Large area of retouching behind Queen's head (Th. C5–6 and D5–6) |
| | 18/12 | As Cyl. 8 |
| Cyl. 13. | 15/3 | As Cyl. 8 |
| | 15/5 | As Cyl. 8 but more prominent |
| Cyl. 14 | 6/11 | Vertical white scratch on Queen's neck (Th. E–F4) |
| | 18/7 | White flaw at back of Queen's dress (Th. F5) |

**Coils**
Printed in continuous reels from double pane cylinders P2, P3 or P4 (vertical) or single pane P1 (sideways).

**Head A**
Gum Arabic. Shade (2) Deep olive-brown

| Code No. | Number in roll | Face value | |
|---|---|---|---|
| H | 480 | £8 | Sideways delivery |
| A | 960 | £16 | Vertical delivery |

**Sheet Markings**
Guide holes: Perf. Type A, in double "SON" box opposite rows 14/15, at left (no dot) or right (dot). In addition a single traffic light type box appears above and below the eighth vertical row in the no dot pane only (latter only used in conjunction with perforation Type F (L)*).

Perf. Type F (L)*, boxed above and below the eighth vertical row in the no dot pane only. The usual "SON" boxes opposite rows 14/15 remain.

**Others**: As given in General Notes

---

## 1968 (16 September). 4d. Change to one 4 mm. Centre phosphor band. PVA Gum

**U13** (=SG 732)

| | | | Mint | Used |
|---|---|---|---|---|
| ✓ | 4d. | (2) Deep olive-brown (A) Head A | 10 | 10 |
| | | (2) Deep olive-brown (B) Head B | 25 | 10 |
| | | (3) Deep olive-sepia | 25 | 10 |
| | b. | White patch (Cyl. 13 No dot, R. 20/12) | 10·00 | |
| | c. | Nick in hair (Cyl. 15 Dot, R. 16/5) | 10·00 | |

For illustrations of Nos. U13b/c see Nos. U12c/d.

No. U13 also occurs with the phosphor omitted but since a single stamp would be indistinguishable from No. U12b it is only listed when in a complete se-tenant booklet pane (see No. UB3a).

**Cylinder Numbers** (Blocks of Six)
Perforation Type A

**(a) Shade (2) Deep olive-brown**

| Cylinder No. | No dot | Dot |
|---|---|---|
| 4 | 2·50 | 2·50 |
| 12 | 2·50 | 2·50 |
| 13 | 70·00 | 70·00 |
| 14 | 3·00 | 3·00 |
| 15 | 3·00 | 3·00 |

**(b) Shade (3) Deep olive-sepia**

| | | |
|---|---|---|
| 14 | 3·00 | 3·00 |
| 15 | 3·00 | 3·00 |

The notes, concerning cylinders 12 and 15, under No. U12 also apply here.

**Minor Constant Sheet Flaws**

| Cyl. 4. | 1/1 | Nick in neck (Th. F5) |
|---|---|---|
| | 1/13 | Nick in neck (Th. F5) |
| | 2/9 | Coloured flaw in Queen's hair (Th. C4) |
| | 19/1 | Flaw on lower rim of Queen's diadem shows as missing pearls (Th. C5) |
| | 20/8 | Scar on Queen's forehead (Th. C2–3) |
| Cyl. 12 | 18/12 | Diagonal line through back of Queen's hair (Th. C5) |
| Cyl. 12. | 15/3 | Diagonal coloured line on Queen's shoulder and dress (Th. F–G4) |
| | 15/5 | Prominent retouch on Queen's neck just below jawline (Th. E3–4) |
| Cyl. 13 | 9/12 | Large area of retouching behind Queen's head (Th. C5–6 and D5–6) |
| | 18/12 | As Cyl. 12 |
| Cyl. 13. | 15/3 | As Cyl. 12 |
| | 15/5 | As Cyl. 12, but more prominent |
| Cyl. 15. | 5/12 | Two small white dots on Queen's shoulder (Th. F–G4). Later retouched |
| | 17/12 | White scratch in background above value, extending to Queen's shoulder. Later retouched but flaw still shows on Queen's shoulder |

**Coils**
Printed in continuous reels from double pane cylinder P3 (vertical) or single pane P5 (sideways). Head A

| Code No. | Number in roll | Face value | |
|---|---|---|---|
| H | 480 | £8 | Sideways delivery |
| A | 960 | £16 | Vertical delivery |

**Sheet Markings**
Guide holes: As for perf. Type A under Nos. U11/12
Others: As given in General Notes

---

## ◼ 4d. bright vermilion, Type U1 (1969)

**1969 (6 January). 4d. Colour changed. One 4 mm. Centre Phosphor band**

U14 (=SG 733)

A. PVA Gum

|  |  | Mint | Used |
|---|---|---|---|
| 4d. | Bright vermilion (A) Head A | 25 | 25 |
|  | (B) Head B | 10 | 10 |
| a. | *Tête-bêche* (horiz. pair) | £3800 |  |
| b. | Uncoated paper (,70)** | 6·00 |  |
| c. | Phosphor omitted | 1·25 |  |
| d. | Red nick in "D" (Cyl. 4 Dot. R. 1/4) | 10·00 |  |
| e. | White patch (Cyl. 13 Dot, R. 20/12) | 10·00 |  |
| f. | Nick in hair (Cyl. 15 Dot. R. 16/5) | 10·00 |  |
| g. | Imperf. between stamp and top margin | £180 |  |
| h. | Error. Two bands* | 60·00 |  |
| s. | Opt. "Specimen" (14 mm.) | 45·00 |  |

U15 (=SG 733Eg)

B. Gum Arabic. (20 February 1969)

|  |  | |
|---|---|---|
| 4d. | Bright vermilion (A) Head A (booklets) | 2·00 |
|  | (B) Head B (multi-value coil) | 10 |
| a. | Phosphor omitted | £1650 |
| b. | Diagonal scratch in background (Multi-value coil) | 6·00 |

**Uncoated paper. No. U14b comes from the £1 Stamps for Cooks Booklet (see Nos. UB16ab and UB17ab); see also General Notes.

Nos. U14 and U16/A from the £1 Stamps for Cooks Booklet (ZP1) show slight differences compared with stamps from normal sheets and all other booklets. The main stem of the "4 "is thicker and it is only 0·6 mm. from its foot to the base of the design compared with 0·9 mm. on stamps from sheets and all other booklets. Also, the cross-bar of the "4", normally opposite the point of the Queen's gown, is lower on the £1 booklet stamps. See under Machin Heads in General Notes.

**Misplaced Phosphor Bands,** *No. U14h comes from Method pane UB17af which has the central phosphor bands printed over the vertical perforations at each side.

No. U15B comes from the multi-value coil strip, issued 27 August 1969, which is listed as No. U32 and U15A from the February and part of March 1969 6s. Barn Owl and Jay Booklets (QP46/7) and also part of May 1969 10s. Mary Kingsley Booklets (XP8).

For illustrations of Nos. U14e/f, see Nos. U12c/d.

U14d
Believed later retouched

U15b

**Cylinder Numbers (Blocks of Six)**
PVA Gum. Perforation Type A

| Cylinder No. | No dot | Dot |
|---|---|---|
| 4 (Head A) | 2·00 | 2·00 |
| 10 (Head A) | 2·00 | 2·00 |
| 13 (Head A) | 2·00 | 2·00 |
| 15 (Head B) | 2·50 | 2·50 |
| 16 (Head B) | 5·50 | 5·50 |
| 17 (Head B) | 2·50 | 2·50 |

The note about the cylinder number being close to the stamp on Cylinder 15 mentioned under No. U12 also applies here.

**Minor Constant Sheet Flaws**

| Cyl. 4. | 1/1 | Nick in neck (Th. F5) |
|---|---|---|
|  | 1/13 | Nick in neck (Th. F5) |
|  | 19/1 | Flaw on lower rim of Queen's diadem shows as missing pearls (Th. C5) |
|  | 20/8 | Scar on Queen's forehead (Th. C2–3) |
| Cyl. 10 | 18/12 | Diagonal line through back of Queen's hair (Th. C5). |
| Cyl. 10. | 15/3 | Diagonal coloured line on Queen's shoulder and dress (Th. F–G4) |
|  | 15/5 | Prominent retouch on Queen's neck just below jawline (Th. E3–4) |
| Cyl. 13 | 9/12 | Large area of retouching behind Queen's head (Th. C5–6 and D5–6) |
|  | 18/12 | As Cyl. 10 |
| Cyl. 13. | 15/3 | As Cyl. 10 |
|  | 15/5 | As Cyl. 10, but more prominent |
| Cyl. 15. | 17/12 | Scratch on Queen's shoulder at left (Th. F3) |
| Cyl. 17 | 4/7 | Small coloured spot in band of diadem (Th. B4) |
|  | 7/3 | Small retouch on Queen's shoulder (Th. F3) |
|  | 18/4 | Small flaw in band of diadem (Th. B4) |
| Cyl. 17. | 19/10 | White scratch at back of Queen's shoulder (Th. F5) |

**Coils**
PVA Gum. Printed in continuous reels from double pane cylinder P3 (vertical) or single pane P5 (Head A) and P7 (Head B) (sideways)

| Code No. | Number in roll | Face value |  |
|---|---|---|---|
| H | 480 | £8 | Sideways delivery Head A or Head B |
| A | 960 | £16 | Vertical delivery Head A |

One centre band, gum arabic. Multi-value coil, see No. U32.

**Sheet Markings**
**Guide holes:** As for perf. Type A under Nos. U11/12
**Others:** As given in General Notes

## 1969 (6 January) 4d. bright vermilion

**A. One Side Phosphor band at left\*. PVA Gum. Head B**
From 10s. Booklets XP7/12 and £1 Booklet ZP1
**U16** (=SG 734)

|  |  | Mint | Used |
|---|---|---|---|
| 4d. | Bright vermilion | 1·50 | 1·90 |
| b. | Uncoated paper (,70)\*\* | £275 | |
| c. | Error. One 9·5 mm. phosphor band | £225 | |
| d. | Phosphor omitted on front but printed at left on the gummed side | £325 | |
| s. | Optd. "Specimen" (14 mm.) | £275 | |

**B. One Side Phosphor band at right\*. PVA Gum. Head B**
From £1 Booklet ZP1 only (1 December 1969)
**U16A** (=SG 734Eb)

|  |  | Mint | Used |
|---|---|---|---|
| 4d. | Bright vermilion | 1·75 | 2·50 |
| b. | Uncoated paper (,70)\*\* | £275 | |
| c. | Phosphor omitted on front but printed at right on the gummed side | £325 | |
| s. | Optd. "Specimen" (14 mm.) | £275 | |

\*The one side band stamps were produced by applying a 9·5 mm. band over the vertical perforations between the 4d. and its adjoining stamp in the booklet panes. In theory the width of the band on a single stamp should be 4¾ (or 4·75) mm. but this will vary if the band has not been perfectly positioned.

\*\*Uncoated paper. Nos. U16b and U16Ab came from the se-tenant pane of 15 in the £1 Stamps for Cooks Booklet (see No. UB2ab.); see also General Notes.

No. U16 also occurs with the phosphor omitted but since a single stamp would be indistinguishable from No. U14c it is only listed when in a complete se-tenant booklet (see No. UB4a).

No. U16Ac came from the se-tenant pane No. UB2ad of which three examples are believed to exist.

See note after No. U15 describing the differences between 4d. stamps in the £1 Booklet (ZP1) and those in sheets and all other booklets.

## 5d., Type U1 (1968-70)

### 1968 (1 July). 5d. Two 9·5 mm. Phosphor bands. PVA Gum.

**U17** (=SG 735)

|  |  | Mint | Used |
|---|---|---|---|
| 5d. | (1) Royal blue (A) Head A | 10 | 10 |
| | (2) Deep blue (B) Head B | 10 | 15 |
| a. | Imperforate (pair) | £250 | |
| ab. | Imperf. between stamp and top margin | | |
| b. | Uncoated paper ('70)\*\* | 20·00 | |
| c. | Two bands and phosphor coating (Cyl. 15) | £325 | |
| d. | Phosphor omitted. Shade (1) | 2·00 | |
| da. | Phosphor omitted. Shade (2) | 3·00 | |
| db. | Right-hand band omitted | | |
| e. | Phosphor omitted on front but printed on the gummed side | £325 | |
| f. | Error. One 9.5 mm. phosphor band | 55·00 | |
| g. | Neck retouch (Cyls. 7, 10, 11, 13 No dot, R. 18/1 and Cyl. 15 R. 19/1) | 10·00 | |
| h. | Scratch severing neck (Cyl. 13 No dot, R. 19/4) | 25·00 | |
| s. | Optd. "Specimen" (14 mm.) | 60·00 | |

No. U17a comes from the original state of cylinder 15 which is identifiable by the screening dots in the gutters (see note after cylinder number list). This must not be confused with imperforate stamps from cylinder 10, a large quantity of which was stolen from the printers early in 1970.

\*\*Uncoated paper. No. U17b comes from the £1 Stamps for Cooks Booklet (see Nos. UB2ab and UB20ab and b); see also General Notes.

No. U17c is thought to result from the issue, in error, of stamps on phosphor-coated paper, intended for experiments only. Examples were purchased from various sources in 1972.

No. U17 from the £1 Stamps for Cooks Booklet (ZP1) and cylinders 7, 10 and 11 (no dot and dot panes) show slight differences compared with stamps from cylinder 1 (no dot and dot) and all other booklet panes. The "5D" is slightly thicker and is positioned fractionally lower than on stamps from cylinder 1 and all other booklet panes. See under Machin Heads in the General Notes.

No. U17 is known postmarked at Trafalgar Square (London) on 29 June and at Dorking and Guildford on 30 June 1968.

***Tête-bêche* Pairs.** Examples of No. U17 in *tête-bêche* pairs were not issued.

U17g                                    U17h

This variety is due to damage on the multipositive. Cyl. 1 is normal and the most marked retouch is on cyl. 11. Cyl. 15 was formed by moving up one row of the multipositive (which is 28 rows by 31 columns) and the variety occurs on R. 19/1. All on no dot panes.

**Cylinder Numbers** (Blocks of Six)
Perforation Type A

| Cylinder No. | No dot | Dot |
|---|---|---|
| 1 (Shade 1)(Head A) | 2·50 | 2·50 |
| 7 (Shade 2)(Head B) | 4·75* | 2·00 |
| 10 (Shade 2)(Head B) | 4·75* | 2·00 |
| 11 (Shade 2)(Head B) | 10·00* | 8·50 |
| 13 (Shade 2)(Head B) | £800* | £450 |
| 15 (Shade 2)(Head B) | 6·00* | 3·50 |

Cyl. 15 dot has a smudge so that it looks like "151".

Original printings of cylinder 15 (no dot and dot) had screening dots extending through the gutters of the stamps and into the margins of the sheet. Later the cylinder was cleaned and re-chromed.

**Minor Constant Sheet Flaws**

| Cyl. 1 | 7/1 | Coloured spot in band of diadem (Th. C5) |
|---|---|---|
| | 7/5 | Short white flaw in Queen's hair (Th. C4) |
| | 12/2 | White flaw in band of diadem (Th. B4) |
| Cyl. 1. | 1/11 | Pale patch in background below top bar of "5" (Th. G1) |
| | 20/4 | White spot in band of diadem (Th. C5) |
| Cyl. 7 | 18/2 | Scratch on Queen's shoulder (Th. F4) |
| Cyl. 7. | 1/10 | White flaw on Queen's forehead (Th. C3) |
| | 14/12 | Small retouch on Queen's shoulder (Th. G4) |
| Cyl. 10 | 15/8 | Coloured flaw below Queen's earring (Th. D4) |
| | 18/2 | Scratch on Queen's shoulder (Th. F4) |
| | 20/5 | Two diagonal scratches on Queen's neck (Th. E3–4, F4 and G4) |
| | 20/6 | Retouch on Queen's neck (Th. E4) |
| Cyl. 13 | 5/6 | White flaw in Queen's hair (Th. C3) |
| | 12/4 | White ring flaw on Queen's forehead (Th. C2) |
| | 13/3 | Flaw on Queen's shoulder (Th. G3) |
| | 14/5 | Necklace flaw (Th. E4) |
| | 18/2 | Coloured flaw on Queen's neck (Th. F5) |
| Cyl. 15 | 16/8 | Coloured flaw below Queen's earring (Th. D4) |
| | 19/2 | Scratch on Queen's shoulder (Th. F4) |
| Cyl. 15. | 1/10 | Scratch on Queen's nose (Th. C2) |

**Coils**

Printed in continuous reels from double pane cylinders S1, S3 or S4 (vertical) or single pane S2 (sideways). Head B

| Code No. | Number in roll | Face value | |
|---|---|---|---|
| AF | 480 | £10 | Sideways delivery |
| AE | 960 | £20 | Vertical delivery |

**Sheet Markings**

Phosphor cylinder number "Ph 1" found on the later printings of cyl. 15 dot, right margin (price £30 block of 6).
**Guide holes:** In double "SON" box (or "SO" box cyl. 10) opposite rows 14/15, at left (no dot) or right (dot). In addition a single traffic light type box appears above and below the eighth vertical row in the no dot pane only. (These would only be used in conjunction with perforation Type F (L)*.)
**Others:** As given in General Notes.

## 6d., Type U1 (1968)

**1968 (5 February). 6d. Two 9·5 mm. Phosphor bands. PVA Gum**

**U18** (=SG 736)

| | Mint | Used |
|---|---|---|
| 6d. (1) Bright reddish purple (shades) (A) Head A | 20 | 25 |
| (2) Bright magenta | 8·00 | 6·00 |
| (3) Claret | 50 | 45 |
| (1) Bright reddish purple (B) Head B (coils) | 15·00 | 6·00 |
| (3) Claret | 80·00 | 35·00 |
| a. Phosphor omitted. Shade (1) | 6·50 | |
| ab. Phosphor omitted. Shade (3) | 15·00 | |
| b. Hair flaws (Cyl. 2 No dot, R. 18/1) | 10·00 | |
| c. Background retouch (Cyl. 2 Dot, R. 11/1) | 10·00 | |
| d. Diadem flaw (Cyl. 3 No dot, R. 2/3) | 10·00 | |
| e. Two spots in front of neck (Vert. coil, Roll 12)((1) Head B) | 20·00 | |
| f. Retouch above 6 D (Vert. coil) ((1) Head B) | 20·00 | |

U18b Two coloured lines crossing base of diadem, one extending in curves through the hair

U18c Large circular retouch above value

U18d Coloured flaw in band of diadem

U18e Two spots in front of neck

U18f

## Cylinder Numbers (Blocks of Six)
Perforation Type A
(a) Shade (1) Bright reddish purple

| Cylinder No. | No dot | Dot |
|---|---|---|
| 2 | 7·00 | 5·50 |
| 3 | 3·50 | 3·50 |
| 4 | 45·00 | 45·00 |
| 5 | 4·00 | 4·00 |

(b) Shade (2) Bright magenta

| | | |
|---|---|---|
| 3 | 55·00 | 55·00 |

(c) Shade (3) Claret

| | | |
|---|---|---|
| 5 | 8·50 | 8·50 |

### Minor Constant Sheet Flaws

| | | |
|---|---|---|
| Cyl. 2. | 2/4 | White flaw in band of diadem (Th. B4) |
| | 4/4 | Coloured line in band of diadem (Th. B3–4) |
| | 4/11 | Small retouch on Queen's collar (Th. G4) |
| | 10/11 | Vertical flaws in Queen's hair and in band of diadem (Th. B–C4) |
| Cyl. 3 | 13/5 | Two small white flaws on Queen's neck above necklace (Th. F3) |
| | 19/9 | Small coloured dot in band of diadem (Th. B3) |
| Cyl. 3. | 5/3 | Line of white dashes on Queen's collar (Th. G3–4) |
| | 11/5 | Small retouch on Queen's collar (Th. G4) |
| Cyl. 4 | 11/10 | Small background retouch left of Queen's forehead (Th. B2) |
| Cyl. 5 | 18/1 | White tail below D |

### Coil
Vertical delivery printed in continuous reels from cylinder Q2. Head B

| Code No. | Number in roll | Face value |
|---|---|---|
| J | 480 | £12 |

### Sheet Markings
**Phosphor cylinder number:** "Ph 1" found on a later printing from cyl. 5 dot, right margin (price £140, block of 6).
**Guide holes:** In double "SON" box opposite rows 14/15, at left (no dot) or right (dot). In addition a single traffic light type box appears above and below the eighth vertical row in the no dot pane only (These would only be used in conjunction with perforation Types F (L)*.)
**Others:** As given in General Notes

## ■ 7d., Type U2 (1968)

**1968 (1 July). 7d. Two 9.5 mm. Phosphor bands. PVA Gum. Head B**

<u>U19</u> (=SG 737)

| | | Mint | Used |
|---|---|---|---|
| ✓ | 7d. Bright emerald | 40 | 35 |
| | a. Phosphor omitted | 95·00 | |

No. U19 is known postmarked at Dorking and at Guildford on 30 June 1968.

### Cylinder Numbers (Blocks of Six)
Perforation Type A

| Cylinder No. | No dot | Dot |
|---|---|---|
| 3 | 4·50 | 4·50 |
| 4 | 15·00 | 12·00 |

### Minor Constant Sheet Flaws

| | | |
|---|---|---|
| Cyl. 3 | 8/6 | Flaw in background by Queen's collar (Th. F5) |
| | 12/6 | Dark flaw on jewel in band of diadem (Th. C5) |

### Sheet Markings
**Phosphor cylinder number:** "Ph 1" found on all sheets from cyl. 4 dot, right margin (Price £55, block of 6)
**Guide holes:** in single hand engraved box opposite rows 14/15, at left (no dot) or right (dot)
**Marginal arrows:** "W" shaped, hand engraved at top, bottom and sides on cyl. 3, photo-etched on cyl. 4
**Others:** As given in General Notes

## ■ 8d. Bright vermilion, Type U2 (1968)

**1968 (1 July). 8d. Two 9·5 mm. Phosphor bands. PVA gum. Head A**

U20 (=SG 738)

| | | Mint | Used |
|---|---|---|---|
| ✓ | 8d. Bright vermilion | 20 | 45 |
| | a. Phosphor omitted | £425 | |

No. U20 is known postmarked at Dorking and at Guildford on 30 June 1968.

**Cylinder Numbers (Blocks of Six)**
Perforation Type A

| Cylinder No. | No dot | Dot |
|---|---|---|
| 2 | 2·50 | 2·50 |

**Sheet Markings**
**Guide holes**: In double "SON" box opposite rows 14/15, at left (no dot) or right (dot). In addition a single traffic light type box appears above and below the eighth vertical row in the no dot pane only. (These would only be used in conjunction with perforation Type F (L)*.)
**Others**: As given in General Notes

## ■ 8d. Light turquoise-blue, Type U2 (1969)

**1969 (6 January). 8d. Colour changed. Two 9·5 mm. Phosphor bands. PVA Gum. Head B**

U21 (=SG 739)

| | | Mint | Used |
|---|---|---|---|
| ✓ | 8d. Light turquoise-blue | 50 | 60 |
| | a. Phosphor omitted | 65·00 | |
| | b. Left band omitted | | |
| | c. Missing pearls (Cyl. 3 No dot, R. 19/2) | 10·00 | |

U21c

**Cylinder Numbers (Blocks of Six)**
Perforation Type A

| Cylinder No. | No dot | Dot |
|---|---|---|
| 3 | 10·00* | 7·00 |

**Minor Constant Sheet Flaw**
Cyl. 3. 19/2 White flaw by Queen's mouth (Th. D2)

**Sheet Markings**
**Guide holes**: In single "SN" box opposite rows 14/15, at left (no dot) or right (dot). In addition a single traffic light type box appears above and below the eighth vertical row in the no dot pane only. (These would only be used in conjunction with perforation Type F (L)*.)
**Others**: As given in General Notes.

**Colour trials**
On coated paper with PVA gum. Perf 15 × 14 in blue, greenish blue, dull greenish blue, ultramarine, deep bright magenta, deep bright mauve, plum, purple, deep bluish violet, bright emerald or deep green.

### ■ 9d. Type U2 (1967-68)

**1967 (8 August). 9d. Two 9·5 mm. Phosphor bands. Head A**

U22 (=SG 740)

| A. Gum Arabic | | Mint | Used |
|---|---|---|---|
| 9d. | Myrtle-green | 40 | 25 |
| a. | Phosphor omitted | 40·00 | |
| b. | Dots below necklace (Cyl. 2 Dot, R. 9/6) | 10·00 | |

U23 (=SG 740Ev)

| B. PVA Gum (29 November 1968) | | | |
|---|---|---|---|
| 9d. | Myrtle-green | 50 | |
| a. | Phosphor omitted | 70·00 | |

No. U22 is known pre-released on 7 August at Bournemouth and Torquay.

U22b

**Cylinder Numbers (Blocks of Six)**

**Gum Arabic**
Perforation Type F (L)*

| Cylinder No. | No dot | Dot |
|---|---|---|
| 2 | 6·00 | 6·00 |

Perforation Type A

| | | |
|---|---|---|
| 2 | 35·00 | 30·00 |

**PVA Gum**
Perforation Type A

| | | |
|---|---|---|
| 2 | 5·50 | 5·50 |

Cylinder 2 has the number close to the stamp resulting in the dot often being removed by the perforations. The no dot cylinder can be distinguished by a horizontal line below R. 20/2, although this may be trimmed off if the margin is narrow.

**Minor Constant Sheet Flaws**

| Cyl. 2 | 2/7 | Coloured line in gutter above stamp (Th. above A4–6) |
|---|---|---|
| | 3/12 | Retouch on Queen's shoulder (Th. F4) |
| | 6/2 | Pale area on Queen's shoulder (Th. F4). Retouched on PVA |
| | 6/7 | Dark patches on Queen's neck (Th. E–F3). Less noticeable on PVA |
| | 7/3 | Dark spot over "D" of value (Th. F6) |
| Cyl. 2. | 6/10 | Coloured line across Queen's shoulder and dress (Th. F–G4) |
| | 8/11 | Retouch on Queen's forehead (Th. B–C2) |
| | 10/4 | Coloured spot at rear of diadem (Th. C5) |
| | 14/8 | Two white flaws on Queen's neck by hair (Th. D–E4). Retouched on PVA |
| | 14/11 | Retouch on Queen's neck by necklace (Th. E4) |
| | 15/11 | Retouch on Queen's dress at front (Th. G3) |
| | 19/10 | Retouch on Queen's shoulder (Th. F4) |

**Sheet Markings**
**Phosphor cylinder number:** "Ph 1" found on a later printing from cyl. 2 dot, right margin (Price £850 block of 6)
**Guide holes:** Perforation Type A, in double "SON" box opposite

rows 14/15, at left (no dot) or right (dot). In addition a single traffic light type box appears above and below the eighth vertical row in the no dot pane only (latter only used in conjunction with perforation Type F (L)*).
Perforation Type F (L)*, boxed above and below the eighth vertical row in the no dot pane only. The usual "SON" boxes opposite rows 14/15 remain.
**Others:** As given in General Notes

## ■ 10d. Type U1 (1968)

**1968 (1 July). 10d. Two 9·5 mm. Phosphor bands. PVA gum. Head C**

**U24** (=SG 741)

| | | Mint | Used |
|---|---|---|---|
| 10d. | Drab | 50 | 50 |
| a. | Uncoated paper (69)* | 30·00 | |
| b. | Phosphor omitted | 55·00 | |
| c. | Neck flaw (Cyl 1, R. 2/12) | 10·00 | |

*Uncoated paper-see General Notes.
No. U24 is known postmarked at Dorking and at Guildford on 30 June 1968.

U24c
Flaw comprises dark spots surrounded by white "halo" caused by lack of screening dots

**Cylinder Number** (Block of Six)
Single pane cylinder
Perforation Type F (L)

| Cylinder No. | No dot |
|---|---|
| 1 | 6·00 |

**Minor Constant Sheet Flaw**
Cyl. 1 20/5 Coloured flaw in Queen's hair (Th. B3)

**Sheet Markings**
**Guide holes:** Through marginal arrow above vertical rows 6/7 and below vertical row 10
**Others:** As given in General Notes

## ■ 1s. Type U1 (1967-68)

**1967 (5 June). 1s. Two 9·5 mm. Phosphor bands. Head C**

**U25** (=SG 742/Ea)

| A. Gum Arabic | | Mint | Used |
|---|---|---|---|
| 1s. | (1) Light bluish violet | 45 | 25 |
| | (2) Pale bluish violet | 2·25 | 50 |
| a. | Phosphor omitted | 80·00 | |
| b. | Background retouches (Cyl. 3 No dot, R. 20/5) | 10·00 | |

**U26** (=SG 742E)

| B. PVA Gum (26 April 1968) | | | |
|---|---|---|---|
| 1s. | Pale bluish violet | 45 | |
| a. | Phosphor omitted | 3·50 | |

No. U25(1) is known pre-released on 25 May at Gravesend.

U25b
Retouching extends from behind the Queen's neck to the base of the design where it is most noticeable. There are also minor retouches on the Queen's shoulder and on her dress

**Cylinder Numbers (Blocks of Six)**

**Gum Arabic**
Double pane cylinder
Perforation Type F (L)*
Shade (1) Light bluish violet

| Cylinder No. | No dot | Dot |
|---|---|---|
| 3 | 5·50 | 5·50 |

Single pane cylinder
Perforation Type F (L)*
Shade (2) Pale bluish violet

| | | |
|---|---|---|
| 11 | 11·00 | |

**PVA Gum**
Single pane cylinder
Perforation Type F (L)
Shade (2) Pale bluish violet

| | | |
|---|---|---|
| 11 | 5·50 | |

**Minor Constant Sheet Flaws**

| | | |
|---|---|---|
| Cyl. 3 | 1/10 | Retouch in background above diadem (Th. A5) |
| | 2/2 | Light diagonal line extending from lowest point of Queen's hair to bottom right-hand corner (E5 through to G6) |
| | 2/3 | White spot in background left of Queen's shoulder (Th. G2) |
| | 9/12 | White spot in background to right of Queen's necklace (Th. E5) |
| | 11/11 | Coloured spot in band of diadem (Th. B4) |
| | 17/2 | As 11/11 but Th. B3 |
| | 18/12 | Coloured spot in hyphen of value |
| | 19/10 | Coloured scratch through Queen's neck and background below portrait |
| | 20/4 | Horizontal scratch through Queen's neck and into background at right |
| Cyl. 3. | 1/8 | White spot in background at top of stamp (Th. A4) |

7/8 Coloured flaw in Queen's hair to right of earring (Th. D4)

8/4 Coloured flaw in Queen's hair (Th. B3)

9/7 Retouch to background to right of Queen's ear (Th. D5)

19/8 Coloured spot in background above diadem emblems (Th. B5)

Cyl. 11 7/8 Coloured spot by band of diadem, also small spot in background at rear of diadem (Th. B4 and C5)

7/9 Diagonal coloured line in background behind Queen's neck (Th. F5)

15/4 Disturbed area in background at rear of diadem (Th. C–D5)

16/9 Diagonal coloured scratches extending the depth of the stamp behind the Queen's portrait

18/7 Diagonal coloured scratch about 10 mm. long at left of Queen's portrait

19/2 White flaw in Queen's hair to right of ear (Th. D4)

**Sheet Markings**

**Guide holes**: Perforation Type F (L)*, boxed above and below the eighth vertical row in the no dot pane only. In addition double "S O N" box appears opposite rows 14/15, at left (no dot) or right (dot). (These would only be used in conjunction with perforation Type A.)

Perforation Type F (L), through marginal arrow above vertical rows 6/7 and below vertical row 10

**Others**: As given in General Notes

**Colour trials.** On coated paper with PVA gum. Perf 15 × 14. In dull olive-grey, olive-grey, light emerald, light violet-blue, pale magenta, mauve, pale chestnut, pale olive-green, turquoise-blue or slate-blue.

○━━━━━━━━━

## ■ 1s.6d. Type U1 (1967-69)

### 1967 (8 August). 1s.6d. Two 9·5 mm. Phosphor bands. Head A

**U27** (=SG 743)

| A. Gum Arabic | | Mint | Used |
|---|---|---|---|
| 1s.6d. (1) Greenish blue and deep blue | | 50 | 50 |
| (2) Prussian blue and indigo (phosphor omitted) | | 11·00 | |
| a. Greenish blue omitted | | £150 | |
| b. Phosphor omitted. Shade (1) | | 6·00 | |
| c. Retouch on dress (Cyl. 2A, R. 7/12) | | 12·00 | |
| d. Neck retouch (Cyl. 2A, R. 19/4) | | 12·00 | |
| e. Neck retouch (Cyl. 2A, R. 20/3) | | 12·00 | |

**U28** (=SG 743Ev)

| B. PVA Gum (28 August 1968) | | | |
|---|---|---|---|
| 1s.6d. (1) Greenish blue and deep blue | | 75 | |
| (2) Prussian blue and indigo | | 2·25 | 1·50 |
| a. Greenish blue omitted | | £200 | |
| b. Imperf. top margin. Shade (2) | | 80·00 | |
| c. Phosphor omitted. Shade (1) | | 14·00 | |
| d. Error. One 9·5 mm. phosphor band | | 20·00 | |
| e. Greenish blue omitted and one 9·5 mm. phosphor band | | £225 | |

No. U27 is known pre-released on 7 August at Bournemouth and Torquay.

U27c U27d

U27e

## Cylinder Numbers (Blocks of Four)

**Gum Arabic**
Single pane cylinders.
Perforation Type A

| Cylinder No. | No dot |
|---|---|
| 2A (deep blue) – 2B (greenish blue) | 7·50 |
| 3A (deep blue) – 2B (greenish blue) | 15·00 |
| 5A (indigo) – 2B (Prussian blue)(phosphor omitted) | £180 |

**PVA Gum**

| | |
|---|---|
| 3A (deep blue) – 2B (greenish blue) | 7·50 |
| 3A (indigo) – 1B (Prussian blue) | 20·00 |
| 3A (indigo) – 2B (Prussian blue) | 18·00 |

### Minor Constant Sheet Flaws

| | | |
|---|---|---|
| Cyls. 2A–2B | 3/12 | Coloured spot in band of diadem (Th. B4) |
| | 7/8 | Coloured spots on Queen's collar (Th. G3) |
| | 14/1 | Coloured spot on Queen's shoulder (Th. F4–5) |
| | 17/3 | Coloured spot on Queen's temple (Th. C3) |
| | 18/4 | Coloured spot on Queen's shoulder (Th. F5) |
| | 20/2 | Pale patch on Queen's neck (Th. E3–4) |
| | 20/7 | Retouch on Queen's neck (Th. E4) |
| Cyls. 3A–2B | 3/12 | As for cyls. 2A–2B |
| Cyls. 5A–2B | 19/1 | Retouch on Queen's shoulder (Th. F5) |

### Sheet Markings

**Cylinder numbers:** Boxed, opposite R. 19/1
**Guide holes:** In single traffic light type box opposite rows 14/15, at both sides
**Colour register marks:** Opposite rows 3/4 and 17/18, at both sides
**Autotron marks (solid):** Deep blue and greenish blue opposite rows 7/8, left margin
**Colour designations:** G1 (greenish blue) opposite rows 7/8 and G2 (deep blue) opposite rows 5/6 both reading up in right margin
**Traffic lights (boxed):** Deep blue and greenish blue opposite row 19, right margin
**Others:** As given in General Notes

### Colour trials

On coated paper with PVA gum. Perf 15×14 in rose-pink and deep blue-green, lilac and deep bright blue, pale bright blue and deep ultramarine, bright mauve and bright ultramarine, light violet and bluish violet, olive-yellow and brown olive, pale magenta and deep carmine and pale dull green and deep bright purple.

---

## 1969 (10 December). 1s.6d. Change to Phosphorised paper. PVA Gum. Head A

**U29** (=SG 743c)

| | Mint | Used |
|---|---|---|
| 1s.6d. Prussian blue and indigo | 80 | 80 |
| a. Prussian blue omitted | £425 | |

No. U29 was an experimental issue and the small printing represented approximately three months normal issue. After the supply was exhausted No. U28 again became the normal issue.

### Cylinder Numbers (Block of Four)
Single pane cylinders.
Perforation Type A

| Cylinder No. | No dot |
|---|---|
| 5A (indigo) – 2B(Prussian blue) | 12·00 |

### Minor Constant Sheet Flaws

| | | |
|---|---|---|
| Cyls. 5A–2B | 12/5 | Two white spots on Queen's dress (Th. G3) |
| | 19/1 | Retouch on Queen's shoulder (Th. F5) |

### Sheet Markings
All the same as for Nos. U27/8

---

## ■ 1s.9d. Type U1 (1967–70)

### 1967 (5 June). 1s.9d. Two 9·5 mm. Phosphor bands. Head A

**U30** (=SG 744)

| A. Gum Arabic | | Mint | Used |
|---|---|---|---|
| 1s.9d. | (1) Dull orange and black | 50 | 45 |
| | (2) Bright orange and black | 1·75 | 70 |
| a. | Phosphor omitted | 55·00 | |

**U31** (=SG 744Ev)

| B. PVA Gum (16 November 1970) | | |
|---|---|---|
| 1s.9d. Bright orange and black | | 75 |

No. U30 is known pre-released on 25 May at Gravesend. The bright orange shade occurs on whiter paper and may be due to this.

### Cylinder Numbers (Blocks of Four)

**Gum Arabic**
Single pane cylinders
Perforation Type A

| Cylinder No. | No dot |
|---|---|
| 1A (black) – 1B (dull orange) | 14·00 |
| 1A (black) – 1B (bright orange) | 20·00 |

**PVA Gum**

| | |
|---|---|
| 1A (black) – 1B (dull orange) | † |
| 1A (black) – 1B (bright orange) | 20·00 |

### Minor Constant Sheet Flaws

| | | |
|---|---|---|
| Cyls. 1A–1B | 4/6 | White spot in Queen's ear (Th. D4) |
| | 5/7 | Coloured spots on Queen's upper lip (Th. D2) |
| | 5/10 | White patch in Queen's hair (Th. B4) |
| | 8/1 | Coloured flaw on Queen's neck (Th. E4) |
| | 13/1 | Retouch on Queen's shoulder (Th. F3–4) |
| | 20/1 | Pale patch in Queen's hair (Th. C4) |

### Sheet Markings

**Cylinder numbers:** Boxed, opposite R. 19/1
**Guide holes:** In single traffic light type box opposite rows 14/15, at both sides
**Colour register marks:** Opposite rows 3/4 and 17/18, at both sides
**Autotron marks (solid):** Black and orange opposite rows 7/8, left margin
**Colour designations:** G1 (orange) opposite rows 7/8 and G2 (black) opposite rows 5/6 both reading up in right margin
**Traffic lights (boxed):** Black and orange opposite row 19, right margin
**Others:** As given in General Notes

## ■ Multi-value coil strip (1969)

**1969 (27 August). Strip of five (2d. + 2d. + 3d. + 1d. + 4d. *Se-tenant*) each with one 4 mm. Centre phosphor band. Gum Arabic. Head B**

**U32** (=SG 725m)

| | | Mint | Used |
|---|---|---|---|
| 1d. | Light olive (No. U4), 2d. lake-brown (No. U7 × 2), 3d. violet (No. U8) and 4d. bright vermilion (No. U15) | | 1·25 |

No. U32 was issued in strips from stamp vending machines taking a shilling or a decimal five pence piece. Complete coils only were available from the Philatelic Bureau in Edinburgh. For listed varieties, see Nos. U4a, U8d and U15b.

A new type of perforation was adopted for these coils. The paper was drawn, gum upwards, over a cylinder containing short points pushing up pimples from the undersurface which were then shaved off.

It is understood that gum arabic was used for these coils, as also for the next decimal multi-value coil, because it is more brittle than PVA and facilitates the clean removal of the perforations.

### Coils

Sideways delivery printed in continuous reels from cylinders B3-D3-M3-P6 (1d., 2d., 3d., 4d, B4-D3-M3-P6 or B5-D3-M3-P6

| Code No. | Number in roll | Face value |
|---|---|---|
| GS | 1500 (300 strips) | £15 |
| GL | 3000 (600 strips) | £30 |

### Presentation Pack

| UPP1 | (Issued 5 March 1969) Fourteen values | 12·00 |
|---|---|---|
| | a. With German text | £150 |

The issued Pack contained one each of the low value definitive stamps (½d. to 1s.9d.). The 4d. and 8d. were in the changed colours (Nos. U14 and U21 respectively).

UPP1 also exists with a Japanese insert card.

### First Day Covers

On official covers prepared and issued by the Post Office and stamps franked with circular "FIRST DAY OF ISSUE" postmarks.

| UFC1 | (5.6.67) | 4d., 1s, 1s. 9d. | 3·00 |
|---|---|---|---|
| UFC2 | (8.8.67) | 3d., 9d., 1s. 6d. | 3·00 |
| UFC3 | (5.2.68) | ½d., 1d., 2d., 6d. | 3·00 |
| UFC4 | (1.7.68) | 5d., 7d., 8d., 10d. | 3·00 |
| UFC5 | (1.12.69) | "Stamps for Cooks" pane stamps, four covers | 20·00 |

There was no F.D.C. service for the 4d. red and 8d. turquoise-blue values.

*The price is for covers with complete panes with recipe attached. The Milk Marketing Board issued a special handstamp cancellation reading "Visit the Stamps for Cooks Exhibition, Milk Marketing Board, Thames Ditton, Surrey".

Multi-value Coil Strip (1969)

# SECTION UB
Machin £.s.d. Issues
1967-70. Booklet Panes in Gravure

## General Notes

**Introduction.** All panes were printed in Gravure by Harrison & Sons. See the detailed notes under Section U for information on printing, paper and gum. Reference to the note, "Booklet Cylinder Flaws", at the beginning of Section SB describes the panes which were printed from 21-row cylinders. These panes are found with varieties and the cylinder number in either the top or bottom row of the pane. In this Section the Panes of Six of the 1d., 3d., 4d. (both colours) and 5d. were printed from 21-row cylinders.

**Booklet errors.** Those listed as "Part perf. pane" have one row of three stamps imperforate on three sides.

Booklet Cylinder Number

**Booklet cylinder numbers.** These are listed for the Panes of Six only and the other panes had cylinder numbers engraved so that they did not occur in the finished booklet. The cylinders

employed are recorded for reference. The cylinder numbers being hand-engraved varied as to their position in relation to the stamp so that some were invariably trimmed. A pane which shows a complete cylinder number placed away from the stamp will only exist with badly trimmed perforations on the opposite side.

**Booklet cylinder flaws.** Cylinder flaws on booklet stamps are listed under the panes in which they occur as in Section SB. The flaws are priced in panes since this is the preferred method of collecting wherever possible. In consequence when checking varieties on single stamps it will be necessary to look at the lists of the sheet and coil stamps as well as the booklet panes.

When quoting the position on booklet panes no attention is paid to the labels. Therefore a flaw on the first stamp in the pane No. UB13 (4d. (2) and pair of labels) will be described as being on "R. 1/1". Since this Catalogue is primarily concerned with stamps we do not list flaws which sometimes occur in the wording of the labels from booklet panes.

**Booklet pane prices.** The prices quoted are for panes in mint condition, good perforations all round and complete with binding margin. Prices for complete booklets in Appendix HA are for booklets with average perforations.

## CHECKLIST OF MACHIN £.s.d. BOOKLET PANES

| UB No. | Face Value | Phos. Bands | Gum | Head | Size of Pane | Further description | Page |
|---|---|---|---|---|---|---|---|
| 1 | 1d. | 2 | PVA | B | 6 | Yellowish olive | 120 |
| 2 | 6 × 1d. | 2 | | | | | |
| | 3 × 4d. | 1L | PVA | B | 15 | "Baked Stuffed Haddock" recipe | 120 |
| | 3 × 4d. | 1R | | | | | |
| | 3 × 5d. | 2 | | | | | |
| 3 | 4 × 1d. | 1C | PVA | B | 6 | 4d. in sepia | 121 |
| | 2 × 4d. | 1C | | | | | |
| 4 | 4 × 1d. | 2 | PVA | B | 6 | 4d. in bright vermilion | 121 |
| | 2 × 4d. | 1L | | | | | |
| 5 | 2 × 1d. | 2 | PVA | B | 4 | 1d. at left | 122 |
| | 2 × 3d. | 2 | | | | | |
| 5a | 2 × 1d. | 2 | PVA | B | 4 | 1d. at right | 122 |
| | 2 × 3d. | 2 | | | | | |
| 6 | 3d. | 1C | PVA | B | 6 | Violet | 122 |
| 7 | 4d. | 2 | GA | A | 6 | Deep sepia | 123 |
| 8 | 4d. | 2 | GA | A | 6 | Deep olive-brown | 123 |
| 9 | 4d. | 2 | PVA | A | 6 | Deep olive-brown | 123 |
| 10 | 4d. | 2 | PVA | B | 4 | Deep olive-brown | 123 |
| 11 | 4d. | 1C | PVA | A | 6 | Deep olive-brown | 124 |
| 12 | 4d. | 1C | PVA | B | 4 | Deep olive-sepia | 124 |
| 13 | 4d. | 1C | PVA | B | 4 | Deep olive-sepia, including 2 labels | 124 |
| 14 (A) | 4d. | 1C | PVA | A | 6 | Bright vermilion | 125 |
| 14 (B) | 4d. | 1C | PVA | B | 6 | Bright vermilion | 125 |
| 14 (b) | 4d. | 1C | GA | A | 6 | Bright vermilion | 125 |
| 15 | 4d. | 1C | PVA | B | 4 | Bright vermilion | 125 |
| 16 | 4d. | 1C | PVA | B | 15 | "Stuffed Cucumber" and "Method" recipe | 126 |
| 17 | 4d. | 1C | PVA | B | 15 | "Method" for Braised Shoulder of Lamb recipe | 126 |
| 18 | 4d. | 1C | PVA | B | 4 | Bright vermilion, including 2 labels | 127 |
| 19 | 5d. | 2 | PVA | B | 6 | Deep Blue | 127 |
| 20 | 5d. | 2 | PVA | B | 15 | "Method" for Cream of Potato Soup recipe | 128 |

## ■ 1d. Panes of six

6 × 1d. (two bands). Head B.
Shade (2) Yellowish olive
From 4s.6d. Booklets LP45/59 and 10s. Booklets XP4/5

| | | Perf. Type | |
|---|---|---|---|
| | | *I* | *Ie* |
| UB1 | Pane of 6 × 1d. (containing No. U2 × 6) (25.3.68) | 2·00 | 2·50 |
| | a. Part perf. pane* | | |
| | b. Imperf. pane* | £5000 | |
| | c. Phosphor omitted | 32·00 | |

*Booklet error see General Notes.

**Booklet Cylinder Numbers**
Panes of Six (21-row cylinders)

| | | Perforation Type I | |
|---|---|---|---|
| Pane No. | Cylinder No. | No Dot | Dot |
| UB1 | F1 | £100 | £100 |
| UB1 | F1T | £100 | £100 |
| UB1 | F3 | 5·50 | 5·50 |
| UB1 | F3T | 5·50 | 5·50 |

In the above and all other 21-row cylinders, which are printed continuously on the web, the perforated web is cut at every 20th row to make sheets of 480. Consequently on successive sheets the cylinder number appears one row lower and thus a pane can have it adjoining the top or bottom row. Where the cylinder number adjoins the top row of the pane it is designated by the letter "T".

Examples of Cyl. No. pane F1 (lower position) are known with forged cylinder number.

## ■ "Stamps for Cooks" *se-tenant* pane of 15

*Se-tenant* Booklet Pane with recipe label
Pane of fifteen comprising 6 × 1d. (two bands) with 3 × 4d. (one side band at left), 3 × 4d. (one side band at right), 3 × 5d. and se-tenant recipe label. Head B "Baked Stuffed Haddock" recipe from £1 "Stamps for Cooks" Booklet ZP1

**A. Stapled**

| UB2 | Pane of 3 × 4d./1d./5d./1d./4d. (containing Nos. U2 × 6, U16 × 3, U16A × 3, U17 × 3) (1.12.69) | 35·00 |
|---|---|---|
| | b. Phosphor omitted | £500 |
| | c. One 9·5 mm. phosphor band on each stamp, except first vertical row which has phosphor omitted | £700 |
| | d. Mole on cheek (R. 1/2) | 55·00 |
| | e. White spot in necklace | 55·00 |
| | s. Optd. "Specimen" (14 mm.) | £3500 |

**B. Stitched**

| UB2a | Pane of 3 × 4d./1d./5d./1d./4d. (containing Nos. U2 × 6, U16 × 3, U16A × 3, U17 × 3) | 8·50 |
|---|---|---|
| | ab. Uncoated paper* | £900 |
| | ac. Phosphor omitted | £150 |
| | ad. Phosphor omitted from front, but shown on gummed side | £2250 |
| | ae. Mole on cheek (R. 1/2) | 12·00 |
| | af. White spot in necklace | 12·00 |
| | ag. One 9·5 mm. phosphor band on each stamp except for first vertical row which has phosphor omitted | £750 |
| | ah. As ag but phosphor omitted from first two vertical rows and one 9·5 mm. band at left on rows containing 5d., 1d., 4d. | £2250 |
| | aj. One 9·5 mm. band at right on first row at left and phosphor omitted from vertical rows 1d., 5d., 1d., 4d. | |

*Uncoated paper–Nos. UB2e and UB2af are repairs of the multipositive 'Broken necklace' variety (UB16b, etc). See General Notes for Section U.

**Booklet Cylinder Numbers**
In the £1 Booklet (ZP1) the cylinder numbers were always trimmed off, however, the cylinders known to have been used were F7 (1d.), N8 (4d.) and R5 (5d.).

UB2

UB2d, UB2ae(1d.)

UB3

UB4

## ■ **1d. and 4d. Sepia** *se-tenant* **pane of six**

*Se-tenant* Booklet Panes of Six
4 × 1d. (centre band) with vertical pair 4d. sepia (centre band).
Head B
From 10s. Booklet XP6

| | | Perf. Type | | |
|---|---|---|---|---|
| | | *I* | *I(½v)* | *P* |
| UB3 | Pane of 2 × 1d./1d./4d. (containing Nos. U3 × 4, U12 × 2) (16.9.68) | 4·00 | 14·00 | 5·00 |
| a. | Phosphor omitted | 30·00 | 65·00 | 45·00 |
| b. | Centre band on second and third vert. rows and missing phosphor on first row (2 × 1d.) | | | |
| c. | Centre band on first and second vert. rows and missing phosphor on third row (2 × 4d.) | | | |
| d. | Centre band on second vert. row only | | | |

**Booklet Cylinder Numbers**
*Se-tenant* pane of six (20-row cylinder)
One centre band

| | | Perforation Type I | |
|---|---|---|---|
| Pane No. | Cylinder No. | *No Dot* | *Dot* |
| UB3 | F4 (1d.), N5 (4d.) sepia | 28·00 | 30·00 |

## ■ **1d. and 4d. Bright vermilion** *se-tenant* **pane of six**

*Se-tenant* 4 × 1d. (two bands) with vertical pair 4d. bright vermilion (one left side band). Head B
From 10s. Booklets XP7/12

| | | Perforation Type P |
|---|---|---|
| UB4 | Pane of 2 × 1d./1d./4d. (containing Nos. U2 × 4, U16 × 2) (6.1.69) | 3·50 |
| a. | Phosphor omitted | £160 |

**Booklet Cylinder Numbers**
*Se-tenant* pane of six (20-row cylinder)
Two bands

| | | Perforation Type P |
|---|---|---|
| Pane No. | Cylinder No. | *No Dot* |
| UB4 | F4 (1d.), N5 (4d. vermilion) | 15·00 |

UB5

UB5a

## 1d. and 3d. *se-tenant* pane of four

Pair 1d. (two bands) with pair 3d. (two bands). Head B
From 2s. Booklets N P27/9
Pane UB5 Pane of four with 1d. at left
Pane UB5a Pane of four with 1d. at right

| | | Perf. Type | | |
|---|---|---|---|---|
| | | *I* | *I(½v)* | *AP* |
| UB5 | Pane of 2 × 1d./3d. (containing Nos. U2 × 2, U10 × 2) (6.4.68) | 7·00 | £275 | 3·00 |
| b. | One 9·5 mm. phosphor band on each stamp | 22·00 | £250 | 15·00 |
| c. | Phosphor omitted | £100 | | 75·00 |
| UB5a | Pane of 2 × 3d./1d. (containing Nos. U2 × 2, U10 × 2) (6.4.68) | 7·00 | 18·00 | 3·00 |
| ab. | One 9·5 mm. phosphor band on each stamp | 22·00 | 50·00 | 15·00 |
| ac. | Phosphor omitted | £100 | £150 | 75·00 |

**Booklet Cylinder Numbers**
*Se-tenant* panes of four
In the 2s. Booklets (NP27/9) the cylinder numbers were always trimmed off, but cylinders F2 and K3 were used.

## 3d. Panes of six

Panes of Six
6 × 3d. (centre band). PVA gum. Head B
From 10s. Booklets XP4/5

| | Perf. Type | |
|---|---|---|
| | *I* | *Ie* |
| UB6   Pane of 6 × 3d.(containing No. U9 × 6) (25.3.68) | 25·00 | 30·00 |
|    a.   Phosphor omitted | | |

**Booklet Cylinder Numbers**
Panes of Six (21-row cylinder)

| | | Perforation Type I | |
|---|---|---|---|
| Pane No. | Cylinder No. | *No Dot* | *Dot* |
| UB6 | K2 | £150 | £150 |
| UB6 | K2 T | £150 | £150 |

## ■ 4d. Deep olive-brown panes of six

Panes of Six (two bands)
6 × 4d. (two bands). Gum Arabic. Head A
(a) Shade (1) Deep sepia
From 6s. Booklets QP28/32

| | | Perf. Type | |
|---|---|---|---|
| | | I | Ie |
| UB7 | Pane of 6 × 4d. (containing No. U11 × 6) (21.9.67) | 10·00 | 12·00 |
| a. | Phosphor omitted | 28·00 | |

(b) Shade (2) Deep olive-brown
From 6s. Booklets QP33/6

| | | Perf. Type | |
|---|---|---|---|
| UB8 | Pane of 6 × 4d. (containing No. U11 × 6) (1.68) | 12·00 | 14·00 |
| a. | Part perf. pane* | £3500 | |
| b. | Phosphor omitted | 32·00 | |

*Booklet error–see General Notes.

6 × 4d. (two bands). PVA gum. Head A
From 4s.6d. Booklets LP45/6, 6s. Booklets QP37/40 and 10s. Booklets XP4/5

| | | Perf. Type | |
|---|---|---|---|
| UB9 | Pane of 6 × 4d. (containing No. U12 × 6) (25.3.68) | 1·50 | 1·75 |
| a. | One 9·5 mm. phosphor band on each stamp | £190 | |
| b. | Phosphor omitted | 25·00 | |
| c. | Patch on cheek (R. 1/2 or 2/2) | 10·00 | |

UB9c, UB11b
From 10s. Booklet

**Booklet Cylinder Numbers**
Panes of Six (21-row cylinders)

**Gum Arabic**

| Pane No. | Cylinder No. | No Dot | Dot |
|---|---|---|---|
| (a) Shade (1) Deep sepia | | | |
| UB7 | N1 | 22·00 | 22·00 |
| UB7 | N1 T | 22·00 | 22·00 |
| (b) Shade (2) Deep olive-brown | | | |
| UB8 | N1 | 22·00 | 22·00 |
| UB8 | N1 T | 22·00 | 22·00 |
| **PVA Gum** | | | |
| UB9 | N1 | 6·75 | 6·75 |
| UB9 | N1 T | 6·75 | 6·75 |
| UB9 | N2 | 6·00 | 6·00 |
| UB9 | N2 T | 6·00 | 6·00 |

## ■ 4d. Deep olive-brown panes of four

Panes of Four (two bands)
4 × 4d. (two bands). PVA gum. Head B
From 2s. Booklets NP27/31

| | | Perf. Type | | |
|---|---|---|---|---|
| | | I | I(½v) | AP |
| UB10 | Pane of 4 × 4d. (containing No. U12 × 4) (6.4.68) | 4·00 | 15·00 | 2·50 |
| a. | One 9·5 mm. phosphor band on each stamp | | 25·00 38·00 | 22·00 |
| b. | Phosphor omitted | 25·00 | 70·00 | 18·00 |
| c. | Dot on "D" (R. 1/2) | 20·00 | † | † |
| ca. | Retouched state | 10·00 | † | † |

UB10c

**Booklet Cylinder Numbers**
In the 2s. Booklets (NP27/31) the cylinder numbers were always trimmed off, however, the cylinder known to have been used was N3.

### ◼ **4d. Deep olive-brown pane of six**

Panes of Six (centre band)
6 × 4d. (centre band). PVA gum. Head A
From 4s.6d. Booklets LP47/8, 6s. Booklets QP41/5 and 10s.
Booklet XP6

| | | Perf. Type | |
|---|---|---|---|
| | | *I* | *Ie* |
| UB11 | Pane of 6 × 4d. (containing No. U13 × 6) (16.9.68) | 2·50 | 3·00 |
| | a. Part perf. pane* | £3500 | |
| | b. Patch on cheek (R. 1/2 or 2/2) | 10·00 | |

No. UB11 also occurs with the phosphor omitted but since a single pane would be indistinguishable from No. UB9b it is only listed there.
*Booklet error–see General Notes.

**Booklet Cylinder Numbers**
Panes of Six (21-row cylinders)

| Pane No. | Cylinder No. | No Dot | Dot |
|---|---|---|---|
| UB11 | N1 | 6·00 | 6·00 |
| UB11 | N1 T | 6·00 | 6·00 |
| UB11 | N2 | 6·00 | 6·00 |
| UB11 | N2 T | 6·00 | 6·00 |

### ◼ **4d. Deep olive-sepia panes of four**

Panes of Four (centre band)
4 × 4d. (centre band). PVA gum. Head B
From 2s. Booklets NP31a/33

| | | Perf. Types | | | |
|---|---|---|---|---|---|
| | | *I* | *I(½v)* | *AP* | *P* |
| UB12 | Pane of 4 × 4d. (containing No. U13 × 4) (16.9.68) | 24·00 | 35·00 | 2·50 | 2·50 |
| | a. Phosphor omitted | * | * | * | 50·00 |
| | b. Dot on "D" retouched | 27·00 | † | † | † |

*Phosphor omitted errors exist from these booklets in Perf. Types I and AP, but the panes are identical with No. UB10b.

**Booklet Cylinder Numbers**
In the 2s. Booklets (NP31/3) the cylinder number was always trimmed off, however, the cylinder known to have been used was N3.

UB13, UB18

### ◼ **4d. Deep olive-sepia *se-tenant* pane**

*Se-tenant* with printed labels
2 × 4d. (centre band). with two labels. PVA gum. Head B
"£4,315 FOR YOU AT AGE 55" (1st label) and "SEE OTHER PAGES" (2nd label) from 2s. Booklets NP30/3

| | | Perf. Types | | | |
|---|---|---|---|---|---|
| | | *I* | *I(½v)* | *AP* | *P* |
| UB13 | Pane of 2 × label/4d. (containing No. U13 × 2) (16.9.68) | 3·50 | 12·00 | 1·00 | |
| | | | | | 2·75 |
| | a. Phosphor omitted | 75·00 | | 60·00 | |
| | b. Damaged pearls in crown (R. 1/2) | | | | |

UB13b, UB18b

**Booklet Cylinder Numbers**
In the 2s. Booklets (NP30/3) the cylinder number was always trimmed off, however, the cylinder known to have been used was N6.

## ◼ 4d. Bright vermilion pane of six

Panes of Six
6 × 4d. (centre band). PVA gum.
From 4s.6d. Booklets LP49/59, 6s. Booklets QP46/55 and 10s.
Booklets XP7/12

| | | *Perf. Type* | |
|---|---|---|---|
| | | *I* | *Ie* |
| UB14 | Pane of 6 × 4d. (containing No. U14 × 6) (6.1.69) (A)  Head A | 1·75 | 2·00 |
| | (B) Head B | 2·50 | |
| a. | Phosphor omitted | 35·00 | |
| b. | Gum arabic (Head A) | £150 | |
| ba. | Gum arabic (Head A). Phosphor omitted | £600 | |

**Booklet Cylinder Numbers**
Panes of Six (21-row cylinders)

| Pane No. | Cylinder No. | No Dot | Dot |
|---|---|---|---|
| UB14 (A) | N1 (Head A) | 7·00 | 7·00 |
| UB14 (A) | N1 T | 7·00 | 7·00 |
| UB14 (A) | N1 (gum arabic) | £325 | £325 |
| UB14 (A) | N1 T (gum arabic) | £325 | £325 |
| UB14 (A) | N2 (Head A) | 7·00 | 7·00 |
| UB14 (A) | N2 T (Head A) | 7·00 | 7·00 |
| UB14 (A) | N7 (Head B) | 10·00 | 10·00 |
| UB14 b | N7 T (gum arabic) | 10·00 | 10·00 |

Stamps from booklet cylinder N7 show screening dots within the face value and in the margins.

## ◼ 4d. Bright vermilion pane of four

Panes of Four
4 × 4d. (centre band). PVA gum. Head B
From 2s. Booklets NP34/45

| | | *Perf.Types* | | |
|---|---|---|---|---|
| | | *I* | *I(½v)* | *P* |
| UB15 | Pane of 4 × 4d. (containing No. U14 × 4) (3.3.69) | 3·50 | 16·00 | 90 |
| a. | Phosphor omitted | 60·00 | £150 | 55·00 |
| b. | Dot on "D" retouched | 6·50 | † | † |
| c. | Two narrow phosphor bands over perforations | † | † | £150 |

**Booklet Cylinder Numbers**
In the 2s. Booklets (NP34/45) the cylinder number was always trimmed off, however, the cylinder known to have been used was N3.

UB16

## 4d. Bright vermilion pane of fifteen

Pane of Fifteen with recipe label
15 × 4d. (centre band). Panes of fifteen *se-tenant* with recipe
label. PVA gum. Head B
"Stuffed Cucumber" recipe and "Method" from £1 "Stamps for
Cooks" Booklet ZP1

### A. Stapled

| UB16 | Pane of 15 × 4d. (containing No. U14 × 15) (1.12.69) | 18·00 |
|---|---|---|
| b. | Broken necklace (R. 1/1) | 23·00 |
| c. | Tail on "4" (R. 1/4) | 25·00 |
| s. | Opt. "Specimen" (14 mm.) | £675 |

### B. Stitched

| UB16a | Pane of 15 × 4d. (containing No. U14 × 15) | 3·00 |
|---|---|---|
| ab. | Uncoated paper ('70)* | £150 |
| ac. | Phosphor omitted | £110 |
| ad. | Broken necklace (R. 1/1) | 5·75 |
| ae. | Tail on "4" (R. 1/4) | 9·00 |

### A. Stapled

| UB17 | Pane of 15 × 4d. (containing No. U14 × 15) (1.12.69) | 18·00 |
|---|---|---|
| b. | Broken necklace (R. 1/1) | 23·00 |
| c. | Spot over eye (R. 2/2) | 25·00 |
| s. | Opt. "Specimen" (14 mm.) | £675 |

### B. Stitched

| UB17a | Pane of 15 × 4d. (containing No. U14 × 15) | 3·00 |
|---|---|---|
| ab. | Uncoated paper ('70)* | £130 |
| ac. | Phosphor omitted | £160 |
| ad. | Broken necklace (R. 1/1) | 6·00 |
| ae. | Spot over eye (R. 2/2) | 8·00 |
| af. | Two narrow bands on each stamp | £600 |

*Uncoated paper–see General Notes for Section U.
   The note below No. U15, describing No. U14h, also applies
to pane UB17af.

UB17

"Method" only for Braised Shoulder of Lamb from £1 "Stamps
for Cooks" Booklet ZP1

UB16b, UB16ad, UB17b, UB17ad
This is a multipositive flaw which was repaired and appears as a white spot on pane UB2 (UB2e and UB2af)

UB16c, UB16ae

UB17c, UB17ae Later retouched on UB17 and exists retouched only on UB16

**Booklet Cylinder Numbers**
In the £1 Booklet (ZP1) the cylinder number was always trimmed off, however, the cylinder known to have been used was N9.

## ■ **4d. Bright vermilion** *se-tenant* **pane**

*Se-tenant* with printed labels
2 × 4d. (centre band). PVA gum. Head B
"£4,315 FOR YOU AT AGE 55" (1st label) and "SEE OTHER PAGES" (2nd label) from 2s. Booklets NP34/45

| | | Perf. Types | | |
|---|---|---|---|---|
| | | I | I(½v) | AP | P |
| UB18 | Pane of 2 x label/4d. (containing No. U14 × 2) (3.3.69) | 3·25 | 20·00 | £800 | 1·00 |
| | a. Phosphor omitted | 90·00 | £160 | | 70·00 |
| | b. Damaged pearls in crown (R. 1/2) | | | | |

**Booklet Cylinder Numbers**
In the 2s. Booklets (NP34/45) the cylinder number was always trimmed off, however, the cylinder known to have been used was N6.
For illustration of No. UB18b, see No. UB13b.

## ■ **5d. Pane of six**

6 × 5d. (two bands). PVA gum. Head B
From 5s. Booklets HP26/38 and 10s. Booklets XP6/12

| | | Perf. Type | |
|---|---|---|---|
| | | I | Ie |
| UB19 | Pane of 6 × 5d. (containing No. U17 × 6) (27.11.68) | 1·75 | 2·00 |
| | a. Imperf. pane* | £2750 | |
| | b. Part perf. pane* | £1800 | |
| | c. Phosphor omitted | 40·00 | |
| | ca. Third and fourth phosphor bands from left omitted | £120 | |
| | d. White flaw on diadem (R. 1/2 or 2/2) | 5·50 | |
| | e. Scratch through hair (R. 1/1 or 2/1) | 9·00 | |

*Booklet errors–see General Notes.
No. UB19ca is known with cylinder number R3T. Single variety is No. U17db.

UB19d

UB19e

**Booklet Cylinder Numbers**
Panes of Six (21-row cylinders)

| Pane No. | Cylinder No. | No Dot | Dot |
|---|---|---|---|
| UB19 | R2 | 4·75 | 4·75 |
| UB19 | R2 T | 4·75 | 4·75 |
| UB19 | R3 | 4·75 | 4·75 |
| UB19 | R3 T | 4·75 | 4·75 |

UB20

## 5d. Pane of fifteen

Pane of Fifteen with recipe label
15 × 5d. (two bands). Panes of fifteen se-tenant with recipe label. PVA gum. Head B
"Method" only for Cream of Potato Soup from £1 "Stamps for Cooks" Booklet ZP1

### A. Stapled

| UB20 | Pane of 15 × 5d. (containing No. U17 × 15) | |
|---|---|---|
| | (1.12.69) | 25·00 |
| b. | Uncoated paper ('70)* | £300 |
| c. | White flaw below collar (R. 1/2) | 32·00 |
| d. | Flaw on shoulder (R. 1/2) | 32·00 |
| s. | Opt. "Specimen" (14 mm.) | £900 |

### B. Stitched

| UB20a | Pane of 15 × 5d. (containing No. U17 × 15) | 4·00 |
|---|---|---|
| ab. | Uncoated paper ('70)* | £350 |
| ac. | Phosphor and recipe omitted | £750 |
| ad. | One 9·5 mm. band on each stamp | £800 |
| ae. | Phosphor omitted | £200 |
| af. | White flaw below collar (R. 1/2) | 7·00 |
| ag. | Flaw on shoulder (R. 1/2) | 7·00 |

*Uncoated paper—see General Notes for Section U.

UB20c, UB20af          UB20d, UB20ag

Both varieties occur on the same stamp on the primary sheet and seem to be two states of the same retouch, other states exist.

### Booklet Cylinder Numbers

In the £1 Booklet (ZP1) the cylinder number was always trimmed off, however, the cylinder known to have been used was R6 for UB20.

# SECTION UC

Machin £.s.d. Issues
1969. High Values. Recess-printed

## General Notes

**Introduction.** The four high values, in similar design to the low values, were issued on 5 March, 1969 thus completing the Machin definitive series.

**Printers.** The Machin high values were recess-printed by Bradbury, Wilkinson & Co. Ltd. on rotary sheet-fed machines.

**Paper.** Unwatermarked lightly coated paper was used for all values. Several types of coated paper appear to have been used and generally there is only a slight response to the chalky test. Variations in the thickness of the paper also exist. Shades are known but it is probable that they are due to the variations in the coating and thickness of the paper rather than to the use of different inks.

**Gum.** Only PVA gum was used for the Machin high values.

Diagram showing the printer's sheet comprising four Post Office panes, the method of perforation, and the positions of the plate numbers and perforation guide holes

**Sheet details.** The printer's sheets comprised 160 stamps in four panes of 40 each arranged in five rows of eight stamps (see diagram above), the sheet being guillotined into four before issue.

**Perforation.** All values are comb perforated 12. The printer's sheet was perforated as a complete sheet with perforation Type A*; therefore, the characteristics of each individual pane are different as is clearly shown in the diagram above. Perforator Type A* is described in Appendix G.

**Plate Numbers.** See the General Notes for Section T for an illustration of these. Each printer's sheet produces four plate numbers comprising a "whole number" and "A", "B" and "C" numbered panes and these appear below stamp 7 in the bottom row of each pane, as shown in the diagram above. The arrangement of the panes is the same for all plates of all the values.

Guide hole and plugged impression

**Perforation Guide Holes.** The Machin high values have a single guide hole opposite the first row of stamps, in the left-hand margin of the "whole" number panes and in the right-hand margin of the "A" plates as shown in the diagram of the printer's sheet. Additionally for plate 2 of the 2s.6d., and 5s., and plate 1 of the 10s., there are "blind" perforation guide holes slightly below the punched holes.

The punched holes are usually heavily rimmed with colour and may be either partly or completely trimmed off. The appearance of the "blind" holes ranges from a thin outline to being completely coloured in.

**U3.** Queen Elizabeth II

(Des. after plaster cast by Arnold Machin)

### ■ 1969. Type U3

#### 1969 (5 March). 2s.6d. Brown

UC1 (=SG 787)

| | Mint | Used |
|---|---|---|
| 2s.6d. Brown | 35 | 30 |

**Plate Numbers** (Blocks of Four)

| Plate No. | |
|---|---|
| | 7·00 |
| 2 | 7·00 |
| 2A | 7·00 |
| 2B | 7·00 |
| 2C | 7·00 |
| 3 | 7·00* |
| 3A | 7·00 |
| 3C | 7·00 |
| 6 | 10·00 |
| 6A | 10·00 |
| ✓ 6B | 10·00 |
| 6C | 10·00 |

*This contains the recorded minor constant flaw.

**Minor Constant Flaw**
Pl. 3A 5/8 Dot to right of Queen's eye (Th. D–E4)
**Quantities Printed.** Pl. 2/2C 7,840,000; Pl. 3/3C 27,200,000; Pl. 6/6C 9,360,000

●————————

#### 1969 (5 March). 5s. Crimson-lake

UC2 (=SG 788)

| | Mint | Used |
|---|---|---|
| 5s. Crimson-lake | 1·75 | 60 |

**Plate Numbers** (Blocks of Four)

| Plate No. | |
|---|---|
| 2 | 16·00 |
| ✓ 2A | 16·00 |
| 2B | 16·00 |
| 2C | 16·00 |
| 3 | 15·00 |
| 3A | 15·00 |
| 3B | 15·00 |
| 3C | 15·00 |

**Quantities Printed.** Pl. 2/2C 8,480,000; Pl. 3/3C 15,200,000

●————————

#### 1969 (5 March). 10s. Deep ultramarine

UC3 (=SG 789)

| | Mint | Used |
|---|---|---|
| 10s. Deep ultramarine | 6·00 | 7·00 |

**Plate Numbers** (Blocks of Four)

| Plate No. | |
|---|---|
| 1 | 45·00 |
| 1A | 45·00 |
| 1B | 45·00 |
| 1C | 45·00 |

**Quantities Printed.** Pl. 1/1C 8,880,000
●————————

#### 1969 (5 March). £1 Bluish black

UC4 (=SG 790)

| | Mint | Used |
|---|---|---|
| £1 (1) Bluish black | 3·00 | 1·50 |
| (2) Indigo | | £750 |

The indigo shade, from plate 3B, was due to a faulty ink mix and has been confirmed by analysis.

**Plate Numbers** (Blocks of Four)

| Plate No. | |
|---|---|
| 3 | 35·00 |
| 3A | 35·00 |
| 3B | 35·00 |
| (3C*) | † |
| 4 | 48·00 |
| 4A | 48·00 |
| 4B | 48·00 |
| 4C | 48·00 |

*This plate number block is not known as there was a fault on the plate and only the left half of this pane was issued.

New plates were made for the decimal £1 in 1970, but in single pane settings of 100 (10 × 10) in place of the plates of four panes each of 40 (8 × 5). Plate blocks of four from Plate 3 of the decimal issue (No. UC11 in Vol. 4 of this catalogue) can easily be distinguished from Plate 3 blocks of the pre-decimal issue as they show part of the "TOTAL SHEET VALUE" inscription in the margin opposite R. 9/10.

However, specialists may also recognise single stamps by studying the background shading under a strong magnifying glass, particularly in the top left and bottom right corners. The pre-decimal issue has thicker horizontal lines of shading whilst the decimal issue has thicker vertical lines, each caused by the direction in which the transfer roller was rocked, both plates being produced by the conventional process of rocking in impressions from the die. (Illustrations taken from top left corner)

On 6 December 1972 the £1 value was reissued with the value shown in a new style.

UC4 Pre-decimal issue Thicker horizontal lines    UC11 Decimal issue Thicker vertical lines

**Quantities Printed.** Pl. 3/3C 3,760,000; Pl. 4/4C 2,800,000

**Proofs**
Imperforate in the £1 design TYPE U3 each mounted on a Bradbury Wilkinson card and marked "Approved by the Queen" signed and dated "14 Jan/Feb. 1968" in blue. The stamps are printed in the approved colours of Nos. UC1 to 4
Card inscribed in red "A1" with £1 in brown as No. UC1
Card inscribed in red "A2" with £1 in crimson-lake as No. UC2
Card inscribed in red "A3" with £1 in deep ultramarine as No. UC3
Card inscribed in red "A4" with £1 in issued colour as No. UC4

As above but 2s.6d., 5s., 10s., and £1 imperforate proofs in the issued colours mounted on Bradbury Wilkinson card

Card with four values imperforate inscribed "AS SUBMITTED 20.3.68"

The above were originally in the Bradbury Wilkinson archive later acquired by De La Rue and sold by them in 2000.

## Presentation Pack

| | | |
|---|---|---:|
| UPP2 | (issued 5 March 1969) Four values | 16·00 |
| | a. With German text | 80·00 |

The issued Pack contained one each of Nos. UC1/4.
UPP2 also exists with a Japanese insert card.

## First Day Cover

| | | |
|---|---|---:|
| UFC6 | (5.3.69) 2s.6d., 5s., 10s., £1 | 9·50 |

# SECTION W

Special Issues
(1953-70)

## General Notes

**Special issues.** Until 1966 it had been the policy of the Post Office to restrict commemorative issues to celebrating particular events, such as anniversaries or exhibitions, conferences and festivals, etc. The introduction of the Landscape series in May 1966 heralded a new departure as this was followed by pictorial sets showing British Birds, Paintings, Bridges, Cathedrals, etc. and Technological Achievements. These cannot be described as being commemorative stamps, yet it is obviously convenient and logical for them to be listed here and so we have headed this Section Special Issues.

**Se-tenant combinations.** *Se-tenant* means joined together. Some sets include stamps of different design arranged se-tenant as blocks or strips and, in mint condition, these are usually collected unsevered as issued. Where such combinations exist, the individual stamps are priced normally as mint and used singles.

**Printers.** All the £.s.d. special issues were printed in photogravure by Harrison & Sons with the exception of the 1964 2s.6d. Shakespeare and 1966 2s.6d. Westminster Abbey which were recess-printed by Bradbury, Wilkinson & Co. and the 1969 Post Office Technology and 1970 Commonwealth Games issues which were printed by De La Rue & Co. by lithography.

Generally, the double-sized stamps were printed on continuous reels of paper on the web in double pane width, i.e. 240 stamps consisting of two panes (no dot and dot) each of 120 stamps arranged in twenty rows of six stamps, the panes being guillotined before issue. However, the higher values were often printed in single panes, either on reel or sheet-fed machines. After the listing of each issue we give the sheet arrangement and state whether printed in the reel or in sheets.

**Queen's portrait.** The portrait from the photograph by Dorothy Wilding Ltd. was used from the 1953 Coronation to the 1966 Westminster Abbey issues. This was replaced on the 1966 Landscapes to 1967 Christmas by the profile coinage design by Mrs. Mary Gillick, adapted by David Gentleman. The third, and final, change was made on the 1968 Bridges issue with the introduction of design from a plaster cast by Arnold Machin. The Machin head can be distinguished from the Gentleman adaptation of the Gillick profile by two, instead of one, laurel leaves on top of the Queen's head.

**Paper.** The same type of paper as for the definitive issues was used up to the 1960 General Letter Office issue and thereafter chalk-surfaced paper was used.

**Screen.** The 200-line screen as used for the Wilding definitives was employed up to the 1960 Europa issue but thereafter Harrisons used a finer 250-line screen.

**Watermarks.** These are illustrated in Section SA and were used as follows:

**Tudor Crown**          1953 Coronation issue
**St. Edward's Crown**          1957 World Scout Jubilee and Inter-Parliamentary Union and 1958 Commonwealth Games
**Crowns**          All later issues until 1967 Wild Flowers and British Discovery and Invention
**No watermark**          1967 Paintings and Sir Francis Chichester and all issues from 1967 Christmas onwards
The watermark normally appears sideways on upright designs. On certain stamps, the 2½d. and 3d. 1962 Productivity Year,

the 1963 Freedom from Hunger and Paris Postal Conference issues, the watermark is normally inverted. These stamps were printed on the web and for technical reasons the paper had to be re-reeled and, to save time and expense, it was decided to print on the paper wound in the reverse direction to normal, thus resulting in the watermark being inverted. A large proportion of the printing for the 1967 Wild Flowers 9d. was similarly treated. Other inverted watermark varieties on commemorative issues are normally from sheet-printed issues where the paper has been accidentally fed the wrong way and these are often quite scarce.

**Gum.** The distinction between gum arabic and PVA gum is explained in the General Notes relating to Section UA. It is sufficient to state here that gum arabic was used for all commemorative stamps up to the 1967 Christmas issue and thereafter Harrisons and De La Rue only used PVA gum.

**Perforation.** Harrisons used the same 15 × 14 comb perforation as for the Wilding definitives but some of the upright designs are perforated 14 × 15. The 1964 2s.6d. Shakespeare and 1966 2s.6d. Westminster Abbey were comb perforated 11 × 12 by Bradbury, Wilkinson and the 1969 Post Office Technology and 1970 Commonwealth Games issues were comb perforated 13 ½ × 14 by De La Rue.

Cylinder and plate blocks are listed according to the perforator type as described in Appendix G together with abbreviations for the side and horizontal margins of the listed block. These are usually from the bottom left corner, therefore the first letter refers to the left margin and the second to the bottom margin. For details see page 2 in Section S.

**Phosphor bands.** See the General Notes for Section S for a detailed description of these. In the special issues they were applied as follows:

Blue: From 1962 N.P.Y. to 1965 Salvation Army and 1965 I.T.U. Generally 8 mm. but occasionally 9·5 mm. bands.
Violet 8 mm. bands: Other 1965 issues to 1966 Christmas.
Violet 9·5 mm. bands: 1967 E.F.T.A. to 1970 Christmas.

From 1962 until the 1967 Wild Flowers set the special issues appeared both with and without phosphor bands. From the 1967 British Paintings set onwards it was intended that all special issues should appear only with phosphor bands. However, it is quite common practice for sheets to be issued with the phosphor accidentally omitted and these are listed as varieties.

**Methods of Application.** All three methods, photogravure, flexography and typography were utilised to apply the phosphor bands to £.s.d. special issues (for the characteristics of each method see Section S Notes).

In the light of considerable research it now appears that from 1962 until 1969 the bands were applied either by flexography or photogravure, the only exceptions being the two special issues printed by De La Rue which had the bands applied by typography. These two issues used a slightly different substance known as SA, sulphanilic acid being the activator.

It is known that the first phosphor issue, 1962 National Productivity Year set, had the bands printed on the web by flexography and the following reel-fed issues used the same process or photogravure. Flexography was used for the few sheet-fed issues. Since 1970 Harrisons have only used photogravure to apply the bands, and phosphor cylinder numbers were introduced.

Some difficulty can arise in distinguishing between

phosphor bands applied by photogravure and those printed by flexography. The latter often do not run to the bottom of the sheet or show a break in the bottom margin. They also show, in some instances, a vertical split in the centre of the band.

In some instances the cylinders or stereos used to apply the bands were made-up with a narrow band at one side or both sides of the sheet. These narrow bands vary in size, as do the normal bands, but most are 6 mm. wide. Where such varieties occur they are included, listing being for a single stamp with vertical margin attached. Note that the 6 mm. band listings refer to the width of the band *as printed*, not the width of the part of the band that falls on the stamp.

**Phosphor cylinder numbers.** Starting with the 1970 Anniversaries issue cylinder numbers were introduced on the phosphor cylinders as an additional check on tracing errors in applying the bands.

**Cylinder varieties and minor constant flaws.** We have only listed or recorded those we have actually seen and know to be constant in the position given. Others have been reported and may be added in future editions as examples become available for inspection. To pinpoint the position of the flaws we give the reference according to the S.G. Thirkell Position Finder where this is appropriate. Please note that for designs which lack outer frame lines the position finder should be placed over the outside of the perforation. For further information see the General Notes to Section S under "Varieties" and "Varieties in Cylinder Blocks".

**Flaws on Phosphor Issues.** In the recorded lists of flaws on stamps which come both ordinary and phosphor, "O" means that the flaw occurs only on the ordinary stamp, "P" phosphor only and "OP" on ordinary and phosphor.

**Multicoloured stamps.** Colour descriptions are taken from the traffic lights to identify the colours of the cylinder numbers and also missing colour errors. Where colours are superimposed one over another, the colours that result will be different from those described. So far as possible we have followed the normal practice giving the colours starting first with the most prominent one in the centre of the stamp and then moving outwards, usually ending with the colours of the inscriptions, background and Queen's head.

**Presentation Packs.** Special Packs comprising slip-in cards with printed commemorative inscriptions and descriptive notes on the back and with protective covering, were introduced in 1964 with the Shakespeare issue. These are listed and priced.

Issues of 1968-69 (British Paintings to the Prince of Wales Investiture) were also issued in packs with text in German for sale through the Post Office's German Agency and these are also listed.

Subsequently, the packs sold in Germany, Japan and the Netherlands were identical to the normal English version with the addition of a separate printed card in German, Japanese or Dutch. These are noted where they exist.

Spelling errors on insert cards exist, but these are outside the scope of this catalogue.

**Reprinted insert cards.** In 1988 permission was granted to a British stamp dealer by the Post Office to reproduce, from an original, 1,000 sets of the Dutch insert cards for the 1969 Ships to the 1970 Literary Anniversaries issues.

**"Specimen" and "Cancelled" stamps.** The former practice of distributing these ceased during the reign of King George VI but occasionally such overprints were applied to Elizabethan Special Issues for advance publicity or exhibition purposes and these are listed.

Various issues of 1964, 1965 and 1966 are known overprinted "CANCELLED", usually without gum. These were for use in trials carried out by the Forensic Department of the Post Office, and should not have reached the general public.

Issues of 1969/70 are known with "CANCELLED" applied with a violet rubber handstamp (26 × 3½ mm.), generally across a corner of the stamps. This practice was introduced in

an attempt to defeat the postal use of the stamps prior to their first day of issue and which could be obtained from advance publicity material distributed to shops supplied by the Post Office Agency in West Germany. When it was realised that the use of the rubber handstamp created material of a collectable nature the practice was discontinued but the following are known to exist, Nos. W159/97. The Machin 1969 high values, Nos. U33/6 were similarly obliterated. Later stamps were cancelled by a red pen line across the corner. Such publicity material is outside the scope of this catalogue.

**Encapsulated Stamp Sets.** Starting with the 1969 Post Office Technology set, publicity notices were prepared for a number of commemorative issues. These comprised complete sets of stamps mounted on card with details of issue date, description, designer and printer and encapsulated in perspex.

Scientific analysis of the stamps in these cards has concluded that they are printed on unsurfaced paper, unlike the issued stamps which are all on chalk-surfaced paper.

As the stamps cannot be removed from the perspex casing they are not individually listed, but those cards which we have seen are noted.

**Withdrawal dates.** The earlier commemorative issues were left on sale until exhaustion and definite withdrawal dates are not always known, but starting with 1963 Red Cross issue the Post Office announced a standard practice to keep commemorative stamps on sale at the Philatelic Bureau for twelve months from date of issue unless sold out before. All £.s.d. stamps were invalidated as from 1 March 1972.

**Quantities.** Up to the end of the 1962 issues (N.P.Y.) it is believed that stamps were sold to exhaustion except where a definite withdrawal date was announced, and so the printing figures are quoted as being the Quantities Sold:. Starting with the 1963 Freedom from Hunger issue the quantities are stated as being the number sold, issued or printed. These are defined as follows:

**Sold**: Actual Quantities Sold after accounting for undistributed stocks and unsold stocks returned to stores for destruction.

**Issued**: Quantities issued from Post Office Stores Department to post offices, including the Philatelic Bureau. These figures are given for the 1965 issues (Churchill to I.T.U.) and for which we do not have actual sales figures. Some may have been Withdrawn: and destroyed.

**Printed:** Quantities actually supplied by the printers. These often differ from advance announcements of quantities ordered, owing to spoilage, etc.

Recent research at the BPMA has revealed that quantities noted in the printers' reports frequently differ from those previously announced by the Post Office and published in the philatelic press. There are also cylinder combinations recorded that have not been reported or listed in this catalogue. This research has not been incorporated into this edition as it is not clear whether they were ever put on sale.

We also quote figures for sales of Presentation Packs and these were only made available after the total Quantities Sold, etc., had been announced. The quantities for Packs are not additional as they have already been included in the figures for the numbers sold, issued or printed.

We have noticed slight variations in the figures given for Quantities Sold, etc., stated in other publications and would point out that the figures we have given are those furnished to us by the Post Office. However, the differences are insignificant. See note above Type No. W 178.

**Sheet markings.** Reference should be made to the descriptions of sheet markings given in the General Notes for Section S, as most of these apply to this section and the information given there is not repeated here. In the commemorative issues the markings are most interesting as they begin with the same basic markings as for the definitives for the first monocoloured issues but as more colours were introduced other markings began to appear. They are described here in the order of their appearance.

Normal at side
Harrison

At foot

De La Rue

Cylinder Numbers

**Cylinder Numbers.** These are described in Section S but we show above how they occur on stamps printed in more than one colour. In the listing of cylinder number blocks for stamps printed in more than one colour we give the colour of each cylinder number in order, reading downwards. The information is sometimes helpful in connection with varieties and flaws where more than one cylinder has been used for the same colour in combination with others.

**Plate Numbers.** The Plate Numbers used by Bradbury, Wilkinson for the 2s.6d. Shakespeare and the 2s.6d. Westminster Abbey are as shown in our notes on the sheet markings for Section T. It should be stated that some of the sheet-fed commemorative stamps were printed by Harrisons on a Linotype and Machinery No. 4 press which uses curved plates and on these the cylinder numbers are, strictly speaking, plate numbers. However, as they appear just like the cylinder numbers they are referred to as such.

**Colour Register Marks.** These are coloured crosses of very fine lines, one for each colour superimposed as illustrated. They appear on all sheets of stamps printed in more than one colour, starting with the 1960 Europa issue.

Photo-etched Solid

Stippled

**Autotron Marks.** Coloured bars which may be photo-etched solid or stippled (dotted lines). They serve as an electronic control on colour registration and were first used on the 1961 C.E.P.T. issue.

**Colour Designations.** These consist of colour names usually preceded by a figure and the letter "G" which stands for "Gear". They are usually trimmed off but sometimes appear on extra wide right-hand margins on double and single pane reel-fed printings. They are to indicate which side the cylinder should be fitted and aligned with the colour gear in the press. They are not always shown in the colour indicated. They began to be used on the 1961 C.E.P.T. issue, but do not appear on correctly trimmed sheets of £.s.d. stamps after the 1969 Notable Anniversaries issue.

Boxed                    Partially Boxed

Harrison

De La Rue

**"Traffic Lights".** This term is used to denote coloured check dots which were first introduced on the 1962 N.P.Y. issue. They are intended as a means of checking sheets for missing colours before delivery to the Post Office. They may be fully boxed or partially boxed as shown but we have not distinguished between these. We quote the colours in the order of their appearance reading downwards. Sometimes they are in the same order as the cylinder numbers in which case we state this to save space. Rather larger dots were used by De La Rue.

**Coloured Crosses.** These are most usually found on sheet-fed printings and they serve as trimming lines and as an additional check on colour registration. They are often trimmed off. They first appeared on the 1s.3d. 1964 Botanical stamp.

(a)        (b)        (c)

De La Rue

**Perforation Guide Holes.** At first the styles as shown in the General Notes for Section S were used but the types illustrated above were introduced as follows:

    (a)  Double "SON" box for the 6d. 1965 Parliament
    (b)  Single "SON" box for the 4d. 1966 Landscapes
    (c)  Single "SON" box for the 4d. 1966 World Football Cup

The letters stand for "Selvedge", "Off-side" and "Near-side" and they appear in the reverse order on the other side of the sheet. The "S" or "S O" and part of the box are liable to be trimmed off. We also show the styles used by De La Rue for the 1969 Post Office Technology set and 1970 Commonwealth Games issue respectively.

TOTAL SHEET VALUE    £ 4. 10. 0.

`**Total Sheet Values.** As an aid to counter clerks in stocktaking and in selling stamps by the sheet, the "TOTAL SHEET VALUE" and amount was printed in the margin. This practice was introduced with the 1969 Anniversaries issue and this was presumably found to be necessary with the introduction of stamps of unusual size and sheet make-up.

**Embossed head.** Starting with the 1968 British Paintings set the Queen's head was sometimes embossed over the gold printing.

This gives rise to missing embossing varieties which are listed, although we do not list misplaced embossing. Provision is also made for an embossed dot in the traffic lights.

This index gives an easy reference to the inscriptions and designs of the Special Stamps 1953 to 1970. Where a complete set shares an inscription or type of design, then only the catalogue number of the first stamp is given. Paintings, inventions, etc., are indexed under the name of the artist or inventor, where this is shown on the stamp.

---

W1

(Des. E. G. Fuller)

W2

(Des. Michael Goaman)

W3

(Des. Edmund Dulac)

W4

(Des. M. C. Farrar-Bell)
(Portrait by Dorothy Wilding Ltd (except 1s.3d.))

## 1953 (3 June). Coronation of Queen Elizabeth II

Type **W1/4.**

Watermark Tudor Crown, Type W.22

**W1** (=SG 532)

|  | Mint | Used |
|---|---|---|
| 2½d. carmine-red | 20 | 25 |
| a. Missing pearl (Cyl. 3 Dot, R. 1/4) | 30·00 | |
| b. Pearls retouched | 22·00 | |

**W2** (=SG 533)

|  | Mint | Used |
|---|---|---|
| 4d. ultramarine | 1·10 | 1·90 |
| a. Daffodil leaf flaw (Cyl. 1 No dot, R. 19/1) | 20·00 | |

**W3** (=SG 534)

|  | Mint | Used |
|---|---|---|
| 1s.3d. deep yellow-green | 5·00 | 3·00 |
| a. Clover leaf flaw (Cyl. 2 No dot, R. 20/1) | 25·00 | |

**W4** (=SG 535)

|  | Mint | Used |
|---|---|---|
| 1s.6d. deep grey-blue | 10·00 | 4·75 |
| a. Mis-shapen emblems (Cyl. 1 Dot, R. 1/6) | 30·00 | |

| b. Thistle flaw (Cyl. 1 Dot, R. 16/5) | 35·00 |
|---|---|

| First Day Cover (W1/4) | 75·00 |
|---|---|

Nos. W1/4 are known used from an Army Post Office in Egypt and Lambeth, London S.W. on 2 June 1953. The latter example was an error as the U.K. offices were closed on 2 June.

Reprints, in black, of these four stamps were included in the Penrose Annual for 1954. These reprints were printed in photogravure by Harrisons, on ungummed paper, but were perforated. They were inscribed on the reverse "Reproduction only no postal or philatelic value".

For a £1 value as Type W3 see No. MS2147 Concise Catalogue.

W1a          W1b

Normal          W3a

W2a          W4a

W4b

**Cylinder Numbers** (Blocks of Six)
Perforation Type A (E/I)

|  | Cylinder No. | No dot | Dot |
|---|---|---|---|
| 2½d. | 1 | 5·50 | 5·50 |
|  | 2 | 1·75 | 1·75 |
|  | 3 | 1·75 | 1·75 |
|  | 4 | 1·75 | 1·75 |
| 4d. | 1 | 25·00* | 7·50 |
| 1s.3d. | 2 | 55·00* | 35·00 |
| 1s.6d. | 1 | 70·00 | 70·00 |

**Minor Constant Flaws**

2½d. Cyl. 1 no dot
19/2 Spur to top of A of POSTAGE

2½d. Cyl. 3 dot
13/2 Bulge on left-hand fraction bar

2½d. Cyl. 4 no dot
  1/3 White flaw in diadem (Th. A7)
  1/4 White spur on left-hand crown (Th. B2)
  7/1 Red spot behind hair level with earring (Th. D8–9)
  14/2 Red spot on face level with earring (Th. D7)
  17/1 White spot on branch below left-hand crown (Th. C3)

4d. Cyl. 1 dot
  1/4 Retouched stem of daffodil (Th. F2–3)

1s.3d. Cyl. 2 dot
  2/6 Retouch behind upper part of E of E R and white flaw at top of sceptre (Th. B4)

1s.6d. Cyl. 1 no dot
  18/2 Malformed foot to R of REVENUE

1s.6d. Cyl. 1 dot
  19/1 White flaw on wreath below R of REVENUE (Th. B9)

**Sheet Details**
Sheet size: 120 (6 × 20). Double pane reel-fed

**Sheet markings:**
**Cylinder numbers:** Opposite R. 18/1
**Guide holes:** Boxed opposite rows 14/15, at left (no dot) or right (dot)
**Marginal arrows:**
"V" shaped, hand engraved at top and bottom of sheet
"W" shaped, photo-etched at both sides
**Marginal rule:** At bottom of sheet

**Imprimaturs from the National Postal Museum Archives**
Nos. W1/4 imperforate, watermark Type W.22

| | |
|---|---|
| Watermark upright (set of 4) | £9000 |

**Quantities Sold:**
2½d. 415,034,000; 4d. 19,816,000; 1s.3d. 8,012,000;
1s.6d. 5,987,200

**W5**. Scout Badge and "Rolling Hitch"

(Des. Mary Adshead)

**W6**. "Scouts coming to Britain"

(Des. Pat Keely)

**W7**. Globe within a Compass

(Des. W. H. Brown)

## 1957 (1 August). World Scout Jubilee Jamboree

Commemorating the 50th Anniversary of the founding of the Boy Scout Movement. The Jubilee Jamboree was held at Sutton Coldfield.

Types **W5/7**. Watermark St. Edward's Crown, Type W.23

**W5** (=SG 557)

| | Mint | Used |
|---|---|---|
| 2½d.  carmine-red | 50 | 50 |
|   a. Broken rope strand (Cyl. 4 Dot, R. 1/1) | 25·00 | |
|   b Neck retouch (Cyl. 5 No dot, R. 11/5) | 25·00 | |

**W6** (=SG 558)

| | Mint | Used |
|---|---|---|
| 4d.  ultramarine | 75 | 1·50 |
|   a. Solid pearl at right (Cyl. 1 No dot, R. 14/5) | 25·00 | |

**W7** (=SG 559)

| | Mint | Used |
|---|---|---|
| 1s.3d.  green | 4·50 | 4·50 |
|   a. Major retouch (Cyl. 1 Dot, R. 2/4) | 30·00 | |

| | | |
|---|---|---|
| First Day Cover (W5/7) | | 25·00 |

W5a                    W5b

W6a

W7a

**Quantities Sold:**
Sheets and coils: 2½d. 137,235,286; 4d. 9,318,477;
1s.3d. 3,820,478

**Coils:**

| Value | Size | Printed | Sold | Size | Printed | Sold |
|---|---|---|---|---|---|---|
| 2½d. | 4800 | 487 | 23 | 480 | 100 | 49 |
| 4d. | 4800 | 480 | 21 | 480 | 100 | 37 |
| 1s.3d. | 4800 | 482 | 20 | 240 | 100 | 33 |

**Total number of coil stamps sold or used on covers:**
2½d. 133,920; 4d. 118,560; 1s.3d. 103,920
  Only 60,632 covers were serviced and 14 large rolls of each
value were used for this purpose.
**Withdrawn:** 11.9.57

**Cylinder Numbers** (Blocks of Six)
Perforation Type A (E/1)

|  | Cylinder No. | No dot | Dot |
|---|---|---|---|
| 2½d. | 4 | 4·50 | 4·50 |
|  | 5 | 4·50 | 4·50 |
| 4d. | 1 | 18·00 | 18·00 |
| 1s.3d. | 1 | 30·00 | 30·00 |
| Perforation Type B (I/P) | | | |
| 4d. | 1 | 5·75 | 5·75 |
| Perforation Type C (E/P) | | | |
| 4d. | 1 | † | 5·75 |

**Minor Constant Flaws**

2½d. Cyl. 4 dot
    11/2 Red spot over Queen's left eyebrow, later retouched
        (Th. C9)
    14/1 Red spot in rope between L E (Th. G5)
    16/5 White spot in rope at junction with fifth line at left
        (Th. C1)
    17/3 Red spot in large 2 just left of curve
    19/2 White dot after small 2
    20/4 White stop after M

2½d. Cyl. 5 dot
    13/4 Red spot in top of A

1s.3d. Cyl. 1 dot
    18/2 Green spot in compass point above badge (Th. E2)

**Coils**

Special rolls were prepared of this issue for servicing first
day covers mechanically. They were produced from different
cylinders and printed on continuous reels of paper. The
cylinders bore 126 impressions in 21 rows of six. The cylinders
were numbered J1 for the 2½d. and 4d. and J2 for the 1s.3d.
The reels were cut so as to provide single rolls of 4800 stamps,
numbered 1 to 6. Some very minor flaws have been noted on
these coil stamps.
    The rolls were put on sale at the London Chief Office but as
the quantities were too large for stamp collectors, some were
rewound into smaller rolls of 480 for the 2½d. and 4d. and 240
for the 1s.3d. and put on sale there on 2 September.

**Sheet Details:** Sheet size: 120 (6 × 20). Double pane reel-fed

**Sheet markings:**
**Cylinder numbers:** Opposite R. 18/1
**Guide holes:** Opposite rows 14/15, at left (no dot) or right (dot)
**Marginal arrows:**
"V" shaped, hand engraved at top and bottom of sheet
"W" shaped, hand engraved on both sides
**Marginal rule:** At bottom of sheet

**Imprimaturs from the National Postal Museum Archives**
Nos. W5/7 imperforate, watermark Type W.23

| Watermark upright (set of 3) | £6750 |
|---|---|

**W8**

(Des. M. C. Farrar-Bell and adopted by
Frank Langfield with added lettering)

———————————

**1957 (12 September). 46th Inter-Parliamentary
Union Conference**

To mark the 46th Conference held at Church House,
Westminster. The Union was founded in 1889.

Watermark St. Edward's Crown, Type W.23

Type **W8.**

**W8** (=SG 560)

|  |  | Mint | Used |
|---|---|---|---|
| 4d. | ultramarine | 1·00 | 1·00 |
| a. | Broken wreath (R. 2/6) | 25·00 | |
| b. | Broken frame (R. 12/5) | 25·00 | |
| c. | Partial double frame line (R. 17/3, 17/6 and 18/6) | 25·00 | |

| First Day Cover (W8) | £140 |
|---|---|

W8a

W8b  W8c

**Cylinder Numbers** (Blocks of Six)
Perforation Type B (I/P)

|  | Cylinder No. | No dot | Dot |
|---|---|---|---|
| 4d. | 2 | 7·00 | |

Perforation Type C (E/P)

|  |  |  |  |
|---|---|---|---|
| 4d. | 2 | 7·00 | |

**Minor Constant Flaws**

4d. Cyl. 2 no dot
    1/5 Blue blob in frame over last N of CONFERENCE (Th. E6)
    1/6 Outline of left-hand jewel of diadem incomplete (Th.
       A–B3)
    2/1 Line joining shamrock leaf to bottom frame (Th. G–H1)
    3/2 Blue scratch on right frame near bottom (Th. H6)
    8/7 Small break in frame opposite last E in CONFERENCE
    14/6 Fine scratch from ear right across neck (Th. E4)
    15/8 Blue blob in bottom right corner (Th. H6)

18/1 Blue spot below A of POSTAGE

**Sheet Details**
Sheet size: 240 (12 × 20). Single pane reel-fed

**Sheet markings:**
**Cylinder number:** Opposite R. 18/1
**Guide holes:** Six. Opposite rows 1 and 7/8 at both sides and
also boxed opposite rows 14/15 at both sides
**Marginal arrows:** "V" shaped, hand engraved at top and
bottom of sheet
"W" shaped, etched in photogravure at both sides
**Marginal rule:** At bottom of sheet

**Imprimatur from the National Postal Museum Archives**
No. W8 imperforate, watermark Type W.23

| Watermark upright | £2250 |
|---|---|

**Quantity Sold:** 10,472,160

**Withdrawn:** 13.10.57

———————————

**W9**. Welsh Dragon

(Des. Reynolds Stone)

**W10**. Flag and Games Emblem

(Des. W. H. Brown)

**W11**. Welsh Dragon

(Des. Pat Keely)

SPECIMEN

A

## 1958 (18 July). Sixth British Empire and Commonwealth Games

The 1958 Empire and Commonwealth Games were held at Cardiff.

Watermark St. Edward's Crown, Type W.23

Types **W9/11**.

**W9** (=SG 567)

| | | Mint | Used |
|---|---|---|---|
| 3d. | deep lilac | 20 | 20 |
| a. | Short scale (Cyl. 2 Dot, R. 1/1) | 25·00 | |
| b. | Shoulder flaw (Cyl. 2 Dot, R. 12/2) | 25·00 | |
| c. | Shoulder flaw retouched | 25·00 | |
| d. | Body flaw. State II (Cyl. 2 Dot, R. 20/3) | 25·00 | |
| e. | Body flaw. State III | 25·00 | |
| f. | Retouched face (Cyl. 7 Dot, R. 10/6) | 25·00 | |
| g. | "H" flaw (Cyl. 7 Dot, R. 11/2) | 30·00 | |
| h. | "H" flaw retouched | 25·00 | |
| s. | "Specimen", Type A | 50·00 | |

**W10** (=SG 568)

| | | | |
|---|---|---|---|
| 6d. | reddish purple | 40 | 45 |
| s. | "Specimen", Type A | 50·00 | |

**W11** (=SG 569)

| | | | |
|---|---|---|---|
| 1s.3d. | green | 2·25 | 2·40 |
| s. | "Specimen" Type A | 50·00 | |

| First Day Cover (W9/11) | 85·00 |
|---|---|

Normal W9a
Part of the shading is missing on the scale near "M" of "EMPIRE".

W9b W9c
White flaw on shading of dragon's body above shoulder. Later retouched with an irregular pattern of dots.

W9d W9e
Flaw on body above second "E" of "EMPIRE". This is a progressive flaw. Initially normal, the first stage showed the faintest outline of the flaw. State II shows the flaw solid and state III with a dark outline and pale centre.

W9f
The retouches across the Queen's cheek and below the chin are quite marked on Cyl. 7 dot, R. 10/6 but there are other minor retouches in this position in stamp No. 6 in rows 2 to 13.

W9g
White flaw crossing line behind dragon's left foreleg shows as a letter "H". After retouching there is a light vertical line across the flaw.

**Cylinder Numbers** (Blocks of Six)
Perforation Type A (E/I)

| | Cylinder No. | No dot | Dot |
|---|---|---|---|
| 3d. | 2 | 1·75 | 1·75 |
| | 7 | 3·50 | 3·50 |
| 6d. | 1 | 4·25 | 4·25 |
| 1s.3d. | 1 | 16·00 | 16·00 |

**Minor Constant Flaws**

3d. Cyl. 2 no dot
13/1 Dark diagonal line across last two fins of dragon's tail; later the upper line was touched out (Th. F–G9)
19/3 Dots to left of right stroke of H in BRITISH (Th. D2)

3d. Cyl. 7 no dot
8/4 White spot on M in EMPIRE; later retouched (Th. E2)

3d. Cyl. 7 dot
3/4 White flaw on fin of dragon's tail above E of COM-MONWEALTH (Th. F8)
4/5 Break in left frame by top of 3 (Th. E1)
20/3 White flaw on dragon's ankle above N of COMMON-WEALTH (Th. F7)

6d. Cyl. 6 no dot
18/6 Dot between O and N of COMMONWEALTH (Th. A6)

6d. Cyl. 6 dot
10/1 BRI thicker than normal and retouch under left corner of flag (Th. G3)
11/1 IRE thicker than normal
16/1 IR thicker than normal
20/3 Dent in bottom frame below Queen (Th. H10–11)

1s.3d. Cyl. 3 no dot
12/3 Retouched background above RE of EMPIRE (Th. G5)

1s.3d. Cyl. 3 dot
16–19 /5Vertical scratch of varying length in left-hand margin, petering out in rows 18/19

**Sheet Details**
Sheet size: 120 (6 × 20). Double pane reel-fed

**Sheet markings:**
**Cylinder numbers:** Opposite R. 18/1
**Guide holes:** Boxed opposite rows 14/15, at left (no dot) or right (dot)
**Marginal arrows:** "V" shaped, hand engraved at top and bottom of sheet
"W" shaped, photo-etched at both sides
In the early printings of the 6d. the arrow was omitted in the right margin on the no dot pane, and in the left margin on the dot pane. Later they were inserted by hand engraving and appear quite rough
**Marginal rule:** At bottom of sheet

**Imprimaturs from the National Postal Museum Archives**
Nos. W9/11 imperforate, watermark Type W.23

| Watermark upright (set of 3) | £6750 |
|---|---|

**Quantities Sold:** 3d. 320,400,000; 6d. 28,595,880; 1s.3d. 9,870,000

W.24

**Crowns Watermark**
The Multiple Crowns watermark, Type W.24, was used for all the following special issues up to the 1967 Wild Flowers issue.

**W12**. Postboy of 1660          **W13**. Posthorn of 1660

(Des. Reynolds Stone)          (Des. Faith Jaques)

**1960 (7 July). Tercentenary of Establishment of General Letter Office**

Charles II Act of 1660 establishing the G.P.O. legally settled the Post Office and was the first of a long series of laws for the regulation of postal matters.

The watermark is sideways on the 1s.3d.

Types **W12/13.**

**W12** (=SG 619)

| | Mint | Used |
|---|---|---|
| 3d. deep lilac | 50 | 50 |
| a. Broken mane (Cyl. 1 No dot, R. 17/2) | 35·00 | |
| b. Face scratch (Cyl. 1 Dot, R. 17/3) | 25·00 | |

**W13** (=SG 620)

| | Mint | Used |
|---|---|---|
| 1s.3d. green | 3·75 | 4·25 |

| First Day Cover (W12/13) | 55·00 |
|---|---|

W12a          W12b
Scratch extends from eye to hair

**Cylinder Numbers** (Blocks of Six)
Perforation Type A (E/1)

| | Cylinder No. | No dot | Dot |
|---|---|---|---|
| 3d. | 1 | 4·50 | 4·50 |
| Perforation Type B (P/I) | | | |
| 1s.3d. | 1 | 25·00 | |
| Perforation Type C (P/E) | | | |
| 1s.3d. | 1 | 25·00 | |

For Types B and C the 1s.3d is with sheet orientated showing head to right.

**Minor Constant Flaws**

3d. Cyl. 1 no dot
1/2 White dot in bottom of large C (Th. B1)
10/5 White notch in bottom frame below r of Letter (Th. H7)
13/1 r of Letter weak (Th. G7)

15/6 White patch on left foreleg of horse (Th. E5)

**3d. Cyl. 1 dot**
11/6 White dot in hair near top of ear (Th. D12)
20/5 White nick in back of boy (Th. D4)

**1s.3d. Cyl. 1 no dot**
1/18 White bulge inside 0 of 1960 (Th. E7)
2/20 White bulge on stem of acorn under horn (Th. L3)
5/19 White spot in centre of leaf on right of portrait (Th. G6)
6/5 White dot at junction of two acorns under Queen's shoulder (Th. G5)

**Sheet Details**
**Sheet sizes:**
3d. 120 (6 × 20). Double pane reel-fed; 1s.3d. 120 (20 × 6). Single pane reel-fed

**Sheet markings:**
**Cylinder numbers:** 3d. opposite R. 18/1; 1s.3d. opposite R. 4/1
**Guide holes:**
3d. opposite rows 14/15, at left (no dot) or right (dot)
1s.3d. Six. Above and below vertical rows 1, 7/8 and boxed above and below 14/15
**Marginal arrows (hand engraved):**
3d. "V" shaped at top and bottom of sheet; "W" shaped on both sides
1s.3d. "V" shaped on both sides: "W" shaped at top and bottom of sheet.
**Marginal rule:** 3d. at bottom of sheet and 1s.3d. at right-hand side

**Imprimaturs from the National Postal Museum Archives**
Nos. W12/13 imperforate, watermark Type W.24

Watermark upright (3d.) or sideways (1s.3d.) (set of 2)   £4500

**Quantities Sold:** 3d. 143,390,520; 1s.3d. 6,090,840

**Withdrawn:** 31.12.60

---

> **Chalk-surfaced paper**
> All the following special issues are on chalk-surfaced paper, unless otherwise stated.

**W14.** Conference Emblem

(Des. Reynolds Stone, emblem by P. Rahikainen)

**Miniature Sheets**
On the occasion of the Eurostamp–1962 London Stamp Exhibition, organised with the help of the Council of Europe, a miniature sheet, size 114 × 124 mm., was produced comprising three each of Nos. W14/15 se-tenant in a block of six (2 × 3) printed in grey-blue, imperforate and surrounded by a brown frame and inscriptions in black on white unwatermarked gummed paper. The stamps were printed by Harrison & Sons in photogravure and the rest of the sheet was printed by Wm. Clowes & Sons by letterpress. The sheet had no franking value.

A similar sheet exists, size 110 × 125 mm., but with the stamps printed in black and surrounded by a green frame and inscription giving details of the issue in red. The stamps were printed in photogravure and the rest of the sheet by letterpress by Harrison & Sons. The sheet had no franking value.

---

**1960 (19 September). First Anniversary of European Postal and Telecommunications Conference**

Celebrating the first Anniversary of the Conference of European Postal and Telecommunications Administrations.
**Type W14**
**W14** (= S.G.621)

|  | Mint | Used |
|---|---|---|
| 6d. bronze-green and purple | 2·00 | 50 |
| a. Broken diadem (R. 1/2) | 25 | |
| b. Blurred "E" (R. 13/5) | 25 | |

**W15** (=SG 622)

|  | Mint | Used |
|---|---|---|
| 1s.6d. brown and blue | 9·50 | 5·00 |
| a. Broken diadem (R. 1/2) | 35 | |
| b. Major retouch (R. 9/2) | 35 | |
| c. Blurred "E" (R. 13/5) | 16·00 | |

| First Day Cover (W14/15) | | 65·00 |
|---|---|---|

**Printing Screen.** Nos. W14/15 were the last photogravure commemoratives from Harrisons to utilise the 200-line screen. On the 1s.6d. a 200-line screen was used for the portrait and the new 250-line version for the background.

W14/15a                     W14b, W15c

---

W15b

**Cylinder Numbers** (Blocks of Four)
Perforation Type A (E/1)

| Cylinder No. | No dot | Dot |
|---|---|---|
| Perforation Type B (E/P) | | |
| 6d.  1 (purple)–1A (green) | 8·50 | |
| 1s.6d.  2 (blue) –1A (brown) | 45·00 | |
| Perforation Type C (I/P) | | |
| 4d.  1 (purple) – 1A (green) | 8·50 | |
| 1s.6d.  2 (blue) – 1A (brown) | 45·00 | |

The same cylinder 1A was used for both values.

**Minor Constant Flaws**

6d. Cyls. 1–1A no dot
  1/4 Pale purple spots in bottom of oval and below bottom frame (Th. G9–10 and H10)
  6/2 Two short lines in scroll above T of TELECOMMUNI-CATIONS (Th. E2)
  9/3 Small coloured line in scroll above E of EUROPEAN (Th. B1)
  12/2 Dot in M of ADMINISTRATION
  19/1 Vertical seratch left of scroll containing EUROPEAN (Th. B–D1)
  20/5 Two scratches in scroll left of C of CONFERENCE (Th. A12)

1s.6d. Cyls. 2–1A no dot
  10/4 Retouch to spine of P of EUROPA
  12/2 Dot in M of ADMINISTRATION
  17/4 Dotted retouch above CO (Th. F4)
  18/5 Retouch in background above first M of TELECOM-MUNICATIONS

**Sheet Details**
Sheet size: 120 (6 × 20). Single pane reel-fed

**Sheet markings:**
**Cylinder numbers**: Bottom margin below R. 20/5
**Guide holes**: Opposite rows 1 and 7/8, at both sides and boxed opposite rows 14/15, at both sides
**Marginal arrows (hand engraved)**: "V" shaped at top and bottom and "W" shaped at both sides
**Marginal rule**: At bottom of sheet
**Colour register marks**: Opposite rows 2 and 19 at both sides

**Imprimaturs from the National Postal Museum Archives**
Nos. W14/15 imperforate, watermark Type W.24

| Watermark upright (set of 2) | £4500 |
|---|---|

**Quantities Printed**: 6d. 16,990,320; 1s.6d. 7,682,520

**Withdrawn**: 31.12.60, but placed on sale again during Stampex exhibition in March 1961

**W15**. Thrift Plant      **W16**. Growth of Savings

(Des. Peter Gauld)      (Des. Michael Goaman)

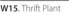

**W17**. Thrift Plant

(Des. Michael Goaman)

## 1961 (28 August). Post Office Savings Bank Centenary

To mark the centenary of the establishment of the P.O. Savings Bank.
Types **W15/17**

The watermark is sideways on the 2½d.

**A. TIMSON Machine**
  2½d. Cyls. 1E–1F no dot. Deeply shaded portrait (dull black)
  3d. Cyls. 3D–3E no dot. Sharp portrait with good contrast and bright highlights

**W16** (=SG 623A)

| | Mint | Used |
|---|---|---|
| 2½d.  dull black and red | 25 | 25 |
| a.  Dull black (Queen's Head) omitted | £25000* | |
| b.  Forehead retouch (R. 4/19) | 25·00 | |

**W17** (=SG 624A)

| | Mint | Used |
|---|---|---|
| 3d.  orange-brown and violet | 20 | 20 |
| a.  Orange-brown omitted | £550 | |
| b.  Perf. through right sheet margin | 35·00 | 38·00 |
| ba.  Do. and orange-brown omitted | £1250 | |
| c.  Extension hole in top or bottom sheet margin | 6·00 | |
| d.  Nick in "S" (R. 9/3) | 25·00 | |
| e.  Nick retouched | 20·00 | |

**W18** (=SG 625A)

| | Mint | Used |
|---|---|---|
| 1s.6d.  red and blue | 2·50 | 2·25 |
| a.  Phantom oval in light blue (R. 19/3) | 30·00 | |

| First Day Cover (W16/18) | | 75·00 |
|---|---|---|

## B. THRISSELL Machine

2½d. Cyls. 1D–1B no dot or dot. Lighter portrait (grey-black)
3d. Cyls. 3C–3B no dot or dot. Dull portrait, lacking in contrast

**W19** (=SG 623B)

| | | Mint | Used |
|---|---|---|---|
| W19 | 2½d. grey-black and red | 2·25 | 2·25 |

**W20** (=SG 624B)

| | | Mint | Used |
|---|---|---|---|
| W20 | 3d. orange-brown and violet | 40 | 40 |
| | a. Orange-brown omitted | £1500 | |
| | b. Notch in flower (No dot, R. 7/1) | 25·00 | |
| | c. Notch in leaf (No dot, R. 14/4) | 25·00 | |

A very small quantity of all values was pre-released at the Chorley, Lancs., P.O. on 21 August, 1961.

*No. W16a dull black omitted. The price is for certificated examples without the grey ghosting present on some stamps.

W16b

W17d
Nick in S

W17e
Nick filled in but centre of S is narrower

W18a

W20b                    W20c

**Cylinder Numbers** (Blocks of Four)
**A. Timson printings:** Single pane cylinders only (no dot). Nos. W16/18
Perforation Type A (E/1)

| | Perforation types | | |
|---|---|---|---|
| Cylinder No. | B | C | F(L) |
| 2½d. 1E (black)–1F (red)* | 2·50 (P/I) | 2·50 (P/E) | † |
| 3d. 3D (violet)–3E (brown) | 1·50 (E/P) | 1·50 (I/P) | 70·00 (P/E) |
| 1s.6d. 2E (blue)–2C (red) | 14·00 (E/P) | 14·00 (I/P) | † |

*The black number is superimposed over the red.

**B. Thrissell printings:** Double pane cylinders. Nos. W19/20

| | Perforation Type A | |
|---|---|---|
| Cylinder Nos. | No dot | Dot |
| 2½d. 1D (black)–1B (red) | 10·00 (I/E) | 10·00 (I/E) |
| 3d. 3C (violet)–3B (brown) | 10·00 (E/1) | 2·50 (E/I) |

In the 2½d. dot pane the dot was omitted in error after 1B.

In the 3d. no dot pane "3E" was wrongly inserted and the "C" was engraved over the "E".

Two blocks of four are needed to show both cylinders in the 3d. no dot Thrissell printing as the numbers are below R. 20/2 and R. 20/5 on the bottom margin.

For Types B and C the 2½d. is with sheet orientated showing head to right.

**Minor Constant Flaws**

2½d. Cyls. 1E–1F no dot
1/13 Two white dots on right curve below last S of SAVINGS
1/16 Two black dots right of Queen's left eye (Th. D4)
1/17 State I. Dark red patch left of top thrift flower (Th. H3) State II. Later printings show whitish patch
2/3  White horizontal line from Queen's hair to OF of OFFICE (Th. C3)
5/3 White spot on top of right arm of V of SAVINGS

3d. Cyls. 3D–3E no dot
8/1 Diagonal retouch across Queen's cheek from right of her left eye to nose (Th. D9–10)
11/5 Brown spot on squirrel s neck (Th. D5)
17/1 Retouch on Queen's chin (Th. E9)
17/2 Retouch on neck (Th. E10)
19/2 Retouch above necklace (Th. E–F10)
20/1 Vertical violet line on branch in bottom right corner (Th. FG13)

3d. Cyls. 3C–3B no dot
1/4 Additional serif at top of K of BANK
3/3 Notch in upper right leaf on lowest right-hand branch of tree (Th. E7)
4/2 Retouch on neck below earring (Th. E10)
4/6 Dot in B of BANK
7/3 Retouch above necklace (Th. E10)

**Sheet sizes:**

| Sheet Details | Timson | Thrissell |
|---|---|---|
| 2½d. 120 (20 × 6) | Single pane reel-fed | Double pane reel-fed |
| 3d. 120 (6 × 20) | Single pane reel-fed | Double pane reel-fed |
| 1s.6d. 120 (6 × 20) | Single pane reel-fed | |

**Sheet markings:**
**Cylinder numbers:**

| | | |
|---|---|---|
| 2½d. | Bottom margin below R. 6/19 | Bottom margin below R. 6/19 |
| 3d. | Bottom margin below R. 20/5 | Bottom margin below R. 20/2 and R. 20/5 |
| 1s.6d. | As 3d. | |

**Guide holes:**

| | | |
|---|---|---|
| 2½d. | Above and below vertical rows 1, 7/8 and (boxed) 14/15 | Below vertical rows 14/15 (no dot) or above (dot), boxed |
| 3d. | Opposite rows 1, 7/8 and (boxed) 14/15, both sides | Opposite rows 14/15, at left (no dot) or right (dot), boxed |
| 1s.6d. | As 3d. | |

**Marginal arrows (hand engraved):**

| | | |
|---|---|---|
| 2½d. | "V" shaped on both sides; "W" shaped at top and bottom "V" shaped, all round | As Timson |
| 3d. | | "V" shaped, at top and bottom; "W" shaped at both sides |
| 1s.6d. | "V" shaped, at top and bottom; "W" shaped, at both sides | |

**Marginal rules:**

| | | |
|---|---|---|
| 2½d. | At right-hand side | As Timson |
| 3d. | At bottom | As Timson |
| 1s.6d. | At bottom | |

**Colour register marks:**

| | | |
|---|---|---|
| 2½d. | Above and below vertical rows 2/3 and 17/18 | Below vertical rows 2/3 and 17/18 (no dot) or above (dot) |
| 3d. | Opposite rows 3/4 and 17/18 at both sides | Opposite rows 3/4 and 17/18 at left (no dot) or right (dot) |
| 1s.6d. | Opposite rows 2/3 and 18/19 at left (no dot) or right (dot) | |

**Colour designations (usually trimmed off):**

2½d. None
3d. BROWN opposite row 11 and BLUE opposite row 12, right margin, dot pane
1s.6d. RED opposite row 15 and BLUE opposite row 16, right margin

In the case of marginal copies the differences in sheet markings, in conjunction with the different types of perforators used, provide helpful clues for identifying the printing machine used.

Autotron markings were engraved on the Thrissell cylinders during the printing run.

**Imprimaturs from the National Postal Museum Archives**
Nos. W16/18 imperforate, watermark Type W.24

| | |
|---|---|
| Watermark upright (3d., 1s.6d.) or sideways (2½d.) (set of 3) | £6750 |

**Quantities Sold**: 2½d. 24,720,000; 3d. 114,360,000; 1s.6d. 7,560,000

W18. C.E.P.T. Emblem

W19. Doves and Emblem

W20. Doves and Emblem

(All values des. Michael Goaman, doves by T. Kurpeschoek)

## 1961 (18 September). European Postal and Telecommunications (C.E.P.T.) Conference

Representatives of 19 countries met at Torquay on 11 September for the Second Anniversary Conference of the European Postal and Telecommunications Administrations.

These were the first stamps of Great Britain to be printed in three colours
Types **W18/20**
**W21** (=SG 626)

| | | | Mint | Used |
|---|---|---|---|---|
| 2d. | orange, pink and brown | | 15 | 15 |
| | a. | Orange omitted | £18000 | |
| | b. | White ear (Dot, R. 11/2) | 25·00 | |

**W22** (=SG 627)

| | | | Mint | Used |
|---|---|---|---|---|
| 4d. | buff, mauve and ultramarine | | 15 | 15 |

**W23** (=SG 628)

| | | | Mint | Used |
|---|---|---|---|---|
| 10d. | turquoise, pale green and Prussian blue | | 15 | 50 |
| | a. | Pale green omitted | £22500 | |
| | b. | Turquoise omitted | £7000 | |

| | |
|---|---|
| First Day Cover (W21/63) | 6·00 |

W21b

**Cylinder Numbers** (Blocks of Four)

| Cylinder Nos. | Perforation Type A (E/I) | |
|---|---|---|
| | No dot | Dot |
| 2d. 1A (brown)–1B (orange)1C (pink) | 1·50 | 1·50 |
| 4d. 2E (ultramarine)–2B (buff)–2C (mauve) | 1·50 | 1·50 |
| 10d. 3G (Prussian blue)–3D (green)–3A (turquoise) | 2·50 | 2·50 |

The panes were transposed, the dot being on the left and the no dot on the right.

**Minor Constant Flaws**

2d. Cyls. 1A–1B–1C no dot
  6/4 Pale spot on neck below necklace (Th. F10)
  17/4 Dot in lower right pink horn (Th. F12)
  18/1 Diagonal dark brown patch across Queen's cheek. Later retouched (Th. E10)

2d. Cyls. 1A–1B–1C dot
  6/4 Small white dot to left of P
  18/6 Hairline from right-hand frame to sheet margin (Th. E13–14)

4d. Cyls. 2E–2B–2C dot
  5/3 Flaw at top right of E
  12/6 Dark patch above diadem (Th. A8)
  15/3 Flaw down Queen's forehead and nose (Th. C–D6)
  17/6 Pale patch on cheek (Th. D7)

10d. Cyls. 3G–3D–3A no dot
  4/6 White patch above Queen's right eye (Th. C10)
  6/1 Pale patch to right of Queen's neck (Th. E1213, F1213)
  10/3 White patch on Queen's forehead (Th. C10). Started during the run gradually becoming more prominent
  15/5 Small white patch at top centre of Queen's forehead (Th. C10)

10d. Cyls. 3G–3D–3A dot
  4/3 Break in loop of posthorn around P (Th. C7)
  4/6 Notch in frame at top right (Th. A13)
  14/2 Dark patch to right of lower right posthorn (Th. C8)

**Sheet Details**
Sheet size: 120 (6 × 20). Double pane reel-fed

**Sheet markings:**
**Cylinder numbers:** Bottom margin below R. 20/5
**Guide holes:** Opposite rows 14/15, at left (dot) or right (no dot), boxed
**Marginal arrow (hand engraved):** "V" shaped at top and bottom; "W" shaped at both sides
**Marginal rule:** At bottom of sheet
**Colour register marks:**
2d. Opposite rows 2/3 and 17/18 at left (dot) or right (no dot)
4d. Opposite rows 2/3 and 18/19 at left (dot) or right (no dot)
10d. None
**Autotron marks (solid):**
2d. Respectively brown, pink and orange opposite rows 18/20, at left (dot) or right (no dot)
4d. Respectively ultramarine and mauve opposite rows 18/19, at left (dot) or right (no dot)
10d. Respectively Prussian blue, green and turquoise opposite rows 18/20, at left (dot) or right (no dot)
**Colour designations:**
2d. BROWN in right margin reading upwards opposite rows 14/13 (no dot)
4d. YELLOW, MAUVE, BLUE respectively in right margin opposite rows 11/12, 12/13 and 13 (no dot)
10d. None

**Imprimaturs from the National Postal Museum Archives**
Nos. W21/23 imperforate, watermark Type W.24

| Watermark upright (set of 3) | £3000 |
|---|---|

**Quantities Sold:** 2d. 47,530,920; 4d. 7,614,480; 10d. 5,427,780

**W21.**
Hammer Beam Roof, Westminster Hall

**W22.**
Palace of Westminster

(Des. Faith Jaques)

**1961 (25 September). Seventh Commonwealth Parliamentary Conference**

The Empire Parliamentary Association was formed at the Coronation of King George V and in 1948 its name was changed to its present form.
Types **W21/22**

The watermark is sideways on the 1s.3d.

**W24** (=SG 629)

| | | Mint | Used |
|---|---|---|---|
| 6d. | purple and gold | 25 | 25 |
| a. | Gold omitted | £2400 | |

**W25** (=SG 630)

| | | | |
|---|---|---|---|
| 1s.3d. | green and blue | 2·50 | 2·75 |
| a. | Blue (Queen's head) omitted | £35000 | |
| b. | Green omitted | | |

| First Day Cover (W24/25) | 30·00 |
|---|---|

**Cylinder Numbers** (Blocks of Four)

| Cyl. Nos. (No dot) | Perforation Types | |
|---|---|---|
| | Type B | Type C |
| 6d. 1B (gold)–1D (purple) | 2·00 (E/P) | 2·00 (I/P) |
| 1s.3d. 2A (green)–2B (blue) | 15·00 (P/I) | 15·00 (P/E) |

For Types B and C the 1s.3d. is with sheet orientated showing head to right.

**Minor Constant Flaws**

6d. Cyls. 1B–1D no dot
  3/4 Dot in middle bar of second E in CONFERENCE
  5/5 Enlarged white patch in Queen's hair (Th. C7)
  6/3 Two small retouches in neck above necklace (Th. F7–8)
  10/3 Patch of retouching below crossed maces (Th. G5–6)

1s.3d. Cyls. 2A–2B no dot
  5/4 White patch on Queen's forehead (Th. D4)
  6/2 Small white vertical line on Queen's forehead (Th. C–D4)

**Sheet Details**
**Sheet sizes:** 6d. 120 (6 × 20); 1s.3d. 120 (20 × 6). Single pane reel-fed

**Sheet markings:**
**Cylinder numbers:** Bottom margin below R. 20/5 (6d.) or 6/19 (1s.3d.)
**Guide holes:**
6d. opposite rows 1 and 7/8, at both sides and boxed opposite rows 14/15, at both sides
1s.3d. above and below vertical rows 1 and 7/8 and boxed above and below vertical rows 14/15

**Marginal arrows (hand engraved):**
6d. "V" shaped at top and bottom and "W" shaped at both sides
1s.3d. "V" shaped at both sides and "W" shaped at top and bottom
**Marginal rule:** 6d. at bottom of sheet; 1s.3d. at right side
**Colour register marks:**
6d. Opposite both sides of rows 2/3 and 18/19
1s.3d. Above and below vertical rows 2/3 and 18/19

**Imprimaturs from the National Postal Museum Archives**
Nos. W24/25 imperforate, watermark Type W.24

Watermark upright (6d.) or sideways (1s.3d.) (set of 2)  £4500

**Quantities Sold:** 6d. 16,680,000; 1s.3d. 5,760,000

**W23**. "Units of Productivity"

**W24**. "National Productivity"

**W25**. "Unified Productivity"

(Des. David Gentleman)

The National Productivity Year issue was the first commemorative series to appear with phosphor bands and presents a number of other interesting facets:

The watermark on the 2½d. and 3d. is inverted for the reason explained in the General Notes to this section.

There were several printings on the low values which are characterised by their distinct shades and confirmed by different states of some of the flaws and varieties. It is believed that the second printing of the 2½d. comes from sheets numbered between about 439,000 and 450,000. Only the third printing was used for the phosphor stamps. There was considerable variation in the carmine-red during the printing and carmine-rose shades are quite common.

**2½d.** During the first printing both green cylinders were seriously damaged, hence the major repairs in the later printings.

**3d.** There were several printings of this value which fall into two shade groups. The violet cylinder 2A provided a number of minor flaws and was quickly replaced. It is believed that stamps from this cylinder were supplied only to Canterbury and Chelmsford.

## 1962 (14 November). National Productivity Year

The stamps emphasised the need for greater productivity as an essential element in the continuing prosperity of Great Britain. The watermark is inverted on the 2½d. and 3d.
Types **W23/25**

**A. Ordinary**

**W26** (=SG 631)

| | | Mint | Used |
|---|---|---|---|
| 2½d. | (1) Myrtle-green and carmine-red | 20 | 20 |
| | (2) Deep green and bright carmine-red | 25 | 15 |
| | (3) Blackish olive and carmine-red | 25 | 15 |
| | a. Emblem and arrows retouch (No dot, R. 3/3) (2) | 20·00 | |
| | b. Ditto (3) | 20·00 | |
| | c. Arrow head retouch (No dot, R. 4/4) (2) | 20·00 | |
| | d. Ditto (3) | 20·00 | |
| | e. Retouches, arrows 2 and 6 (No dot, R. 4/5) (2) | 20·00 | |
| | f. Ditto (3) | 20·00 | |
| | g. White nose (Dot, R. 2/6) (1) | 20·00 | |
| | h. Neck retouch (Dot, R. 15/4) (1) | 20·00 | |
| | i. Ditto (2) | 20·00 | |
| | j. Ditto (3) | 20·00 | |
| | k. Smudged red centre cube (Dot R. 18/3) (2) | 20·00 | |
| | l. Ditto (3) | 20·00 | |
| | m. Arrow head retouch (Dot, R. 19/6) (2) | 20·00 | |
| | n. Ditto (3) | 20·00 | |

**W27** (=SG 632)

| | | | |
|---|---|---|---|
| 3d. | (1) Light blue and violet | 50 | 25 |
| | (2) Light blue and deep bluish purple | 60 | 15 |
| | a. Light blue (Queen's head) omitted | £5000 | |
| | b. Lake in Scotland (Cyls. 2A–2B Dot, R. 1/3 | 25·00 | |
| | c. Kent omitted (Cyls. 2C–2B No dot, R. 18/2) | 30·00 | |
| | d. Lake in Yorkshire (Cyls. 2C–2B Dot, R. 19/1) | 25·00 | |
| | e. Forehead line (Cyls. 2D–2B No dot, R. 17/6) | 20·00 | |
| | f. Ditto, removed | 20·00 | |
| | g. Ditto, retouched | 20·00 | |

**W28** (=SG 633)

| | | | |
|---|---|---|---|
| 1s.3d. | carmine, light blue and deep green | 1·50 | 1·75 |
| | a. Light blue (Queen's head) omitted | £15000 | |

| | | |
|---|---|---|
| First Day Cover (W26/8) | | 55·00 |

**B. Phosphor**
(2½d. has one band at left; others have three bands, all applied flexo.)

**WP26** (=SG 631p)

| | | | |
|---|---|---|---|
| 2½d. | blackish olive and carmine-red | 60 | 50 |
| | a. Emblem and arrows retouch (No dot, R. 3/3) | 20·00 | |
| | b. Arrows head retouch (No dot, R. 4/4) | 20·00 | |
| | c. Retouches, arrows 2 and 6 (No dot, R. 4/5) | 20·00 | |
| | d. Neck retouch (Dot, R. 15/4) | 20·00 | |
| | e. Smudged red centre cube (Dot, R. 18/3) | 20·00 | |

| | | |
|---|---|---|
| f. Arrow head retouch (Dot, R. 19/6) | 20·00 | |

**WP27** (=SG 632p)

| | | |
|---|---|---|
| 3d. light blue and violet | 1·50 | 80 |
| a. Left-hand band omitted | | |
| b. Narrow band at left or right (stamp with vert. margin) | 3·00 | |
| c. Forehead line (Cyls. 2D-2B, No dot, R. 17/6) | 20·00 | |
| d. Forehead line removed | 20·00 | |

**WP28** (=SG 633p)

| | | |
|---|---|---|
| 1s.3d. carmine, light blue and deep green | 35·00 | 22·00 |
| a. Narrow band at left or right (stamp with vert. margin) | 48·00 | |

| | |
|---|---|
| First Day Cover (W26/8) | £150 |

About 60 2½d., 350 3d. and 20 1s.3d. were pre-released at a Lewisham post office, London, on 16 and 17 October, 1962.

W26g          W26h/j, WP26d

W26k/l, WP26e
This may not be fully constant

2½d. Arrows numbered for easy identification of varieties and flaws

W26e/f, WP26c
In W26c/d, WP26b the arrowhead alone is retouched with diagonal lines and in W26m/n, WP 26f with irregular dots. Less marked retouches occur in the same area on dot cyl., R.19/2 and 19/4

W26a/b, WP26a
N and arrowhead of emblem strongly shaded with diagonal cuts and dashes, also arrows 4,10 and 14

W27b          W27c    W27d

W27e, WP27c          W27f, WP27d          W27g
The original variety was a horizontal line from Queen's left eye to hair which was later removed, leaving a white gap and this was finally partly filled in by retouching

**Cylinder Numbers** (Blocks of Four)

**(a) Ordinary**

| Cylinder Nos. | Perforation Type A (E/I) | |
|---|---|---|
| | No dot | Dot |
| 2½d. 1D (red)1B (green) (shade 1) | 1·75 | 1·75 |
| 1D−1B (shade 2) | 2·50 | 5·50* |
| 1D−1B(shade 3) | 2·50 | 5·50* |
| 3d. 2A (violet)2B (blue) | 30·00 | 30·00 |
| 2C−2B | 2·75 | 2·75 |
| 2D−2B | 3·50 | 3·50 |
| 1s.3d. 3C (carmine)3B (blue)3E (green) | 8·00 | |

| | No dot | |
|---|---|---|
| | Type B (E/P) | Type C (I/P) |
| 1s.3d. 3C (carmine)3B (blue)3E (green) | 18·00 | 18·00 |

## (b) Phosphor

| | Perforation Type A (E/I) | |
|---|---|---|
| | No dot | Dot |
| 2½d. 1D (red)–1B (green) (shade 3) | 4·25 | 8·00* |
| 3d. 2D (violet)–2B (blue) | 4·25 | 4·25 |
| 1s.3d. 3C (carmine)–3B (blue)–3E (green) | £150 | † |

### Minor Constant Flaws

2½d. Cyls. 1D–1B no dot
1/2 Two small green dots right of arrow 2 (Th. B–C4) all shades, OP
3/2 Scratch through top of bottom right cube (Th. F–E4) all shades, OP
3/4 Minor retouches to face around mouth (Th. D–F10) shades 2/3, OP
5/1 White scratch below Queen's nose and through mouth (Th. D–E10) all shades, OP
17/5 Small retouch to cheek to right of mouth (Th. D10–11) all shades, OP

3d. Cyls. 2C–2B no dot
1/4 Retouch in Scotland (Th. C3), O
6/5 Dark patch above R of PRODUCTIVITY (Th. G6), O
13/5 Line of retouching above blue sea of Ireland (Th. C2), O

3d. Cyls. 2C–2B dot
7/1 Purple line across Solway Firth (Th. D3), O
15/6 Row of dots from Queen's left eye to hair (Th. C11), O

3d. Cyls. 2D–2B no dot
13/5 Lines of retouching above blue sea of Ireland (Th. C2), OP

3d. Cyls. 2D–2B dot
1/3 Retouch in Yorkshire (Th. D4), OP

1s.3d. Cyls. 3C–3B–3E no dot
3/4 White flaw at back of Queen's hair (Th. D12), OP
6/2 Retouch on tail of large blue arrow (Th. D2), OP
13/4 White flaw left of earring (Th. E11), OP

### Sheet Details

Sheet size: 120 (6 × 20)
2½d. and 3d. Double pane reel-fed on a Timson machine
1s.3d. Single pane reel-fed on a new Thrissell machine capable of using five colours

**Sheet markings:**
**Cylinder numbers:** Bottom row below R. 20/5
**Guide holes:**
2½d. and 3d. Opposite rows 14/15 (boxed), at left (no dot) or right (dot)
1s.3d. Opposite rows 1 and 7/8, at both sides and boxed opposite rows 14/15, at both sides
**Marginal arrows (photo-etched):** "W" shaped at top, bottom and sides
**Marginal rule:** At bottom of sheet
**Colour register marks:**
2½d. and 3d. Opposite rows 2/3 and 18/19, at left (no dot) or right (dot)
1s.3d. Opposite rows 2/3 and 18/19, at both sides
**Autotron marks (stippled):**
2½d. and 3d. Bottom margin in various positions
1s.3d. Respectively red, green, blue, green, red below vertical rows 4/6
**Colour designations (usually trimmed off):**
2½d. G GREY (not green) opposite rows 8/9 and G RED opposite row 13, right margin on the dot cylinder
3d. G BLUE opposite rows 8/9 and G MAUVE (Cyl. 2C) opposite row 13 or G PURPLE (Cyl. 2D) opposite rows 6/7, right margin on the dot cylinder
1s.3d. G BLUE opposite row 9 and G GREEN opposite rows 12/3, left margin
**Traffic lights (boxed):**
2½d. Green, red opposite R. 20/6 dot pane
3d. Blue, violet opposite R. 20/6 dot pane

1s.3d. Blue, red, green boxed opposite R. 20/6

### Imprimaturs from the National Postal Museum Archives

**A. Ordinary**
Nos. W26/28 imperforate, watermark Type W.24

| Watermark upright (set of 3) | £6750 |
|---|---|

**B. Phosphor**
Nos. WP26/28 imperforate, watermark Type W.24

| Watermark upright (set of 3) | £6750 |
|---|---|

**Quantities Sold:**

| | Ordinary | Phosphor |
|---|---|---|
| 2½d. | 99,240,000 | 7,320,090 |
| 3d. | 182,580,000 | 13,320,000 |
| 1s.3d. | 8,832,000 | 1,320,000 |

Of the 2½d. ordinary it is estimated that about 62 million came from the first printing. 3 million from the second printing and 34 million from the third printing

**W26.** Campaign Emblem and Family

**W27.** Children of Three Races

(Des. Michael Goaman)

## 1963 (21 March). Freedom from Hunger

The stamps were part of a world-wide co-operative effort to focus attention on the problem of hunger and malnutrition.

The watermark is inverted

Types **W26/27**

**A. Ordinary**

| W29 (=SG 634) | Mint | Used |
|---|---|---|
| 2½d. crimson and pink | 25 | 10 |
| a. Line through MPA (Cyls. 1D–1H Dot, R. 7/2) | 20·00 | |
| b. Broken R in FREEDOM (Cyls. 1D–1H No dot, R. 16/2) | 20·00 | |

| W30 (=SG 635) | | |
|---|---|---|
| 1s.3d. bistre-brown and yellow | 1·90 | 1·90 |

| First Day Cover (WP29/30) | | 52·00 |
|---|---|---|

**B. Phosphor (applied flexo.)**

| WP29 (=SG 634p) | | |
|---|---|---|
| 2½d. One band | 3·00 | 1·25 |

| | | |
|---|---|---|
| a. Line through MPA (Cyls. 1D–1H Dot, R. 7/2) | 20·00 | |
| b. Broken R in FREEDOM (Cyls. 1D–1H No dot, R. 16/2) | 20·00 | |

**WP30 (=SG 635p)**

| | | |
|---|---|---|
| 1s.3d. Three bands | 30·00 | 24·00 |
| a. Vert. pair, one stamp with phosphor omitted, the other with short bands | | |
| b. Narrow band at left or right (stamp with vert. margin.) | 42·00 | |

| | |
|---|---|
| First Day Cover (WP29/30) | 52·00 |

The 2½d. value was pre-released at Chipping Norton on 20 March 1963.

W29a, WP29a
An unsuccessful attempt was made to touch this out

W29b, WP29b

**Cylinder Numbers** (Blocks of Four)

**(a) Ordinary**

| | Perforation Type A (E/I) | |
|---|---|---|
| Cylinder Nos. | No dot | Dot |
| 2½d.  1D (pink)–IG (crimson) | 20·00 | 20·00 |
| 1D–1H | 2·50 | 2·50 |
| 1s.3d.  2E (yellow)2G (brown) | 10·00 | 10·00 |

**(b) Phosphor**

| | | |
|---|---|---|
| 2½d.  1D (pink)–1H (crimson) | 16·00 | 16·00 |
| 1s.3d.  2E (yellow)–2G (brown) | £160 | £160 |

Only the lower halves of sheets from the 2½d. 1D–1G cylinders were released.

In the 1s.3d. the cylinder numbers are reversed, the dot pane being on the left and the no dot pane on the right of the printer s double pane sheet.

The 1s.3d. exists showing a single extension hole for alternate horizontal rows in the left margin. Cylinder blocks from the right-hand side of the sheets are identical to those from perforator Type A.

**Minor Constant Flaws**

2½d. Cyls. 1D–1H no dot
9/6 Dot in upper part of second A of CAMPAIGN, OP
15/2 Retouch from base of portrait to M of CAMPAIGN (Th. E11 and F12–13), OP

2½d. Cyls. 1D–1H dot
8/1 and 7/1 Hairline extends from under GN on 8/1 to CAMPAIGN on 7/1, OP
19/1 Retouch on left cheek and jawbone (Th. D10), OP

1s.3d. Cyls. 2E–2G no dot
1/2 Small white line in extreme right wheatsheaf (Th. C6), OP

**Sheet Details**
Sheet size: 120 (6 × 20). Double pane reel-fed

**Sheet markings:**
**Cylinder numbers**: Bottom row below R. 20/5
**Guide holes**:
2½d. Opposite rows 14/15 (boxed), at left (no dot) or right (dot)
1s.3d. Opposite rows 14/15 (boxed), at left (dot) or right (no dot)
**Marginal arrows (photo-etched)**: "W" shaped at top, bottom and sides
**Marginal rule**: At bottom of sheet
**Colour register marks**:
2½d. Opposite rows 2/3 and 18/19, at left (no dot) or right

(dot)
1s.3d. Opposite rows 2/3 and 18/19, at left (dot) or right (no dot)
**Autotron marks (stippled)**:
2½d. Below vertical rows 2/3, no dot pane
1s.3d. Below vertical rows 2/3, dot pane
**Colour designation**:
1s.3d. G2 in brown opposite row 7 at right, no dot, on wide cut margins
**Traffic lights (boxed)**:
2½d. Red, pink opposite R. 20/6, dot pane
1s.3d. Brown, yellow opposite R. 20/6, no dot pane

**Imprimaturs from the National Postal Museum Archives**

**A. Ordinary**
Nos. W29/30 imperforate, watermark Type W. 24

| | |
|---|---|
| Watermark upright (set of 2) | £4500 |

**B. Phosphor**
Nos. WP29/30 imperforate, watermark Type W. 24

| | |
|---|---|
| Watermark upright (set of 2) | £4500 |

**Quantities Sold:**

| | Ordinary | Phosphor |
|---|---|---|
| 2½d. | 97,050,000 | 2,784,920 |
| 1s.3d. | 9,009,000 | 624,960 |

**Withdrawn**: 1.5.64

**W28**. "Paris Conference"

(Des. Reynolds Stone)

## 1963 (7 May). Paris Postal Conference Centenary

A postal conference was held in Paris to commemorate the centenary of the first international meeting of postal authorities held in 1863.

The watermark is inverted

Type **W28**

**A. Ordinary**

**W31 (=SG 636)**

| | Mint | Used |
|---|---|---|
| 6d.  green and mauve | 50 | 50 |
| a. Green omitted | £5500 | |
| b. White spot in frame line (No dot, R. 19/3) | 20·00 | |

| | |
|---|---|
| First Day Cover (W31) | 16·00 |

**B. Phosphor (applied flexo.)**
**WP31 (=SG 636p)**

| | | |
|---|---|---|
| 6d.  Three bands | 6·00 | 7·00 |
| a. Pair, with and without phosphor | 70·00 | |
| b. Horiz. pair; one stamp without phosphor, the other with two bands | 85·00 | |
| c. Narrow band at left or right (stamp with vert. margin) | 8·00 | |

d. White spot in frame line (No dot,
R. 19/3) 25·00

| First Day Cover (WP31) | 37·00 |
| --- | --- |

W31b, WP31d

**Cylinder Numbers** (Blocks of Four)

| | Perforation Type A (E/I) | |
| --- | --- | --- |
| Cylinder Nos. | No dot | Dot |
| 6d. 2A (mauve)–1B (green) Ordinary | 3·25 | 3·25 |
| 6d. 2A–1B Phosphor | 30·00 | 30·00 |

The panes were reversed, the dot being on the left and the no dot on the right.

**Minor Constant Flaws**

6d. Cyls. 2A–1B no dot
1/1 Flaw in oval frame at 11 o'clock (Th. B9) and lack of definition in top right rose (Th. B13), OP
14/6 First N of CONFERENCE appears white, OP
19/5 Dot under R of CENTENARY, OP
20/5 White spot on ivy stem below first E of CONFERENCE and coloured dot in right frame near top (Th. A13), OP

6d. Cyls. 2A–1B dot
14/2 White spot in R of CONFERENCE, OP

**Sheet Details**
Sheet size: 120 (6 × 20). Double pane reel-fed

**Sheet markings:**
**Cylinder numbers:** Below R. 20/5
**Guide holes:** Opposite row 15 (boxed), at left (dot) or right (no dot)
**Marginal arrows (photo-etched):** "W" shaped at top, bottom and sides
**Marginal rule:** At bottom of sheet
**Colour register marks:** Opposite rows 2/3 and 18/19, at left (dot) or right (no dot)
**Autotron marks (stippled):** Bottom margin, dot pane
**Traffic lights (boxed):** Green, mauve opposite R. 20/6, no dot pane

**Imprimaturs from the National Postal Museum Archives**

**A. Ordinary**
No. W31 imperforate, watermark Type W.24

| Watermark upright | £2250 |
| --- | --- |

**B. Phosphor**
No. WP31 imperforate, watermark Type W.24

| Watermark upright | £2250 |
| --- | --- |

**Quantities Sold:** Ordinary 18,536,400; phosphor 1,430,800

**Withdrawn:** 1.6.64

**W29**. Posy of Flowers

(Des. Stanley Scott)

**W30**. Woodland Life

(Des. Michael Goaman)

## 1963 (16 May). National Nature Week

The Council for Nature organised a Nature Week from 18–25 May in order to draw attention to the natural history movement and the importance of wild life conservation.
The 4½d. value was the first stamp of Great Britain to be printed in five colours.
Types **W29/30**

**A. Ordinary**

| **W32** (=SG 637) | | Mint | Used |
| --- | --- | --- | --- |
| 3d. | yellow, green, brown and black | 15 | 15 |
| a. | Caterpillar flaw (Dot, R. 3/2) | 30·00 | |

| **W33** (=SG 638) | | | |
| --- | --- | --- | --- |
| 4½d. | black, blue, yellow, magenta and brown-red | 35 | 35 |
| a. | Nose retouch (Cyl. 2E, R. 14/4) | 20·00 | |

| First Day Cover (W32/3) | 22·00 |
| --- | --- |

**B. Phosphor**
**WP32** (=SG 637p)

| | | | |
| --- | --- | --- | --- |
| 3d. | Three bands, applied photo. | 55 | 60 |
| a. | Narrow band at left or right (stamp with vert. margin) | 2·00 | |
| b. | Caterpillar flaw (Dot, R. 3/2) | 30·00 | |

**WP33** (=SG 638p)

| | | | |
| --- | --- | --- | --- |
| 4½d. | Three bands, applied flexo. | 2·75 | 3·00 |
| a. | Narrow band at left or right (stamp with vert. margin) | 4·00 | |
| b. | Nose retouch (Cyl. 2E. No dot, R. 14/4) | 20·00 | |
| c. | Error. Two bands | | |

| First Day Cover (WP32/3) | 40·00 |
| --- | --- |

No. W32 is known pre-released on 15 May 1963 at Highbury, London.

W32a, WP32b        W33a, WP33b
Several states exist, later
retouched

## Cylinder Numbers (Blocks of Six)

### (a) Ordinary

| Cylinder Nos. | Perforation Type A (E/I) | |
|---|---|---|
| | No dot | Dot |
| 3d.  1A (black)–3B (brown)–1C (green)–1D (yellow) | 2·00 | 2·00 |
| | No dot | |
| | Rows 12/13 | Rows 18/19 |
| 4½d.  1A (brown-red)–1B (yellow)–1C (magenta)–1D (blue)–2E (black) | 2·75 | 2·75 |
| 1A–1B–1C–1D–3E | 4·00 | 5·50 |

| (b) Phosphor | No dot | Dot |
|---|---|---|
| 3d.  1A (black)–3B (brown)–1C (green)–1D (yellow) | 4·75 | 4·75 |
| | No dot | |
| | Rows 12/13 | Rows 18/19 |
| 4½d.  1A (brown-red)–1B (yellow)–1C (magenta)–1D (blue)–2E (black) | 22·00 | 22·00 |
| 1A–1B–1C–1D–3E | 25·00 | 27·00 |

In the 3d. the panes were reversed, the dot being on the left and the no dot on the right.

In the 4½d. there are two sets of cylinder numbers in the left-hand margin (perf. type E) opposite rows 12/13 and 18/19. In position 18/19 the "1D" is in grey-blue superimposed over an additional "1C" in magenta. Also in position 12/13 the black "2" is superimposed over a black "1". The cylinder numbers are engraved more boldly in position 12/13 and are boxed, the others being without boxes.

### Minor Constant Flaws

3d. Cyls 1A–3B–1C–1D no dot
2/1 Retouch to Queen's left jaw (Th. D–E11), OP
2/5 Dot between top of A and T of NATURE, OP
2/6 White line through top of 3 of value, OP
4/4 Green flaw at bottom right foot of I of NATIONAL, OP
5/4 First N of NATIONAL blurred at top left, OP
6/5 Diagonal green line crosses petals of left-hand daisy (Th. B–C3), OP
7/1 Retouch on Queen's left cheek (Th. D11), OP
9/1 Green dot near centre of N of NATURE, OP
9/2 White flaw at top of left-hand buttercup (Th. B2), OP
10/1 Patch of white to left of Queen's right eye (Th. C10), OP
10/4 Green dot at top right of 2, OP
12/6 White patch just above NA of NATIONAL, OP
13/6 Green spot above EK of WEEK, OP
14/1 White spot above 3 of value (Th. E8), OP
16/6 Dark spot to right of Queen's mouth (Th. E11–12), OP
18/3 Retouch above second A of NATIONAL, later re-touched, appearing as a whitish blob (Th. F5), OP

18/5 White flaw under top left buttercup, at right (Th. C2), OP
19/3 Brown flaw to bottom right of T of NATURE, later retouched, OP
19/5 Large green blob above second A of NATIONAL, later touched out, OP
20/4 White dot between top of 3 of value and leaf (Th. E7–8), OP

3d. Cyls. 1A–3B–1C–1D dot
2/3 White dot just left of top of 3 of value, OP
6/6 Retouch under jaw extending to bottom of ear (Th. E10–11), OP
8/1 Brown dot under right leg of last A of NATIONAL, OP
8/3 Retouch by L of NATIONAL (Th. G6), OP
9/6 Brown dot under right leg of second N of NATIONAL, OP
14/1 Retouch above first E of WEEK, OP
14/4 Retouch left of 3 of value (Th. F–78), OP
15/4 White flaw at bottom of oblique stroke in first N of NATIONAL, OP
15/5 Greyish smear over dot of value, OP
16/5 Retouch from mouth to ear (Th. D11), OP
18/4 Green dot above upper lip (Th. D10), OP
19/6 Small white retouch between 63 of 1963 and dark hairline between 3 of value and leaf (Th. F8), OP

4½d. Cyls. 1A–1B–1C–1D–2E no dot and 1A–1B–1C–1D–3E no dot
3/3 Dark spot under fawn (Th. G10), OP
7/1 Yellow patch above fawn's right ear (Th. E11), OP
14/1 Brown spot in second upper leaf from butterfly (Th. B3), OP
19/3 Retouch in background behind woodpecker (Th. E9), OP

### Sheet Details
Sheet size: 120 (6 × 20). 3d. double pane reel-fed; 4½d. single pane reel-fed

**Sheet markings:**
**Cylinder numbers:**
3d. Below row 20/5
4½d. Opposite rows 18/19 and boxed numbers opposite rows 12/13
**Guide holes:**
3d. Opposite rows 14/15 (boxed), at left (dot) or right (no dot)
4½d. Opposite rows 14/15 (boxed), at both sides
**Marginal arrows (photo-etched):** "W" shaped at top, bottom and sides
**Marginal rule:** At bottom of sheet
**Colour register marks:**
3d. Opposite rows 2/3 and 17/19, at left (dot) or right (no dot)
4½d. Opposite rows 3/4 and 17/18, at left (no dot) or right (dot)
**Autotron marks (stippled):**
3d. Between panes vertically, opposite rows 6/9 (seen either in right or left margin)
4½d. Below vertical rows 1/3 and 4/6 but omitted from rows 1/3 in the first printing
**Colour designations (usually trimmed off):**
3d. G BROWN (rows 4/5), G GREEN (rows 6/7), G YELLOW (row; 8/9), G ORANGE (row 13), left margin dot pane reading downwards
4½d. G1 BROWN G2 YELLOW G3 RED G4 BLUE G5 BLACK in left margin reading downwards opposite rows 5/9
**Traffic lights (boxed):**
3d. Yellow, black, green, brown opposite R. 20/6, no dot pane
4½d. Black, blue, magenta, yellow, brown-red opposite rows 19/20 at right

### Imprimaturs from the National Postal Museum Archives

#### A. Ordinary
Nos. WP32/33 imperforate, watermark Type W.24

| Watermark upright (set of 2) | £4500 |
|---|---|

## B. Phosphor

Nos. WP32/33 imperforate, watermark Type W.24

| Watermark upright (set of 2) | £4500 |
|---|---|

**Quantities Sold:**

| | Ordinary | Phosphor |
|---|---|---|
| 3d. | 148,560,000 | 8,640,000 |
| 4½d. | 12,480,000 | 1,140,000 |

**Withdrawn:** 1.6.64

**W31**. Rescue at Sea

**W32**. 19th-century Lifeboat

**W33**. Lifeboatmen

(Des. David Gentleman)

1963 (31 May). Ninth International Lifeboat Conference The International Lifeboat Conferences are held every four years. In 1963 the Conference was held at Edinburgh from 3 to 5 June. Types **W31/33**

### A. Ordinary

**W34** (=SG 639)

| | | Mint | Used |
|---|---|---|---|
| 2½d. | blue, black and red | 25 | 25 |
| a. | Missing neckline (No dot, col. 1) | 20·00 | |
| b. | Shaded diadem (Dot, R. 20/6) | 20·00 | |

**W35** (=SG 640)

| | | | |
|---|---|---|---|
| 4d. | red, yellow, brown, black and blue | 50 | 50 |
| a. | Spot on boom (R. 6/6) | 20·00 | |
| b. | Spot under I (R. 13/3) | 20·00 | |

**W36** (=SG 641)

| | | | |
|---|---|---|---|
| 1s.6d. | sepia, yellow and grey-blue | 3·00 | 3·25 |

| First Day Cover (W34/6) | 35·00 |
|---|---|

### B. Phosphor (applied flexo.)

**WP34** (=SG 639p)

| | | | |
|---|---|---|---|
| 2½d. | One band | 50 | 60 |
| a. | Missing neckline (No dot, col. 1) | 20·00 | |
| b. | Shaded diadem (Dot, R. 20/6) | 20·00 | |
| c. | White flaw in hair (No dot, R. 9/6) | 20·00 | |

**WP35** (=SG 640p)

| | | | |
|---|---|---|---|
| 4d. | Three bands | 50 | 60 |
| a. | Narrow band at left or right (stamp with vert. margin) | 2·00 | |
| b. | Spot on boom (R. 6/6) | 20·00 | |
| c. | Spot under I (R. 13/3) | 20·00 | |

**WP36** (=SG 641p)

| | | | |
|---|---|---|---|
| 1s.6d. | Three bands | 48·00 | 28·00 |
| a. | Narrow band at left or right (stamp with vert. margin) | 60·00 | |

| First Day Cover (W34/6) | 55·00 |
|---|---|

In the 1s.6d. the grey-blue is lighter on the phosphor stamps, presumably in order to show the phosphor more clearly. All values are known pre-released on 30 May.

W34a, WP34a
Occurs on all stamps in first vertical row in varying degrees

W34b, WP34b
Occurred during the course of printing

WP34c

W35a, WP35b    W35b, WP35c

**Cylinder Numbers** (Blocks of Six)

**(a) Ordinary**

| | Perforation Type A (E/I) | | | |
|---|---|---|---|---|
| | No dot | | Dot | |
| Cylinder Nos. | Row 12 | Row 19 | Row 12 | Row 19 |
| 2½d. 3A (red)–3B (black)–1C (blue) | 2·00 | 2·75 | 2·00 | 2·75 |
| 4d. 1A (blue)–1B (black)–1C (red)–1D (brown)–1E (yellow) | 4·50 | 4·50 | † | † |
| | Row 18 | | | |
| 1s.6d. 3A (blue)–1B (sepia)–1C (yellow) | 21·00 | 21·00 | | |

**(b) Phosphor**

| | | Row 12 | Row 19 | | |
|---|---|---|---|---|---|
| 2½d. | 3A (red)–3B (black)–1C (blue) | 4·50 | 4·50 | 4·50 | 4·50 |
| 4d. | 1A (blue)–1B (black)–1C (red)–1D (brown)–1E (yellow) | 4·50 | 4·50 | † | † |
| | | | Row 18 | | |
| 1s.6d. | 3A (blue)–1B (sepia)–1C (yellow) | £300 | £300 | † | † |

In the 2½d. the cylinder numbers in row 12 are shown as A (red)B (black)1C (blue) in left margin (perf. type E) of left pane and the same in the right margin of right pane but without dot after C.

In the 1s.6d. the 1C is shown twice opposite row 18.

**Minor Constant Flaws**

2½d. Cyls. 3A–3B–1C no dot
7/5 Scratch down Queen's face from hair to chin (Th. C–D11), OP
8/5 Scratch continues from hair to shoulder (Th. C–D11), OP
9/1 White scratch on dress above ENC (Th. F12), OP
11/1 Scratch from hair to ear (Th. C–D12), OP
14/3 Black dot below lower lip (Th. D10), OP

2½d. Cyls. 3A–3B–1C dot
3/4 Retouch left of Queen's ear (Th. C11), OP
9/6 Retouch on Queen's forehead (Th. C10), OP
19/6 Pale grey patch over back of shoulder, normal in State 1 (Th. F12–13), OP

4d. Cyls. 1A–1B–1C–1D–1E no dot
1/6 Retouch on Queen's nose (Th. B–C10), OP
3/5 Vertical line of retouching on Queen's face down to shoulder (Th. C–E11), OP
4/2 Vertical black line through shoulder to just above EN (Th. E–F12), OP
13/1 Pale blue streak across top frame line at apex of sail (Th. A5), OP
13/2 Yellow scratch across main sail from mast to rigging (Th. D6), OP
18/2 Black dot over Queen's left eye (Th. C10), OP
20/2 Blue dot on Queen's neck (Th. E11), OP
20/3 Vertical red line down first N of CONFERENCE, OP

1s.6d. Cyls. 3A–1B–1C no dot
6/5 Length of retouching on Queen's collar (Th. E11–12), OP
15/6 Retouch over Queen's right eye (Th. B10), OP

**Sheet Details**
Sheet size: 120 (6 × 20). 2½d. double pane reel-fed; others single pane reel-fed

**Sheet markings:**
**Cylinder numbers:**
2½d. Boxed opposite R. 12/1 (no dot pane) or R. 12/6 (dot pane)
Also opposite R. 19/1 on both panes without box
4d. Boxed opposite R. 12/1 and without box in left margin opposite rows 17/20
1s.6d. Boxed opposite rows 11/12, left margin and unboxed opposite R. 18/1
**Guide holes:**
2½d. Opposite rows 14/15 (boxed), at left (no dot) or right (dot)
4d. and 1s.6d. Opposite rows 14/15 (boxed), at both sides
**Marginal arrows (photo-etched):** "W" shaped, at top, bottom and sides
**Marginal rule:** At bottom of sheet
**Colour register marks:**
2½d. Opposite rows 3/4 and 18/19. at left (no dot) or right (dot)
4d. Opposite rows 2/3 and 17/18, at both sides

1s.6d. Opposite rows 2/4 and 18/19, at both sides
**Autotron marks (stippled):**
2½d. Blue, black, red below vertical rows 4/6 on dot pane
4d. Yellow. brown, black, red, blue below vertical rows 4/6
1s.6d. Yellow, sepia, blue below vertical rows 4/6
**Colour designations (usually trimmed off):**
2½d. G RED G BLACK G BLUE opposite rows 6, 7 and 9 respectively reading upwards at left (no dot) or right (dot)
4d. G YELLOW G BROWN G BLACK G RED G BLUE in right margin reading upwards opposite rows 14/10
1s.6d. G BLUE G BROWN G YELLOW in left margin reading downwards opposite rows 6/9
**Traffic lights (boxed):**
2½d. Blue, black, red opposite R. 20/6, dot pane
4d. Yellow, brown, black, red, blue opposite R. 20/6
1s.6d. Yellow, sepia, blue opposite R. 20/6

**Imprimaturs from the National Postal Museum Archives**

**A. Ordinary**
Nos. W34/36 imperforate, watermark Type W.24

| Watermark upright (set of 3) | £6750 |
|---|---|

**B. Phosphor**
Nos. WP34/36 imperforate, watermark Type W.24

| Watermark upright (set of 3) | £6750 |
|---|---|

**Quantities Sold:**

| | Ordinary | Phosphor |
|---|---|---|
| 2½d. | 81,405,000 | 4,239,000 |
| 4d. | 7,475,040 | 840,000 |
| 1s.6d. | 7,484,780 | 886,000 |

**Withdrawn:** 1.6.64

**W34**. Red Cross

**W35**. Red Cross

**W36**. Red Cross

(Des. H. Bartram)

---

**1963 (15 August). Red Cross Centenary Congress**

The congress which opened in Geneva on 2 September marked the Centenary of the establishment of the Red Cross organisation.
Type **W34/36**
**W37** (=SG 642)

| A. Ordinary | Mint | Used |
|---|---|---|
| 3d. red and deep lilac | 25 | 25 |
| a. Red omitted | £15000 | |
| b. Repaired cross (Cyls. 2A–2B, No. dot, R. 5/6) | 20·00 | |

**W38** (=SG 643)

| | | |
|---|---|---|
| 1s.3d. red, blue and grey | 3·00 | 3·00 |

**W39** (=SG 644)

| | | |
|---|---|---|
| 1s.6d. red, blue and bistre | 3·00 | 3·00 |
| a. Retouch in C of Cross (R. 14/4) | 20·00 | |
| b. Retouch over 1 of 1/6 (R. 16/4) | 20·00 | |

| First Day Cover (W37/9) | | 40·00 |
|---|---|---|

**B. Phosphor (applied flexo.)**
**WP37** (=SG 642p)

| | Mint | Used |
|---|---|---|
| 3d. Three bands | 1·10 | 1·00 |
| a. Red omitted | £35000 | |
| b. Two bands only | | |
| c. Narrow band at left or right (stamp with vert. margin) | 2·00 | |

**WP38** (=SG 643p)

| | | |
|---|---|---|
| 1s.3d. Three bands | 35·00 | 27·00 |
| a. Narrow band at left or right (stamp with vert. margin) | 48·00 | |

**WP39** (=SG 644p)

| | | |
|---|---|---|
| 1s.6d. Three bands | 35·00 | 27·00 |

| | | |
|---|---|---|
| a. Narrow band at left or right (stamp with vert. margin) | | 55·00 |
| b. Retouch in C of Cross (R. 14/4) | | 55·00 |
| c. Retouch over 1 of 1/6 (R. 16/4) | | 55·00 |

| First Day Cover (W37/9) | | 90·00 |
|---|---|---|

W37b

W39a, WP39b

W39b, WP39c

**Cylinder Numbers** (Blocks of Four)

**(a) Ordinary**

| | Perforation Types | | |
|---|---|---|---|
| | A (E/I) | A (E/I) | E (AE/I) |
| Cylinder Nos. | No dot | Dot | Dot |
| 3d. 2A (lilac)–2B (red) | 2·00 | 2·00 | 5·00 |
| 3A–2B | 2·00 | 2·00 | † |
| 3A–3B | 3·00 | 3·00 | † |
| 1s.3d. 1A (grey)–3B– (blue)–1C (red) | 18·00 | † | † |
| 1s.6d. 1A–(blue)– 1B (red)–1C (bistre) | 18·00 | † | † |

**(b) Phosphor**

| | | | |
|---|---|---|---|
| 3d. 3A (lilac)–2B (red) | 6·50 | 6·50 | † |
| 3A–3B | 6·50 | 6·50 | † |
| 1s.3d. 1A–(grey)–3B (blue)–C (red) | £180 | † | † |
| 1s.6d. 1A–(blue)–1B (red)–1C (bistre) | £180 | † | † |

Perforation Type (AE/I) shows an alternate extension hole in the left margin.

**Minor Constant Flaws**

3d. Cyl. 3A no dot in combination with red cyls. 2B or 3B no dot
  2/3 Lilac coloured spot above t of Centenary. Retouched with cyl. 3B (Th. F10–11), OP

3d. Cyl. 2B no dot in combination with lilac cyls. 2A or 3A no dot
  4/1 Red retouch in top left centre of cross (Th. D4), OP
  7/3 Pale centre to cross (with cyl. 3A only), OP
  3d. Cyl. 3A dot in combination with red cyls. 2B or 3B dot
  4/3 Coloured spur on C of Congress (Th. G9), OP
  15/2 Scratch above 3D. Retouched with cyl. 3B (Th. B8–C9), OP
  17/5 Retouching in and around D of 3D (Th. D9), OP

3d. Cyl. 2B dot in combination with lilac cyls. 2A or 3A dot

16/1 Red retouches in left arm and top left centre of cross
(Th. D3–4), OP
19/1 Red retouch in lower arm of cross (Th. E4), OP
1s.3d. Cyls. 1A–3B–1C no dot
11/4 Diagonal scratch from Queen's nose to jaw (Th. D7),
OP
12/1 White spot to left of Queen's earring (Th. D8), OP
12/5 Dark patch to right of Queen's left eye (Th. C7), OP
15/3 Line through words Red Cross, OP
18/4 Large retouch on Queen's neck (Th. E7), OP
1s.6d. Cyls. 1A–1B–1C no dot
15/3 Large retouch in right arm of cross (Th. C–D8), OP

**Sheet Details**
Sheet size: 120 (6 × 20). 3d. double pane reel-fed; others single
pane reel-fed

**Sheet markings:**
**Cylinder numbers**: Opposite R. 19/1, boxed
**Guide holes:**
3d. Opposite rows 14/15 (boxed), at left (no dot) or right (dot)
1s.3d. and 1s.6d. Opposite rows 14/15 (boxed), at both sides
**Marginal arrows (photo-etched):** "W" shaped, at top, bottom
and sides
**Marginal rule**: At bottom of sheet
**Colour register marks:**
3d. Opposite rows 2/3 and 18/19, at left (no dot) or right (dot)
1s.3d. and 1s.6d. Opposite rows 17/19, at both sides
**Autotron marks (stippled):**
3d. Lilac, red below vertical rows 2/3 on no dot panes
1s.3d. Grey, blue, red below vertical rows 1/3
1s.6d. Blue, red, bistre below vertical rows 1/3 and 4/6
**Colour designations (usually trimmed off):**
3d. G RED in right margin opposite rows 5/6 (Cyls. 3A3B dot)
1s.3d. G1 GREY G2 BLUE G3 YELLOW in right margin reading
downwards opposite rows 9/4
1s.6d. None
**Traffic lights (boxed):**
3d. Lilac, red opposite R. 19/6
1s.3d. Grey, blue, red opposite R. 19/6
1s.6d. Blue, red, bistre opposite R. 19/6

**Imprimaturs from the National Postal Museum Archives**

**A. Ordinary**
Nos. W37/39 imperforate, watermark Type W.24

| Watermark upright (set of 3) | £6750 |
|---|---|

**B. Phosphor**
Nos. WP37/39 imperforate, watermark Type W.24

| Watermark upright (set of 3) | £6750 |
|---|---|

**Quantities Sold:**

|  | Ordinary | Phosphor |
|---|---|---|
| 3d. | 157,277,800 | 10,349,280 |
| 1s.3d. | 7,278,120 | 929,040 |
| 1s.6d. | 6,995,160 | 1,038,840 |

**Withdrawn**: 1.9.64

**W37**. Commonwealth Cable

CANCELLED

B

(Des. Peter Gauld)

**1963 (3 December). Opening of COMPAC**

The Trans-Pacific Cable (COMPAC) was the first telephone
cable to be laid across the Pacific Ocean. It links Canada with
Australia and New Zealand by way of Hawaii and Fiji.
Type **W37**
**A. Ordinary**

| **W40** (=SG 645) | | Mint | Used |
|---|---|---|---|
| 1s.6d. | blue and black | 2·75 | 2·50 |
| a. | Black omitted | £7500 | |
| s. | "Cancelled", Type B, in red | 35·00 | |

| First Day Cover (W40) | 28·00 |
|---|---|

**B. Phosphor (applied flexo.)**
**WP40** (=SG 645p)

| W37 | 1s.6d. | Three bands | 16·00 | 15·50 |
|---|---|---|---|---|
| | a. | Left band omitted | 45·00 | |
| | b. | Narrow band at left or right (stamp with vert. margin) | 23·00 | |

| First Day Cover (WP40) | 40·00 |
|---|---|

The stamp handstamped "CANCELLED" was applied to
Philatelic Bulletin No. 3 (November 1963) so that it only exists
unused, no gum.
No. WP40 has a "blue" phosphor overprint but it is
known with bands giving a short greenish after-glow after
irradiation to ultra-violet light. It is probable that this was
due to contaminated phosphor rather than the use of "green"
phosphor.

**Cylinder Numbers** (Blocks of Four)

| | | Perforation Type F (P/E). No dot | |
|---|---|---|---|
| | Cyl. Nos. | Ordinary | Phosphor |
| 1s.6d. | 1A (blue)–1B (black) | 15·00 | 75·00 |

**Minor Constant Flaws**
1s.6d. Cyls. 1A–1B no dot
17/6 Bulge at top of figure 1 of value (Th. F10), OP
19/1 Extra white dot on Queen's right eye (Th. C10), OP

**Sheet Details**
Sheet size: 120 (6 × 20). Single pane reel-fed

**Sheet markings:**
**Cylinder numbers**: Opposite R. 19/1, boxed
**Guide holes**: at top above R. 1/2 and at bottom below R. 20/4,
cutting marginal arrow
**Marginal arrows (photo-etched):** "W" shaped, at top, bottom
and sides
**Marginal rule**: At bottom of sheet
**Colour register marks**: Opposite rows 1/2 and 17/8, at both
sides
**Autotron marks (stippled)**: Below vertical rows 2/3
**Colour designations**: G1 BLUE (row 9), G2 BLACK (row 12), left

margin
**Traffic lights:** Black, blue (boxed), opposite R. 19/6

**Imprimaturs from the National Postal Museum Archives**

**A. Ordinary**
No. W40 imperforate, watermark Type W.24

| Watermark upright | £2250 |
|---|---|

**B. Phosphor**
No. WP40 imperforate, watermark Type W.24

| Watermark upright | £2250 |
|---|---|

**Quantities Sold:** Ordinary 8,015,880; phosphor 824,280

**Withdrawn:** 1.9.64

**W38**. Puck and Bottom
*(A Midsummer Night s Dream)*

**W39**. Feste
*(Twelfth Night)*

**W40**. Balcony Scene
*(Romeo and Juliet)*

**W41**. Eve of Agincourt
*(Henry V)*

(All the above des. David Gentleman)

**W42**. Hamlet contemplating Yorick's Skull *(Hamlet)*

Des. Christopher and Robin Ironside.
Recess printed, Bradbury, Wilkinson)

**1964 (23 April). Shakespeare Festival**

Issued on the occasion of the 400th Anniversary of the Birth of William Shakespeare. An additional feature of this issue was the introduction of Presentation Packs by the then, General Post Office. The packs include one set of stamps and details of the designs, the designer and the stamp printer. They were issued for this and almost all later commemorative issues.

The 2s.6d. is perf. 11 × 12, comb.

Types **W38/42**

## A. Ordinary
**W41** (=SG 646)

| | | | Mint | Used |
|---|---|---|---|---|
| | 3d. | (1) Yellow-bistre, black and deep violet-blue | 15 | 15 |
| | | (2) Bistre-brown, black and deep violet-blue | 15 | 15 |
| | a. | Black dots across Puck's head (Dot, R. 7/6) | 20·00 | |
| | b. | "Cancelled", Type B | £175 | |

**W42** (=SG 647)

| | | | | Mint | Used |
|---|---|---|---|---|---|
| W39 | 6d. | (1) Yellow, orange, black and yellow-olive | | 30 | 30 |
| | | (2) Yellow, orange, black and olive-green | | 40 | 30 |
| | a. | Broken H (R. 12/3) | | 20·00 | |
| | b. | Missing floorboards (R. 20/1 and 20/2) | | 20·00 | |
| | c. | Olive spots by Queen's mouth (R. 9/6) | | 20·00 | |
| | d. | "Cancelled", Type B | | £175 | |

**W43** (=SG 648)

| | | Mint | Used |
|---|---|---|---|
| 1s.3d. | (1) Cerise, blue-green, black and sepia | 18·00 | |
| | (2) Cerise, turquoise, black and sepia | 75 | 1·00 |
| a. | Watermark inverted | £800 | |
| b. | Large pearl (Dot, R. 13/2) | 10·00 | |
| c. | "Cancelled", Type B (Shade (1)) | £175 | |

**W44** (=SG 649)

| | | Mint | Used |
|---|---|---|---|
| 1s.6d. | (1) Violet, turquoise, black and blue | 1·00 | 85 |
| | (2) Pale violet, turquoise, black and blue | 2·75 | 2·75 |
| a. | Watermark inverted | | £1300 |
| b. | "Cancelled", Type B | £200 | |

**W45** (=SG 650)

| | | | Mint | Used |
|---|---|---|---|---|
| W42 | 2s.6d. | (1) Deep slate-purple | 2·75 | 2·75 |
| | | (2) Blackish brown | 5·00 | 4·00 |
| | | (3) Jet-black | £550 | £225 |
| | a. | Watermark inverted | £550 | |
| | b. | "Cancelled", Type B (jet-black shade) | £450 | |

| | |
|---|---|
| First Day Cover (W41/5) | 12·00 |

| | |
|---|---|
| Presentation Pack (W41/5) | 22·00 |

**B. Phosphor (Three bands) (3d. applied photo.; others flexo.)**
**WP41** (=SG 646p)

| | | | Mint | Used |
|---|---|---|---|---|
| | 3d. | (1) Yellow-bistre, black and deep violet-blue | 25 | 30 |
| | | (2) Bistre-brown, black and deep violet-blue | 30 | 25 |
| | a. | Narrow band at left or right (stamp with vert. margin) | 2·00 | |
| | b. | Black dots across Puck's head (Dot, R. 7/6) | 20·00 | |

**WP42** (=SG 647p)

| | | Mint | Used |
|---|---|---|---|
| 6d. | Yellow, orange, black and yellow-olive | 75 | 1·00 |
| a. | Narrow band at left or right (stamp with vert. margin) | 2·75 | |
| b. | Broken H (R. 12/3) | 20·00 | |
| c. | Missing floorboards (R. 20/1 and 20/2) | 20·00 | |

| | | | | |
|---|---|---|---|---|
| | d. | Olive spots by Queen's mouth (R. 9/6) | 20·00 | |

**WP43** (=SG 648p)

| | | Mint | Used |
|---|---|---|---|
| 1s.3d. | Cerise, turquoise, black and sepia | 4·00 | 6·50 |
| a. | Watermark inverted | £325 | |
| b. | Narrow band at left or right (stamp with vert. margin) | 6·00 | |
| c. | Large pearl (Dot, R. 13/2) | 20·00 | |

**WP44** (=SG 649p)

| | | Mint | Used |
|---|---|---|---|
| 1s.6d. | Violet, turquoise, black and blue | 8·00 | 8·00 |
| a. | Narrow band at left or right (stamp with vert. margin) | 10·00 | |

| | |
|---|---|
| First Day Cover (WP41/4) | 17·00 |

**Shades.** The listed shades of the 6d. to 2s.6d. result from different printings. The 3d. and 6d. shades are quite distinct, the blue-green shade of the 1s.3d. comes from the scarce first printing from cylinder 1B, and although the pale violet in the 1s.6d. may only be due to under-inking, it came from part of the second printing. There were three printings of the 2s.6d. which produced a number of shades, but they fall into the groups listed. The rare jet-black shade exists, possibly from proof sheets issued in error. Most examples have a "CANCELLED" overprint No. W45b.

The 3d. is known with yellow-bistre missing on the top two-thirds of the figures of Puck and Bottom. This occurred on the top row only of a sheet.

W41a, WP41b

W42a, WP42b
Also grey patch on Shakespeare's right cheek. Both later retouched

W42c, WP42d

W42b, WP42c
Other less prominent states of missing floorboards also occur on R. 19/1, 19/2, 19/6 and 20/6

W43a, WP43c

**Cylinder Numbers** (Blocks of Four)

**(a) Ordinary**

| | | Perforation Type A (E/I) | |
|---|---|---|---|
| Cylinder Nos. | | No dot | Dot |
| 3d. | 1A (violet-blue)–1B (black)–1C (bistre) | 1·25 | 1·25 |
| 6d. | 1A (olive-green)–1B (orange)–1C (yellow)–1D (black) | 12·00* | † |
| | Perforation Type A(T) (E/P) | | |
| 1s.3d. | 3A (sepia)–1B (blue-green)–1C (cerise)–1D–(black) | 90·00 | 90·00 |

| 3A–2B (turquoise)–1C–1D | 4·50 | 4·50 |
|---|---|---|
| 1s.6d. 1A (blue)–1B (violet)–1C (black)–1D (turquoise) | 7·00 | 7·00 |

## (b) Phosphor

| | Perforation Type A (E/I) | |
|---|---|---|
| | No dot | Dot |
| 3d. 1A (violet-blue)–1B (black)–1C (bistre) | 2·00 | 2·00 |
| 6d. 1A (olive-green)–1B (orange)–1C (yellow)–1D (black) | 15·00* | † |

| | Perforation Type A(T) (E/P) | |
|---|---|---|
| | No dot | Dot |
| 1s.3d. 3A (sepia)–2B (turquoise)–1C (cerise)–1D (black) | 28·00 | 25·00 |
| 1s.6d. 1A (blue)–1B (violet)–1C (black)–1D (turquoise) | 40·00 | 40·00 |

The 3d. no dot cylinders exist with a false dot after the 1B but this was later removed. In the dot cylinders of the 1s.6d. the dots appear to the left of 1C and 1D.

**Plate Numbers** (Blocks of Four)
Perforation Type A (E/I)

| 2s.6d. Plate 1 | 15·00 |
|---|---|
| Plate 1A | 15·00 |

## Minor Constant Flaws

3d. Cyls. 1A–1B–1C no dot
9/5 White scratch on boards above AL (Th. F/9), OP
19/1 White line in floorboard division above S of FESTIVAL (Th. G8), OP
20/1 White patch on Queen's collar, later retouched (Th. E12), OP

3d. Cyls. 1A–1B–1C dot
2/5 White patch on floorboards above F (Th. G7), OP
7/5 Retouches on Queen's left cheek, later partly re-touched (Th. D11), OP
11/5 Retouch below Queen's left eye (Th. C11), OP
16/2 White spur to bottom arc of 3, OP
20/1 Dark flaw in stage above VA, later retouched (Th. G9), OP

1s.3d. Cyls. 3A–2B–1C–1D no dot
18/2 Outline of Shakespeare's nose cut short, later corrected (Th. C3), OP

1s.6d. Cyls. 1A–1B–1C–1D no dot
1/6 White flaw on stage above EAR (Th. F4-G5), OP
18/1 Black flaw at base of tent over last A of SHAKE-SPEARE (Th. F5), OP
20/2 Vertical scratches on Queen's face (Th. BD11), OP

1s.6d. Cyls. 1A–1B–1C–1D dot
13/3 Flaw on stage above EA (Th. G4), OP

## Sheet Details
**Sheet sizes**:
3d. 120 (6 × 20). Double pane reel-fed
6d. 120 (6 × 20). Single pane reel-fed
1s.3d., 1s.6d. 120 (6 × 20). Double panes sheet-fed
2s.6d. 40 (4 × 10). Double pane sheet-fed
The 1s.3d. and 1s.6d. were printed by the Linotype and Machinery No. 4 machine, a rotary sheet-fed double pane machine.

**Sheet markings**:
**Cylinder numbers**: Opposite R. 19/1, boxed
Plate numbers (2s.6d.): Bottom margin below vertical rows 5/6
**Guide holes**:
3d. Opposite rows 14/15 (boxed), at left (no dot) or right (dot)
6d. Opposite row 13 (boxed), at both sides
1s.3d. Opposite rows 15/16 (boxes only, no holes), at left (no dot) or right (dot)

1s.6d. Opposite rows 14/15 (boxes only, no holes), at left (no dot) or right (dot)
2s.6d. Opposite row 6 (unboxed), at left (Plate 1) or right (Plate 1A)
False boxes appear in both margins opposite rows 14/15 in the 6d. value and these are deleted by a diagonal black line.
**Marginal arrows (photo-etched)**: "W" shaped, at top, bottom and sides (none on 2s.6d.)
**Marginal rule**: At bottom of sheet (except 2s.6d.)
**Colour register marks**:
3d. Opposite rows 2 and 17/18, at left (no dot) or right (dot)
6d. Opposite rows 1/3 and 17/18, at both sides (usually trimmed off)
**Others**: none
**Autotron marks**:
3d. In central gutter alongside rows 14/16
6d. Below vertical rows 1/3: black (stippled), olive (solid), orange (stippled), yellow (solid)
Others, none
**Colour designations (usually trimmed)**:
3d. G BLUE (rows 13/12), G BLACK (rows 9/8), G YELLOW (rows 5/4) reading upwards,
right margin dot pane
Others, none
**Traffic lights (boxed)**: All R. 19/6
3d. Violet-blue, black, bistre
6d. Black, yellow, orange, olive
1s.3d. Black, cerise, turquoise, sepia
1s.6d. Turquoise, black, violet, blue
**Essays**
Set of four gummed perforated esays mounted on Harrison & Sons presentation cards with the face value n black instead of white. .................................................................£24000

**Imprimaturs from the National Postal Museum Archives**

**A. Ordinary**
Nos. W41/45 imperforate, watermark Type W.24

| Watermark upright (set of 5) | £11000 |
|---|---|

**B. Phosphor**
Nos. WP41/44 imperforate, watermark Type W.24

| Watermark upright (set of 4) | £9000 |
|---|---|

**Quantities Sold**:

| | Ordinary | Phosphor |
|---|---|---|
| 3d. | 133,670,000 | 10,427,880 |
| 6d. | 19,238,200 | 1,318,560 |
| 1s.3d. | 7,067,200 | 727,800 |
| 1s.6d. | 6,910,120 | 657,120 |
| 2s.6d. | 3,664,920 | — |
| Pack | 108,541 | — |

**Withdrawn**: 31.3.65 (3d. ordinary sold out earlier)

**W43**. Flats near Richmond Park ("Urban Development")

**W44**. Shipbuilding Yards, Belfast ("Industrial Activity")

**W45**. Beddgelert Forest Park, Snowdonia ("Forestry")

**W46**. Nuclear Reactor, Dounreay ("Technological Development")

(Des. Dennis Bailey)

---

### 1964 (1 July). 20th International Geographical Congress

The first International Geographical Congress was held in 1871; since then one has normally been held at four-yearly intervals. London was chosen in 1964 and the Congress lasted from 20 to 28 July.

Types **W43/46**

**A. Ordinary**

| **W46** (=SG 651) | | Mint | Used |
|---|---|---|---|
| 2½d. | black, olive-yellow, olive-grey and turquoise-blue | 10 | 10 |
| a. | Short line under 2½d. (various) | 10·00 | |
| b. | Line repaired (No dot, R. 18/5) | 20·00 | |
| c. | Retouched lawn (No dot, R. 11/1 and 11/6) | 20·00 | |

| **W47** (=SG 652) | | | |
|---|---|---|---|
| 4d. | orange-brown, red-brown, rose, black and violet | 30 | 30 |
| a. | Violet (face value) omitted | £300 | |
| b. | Red-brown (dock walls) omitted | | |
| c. | Violet and red-brown (dock walls) omitted | £550 | |
| d. | Watermark inverted | £850 | |

| | | | |
|---|---|---|---|
| e. | Scarred neck (R. 20/3) | 20·00 | |

| **W48** (=SG 653) | | | |
|---|---|---|---|
| 8d. | yellow-brown, emerald, green and black | 75 | 85 |
| a. | Green (lawn) omitted | £20000 | |
| b. | Watermark inverted | £1700 | |

| **W49** (=SG 654) | | | |
|---|---|---|---|
| 1s.6d. | yellow-brown, pale pink, black and brown | 3·50 | 3·50 |
| a. | Watermark inverted | 45·00 | |
| b. | Neck flaw (R. 8/4) | 20·00 | |

| First Day Cover (WP46/9) | 22·00 |
|---|---|
| Presentation Pack | £160 |

**B. Phosphor (2½d. applied photo.; others flexo.)**

| **WP46** (=SG 651p) | | | |
|---|---|---|---|
| 2½d. | One band | 40 | 50 |
| a. | Short line under 2½d. (various) | 12·00 | |
| b. | Line repaired (No dot, R. 18/5) | 20·00 | |
| c. | Retouched lawn (No dot, R. 11/1 and 11/6) | 20·00 | |

| **WP47** (=SG 652p) | | | |
|---|---|---|---|
| 4d. | Three bands | 1·25 | 1·25 |
| a. | Narrow band at left or right (stamp with vert. margin) | 2·25 | |
| b. | Scarred neck (R. 20/3) | 20·00 | |

| **WP48** (=SG 653p) | | | |
|---|---|---|---|
| 8d. | Three bands | 2·50 | 2·75 |
| a. | Narrow band at left or right (stamp with vert. margin) | 3·50 | |

| **WP49** (=SG 654p) | | | |
|---|---|---|---|
| 1s.6d. | Three bands | 28·00 | 22·00 |
| a. | Narrow band at left or right (stamp with vert. margin) | 35·00 | |
| b. | Neck flaw (R. 8/4) | 20·00 | |

| First Day Cover (WP46/9) | 22·00 |
|---|---|

A pair of No. WP47 exists with phosphor bands printed diagonally on the gum but omitted from the printed side. This was due to a paper fault which affected the corner of the sheet. A used example of the 4d. (No. W47), is known with the red-brown omitted.

W46a, WP46a

The short lower line occurs on no dot R.5/5, 9/5 (most marked) and 10/2 and on dot R.3/44/5 and 7/5 (short at left). In no. W46b and WP46b the line has been repaired but there remains a short gap unfilled

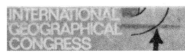

W46c, WP46c

The illustration shows the retouch on R.11/1. On 11/6 it starts further over the line and is less extensive.

W47e, WP47b

W49b, WP49b
Later retouched

## Cylinder Numbers (Blocks of Four)

### (a) Ordinary

| | Cylinder Nos. | Perforation Types | | |
|---|---|---|---|---|
| | | A (E/I) No dot | A (E/I) Dot | F (P/E) No dot |
| 2½d. | 3D (black)–1C (yellow)–1B (grey)–1A (blue) | 1·00 | 1·00 | † |
| 4d. | 1E (orange-brown)–1D (red-brown)–1C (rose)–1B (black)–1A (violet) | † | † | 2·50 |
| 8d. | 1D (brown)–1C (green)–1B (emerald)–1A (black) | 9·00 | † | 5·00 |
| 1s.6d. | 1D (yellow-brown)–1C (pink)–1B (black)–1A (brown) | 20·00 | † | † |

### (b) Phosphor

| | | | | |
|---|---|---|---|---|
| 2½d. | 3D (black)–1C (yellow)–1B (grey)–1A (blue) | 3·00 | 3·00 | † |
| 4d. | 1E (orange-brown)–1D (red-brown)–1C (rose)–1B (black)–1A (violet) | † | † | 7·00 |
| 8d. | 1D (brown)–1C (green)–1B (emerald)–1A (black) | † | † | 14·00 |
| 1s.6d. | 1D (yellow-brown)–1C (pink)–1B (black)–1A (brown) | £150 | † | £140 |

## Minor Constant Flaws

2½d. Cyls. 3D–1C–1B–1A no dot
  2/4 Black line from Queen's left eye to base of back of diadem, later retouched and showing as faint white line (Th. C12–13), O
  4/1 Blue spot on Queen's collar, later retouched (Th. E12), OP
  12/3 Green spot at foot of hills above second N of INTERNATIONAL (Th. F5), OP
  15/2 Blue dot left of oval and above left end of upper value bar, later retouched (Th. E10), OP
  19/3 Green blob above 2 of 20th (Th. E1), OP
  20/3 White dot in portrait oval above right corner of central cross of crown (Th. A12), OP
  20/5 White flaw in hair below central cross of crown (Th. B11), OP

2½d. Cyls. 3D–1C–1B–1A dot
  7/5 Small retouch to right of Queen's nostril (Th. C11), OP
  9/3 Retouch by Queen's left eye, later retouched on phosphor only (Th. B–C12), OP
  12/3 White flaw in h of 20th, OP
  12/5 Blue dot by grey panel opposite value (Th. G10), OP
  13/5 Blue scratch on Queen's left cheek (Th. C11), OP
  15/2 Two diagonal white lines above central cross of crown (Th. A12), OP
  15/4 Blue patch in hills above black arrow (Th. D8) and slight retouch to right of L of GEOGRAPHICAL, OP
  15/5 White flaw in hair above Queen's left eye (Th. B12), OP
  17/4 Retouch on Queen's neck above collar (Th. E12), OP

4d. Cyls. 1E–1D–1C–1B–1A no dot
  1/1 Horizontal black line joining centre of 2 to left frame line, OP

1/2 Black spur on frame line below last S in CONGRESS, OP
1/5 White dot in panel to right of rear cross of crown (Th. B13), OP
1/6 Small flaw under right arm of N of CONGRESS (Th. H2), OP
3/5 White flaw on left of crown (Th. A11), OP
3/6 White spike projecting from back of neck (Th. D12), OP
6/1 Several small black dots on collar (Th. E11–12), OP
7/1 Horizontal line between Queen's lips and ear (Th. C11–12), OP
7/2 Similar retouch but lower down (Th. D11–12), OP
8/1 Violet dot to right of d in value (Th. G12), OP
14/2 Horizontal grey line through NATION, OP
16/5 Broken R in GEOGRAPHICAL, OP
18/1 Break in vertical lines above AT of INTERNATIONAL and small black dot to left of break (Th. E3), OP
20/2 Black dot above Queen's nostril (Th. D11), and break in vertical frame line to left of value, OP
20/5 Corner break in frame line left of value (Th. H9), OP
  Numerous other minor frame breaks are known

8d. Cyls. 1D–1C–1B–1A no dot
  1/1 Extensive retouching to back of Queen's collar (Th. E12–13), OP
  4/2 Dark patch in front of Queen's neck (Th. D–E11), OP
  4/6 Nick in final A of GEOGRAPHICAL, OP
  6/6 Retouch at back of Queen's collar (Th. E13), OP
  7/6 Shading on Queen's forehead, later retouched appearing as white patch (Th. B11–12), OP
  16/4–6 Green line runs through emerald field below brown area, OP
  17/5 Horizontal white line across Queen's face (Th. C11–12), OP
  18/5 Two horizontal white lines across face and chin (Th. C–D11–12), OP

1s.6d. Cyls. 1D–1C–1B–1A no dot
  1/1 Dark flaw in front of Queen's collar (Th. E11), OP
  2/2 White scratch across necklace (Th. D12), OP
  13/3 White dot in panel below rear cross in crown (Th. B13), OP
  20/6 Dark spot below Queen's nose (Th. C12), OP

## Sheet Details
Sheet size: 120 (6 × 20). 2½d. double pane reel-fed; others single pane sheet-fed

**Sheet markings:**
**Cylinder numbers:** Opposite rows 19/20 at left, boxed
**Guide holes:**
2½d. Opposite rows 14/15 (boxed), at left (no dot) or right (dot)
**Others:** Usually trimmed off
**Marginal arrows (photo-etched):** "W" shaped, at top, bottom and sides
**Marginal rule:** At bottom of sheet
**Colour register marks:**
2½d. Opposite rows 2/3 and 18/19, at left (no dot) or right (dot)
**Others:** Above and below vertical rows 1 and 5/6
**Autotron marks (stippled):**
2½d. Black, blue, yellow, grey opposite rows 6/8, at right (no dot) or left (dot)
**Others:** Trimmed off
**Colour designations (usually trimmed):**
2½d. G1 GREY G2 DARK GREEN G3 YELLOW G4 BLACK reading upwards, right margin dot pane
**Others:** Trimmed off
**Traffic lights (boxed):** All opposite rows 19/20 at right
2½d. Black, yellow, blue, grey
4d. Orange-brown, red-brown, rose, black, violet
8d. Brown, green, black, emerald
1s.6d. Order not known

**Imprimaturs from the National Postal Museum Archives**

**A. Ordinary**
Nos. W46/49 imperforate, watermark Type W.24

| | |
|---|---|
| Watermark upright (set of 4) | £9000 |

**B. Phosphor**
Nos. WP46/49 imperforate, watermark Type W.24

| | |
|---|---|
| Watermark upright (set of 4) | £9000 |

**Quantities Sold:**

| | Ordinary | Phosphor |
|---|---|---|
| 2½d. | 109,768,120 | 3,377,520 |
| 4d. | 15,241,680 | 577,800 |
| 8d. | 8,226,800 | 465,720 |
| 1s.6d. | 10,154,040 | 519,000 |
| Pack | 29,952 | — |

**Withdrawn:** 2.7.65 (2½d. ordinary sold out earlier)

**W47**. Spring Gentian

**W48**. Dog Rose

**W49**. Honeysuckle

**W50**. Fringed Water Lily

(Des. Sylvia and Michael Goaman)

**1964 (5 August). Tenth International Botanical Congress**

Botanical Congresses are held every five years each alternate one taking place in Europe. The King of Sweden was Hon. President of the 1964 Congress, which took place in Edinburgh. Types **W47/50**
**A. Ordinary**
**W50** (=SG 655)

| | | Mint | Used |
|---|---|---|---|
| 3d. | violet, blue and sage-green | 25 | 25 |
| a. | Blue omitted | £20000 | |
| b. | Sage-green omitted | £22000 | |
| c. | Broken petal (Cyls. 3A–1B–1C Dot, R. 1/2) | 30·00 | |
| s. | "Cancelled", Type B | 45·00 | |

**W51** (=SG 656)

| | | | |
|---|---|---|---|
| 6d. | apple-green, rose, scarlet and green | 50 | 50 |
| b. | Rose hip flaw (No dot, R. 2/2) | 25·00 | |
| s. | "Cancelled", Type B | 45·00 | |

**W52** (=SG 657)

| | | | |
|---|---|---|---|
| 9d. | lemon, green, lake and rose-red | 1·75 | 2·25 |
| a. | Green (leaves) omitted | £22000 | |
| b. | Watermark inverted | 50·00 | |
| c. | Line through INTER (R. 1/1) | 30·00 | |
| s. | "Cancelled", Type B | 45·00 | |

**W53** (=SG 658)

| | | | |
|---|---|---|---|
| 1s.3d. | yellow, emerald, reddish violet and grey-green | 2·50 | 2·50 |
| a. | Yellow (flowers) omitted | £45000 | |
| b. | Watermark inverted | £2000 | |
| c. | Fruit flaw (R. 14/2) | 25·00 | |
| s. | "Cancelled", Type B | 45·00 | |

| | | |
|---|---|---|
| First Day Cover (W50/3) | | 24·00 |

| | |
|---|---|
| Presentation Pack | £160 |

**B. Phosphor** (applied flexo.)

**WP50** (=SG 655p)

| | | | |
|---|---|---|---|
| 3d. | Three bands | 40 | 40 |
| a. | Right band omitted | | |
| b. | Narrow band at left or right (stamp with vert. margin) | 2·00 | |
| c. | Broken petal (Cyls. 3A–1B–1C Dot, R. 1/2) | 30·00 | |

**WP51** (=SG 656p)

| | | | |
|---|---|---|---|
| 6d. | Three bands | 2·50 | 2·75 |
| a. | Four bands | 18·00 | |
| b. | Narrow band at left or right (stamp with vert. margin) | 3·50 | |
| c. | Rose hip flaw (No dot, R. 2/2) | 25·00 | |

**WP52** (=SG 657p)

| | | | |
|---|---|---|---|
| 9d. | Three bands | 4·50 | 4·00 |
| a. | Narrow band at left or right (stamp with vert. margin) | 5·50 | |
| b. | Line through INTER (R. 1/1) | 30·00 | |

**WP53** (=SG 658p)

| | | | |
|---|---|---|---|
| 1s.3d | Three hands | 25·00 | 20·00 |
| a. | Narrow band at left or right (stamp with vert. margin) | 30·00 | |
| b. | Fruit flaw (R. 14/2) | 45·00 | |

| | | |
|---|---|---|
| First Day Cover (WP50/3) | | 40·00 |

Nos. W50s/53s have the "CANCELLED" handstamp as used on No. W40 applied in black spread over two values. It was used on sample first day covers distributed by the Post Office with the notice announcing the service.

All values were accidentally released before the official date of issue at several post offices and by the Philatelic Bureau. The earliest known date is 27 July.

The, possibly unique, example of No. W53a shows the yellow printed on the gummed side due to a paper fold.

Normal
Petal is broken where the violet overlaps the blue
W50c, WP50c

W51b, WP51c
White flaw in rose hip

W53b, WP53b
Grey-green overlaps centre of fruit

W52c, WP52b

**Cylinder Numbers** (Blocks of Four)

**(a) Ordinary**

| | Cylinder Nos | A (E/I) No dot | A (E/I) Dot | F (P/E) No dot |
|---|---|---|---|---|
| 3d. | 2A (violet)–1B (blue)–1C (sage-green) | 2·00 | 2·00 | † |
| | 3A–1B–1C | 2·00 | 2·00 | † |
| 6d. | 1D (apple-green)–1C (rose)–1B (scarlet)–1A (green) | 3·00 | 3·00 | † |
| 9d. | 2D (lemon)–2C (green)–2B (lake)–2A (rose-red) | † | † | 10·00 |
| 1s.3d. | 1D (yellow)–1C (emerald)–1B (reddish violet)–1A (grey-green) | † | † | 14·00 |

*Perforation Types*

**(b) Phosphor**

| | | | | |
|---|---|---|---|---|
| 3d. | 3A (violet)–1B (blue)–1C (sage-green) | 2·50 | 2·50 | † |
| 6d. | 1D (apple-green)–1C (rose)–1B (scarlet)–1A (green) | 16·00 | 14·00 | † |
| 9d. | 2D (lemon)–2C (green)–2B (lake)–2A (rose- red) | † | † | 24·00 |
| 1s.3d. | 1D (yellow)–1C (emerald)–1B (reddish violet)–1A (grey-green) | † | † | £120 |

**Minor Constant Flaws**

3d. Cyls. 2A–1B–1C and 3A–1B–1C no dot
    1/4 White dot between 3rd and 4th fruits below portrait (Th. E12), OP
    2/4 Curved white line across right petal of left Gentian (Th. C3), OP
    6/1 Small white vertical line on same petal as above (Th. C–D3), OP

3d. Cyl. 3A no dot
    2/5 Retouch on upper lip, OP
    7/5 Blue dash on small leaf pointing left below first flower (Th. F2), OP
    10/5 White dot below first S of CONGRESS, OP
    12/5 Line of damage extends from Queen's upper lip to base of ear (Th. C10–12), OP
    12/6 Line of damage extends from Queen's right cheek across nose to ear (Th. C10–12), OP
    13/1 Clear line of white dots joins SS of CONGRESS, OP
    19/3 White flaw at edge of petal under 3 (Th. C1), OP
    20/2 Retouch from Queen's left eye to ear (Th. B11–C12), OP

3d. Cyls. 2A–1B–1C and 3A–1B–1C dot
    1/4 Small patch of white on Queen's forehead (Th. B10), OP
    5/6 White dot in pod above R of CONGRESS (Th. F12), OP
    15/5 Green dots in leaves above OT of BOTANICAL (Th. E–F7), OP

17/1 Retouch under necklace below earring (Th. D12), O but almost completely repaired on 3A phosphor
19/1 White dot on right petal of partly opened bud (Th. B8), OP
19/2 Retouch between Queen's left eyebrow and hair (Th. B11), OP

3d. Cyl. 2A dot
10/6 Coloured line across Queen's neck (Th. D11), O

3d. Cyl. 3A dot
6/4 Violet dot in Queen's forehead (Th. B10), OP
12/5 Flaw in Queen's left eye, OP
13/3 Thin white line from leaf to R of INTER (Th. G2), OP
13/6 Small white dash above O of BOTANICAL and violet spot above middle of collar (Th. D12), OP
19/6 Diagonal white line above ES of CONGRESS, and retouch from centre of cheek to earring (Th. C11–12), OP
20/1 Light patch in background above 2nd N in INTERNA-TIONAL, OP

6d. Cyls. 1D–1C–1B–1A no dot
2/6 Green flaws in T of INTER, OP
5/4 Green spot between eyebrows (Th. B10), OP
6/4 Retouch above necklace (Th. D11) and green dot on lower petal of flower nearest to portrait (Th. C–D9), OP
10/1 White spot in hair below flowers of crown (Th. B12), OP
11/1 Retouch in Queen's collar (Th. D12), OP
17/2 Small retouch in front of Queen's ear (Th. C11), OP
18/2 Green indent in left side of seed pod (Th. F10), OP
20/1 Green spot in lowest leaf above TE of INTER (Th. F2), OP
20/4 Retouch on Queen's left cheek (Th. C11–12), OP

6d. Cyls. 1D–1C–1B–1A dot
2/6 Green flaws in T of INTER and line of yellow dots on middle leaf at left (Th. D1), OP
4/4 Three scarlet dots to right of Queen's left eye (Th. B11), OP
20/4 Retouch on Queen's left cheek (Th. C11–12), OP
20/5 Two green spots on seed pod (Th. F10), OP

9d. Cyls. 2D–2C–2B–2A no dot
4/4 ON of INTERNATIONAL joined by white line, OP
7/1 Red spot under jewel of necklace (Th. E11), OP
13/2 White dot between two left stamens of lower bloom (Th. F3), OP
14/2 Green dot above Queen's upper lip (Th. C11), OP
14/3 Red dot above Queen's right eye (Th. B10–11), OP

1s.3d. Cyls. 1D–1C–1B–1A no dot
5/1 White line through NI and above C of BOTANICAL, OP
8/3 Grey-green flaw at base of E of CONGRESS, OP
11/1 Retouch on Queen's jaw line and neck (Th. C11), OP
12/6 Horizontal dark line on left-hand bud (Th. B–C12), OP
13/2 Green spot on stem of largest bloom (Th. C5), OP
15/6 Pale patch in background adjoining Queen's lips (Th. C10), OP
18/3 Three dark horizontal dots above L of INTERNATIONAL (Th. G5–6), OP
19/1 Dark spot in leaf below left-hand flower (Th. D–E2), OP
20/1 Tops of IN of INTER joined, OP
20/6 White scratch through seed extending from above C of BOTANICAL to R of CONGRESS (Th. G8–12), OP

**Sheet Details**
Sheet size: 120 (6 × 20)
3d., 6d. double pane reel-fed
9d., 1s.3d. single pane sheet-fed

**Sheet markings:**
**Cylinder numbers:** Boxed, opposite R. 20/1 3d., 19–20/1 others
**Guide holes:**
3d., 6d. Opposite rows 14/15 (boxed), at left (no dot) or right (dot)
9d., 1s.3d. None
**Marginal arrows (photo-etched):** """W" shaped, at top, bottom and sides

**Marginal rule**: At bottom of sheet
**Colour register marks:**
3d., 6d. None
9d., 1s.3d. Above and below vertical rows 1 and 6
**Autotron marks:**
3d. Solid, violet, blue, sage-green opposite rows 4/5 and 15/16 at right (no dot) or left (dot)
6d. Stippled, green, scarlet, rose, apple-green opposite rows 4/6 at right (no dot) or left (dot) and again apple-green, rose, scarlet opposite rows 14/15 at right (no dot) or left (dot)
9d., 1s.3d. None
**Coloured crosses (partly trimmed):**
1s.3d. Above and below vertical rows 1/2
**Others:** None
**Colour designations (usually trimmed off):**
3d. G1 GREEN G2 BLUE G3 MAUVE in right margin of dot panes
**Traffic lights (boxed):**
3d. Violet, blue, sage-green opposite R. 20/6
6d. Apple-green, rose, scarlet, green opposite R. 19–20/6
9d. Lemon, green, lake, rose-red opposite R. 19–20/6
1s.3d. Yellow, emerald, reddish violet, grey-green opposite R. 19–20/6
**Essays**
Perforated and gummed essays on Harrison & Sons presentation card. Various designs ex Goaman archive *from* £5500 each

**Imprimaturs from the National Postal Museum Archives**

**A. Ordinary**
Nos. W50/53 imperforate, watermark Type W.24

| | |
|---|---|
| Watermark upright (set of 4) | £9000 |

**B. Phosphor**
Nos. WP50/53 imperforate, watermark Type W.24

| | |
|---|---|
| Watermark upright (set of 4) | £9000 |

**Quantities Sold:**

| | | Ordinary | Phosphor |
|---|---|---|---|
| | 3d. | 166,491,720 | 6,764,880 |
| | 6d. | 25,361,120 | 996,720 |
| | 9d. | 11,896,060 | 498,460 |
| | 1s.3d. | 15,664,600 | 650,920 |
| | Pack | 16,140 | — |

**Withdrawn:** 2.7.65

**W51**. Forth Road Bridge

**W52**. Forth Road and Railway Bridges

(Des. Andrew Restall)

●━━━━━━━━━━━━━

**1964 (4 September). Opening of Forth Road Bridge**

At that time the largest suspension bridge in Europe and the fourth largest in the world. Opened by Her Majesty The Queen. Types **W51/52**
A. Ordinary

| W54 (=SG 659) | | Mint | Used |
|---|---|---|---|
| 3d. | black, blue and reddish violet | 10 | 10 |
| | a. Imperforate between stamp and top margin | £975 | |
| | b. Dotted 3 (Cyl. 2A Dot, R. 15/1) | 20·00 | |

| W55 (=SG 660) | | | |
|---|---|---|---|
| 6d. | blackish lilac, light blue and carmine-red | 40 | 40 |
| | a. Light blue omitted | £6250 | |
| | b. Watermark inverted | 5·00 | |

| First Day Cover (WP54/5) | | 7·00 |
|---|---|---|

| Presentation Pack (WP54/5) | £400 | |
|---|---|---|

B. Phosphor (3d. applied photo., 6d. flexo.)
**WP54 (=SG 659p)**

| | | | |
|---|---|---|---|
| 3d. | Three bands | 1·00 | 1·50 |
| | a. Narrow band at left or right (stamp with vert. margin) | 2·00 | |
| | b. Dotted 3 (Cyl. 2 A Dot, R. 15/1) | 20·00 | |

**WP55 (=SG 660p)**

| | | | |
|---|---|---|---|
| 6d. | Three bands | 4·50 | 4·75 |
| | a. Watermark inverted | £800 | |
| | b. Narrow band at left or right (stamp with vert. margin) | 5·50 | |

| First Day Cover (WP54/5) | | 18·00 |
|---|---|---|

W54b, WP54b

**Cylinder Numbers** (Blocks of Four)

*(a) Ordinary*

| | Cylinder Nos. | Perforation Type A (E/I) | |
|---|---|---|---|
| | | No dot | Dot |
| 3d. | 1C (blue)–1B (black)–2A (violet) | 1·25 | 1·25 |
| | 1C–1B–3A | 15·00 | 15·00 |
| | 1C–1B–4A | 1·50 | 1·50 |
| | 2C–1B–4A | 2·00 | 2·00 |
| 6d. | 1C (blue)–2B (blackish lilac)–2A (red)* | 2·75 | 2·75 |

| | | Perforation Type A(T) (E/P) | |
|---|---|---|---|
| | | No dot | Dot |
| 6d. | 1C (blue)–2B (blackish lilac)–2A (red)* | 4·75 | 4·75 |

**(b) Phosphor**

| | | Perforation Type A (E/I) | |
|---|---|---|---|
| | | No dot | Dot |
| 3d. | 1C (blue)–1B (black)–2A (violet) | 5·50 | 5·00 |
| | 1C–1B–4A | 24·00 | 24·00 |

| | | Perforation Type A(T) (E/P) | |
|---|---|---|---|
| | | No dot | Dot |
| 6d. | 1C (blue)–2B (blackish lilac)–2A (red)* | 24·00 | 24·00 |

*In the 6d. no dot pane the cylinder numbers are expressed in error thus: 1C2.B.2A

**Minor Constant Flaws**

3d. Cyl. 1C no dot in combination with cyls. 1B–2A or 1B–4A no dot
 4/2 Blue spot to left and above B of BRIDGE, OP
 8/1 Blue spot below B of BRIDGE, OP
 13/6 Blue spot in sky S.W. of moon (Th. B1), O

3d. Cyl. 1C dot in combination with cyls. 1B–2A, 1B–3A or 1B–4A dot
 18/6 Blue dash to left of 3d. (Th. F–G11); also blue spot to left of tanker (Th. G3), latter coincident with a similar violet spot on cyl. 2A

3d. Cyl. 1B no dot in combination with cyls. 1C–2A, 1C–3A, 1C–4A or 2C–4A no dot
 1/3 Detail at rear of diadem is weak (Th. B–C10), OP
 2/3 Scratch on necklace and collar (Th. E9), OP
 4/4 Lack of detail at rear of diadem (Th. B–C10), OP
 8/4 Black flaw on Queen's neck above large jewel (Th. E9), OP
 9/2 White spot on Queen's nose (Th. D8), OP
 9/4 Black scratch on Queen's forehead (Th. C8–9), OP
 14/4 Black spot below Queen's left nostril (Th. D8), OP
 16/4 Loss of detail at back of Queen's neck and collar. Almost normal with cyl. 3A (Th. E10–F10–11), OP
 18/1 Black spots under G of BRIDGE (Th. A10), OP

3d. Cyl. 1B dot in combination with cyls. 1C–2A, 1C–3A, 1C–4A or 2C–4A dot
 2/2 White flaw in sea appears as extra wave (Th. G8), OP
 13/2 Weak top to O of FORTH, OP
 18/4 Small white flaw in hair above Queen's left eye (Th. B9), OP

3d. Cyls. 2A, 3A and 4A no dot (multipositive flaws)
 17/4 White patch at left side of moon (Th. B2), OP. Less pronounced on cyl. 3A
 19/4 Large retouch in sky left of bridge (Th. D1), OP. Most marked on cyl. 4A
 20/1 White tower on hill above funnel (Th. F3), OP. Retouched on cyls. 3A and 4A
 20/4 Large retouch in sky left of moon (Th. A–B1), OP. Most pronounced on cyls. 3A and 4A

3d. Cyls. 1C–1B–2A no dot
 10/6 Violet retouches below 1 and 4 of 1964 (Th. B11 and B13), OP
 18/5 White arc at top left of moon (Th. A–B2), OP

3d. Cyl. 4A no dot in combination with cyls. 1C–1B or 2C–1B no dot
12/6 Faint acute accent over d of 3d (Th. F13), OP
14/4 Small nick in left edge of value panel (Th. D11), OP
16/2 Retouch in sky above funnel (Th. E–F3), OP

3d. Cyl. 4A dot in combination with cyls. 1C–1B or 2C–1B dot
14/2 Violet coloured flaw in sky at left of pylon (Th. E2), OP

3d. Cyls. 2C–1B–4A dot
17/3 Dark patch on skyline under bridge (Th. F5), O

6d. Cyls. 1C–2B–2A no dot
5/1 Small nick in top of 9 of 1964, OP
5/5 Red scratch over D of BRIDGE, OP
7/1 Red scratch over 6 of 6d, OP
7/3 Two small breaks in bridge below portrait (Th. G8), OP
8/2 Black spot on Queen's collar (Th. E10), OP
15/6 Dark red patch below 4 of 1964 (Th. B13), OP
16/1 Black dot in front of D of ROAD, OP
16/5 Mottled portrait, OP
17/6 Mottled portrait, OP
18/4 Black spot in water between left-hand towers of bridge (Th. F1), OP

6d. Cyls. 1C–2B–2A dot
1/4 White scratch on Queen's cheek (Th. D9), OP
15/5 Two small coloured flaws on Queen's forehead (Th. C9); also two small red spots below portrait by bridge (Th. G9), OP
17/2 Diagonal red stroke by value panel (Th. D11), OP
19/1 Queen's face is a mass of white dots (State 1) OP; later appears normal (State 2), O only. Other stamps in the sheet show a similar appearance but this is the most marked

**Sheet Details**
Sheet size: 120 (6 × 20). 3d. double pane reel-fed; 6d. double pane sheet-fed

**Sheet markings:**
**Cylinder numbers:** Opposite R. 19/1, boxed
**Guide holes:**
3d. Opposite rows 14/15 (boxed), at left (no dot) or right (dot)
6d. None
**Marginal arrows (photo-etched):** "W" shaped, at top, bottom and sides
**Marginal rule:** At bottom of sheet
**Colour register marks:**
3d. Opposite rows 2/3 and 17/18, at left (no dot) or right (dot)
6d. Opposite rows 1/2 and 17/18, at left (no dot) or right (dot)
**Autotron marks (solid):**
3d. Black, blue, violet opposite rows 4/6 and violet, blue, black opposite rows 13/15 at right
(no dot) or left (dot)
6d. None
**Colour designations (usually trimmed off):**
3d. G MAUVE G BLUE G BLACK in right margin reading upwards opposite rows 8/4 on dot panes only
6d. None
**Traffic lights (boxed):**
3d. Violet, blue, black opposite R. 19/6
6d. Blue, red, blackish lilac opposite R. 19/6

**Imprimaturs from the National Postal Museum Archives**

**A. Ordinary**
Nos. W54/55 imperforate, watermark Type W.24

| Watermark upright (set of 2) | £4500 |
|---|---|

**B. Phosphor**
Nos. WP54/55 imperforate, watermark Type W.24

| Watermark upright (set of 2) | £4500 |
|---|---|

**Quantities Sold:**

|  | Ordinary | Phosphor |
|---|---|---|
| 3d. | 108,098,480 | 8,020,920 |
| 6d. | 12,055,960 | 1,240,800 |
| Pack | 11,450 | — |

**Withdrawn:** 2.7.65

**W53**. Sir Winston Churchill

**W54**. Sir Winston Churchill

(Des. David Gentleman and Rosalind Dease, from photograph by Karsh)

## 1965 (8 July). Churchill Commemoration

**I. Rembrandt Machine**
Cyls. 1A–1B dot and no dot. Lack of shading detail on Churchill's portrait. Queen's portrait appears dull and coarse. This was a sheet-fed rotary machine.
**A. Ordinary**
Types **W53/54**

| W56 (=SG 661) | | Mint | Used |
|---|---|---|---|
| | black and olive-brown | 10 | 10 |
| a. | Watermark inverted | 3·00 | |
| b. | Vertical scratch (Dot, R. 20/3) | 20·00 | |

**B. Phosphor**
WP56 (=SG 661p)

| 4d. | Three bands | 25 | 25 |
|---|---|---|---|
| a. | Left band omitted | 22·00 | |
| b. | Vertical scratch (Dot, R. 20/3) | 20·00 | |

**II. Timson Machine**
Cyls. 5A–6B no dot. More detail on Churchill's portrait–furrow on forehead, his left eye-brow fully drawn and more shading on cheek. Queen's portrait lighter and sharper. This was a reel-fed, two-colour, 12-in. wide rotary machine. The differences in impression were due to the greater pressure applied by the cylinders.

**Ordinary only**
W57 (=SG 661a)

| 4d. | black and pale olive-brown | 35 | 35 |
|---|---|---|---|

**III. Linotype and Machinery No. 4 Machine**
Cyls. 1A–1B no dot. The Linotype and Machinery No. 4 machine was a sheet-fed rotary press machine. Besides being used for printing the 1s.3d. stamps it was also employed to overprint the phosphor bands on both values.

**A. Ordinary**
W58 (=SG 662)

| 1s.3d. | black and grey | 30 | 40 |
|---|---|---|---|
| a. | Watermark inverted | £100 | |

| First Day Cover (WP56 and W58) | 7·00 |
|---|---|

| Presentation Pack (WP56 and W58) | 70·00 |
|---|---|

**B. Phosphor**
**WP58 (=SG 662p)**

| 1s.3d. | Three bands | 2·50 | 3·00 |
|---|---|---|---|
| | a. Narrow band at left or right (stamp with vert. margin) | | 4·50 |

| First Day Cover (WP56 and W58) | 9·00 |
|---|---|

These are known postmarked 7 July.

Two examples of the 4d. value exist with the Queen's head omitted, one due to something adhering to the cylinder and the other due to a paper fold. The stamp also exists with Churchill's head omitted, also due to a paper fold.

W56b, WP56b

**Cylinder Numbers** (Blocks of Four)

**(a) Ordinary**

| | | Perforation Types | | |
|---|---|---|---|---|
| | | A(T) (E/P) | A(T) (E/P) | F (P/E) |
| | Cylinder Nos. | No dot | Dot | No dot |
| 4d. | 1A (olive-brown)–1B (black) Rembrandt | 1·25 | 1·25 | † |
| 4d. | 5A (olive-brown)–6B (black) Timson | † | † | 2·50 |
| 1s.3d. | 1A (black)–1B (grey) Lino-type and Machinery No. 4 | † | † | 2·5 |

**(b) Phosphor**

| 4d. | 1A (olive-brown)–1B (black) Rembrandt | 2·50 | 2·50 | † |
|---|---|---|---|---|
| 1s.3d. | 1A (black)1B (grey) Lino-type and Machinery No. 4 | † | † | 14·00 |

**Minor Constant Flaws**

4d. Cyls. 1A–1B no dot
1/1 Background retouch left of Churchill's right eye (Th. D2), scratch from Churchill's ear to Queen's chin (Th. D8–11), small background retouch to right of Churchill's left ear (Th. C9), OP
6/6 Queen's face mottled with white streaks (Th. B–D10–12), OP
14/1 Dark patch above Queen's left eye (Th. B11), OP

4d. Cyls. 1A–1B dot
1/6 Vertical line of white dots near hair above Churchill's right eye (Th. A–C3), OP
4/3 Disturbance under Churchill's left eye (Th. D6), OP
7/1 Queen's face mottled with white specks (Th. B–D10–12), OP
7/2 Queen's face mottled with white specks (Th. B–D10–12), OP
20/5 Brown diagonal line on bridge of Queen's nose (Th. C11), OP

The mottled face of the Queen varieties on no dot R. 6/6 and dot R. 7/1 and 7/2 are very marked and occur on ordinary and phosphor but only on some sheets. Many other stamps on this cylinder show signs of mottling

4d. Cyls. 5A–6B no dot (ordinary only)
4/2 Retouch in background between portraits (Th. B9)
6/4 Retouch at top of Churchill's nose (Th. D5)
10/4 Two spots in vertical white line level with Churchill's shoulder (Th. E10)
12/3 Small white flaw by Queen's right eye (Th. C10)
14/5 Background retouch just above Churchill's right shoulder (Th. E–F2) and brown flaw in margin below Churchill's chin (Th. H5)
15/5 Brown flaw left of Churchill's head (Th. A2)

1s.3d. Cyls. 1A–1B no dot
1/4 Line of white dots in Queen's hair (Th. C12), OP
7/1 Small white dot over Queen's left eyelid (Th. C11), OP
15/4 White flaw at base of Queen's neck (Th. D2), OP
19/4 Spur on top jewel of emblems in diadem (Th. A12), OP

**Sheet Details**
Sheet size: 120 (6 × 20)
4d. Rembrandt double pane sheet-fed
Timson single pane reel-fed
1s.3d. L. & M. No. 4 single pane sheet-fed

**Sheet markings:**
**Cylinder numbers:** Opposite R. 19/1, boxed
**Guide holes:**
4d. Timson above vertical row 2 (boxed) and below vertical rows 3/4 (unboxed and over arrow)
**Others:** None
**Marginal arrows (photo-etched):** "W" shaped, at top, bottom and sides; Rembrandt very small at bottom; others normal
**Marginal rule:** At bottom of sheet
**Colour register marks:**
4d. Rembrandt, none
4d. Timson, opposite rows 1/2 and 17/18, at both sides
1s.3d. Above and below vertical rows 1/2 and 6
**Autotron marks (solid):**
4d. Timson: Brown, black above R. 1/2 and 1/3
**Others:** None
**Colour designations:** None
**Traffic lights (boxed):** All R. 19/6
4d. Black, brown; 1s.3d. Grey, black

**Imprimaturs from the National Postal Museum Archives**

**A. Ordinary**
Nos. W56, W58 imperforate, watermark Type W.24

| Watermark upright (set of 2) | £4500 |
|---|---|

**B. Phosphor**
Nos. WP56, WP58 imperforate, watermark Type W.24

| Watermark upright (set of 2) | £4500 |
|---|---|

**Quantities Issued**

| | | Ordinary | Phosphor |
|---|---|---|---|
| 4d. | Rembrandt | 103,217,520 | 10,322,760 |
| 4d. | Timson | 32,040,000 | — |
| 1s.3d. | | 7,893,480 | 864,960 |
| Pack | | 38,500 | — |

**Withdrawn:** 4d. phosphor sold out Dec. 1965, remainder Withdrawn: 28.2.66

**W55**.
Simon de Montfort's Seal

(Des. Stewart R. Black)

**W56**.
Parliament Buildings (after engraving by Hollar, 1647)

(Des. Prof. Richard Guyatt)

---

## 1965 (19 July). 700th Anniversary of Simon De Montfort's Parliament

Simon de Montfort summoned the first parliament representing many cities and shires and it met in various buildings at Westminster in January 1265.
Types **W55/56**

### A. Ordinary

| **W59** (=SG 663) | Mint | Used |
|---|---|---|
| 6d. olive-green | 20 | 20 |
| a. Imperforate between stamp and top margin | £1400 | |

| **W60** (=SG 664) | | |
|---|---|---|
| 2s.6d. black, grey and pale drab | 80 | 1·50 |
| a. Watermark inverted | 40·00 | |

| First Day Cover (W59/60) | | 15·00 |
|---|---|---|
| Presentation Pack (W59/60) | 75·00 | |

### B. Phosphor
**WP59** (=SG 663p)

| 6d. Three bands | 60 | 1·00 |
|---|---|---|

| First Day Cover (WP59) | | 26·00 |
|---|---|---|

Both values were accidentally released in several post offices in the London area on 8 July, the date of issue of the Churchill stamps. Covers are also known with both values, bearing the First Day cancellation of the Philatelic Bureau dated 8 July.

**Cylinder Numbers** (Blocks of Four)

| | Perforation Type A (E/I) | |
|---|---|---|
| Cylinder Nos. | No dot | Dot |
| 6d. 2 (olive-green). Ordinary | 1·50 | 1·50 |
| 6d. 2 Phosphor | 4·25 | 4·25 |

The 2s.6d. sheets had no cylinder numbers. Perforation is Type A(T) (E/P).

**Minor Constant Flaws**

6d. Cyl. 2 no dot
1/1 Background scratch behind right cross of diadem (Th. C11–12), OP
5/3 Small background blemish above jewels in diadem (Th. B11), OP

9/4 Retouch at rear of horse's belly (Th. E4), OP
15/2 Dot below e of Anniversary, OP
17/3 Cut in m of Parliament, OP
17/5 Background retouch to right of diadem (Th. C11), OP

6d. Cyl. 2 dot
10/6 Spur to m of Parliament, OP
14/5 White flaw on Queen's necklace (Th. E10), OP

2s.6d. No numbers
4/1 Vertical line running through river wall and building in centre of stamp (Th. E–F9)
4/6 Vertical line from left of steps at centre through Thames to frame line (Th. G–H7)
6/3 Blemish between 5th and 6th windows of building in front of Westminster Hall (Th. E10)
8/1 White scratches above V of ANNIVERSARY
10/1 Nick in S of ANNIVERSARY

### Sheet Details
**Sheet sizes:**
6d. 120 (6 × 20). Double pane reel-fed
2s.6d. 80 (8 × 10). Single pane sheet-fed

**Sheet markings:**
**Cylinder numbers:** 6d. opposite R. 19/1, boxed; 2s.6d. none
**Guide holes:**
6d. In double photo-etched box opposite rows 14/15, at left (no dot) or right (dot). In the left
margin the boxes are lettered "SON", the "S" being in left box (usually trimmed off), the O below centre line and the "N" above right line. In the right margin the sequence is reversed. The letters are very small and denote respectively selvedge, off-side and near-side
2s.6d. None
**Marginal arrows (photo-etched):** "W" shaped, at top, bottom and sides
**Marginal rule:** At bottom of sheet
**Colour register marks, Autotron marks,Colour designations:** None
**Traffic lights (boxed):**
6d. None
2s.6d. Grey, drab and black opposite R. 9/8, boxed
This shows that the stamp was printed in three colours and accounts for misplacement of the Queen's head downwards in some badly registered sheets

### Imprimaturs from the National Postal Museum Archives

**A. Ordinary**
Nos. W59/60 imperforate, watermark Type W.24

| Watermark upright (set of 2) | £4500 |
|---|---|

**B. Phosphor**
No. WP59 imperforate, watermark Type W.24

| Watermark upright | £4500 |
|---|---|

### Quantities Issued

| | Ordinary | Phosphor |
|---|---|---|
| 6d. | 12,973,800 | 1,537,920 |
| 2s.6d. | 4,055,120 | — |
| Pack | 24,450 | — |

**Withdrawn:** 28.2.66

---

**W57**. Bandsmen and Banner

(Des. M. C. Farrar-Bell)

**W58**. Three Salvationists

(Des. G. Trenaman)

## 1965 (9 August). Salvation Army Centenary

A religious militant movement, the Salvation Army was founded in 1865 by William Booth who became its General in 1880.
Types **W57/58**

### A. Ordinary

**W61** (=SG 665)

|  |  | Mint | Used |
|---|---|---|---|
| 3d. | indigo, grey-blue, cerise, yellow and brown | 25 | 25 |
| a. | Diadem flaw (R. 16/6) | 22·00 | |
| b. | Retouch to V (R. 19/3) | 20·00 | |

**W62** (=SG 666)

|  |  |  |  |
|---|---|---|---|
| 1s.6d. | red, blue, yellow and brown | 1·00 | 1·50 |
| a. | Extra pearl (R. 17/1) | 22·00 | |

| First Day Cover (W61/2) |  |  | 23·00 |
|---|---|---|---|

### B. Phosphor
**WP61** (=SG 665p)

|  |  |  |  |
|---|---|---|---|
| 3d. | One band | 25 | 40 |
| a. | Diadem flaw (R. 16/6) | 22·00 | |
| b. | Retouch to V (R. 19/3) | 20·00 | |

**WP62** (=SG 666p)

|  |  |  |  |
|---|---|---|---|
| 1s.6d. | Three bands | 2·50 | 2·75 |
| a. | Extra pearl (R. 17/1) | 22·00 | |

| First Day Cover (WP61/2) |  |  | 33·00 |
|---|---|---|---|

W61a, WP61a          W61b, WP61b

W62a WP62a

**Cylinder Numbers** (Blocks of Six)

**(a) Ordinary**

| | Cyl. Nos. (No dot) | Perforation Type A (E/I) |
|---|---|---|
| 3d. | 2A (blue)–2B (indigo)–1C (brown)–1D (cerise)–1E (yellow) | 2·00 |
| 1s.6d. | 1A (red)–1B (brown)–1C (blue)–1D (yellow) | 7·00 |

**(b) Phosphor**

| | | |
|---|---|---|
| 3d. | 2A (blue)–2B (indigo)–1C (brown)–1D (cerise)–1E (yellow) | 2·50 |
| 1s.6d. | 1A (red)–1B (brown)–1C (blue)–1D (yellow) | 20·00 |

**Minor Constant Flaws**

3d. Cyls. 2A–2B–1C–1D–1E no dot
1/6 Pale area below D of 3D (Th. G13), OP
2/1 Dark spot on Queen's chin (Th. D11), OP
3/6 Vertical scratch below flag-bearer's collar (Th. D–E4), OP
8/1 Spur at foot of T of SALVATION at bottom of stamp, OP
11/2 Blue scratch in white vertical dividing line to left of Queen's lips (Th. D10); also blue spot to left of flag-bearer's lips (Th. D4), both OP
15/6 Grey flaw protruding from collar under Queen's chin (Th. E11), OP
16/1 Due to faulty registration on the multipositive, the cerise colour is positioned slightly to the right resulting in a white line at left of flag in sky, also cerise colour overlaps ear and face below ear (Th. B–C3 and C4), OP. Note This variety is not an ordinary colour shift and is therefore best collected in a positional block. A similar variety, although much less marked, is found on R. 14/1, also OP
17/4 White spot in lower part of V of SALVATION at bottom of stamp, OP

1s.6d. Cyls. 1A–1B–1C–1D no dot
1/1 Retouch on right arm of left-hand man (Th. D–12), OP
1/4 White flaw on Queen's hair behind ear (Th. D12), OP
15/6 Retouch on right leg of left-hand man (Th. G2), OP
19/3 Diagonal scratch across Queen's forehead and nose (Th. B–C10), OP
20/1 White flaw on Queen's neck by necklace (Th. E11), OP
20/3 Small red flaw at back of Queen's hair (Th. D12), OP
20/5 A wispy line of blue dots by left leg of right-hand man (Th. F7), OP

**Sheet Details**
Sheet size: 120 (6 × 20). Single pane reel-fed

**Sheet markings:**
**Cylinder numbers**:
3d. Opposite rows 18/19 at left, boxed
1s.6d. Opposite row 19 at left, boxed
**Guide holes**: Opposite rows 14/15 (boxed), at both sides
**Marginal arrows (photo-etched)**: "W" shaped, at top, bottom and sides
**Marginal rule**: At bottom of sheet
**Colour register marks**:
Opposite rows 1/2 and 17/18, at both sides
**Autotron marks (solid)**:
3d. Blue, indigo, brown, cerise, yellow below vertical rows 1/3

1s.6d. Red, brown, blue, yellow below vertical rows 1/3
**Colour designations:**
3d. G1 YELLOW G2 RED G3 BROWN G4 BLUE BLACK G5 BLUE
in right margin reading upwards opposite rows 9/3 ("G1 YEL-
LOW" is very faint on some sheets)
1s.6d. G1 YELLOW G2 BLUE G3 BROWN G4 RED in right margin
reading upwards opposite rows 9/3.
**Traffic lights (boxed):**
3d. Blue, indigo, brown, cerise, yellow opposite rows 18/19
at right
1s.6d. Red, brown, blue, yellow opposite rows 18/19 at right

**Imprimaturs from the National Postal Museum Archives**

**A. Ordinary**
Nos. W61/62 imperforate, watermark Type W.24

| | |
|---|---|
| Watermark upright (*set of* 2) | £4500 |

**B. Phosphor**
Nos. WP61/62 imperforate, watermark Type W.24

| | |
|---|---|
| Watermark upright (*set of* 2) | £4500 |

**Quantities Issued**

| | *Ordinary* | *Phosphor* |
|---|---|---|
| 3d. | 54,312,000 | 4,261,200 |
| 1s.6d. | 5,244,120 | 652,320 |

**Withdrawn:** 28.2.66 (3d. ordinary sold out Dec. 1965)

**W59**. Lister s Carbolic Spray

(Des. Peter Gauld)

**W60**. Lister and Chemical Symbols

(Des. Frank Ariss)

## 1965 (1 September). Centenary of Joseph Lister's Discovery of Antiseptic Surgery

Types **W59/60**
**A. Ordinary**
**W63** (=SG 667)

| | | *Mint* | *Used* |
|---|---|---|---|
| 4d. | indigo, brown-red and grey-black | 25 | 15 |
| a. | Brown-red (tube) omitted | £550 | |
| b. | Indigo omitted | £6500 | |
| c. | Corner scratch (No dot, R. 17/1) | 20·00 | |
| d. | Face retouch (No dot, R. 18/1) | 20·00 | |
| e. | Filled e (Dot, R. 20/4) | 20·00 | |

**W64** (=SG 668)

| | | | |
|---|---|---|---|
| 1s. | black, purple and new blue | 1·00 | 1·10 |
| a. | Watermark inverted | £550 | |

| | |
|---|---|
| First Day Cover (W63/4) | 12·00 |

**B. Phosphor**
**WP63** (=SG 667p)

| | | | |
|---|---|---|---|
| 4d. | Three bands | 25 | 25 |
| a. | Brown-red (tube) omitted | £7000 | |
| b. | Narrow band at left or right (stamp with vert. margin) | 1·50 | |
| c. | Error. Two broad bands | 35·00 | |
| ca. | Error. One thin and one broad band | 40·00 | |
| d. | Corner scratch (No dot, R. 17/1) | 20·00 | |
| e. | Face retouch (No dot, R. 18/1) | 20·00 | |

**WP64** (=SG 668p)

| | | | |
|---|---|---|---|
| 1s. | Three bands | 2·00 | 2·50 |
| a. | Watermark inverted | £600 | |
| b. | Narrow band at left or right (stamp with vert. margin) | 3·00 | |
| c. | Error. Two broad bands | 50·00 | |

| | |
|---|---|
| First Day Cover (W63/4) | 15·00 |

Nos. W63/4 exist postmarked 1 August 1965 at Skeabost Bridge
(Skye) (probably a mis-print of 31 August), and can also be
found cancelled 31 August elsewhere.

Nos. WP63c/ca came from a sheet showing misplaced
phosphor bands; No. WP63ca were from the left-hand vertical
row only.

W63e
'e' of 'Antiseptic' nearly filled
by white flaw (later retouched
leaving malformed 'e'

W63c, WP63d

W63d, WP63e
large grey retouch outlines face.
Similar, but more minor flaws can
be found on Row19/2, 20/1.

## Cylinder Numbers (Blocks of Four)

| | Perforation Types | | |
|---|---|---|---|
| | A (E/I) | A (E/I) | F (P/E) |
| Cylinder Nos. | No dot | Dot | No dot |
| 4d. 4A (black)–1B (blue)–1C (red). Ordinary | 4·00 | 2·50 | † |
| 4A–1B–1C. Phosphor | 5·00 | 2·50 | † |
| 1s. 1A (black)–1B (purple)–1C (blue). Ordinary | † | † | 5·50 |
| 1A–1B–1C. Phosphor | † | † | 10·00 |

## Minor Constant Flaws

4d. Cyls. 4A–1B–1C no dot

4/1 Line of white dots under apparatus (Th. H3–4), OP
4/4 Two dark flaws to lower right of apparatus (Th. G5–6), OP
5/6 Prominent retouch in front of Queen's dress (Th. E–F10), OP
6/6 Grey flaw hanging from rear jewel of tiara (Th. B12), OP
10/3 Grey flaw on Queen's forehead (Th. B10), OP
11/4 to 12/4 Grey line under g of Surgery extending across gutter joining frames, OP
11/6 Diagonal grey line from top left corner to apparatus (Th. A1–B2), OP
16/5 Retouch on Queen's forehead (Th. B10), OP
17/2 White flaw in loop of d of value, OP
19/6 Grey spots on Queen's forehead (Th. B10–11), OP
19/6 and 20/6 Grey line extends down right-hand margin, OP
20/3 Vertical grey line from lower left corner of stamp to gutter (Th. H1), OP
20/6 Base of 4 joined to tube by dark line (Th. B7), OP

4d. Cyls. 4A–1B–1C dot

1/4 Blue spot between p and t of antiseptic, OP
8/2 Retouch on Queen's collar (Th. E12), OP
10/2 Diagonal grey line above te of Lister and in front of Queen's collar (Th. F8–E10), OP
13/3 Retouch behind Queen's necklace (Th. D12), OP
18/1 Retouch on Queen's jaw close to ear (Th. D11), OP
19/2 White scratch above ur of Surgery, OP
20/1 Two dark spots at right of Queen's mouth (Th. D11), OP
20/6 Retouch in front of Queen's neck (Th. E10), OP

1s. Cyls. 1A–1B–1C no dot

1/5 Large black spot at rear of Queen's collar (Th. E13), OP
3/1 Retouch along Liste's right shoulder (Th. D3–C4), OP
3/2 Broken frame line behind Queen's portrait was retouched by dots (Th. C13), OP
6/1 Missing portions of jewels left of large cross on diadem heavily retouched (Th. A10), OP
8/1 White retouch on Queen's throat (Th. D11), OP
11/2 Extra pearl half way up necklace (Th. D11), OP
11/3 Small retouch on Queen's left cheek (Th. D11), OP
14/2 Retouch on Queen's collar (Th. E12), OP
15/6 Line from Queen's left eyebrow into hair (Th. B11), OP
16/4 Retouch on back of Queen's collar (Th. E13), OP
17/6 Blue spot normally found by Lister s right wrist is missing (Th. E6), OP
19/1 Dark spot under Queen's nose (Th. C10), OP
20/3 Retouch below Queen's necklace (Th. D12), OP

### Sheet Details
Sheet size: 120 (6 × 20). 4d. double pane reel-fed; 1s. single pane sheet-fed

### Sheet markings:
**Cylinder numbers:** Opposite R. 19/1, boxed
**Guide holes:** Opposite rows 14/15 (boxed), at left (no dot) or right (dot)
**Marginal arrows (photo-etched):** "W" shaped, at top, bottom and sides
**Marginal rule:** At bottom of sheet
**Colour register marks:**
4d. Opposite rows 2/3 and 16/17, at left (no dot)
1s. Above and below vertical rows 1/2 and 5/6
**Autotron marks (solid):**
4d. Black, indigo, brown-red opposite rows 3/5, at right (no dot) or left (dot)
1s. None
**Colour designations:** None
**Traffic lights (boxed):**
4d. Black, indigo, brown-red opposite R. 19/6
1s. Black, purple, blue opposite R. 20/6

### Imprimaturs from the National Postal Museum Archives

**A. Ordinary**
Nos. W63/64 imperforate, watermark Type W.24

| Watermark upright (set of 2) | £4500 |
|---|---|

**B. Phosphor**
Nos. WP63/64 imperforate, watermark Type W.24

| Watermark upright (set of 2) | £4500 |
|---|---|

### Quantities Issued

| | Ordinary | Phosphor |
|---|---|---|
| 4d. | 92,167,440 | 10,732,800 |
| 1s. | 8,368,800 | 1,452,360 |

**Withdrawn:** 15.4.66

**W61**. Trinidad Carnival Dancers

**W62**. Canadian Folk-dancers

(Des. David Gentleman and Rosalind Dease)

---

## 1965 (1 September). Commonwealth Arts Festival

The Festival was aimed at promoting the cultural traditions of Commonwealth countries and was held in London and other centres between 16 September and 2 October.
Types **W61/62**

### A. Ordinary

**W65** (=SG 669)

| | Mint | Used |
|---|---|---|
| 6d. black and orange | 20 | 20 |

**W66** (=SG 670)

| | | |
|---|---|---|
| 1s.6d. black and light reddish violet | 80 | 1·10 |

| | |
|---|---|
| First Day Cover (WP65/6) | 16·50 |

### B. Phosphor
**WP65** (=SG 669p)

| | Mint | Used |
|---|---|---|
| 6d. Three bands | 30 | 50 |
| a. Narrow band at left or right (stamp with vert. margin) | 1·50 | |

**WP66** (=SG 670p)

| | | |
|---|---|---|
| 1s.6d. Three bands | 2·50 | 3·50 |
| a. Narrow band at left or right (stamp with vert. margin) | 3·50 | |
| b. Error. Two broad bands | 30·00 | |
| c. Error. Two bands (9·5 and 6 mm.) | 35·00 | |

| | |
|---|---|
| First Day Cover (WP65/6) | 22·00 |

Nos. W65/6 are known postmarked 1 August 1965 at Skeabost Bridge (Skye) (probably a mis-print for 31 August).

No. WP66c come from the right-hand side of the sheet where the narrow band occurs on the stamp instead of the first vertical row of perforations.

### Cylinder Numbers (Blocks of Four)

| Cylinder Nos. | Perforation Type F(L) (I/E) No dot |
|---|---|
| 6d. 1A (orange)–1B (black). (Ordinary | 1·50 |
| ✓1A–1B. Phosphor | 2·75 |
| 1s.6d. 1A (violet)1B (black). Ordinary | 4·50 |
| ✓1A–1B. Phosphor | 14·00 |

### Minor Constant Flaws

6d. Cyls. 1A–1B (no dot)
  1/2 Damaged right arm of v of Festival, OP
  1/6 Black spot at back of Queen's neck under hair (Th. C12), OP

11/2 S shaped line of white dots on Queen's neck (Th. D–E11), OP
17/1 Pale area in background by right sleeve of central figure (Th. D3–4), OP

1s.6d. Cyls. 1A–1B no dot
  2/3 White flaw under n of Commonwealth, OP
  3/4 Vertical scratch from Queen's ear to neck (Th. C–D12), OP
  5/6 Vertical line from diadem to Queen's neck (Th. B–D11), OP
  7/5 Pale area below C of Commonwealth, OP
  9/2 White triangle in Queen's hair (Th. B11), OP
  13/6 White spot between emblems and rear cross of diadem (Th. B12), OP
  15/1 Diagonal scratch to right of C of Commonwealth (Th. G–12), OP
  20/6 Two dots to right of Queen's left eyebrow (Th. C11), OP

### Sheet Details
Sheet size: 120 (6 × 20). Single pane reel-fed

**Sheet markings:**
**Cylinder numbers:** Opposite R. 19/1, boxed
**Guide holes:** Above vertical rows 3/4 and below vertical row 5, unboxed
**Marginal arrows (photo-etched):** "W" shaped, at top, bottom and sides
**Marginal rule:** At bottom of sheet
**Colour register marks:**
6d. Opposite rows 1/2 and 18/19, at both sides and opposite rows 10/11 (orange only), at left
1s.6d. Opposite rows 1/2, at both sides, rows 9/10 (violet only), at left and rows 18/19, at left and 17/18 at right
**Autotron marks (solid):**
6d. Orange, black above and below vertical rows 3/4
1s.6d. Violet, black above and below vertical rows 3/4
**Colour designations:**
6d. G ORANGE G BLACK reading upwards opposite rows 14/12, right margin
1s.6d. G MAUVE G BLACK reading upwards opposite rows 15/13, right margin
**Traffic lights (boxed):**
6d. Black, orange opposite R. 19/6
1s.6d. Black, violet opposite R. 19/6

### Imprimaturs from the National Postal Museum Archives

**A. Ordinary**
Nos. W65/66 imperforate, watermark Type W.24

| | |
|---|---|
| Watermark upright (set of 2) | £4500 |

**B. Phosphor**
Nos. WP65/66 imperforate, watermark Type W.24

| | |
|---|---|
| Watermark upright (set of 2) | £4500 |

### Quantities Issued

| | Ordinary | Phosphor |
|---|---|---|
| 6d. | 12,264,840 | 1,621,080 |
| 1s.6d. | 5,003,000 | 788,880 |

**Withdrawn:** 15.4.66

**W63**. Flight of Spitfires

**W64**. Pilot in Hurricane

**W65**. Wing-tips of Spitfire and Messerschmitt ME-109

**W66**. Spitfires attacking Heinkel HE-111 Bomber

**W67**. Spitfire attacking Stuka Dive-bomber

**W68**. Hurricanes over Wreck of Dornier DO-1722 Bomber

**W69**. Anti-aircraft Artillery in Action

**W70**. Air-battle over St. Paul's Cathedral

(Des. Andrew Restall (9d.), David Gentleman and Rosalind Dease (others))

### 1965 (13 September). 25th Anniversary of Battle of Britain

The Battle of Britain was the first major campaign in world history to be fought entirely between opposing air forces.

The 4d. values were issued together *se-tenant* in blocks of six (3 × 2) within the sheet

Types **W63/70**

**A. Ordinary**

| | | Mint | Used |
|---|---|---|---|
| **W67** (=SG 671) | | | |
| 4d. | yellow-olive and black | 25 | 25 |
| a. | Block of 6. Nos. W67/72 | 8·00 | 8·00 |
| **W68** (=SG 672) | | | |
| 4d. | yellow-olive, olive-grey and black | 25 | 25 |
| **W69** (=SG 673) | | | |
| 4d. | red, new blue, yellow-olive, olive-grey and black | 25 | 25 |
| b. | Damaged wing (Cyl. 3D Dot, R. 19/3) | 20·00 | |
| **W70** (=SG 674) | | | |
| 4d. | olive-grey, yellow-olive and black | 25 | 25 |
| **W71** (=SG 675) | | | |
| 4d. | olive-grey, yellow-olive and black | 25 | 25 |
| b. | Stuka retouch (Cyl. 1E No dot, R. 2/2) | 20·00 | |
| **W72** (=SG 676) | | | |
| 4d. | olive-grey, yellow-olive, new blue and black | 1·00 | 1·00 |
| b. | New blue omitted | † | £6500 |
| c. | Damaged tailplane (Cyl. 3D Dot, R. 20/3) | 20·00 | |
| **W73** (=SG 677) | | | |
| 9d. | bluish violet, orange and slate-purple | 1·75 | 1·75 |
| a. | Watermark inverted | 85·00 | |
| **W74** (=SG 678) | | | |
| 1s.3d. | light and deep grey, black and light and bright blue | 1·75 | 1·75 |
| a. | Watermark inverted | £175 | |

| First Day Cover (W67/74) | 25·00 |
|---|---|

| Presentation Pack (W67/74) | 70·00 |
|---|---|

No. W72b is only known commercially used on cover from Truro.

## B. Phosphor

**WP67** (=SG 671p)

| | | | |
|---|---|---|---|
| 4d. | Three bands | 50 | 50 |
| a. | Block of 6. Nos. WP67/72 | 10·00 | 12·00 |
| b. | Narrow band at left (stamp with vert. margin) | 2·50 | |

**WP68** (=SG 672p)

| | | | |
|---|---|---|---|
| 4d. | Three bands | 50 | 50 |

**WP69** (=SG 673p)

| | | | |
|---|---|---|---|
| 4d. | Three bands | 50 | 50 |
| b. | Narrow band at right (stamp with vert. margin) | 2·50 | |
| c. | Damaged wing (Cyl. 3D Dot, R. 19/3) | 20·00 | |
| d. | Error. Two bands | | |

**WP70** (=SG 674p)

| | | | |
|---|---|---|---|
| 4d. | Three bands | 50 | 50 |
| b. | Narrow band at left (stamp with vert. margin) | 2·50 | |

**WP71** (=SG 675p)

| | | | |
|---|---|---|---|
| 4d. | Three bands | 50 | 50 |
| b. | Stuka retouch (Cyl. 1E No dot, R. 2/2) | 20·00 | |

**WP72** (=SG 676p)

| | | | |
|---|---|---|---|
| 4d. | Three bands | 50 | 50 |
| b. | Narrow band at right (stamp with vert. margin) | 2·50 | |
| c. | Damaged tailplane (Cyl. 3D Dot, R. 20/3) | 20·00 | |

**WP73** (=SG 677p)

| | | | |
|---|---|---|---|
| 9d. | Three bands | 1·75 | 2·50 |
| a. | Narrow band at left or right (stamp with vert. margin) | 3·50 | |
| b. | Error. Two bands | | |

**WP74** (=SG 678p)

| | | | |
|---|---|---|---|
| 1s.3d. | Three bands | 1·75 | 2·50 |
| a. | Watermark inverted | 5·00 | |
| b. | Narrow band at left or right (stamp with vert. margin) | 3·50 | |

| First Day Cover (W67/74) | 28·00 |
|---|---|

W69b, WP69c

W71b, WP71b
This variety only occurs in combination with cyls. 3A–1B–1C–3D. With cyls. 2A–1B–1C–3D it is normal

W72c, WP72c

**Cylinder Numbers** (Blocks of Twelve (3 × 4) (4d.), Four (9d.), Six (1s.3d.))

**(a) Ordinary**

| | | *Perforation Types* | | |
|---|---|---|---|---|
| | | *A (E/1)* | *A (E/1)* | *F (P/E)* |
| | Cylinder Nos. | No dot | Dot | No dot |
| 4d. | 2A (black)–1B (blue)–1C (red)–3D (olive-grey)–1E (yellow-olive) | 18·00 | 22·00* | † |
| | 3A–1B–1C–3D–1E | 18·00 | 26·00* | † |
| 9d. | 1A (slate-purple)–1B (violet)–1C (orange) | † | † | 10·00 |
| 1s.3d. | 1A (black)–1B (light blue)–1C (light grey)–1D (deep grey)–1E (bright blue) | † | † | 14·00 |

**(b) Phosphor**

| | | | | |
|---|---|---|---|---|
| 4d. | 3A (black)–1B (blue)–1C (red)–3D (olive- grey)–1E (yellow-olive) | 22·00 | 30·00* | |
| 9d. | 1A (slate-purple)–1B (violet)–1C (orange) | † | † | 10·00 |
| 1s.3d. | 1A (black)–1B (light blue)–1C (light grey)–1D (deep grey)–1E (bright blue) | † | † | 14·00 |

**Minor Constant Flaws**

4d. Cyls. 1B–1C–3D–1E no dot in combination with black cyls. 2A or 3A no dot
  1/3 Horizontal scratch retouch under right of cross (Th. F5–7), OP
  1/6 Similar retouch under centre of cross (Th. F3–6), OP
  15/2 Nick in centre line of fuselage at left (Th. D1), OP
  20/1 Small dark area on left wing of bomber (Th. D2), OP

4d. Cyl. 3A no dot
  1/4 Nick in lower curve of B in BRITAIN, OP
  7/2 Black spot in front of Queen's ear (Th. C12), OP
  12/3 White scar across Queen's left cheek (Th. C12), OP
  13/2 Fine vertical line on Queen's left cheek (Th. C12), OP
  18/3 Extra white dot in Queen's hair behind earring (Th. C13), OP

4d. Cyls. 1B–1C–3D–1E dot in combination with black cyls. 2A or 3A dot
  5/3 Dark horizontal line below right arm of cross (Th. F56), OP
  8/1 Dark spot at left end of bomber's wing (Th. C1), OP
  11/2 Line of white dots on pilot's right shoulder (Th. E8–F10), OP
  16/1 Dark spot at right end of bomber's wing (Th. B9), OP
  16/3 Notch in bomber's tail under B of Battle (Th. A4), OP

9d. Cyls. 1A–1B–1C no dot
  11/2 Line across Queen's face under eyes (Th. C10–11), OP
  12/3 Retouch in sky behind hat of man with flag (Th. C1), OP
  20/5 White patch below where vapour trails cross (Th. C5–6), OP

1s.3d. Cyls. 1A–1B–1C–1D–1E no dot
  4/4 Scratch below 1 of 1940 (Th. H5), OP

5/3 Horizontal bright blue line above building at right (Th. F8–10), OP
5/4 Dark line between Br of Britain (Th. G–H5), OP
9/5 Retouches in sky at lower right (Th. D–E9–10), OP
14/4 Blue dot in front of Queen's ear (Th. C12), OP
20/3 Line under value is shorter at right, OP

**Sheet Details**
Sheet size: 120 (6 × 20)
4d. In se-tenant blocks of six, double pane reel-fed
9d. and 1s.3d. Single pane sheet-fed

**Sheet markings:**
**Cylinder numbers:**
4d. and 1s.3d. Opposite rows 18/19 at left, boxed
9d. Opposite R. 19/1, boxed
**Guide holes:**
4d. In double "SON" box opposite rows 14/15, at left (no dot) or right (dot)
**Others:** None
**Marginal arrows (photo-etched):** "W" shaped, at top, bottom and sides
**Marginal rule:** At bottom of sheet
**Colour register marks:**
4d. None
9d. Above and below vertical rows 1/2 and 6
1s.3d. Above and below vertical rows 1/2 and 5/6
There is a large violet blob of colour under vertical rows 1/2 in the 9d. value
**Autotron marks (solid):**
4d. Black, red, blue, olive-grey, yellow-olive opposite rows 3/7, at right (no dot) or left (dot)
**Others:** None
**Colour designations:** None
**Traffic lights (boxed):**
4d. Olive-grey, red, black, blue, yellow-olive opposite rows 18/19 at right
9d. Violet, orange, slate-purple opposite R. 19/6
1s.3d. Deep grey, light blue, light grey, black, bright blue opposite rows 18/19 at right

**Imprimaturs from the National Postal Museum Archives**

**A. Ordinary**
Nos. W67/72 imperforate, watermark Type W.24

| | |
|---|---|
| Watermark upright (se-tenant block of six) | £12500 |

Nos. W73/74 imperforate, watermark Type W.24

| | |
|---|---|
| Watermark upright (2 values) | £4500 |

**B. Phosphor**
Nos. WP67/72 imperforate, watermark Type W.24

| | |
|---|---|
| Watermark upright (se-tenant block of six) | £12500 |

Nos. WP73/74 imperforate, watermark Type W.24

| | |
|---|---|
| Watermark upright (2 values) | £4500 |

**Quantities Issued**

| | Ordinary | Phosphor |
|---|---|---|
| 4d. | 103,417,440 | 11,560,440 |
| 9d. | 6,195,960 | 1,143,120 |
| 1s.3d. | 6,469,440 | 1,239,840 |
| Pack | 28,524 | — |

**Withdrawn:** 31.5.66

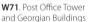

**W71**. Post Office Tower and Georgian Buildings     **W72**. Post Office Tower and Nash Terrace, Regent's Park

(Des. Clive Abbott)

**1965 (8 October). Opening of Post Office Tower**

The tallest building in London, the Post Office Tower is 620 feet high and helps to provide more long distance telephone circuits and more television channels. An additional feature of this issue was the inclusion of the names of both the designer and printers at the foot of the stamps and this became the practice for many later issues until 1969. Watermark sideways on 3d.

Types **W71/72**
**A. Ordinary**

**W75** (=SG 679)

| | | Mint | Used |
|---|---|---|---|
| 3d. | olive-yellow, new blue and bronze-green | 10 | 15 |
| a. | Olive-yellow (tower) omitted | £5500 | £2000 |
| b. | Extra window (Dot, R. 4/18) | 20·00 | |

**W76** (=SG 680)

| | | | |
|---|---|---|---|
| 1s.3d. | bronze-green, yellow-green and blue | 30 | 45 |
| a. | Watermark inverted | 60·00 | |

| | |
|---|---|
| First Day Cover (W75/6) | 6·50 |

| | |
|---|---|
| Presentation Pack (W75/6) | 6·50 |

The one phosphor band on No. WP75 was produced by printing broad phosphor bands across alternate rows of vertical perforations. Individual examples show the band at right or left (same prices either way).

**B. Phosphor**
**WP75** (=SG 679p)

| | | | |
|---|---|---|---|
| 3d. | One band at left | 15 | 15 |
| a. | Band at right | 15 | 15 |
| ab. | Nos. WP75/a (horiz. pair) | 30 | 50 |
| ac. | Error. Broad band se-tenant with missing phosphor (horiz. pair) | 55·00 | |
| b. | Extra window (Dot, R. 4/18) | 20·00 | |

**WP76** (=SG 680p)

| | | | |
|---|---|---|---|
| 1s.3d. | Three bands | 30 | 50 |
| a. | Watermark inverted | 60·00 | |
| b. | Error. Left-hand band omitted | 30·00 | |

| | |
|---|---|
| First Day Cover (W75/6) | 7·00 |

| | |
|---|---|
| Presentation Pack * (WP75/6) | 6·50 |

*See note under withdrawn at end of listing.
The above are known pre-released on 4 October at Aish, South Brent (Devon).

W75b, WP75b

## Cylinder Numbers (Blocks of Four)

### (a) Ordinary

|  | Cylinder Nos. | A (I/E) No dot | A (I/E) Dot | F (P/E) No dot |
|---|---|---|---|---|
| | | *Perforation Types* | | |
| 3d. | 1A (blue)–1B (green)–1C (yellow)* | 1·00 | 1·00 | † |
| 1s.3d. | 1A (yellow-green)–1B (bronze-green)–1C (blue) | † | † | 2·75 |

### (b) Phosphor

|  | Cylinder Nos. | A (I/E) No dot | A (I/E) Dot | F (P/E) No dot |
|---|---|---|---|---|
| 3d. | 1A (blue)–1B (green)–1C (yellow)* | 1·25 | 1·25 | † |
| 1s.3d. | 1A (yellow-green)–1B (bronze-green)–1C (blue) | † | † | 2·75 |

*In the 3d. dot pane the dot after 1C is omitted in error.
For perforation Type A the 3d. is with sheet orientated showing head to left.

### Minor Constant Flaws

3d. Cyls. 1A–1B–1C dot
 1/20 White spot at base of tower (Th. L3), OP
 2/19 Olive-yellow spot below second ground floor window
  of building at base of tower at right (Th. M4), OP
 2/20 Blue spot below SO of HARRISON, OP
 5/2 White spot in O of OFFICE, OP
 5/8 Blue spot surrounded by pale area below T of TOWER,
  OP
 5/16 Pale spot in blue panel to left of 3d. (Th. J4), OP

1s.3d. Cyls. 1A–1B–1C no dot
 1/5 Pale area around lower tip of 3 of 1/3, OP
 3/1 Small retouch below T of TOWER (Th. C–D1), OP
 4/1 Horizontal line of retouching below 1/3 (Th. D11–12),
  OP
 6/2 Scratch in sky above roof of left-hand terrace (Th. E2),
  OP
 10/3 Dark spot to left of Queen's nose (Th. C8), OP
 10/4 Retouch to background at top right of 1 of 1/3, OP
 15/4 White scratch through E and over R of TOWER, OP

### Sheet Details

**Sheet sizes:**
3d. 120 (20 × 6). Double pane reel-fed
1s.3d. 120 (6 × 20). Single pane sheet-fed

**Sheet markings:**
**Cylinder numbers:**
3d. Above vertical row 2, boxed
1s.3d. Opposite R. 19/1, boxed
**Guide holes:**
3d. In double "SON" box above vertical rows 6/7 (no dot) or below (dot)
1s.3d. None
**Marginal arrows (photo-etched):** "W" shaped, at top, bottom and sides
**Marginal rule:** 3d. At left of sheet; 1s.3d. At bottom of sheet
**Colour register marks:**
3d. None
1s.3d. Above and below vertical rows 1/2 and 5/6
**Autotron marks (solid):**
3d. Yellow, green, blue below vertical rows 15/17 (no dot) or above (dot)
1s.3d. None

**Colour designations:** None
**Traffic lights (boxed):**
3d. Yellow, green, blue reading left to right below vertical row 2
1s.3d. Yellow-green, bronze-green, blue opposite R. 19/6

### Imprimaturs from the National Postal Museum Archives

**A. Ordinary**
Nos. W75/76 imperforate, watermark Type W.24

| Watermark upright (1s.3d.) or sideways (3d.) (set of 2) | £4500 |
|---|---|

**B. Phosphor**
Nos. WP75/76 imperforate, watermark Type W.24

| Watermark upright (1s.3d.) or sideways (3d.) (set of 2) | £4500 |
|---|---|

### Quantities Issued

|  | Ordinary | Phosphor |
|---|---|---|
| 3d. | 51,291,120 | 4,274,880 |
| 1s.3d. | 5,722,320 | 1,107,480 |
| Pack | 25,060 (ordinary and phosphor) | |

**Withdrawn:** 30.6.66
When the Post Office Tower was opened on 19 May 1966 these stamps were issued from automatic machines giving a block of four of the 3d. and a pair of the 1s.3d. dispensed in envelopes, and packs were also issued from a machine. These continued to be available after the stamps had been withdrawn everywhere else and early in 1968 the ordinary stamps were replaced by phosphor stamps and packs. These were withdrawn on the introduction of decimal currency.

**W73**. U.N. Emblem

**W74**. I.C.Y. Emblem

(Des. Jeffery Matthews)

**1965 (25 October). 20th Anniversary of the United Nations**

Commemorating the 20th Anniversary of the formation of the United Nations in 1945. 1965 was also designated International Co-operation Year and the symbol of the clasped hands is shown on the 1s.6d. value.
Types **W73/74**
**A. Ordinary**

| W77 (=SG 681) | | Mint | Used |
|---|---|---|---|
| 3d. | black, yellow-orange and light blue | 25 | 20 |
| a. | Broken circle (Dot, R. 11/4) | 30·00 | |
| b. | Lake in Russia (Dot, R. 19/3) | 30·00 | |
| c. | Flying saucer flaw (Dot, R. 18/3) | 25·00 | |
| d. | Retouched | 20·00 | |
| e. | Imperf. between stamp and top margin* | | £1800 |

| W78 (=SG 682) | | | |
|---|---|---|---|
| 1s.6d. | black, bright purple and light blue | 1·00 | 80 |
| a. | Watermark inverted | | £2000 |

| First Day Cover (W77/8) | | 12·00 |
|---|---|---|

**B. Phosphor**
**WP77 (=SG 681p)**

| | | | |
|---|---|---|---|
| 3d. | One centre band | 25 | 30 |
| ✓ a. | Broken circle (Dot, R. 11/4) | 30·00 | |
| ✓ b. | Lake in Russia (Dot, R. 19/3) | 30·00 | |
| c. | Flying saucer flaw (Dot, R. 18/3) | 25·00 | |
| d. | Retouched | 20·00 | |

**WP78 (=SG 682p)**

| | | | |
|---|---|---|---|
| 1s.6d. | Three bands | 2·75 | 3·00 |
| a. | Error. Two bands | 35·00 | |

| First Day Cover (WP77/8) | | 14·00 |
|---|---|---|

*No. W77e was caused by a paper fold.

W77a, WP77a          W77b, WP77b

W77c, WP77c
Stroke over "S" of
"ANNIVERSARY" and smudge

W77d, WP77d
Retouched.
Smudge removed

**Cylinder Numbers** (Blocks of Four)

**(a) Ordinary**

| | | Perforation Types | | |
|---|---|---|---|---|
| | | A (E/I) | A (E/I) | F (P/E) |
| | Cylinder Nos. | No dot | Dot | No dot |
| 3d. | 1A (black)–1B (blue)–1C (orange)* | 2·00 | 2·00 | |
| 1s.6d. | 1A (black)–1B (blue)–1C (purple) | † | † | 5·50 |

**(b) Phosphor**

| | | | | |
|---|---|---|---|---|
| 3d. | 1A (black)–1B (blue)–1C (orange)* | 2·50 | 2·50 | † |
| 1s.6d. | 1A (black)–1B (blue)–1C (purple) | † | † | 15·00 |

*In the 3d. dot pane the dot is before instead of after the "1C".

**Minor Constant Flaws**
3d. Cyls. 1A–1B–1C no dot
1/1 Diagonal scratch across Queen's face (Th. C11–12), OP
1/4 Round pale grey flaw by Queen's left eye (Th. C11–12), OP
2/2 Pale patch on Queen's neck (Th. E12), OP
8/5 Dotted white scratch on right side of 0 of large 20 (Th. D8–9), OP
9/2 Black flaw in lower loop of 3, OP
10/4 Small break in middle of S of ANNIVERSARY, OP
13/1 Curved white scratch in bottom right-hand corner of blue panel (Th. H9–10), OP
14/4 Scratch on Queen's neck by necklace (Th. E12), OP
15/6 Black spot on Queen's forehead (Th. C11), OP
19/4 Horizontal white scratch over VERSARY, OP
20/6 Black flaws between laurel leaves over middle of large 2 (Th. D3), OP

3d. Cyls. 1A–1B–1C dot
20/1 White scratch through ARY U, OP

1s.6d. Cyls. 1A–1B–1C no dot
2/1 White scratch behind Queen's neck (Th. D12–E12), OP
5/1 Small patch of white dots to right of Queen's head (Th. B13), OP
6/2 Pale patch to left of top of large U (Th. B1), OP
10/1 Pale patch in background to left of Queen's mouth (Th. D10), OP
11/2 Pink spot central below large N (Th. F7), OP
15/1 White scratch in base of large U, (Th. E2), OP
20/1 Vertical white scratch in background behind Queen's head (Th. C–D13), OP
20/5 Retouch to background within upper thumb of symbol (Th. B5), OP

**Sheet Details**
Sheet size: 120 (6 × 20). 3d. double pane reel-fed; 1s.6d. single pane sheet-fed

**Sheet markings:**
**Cylinder numbers:** Opposite R. 19/1, boxed
**Guide holes:**
3d. In double "SON" box opposite rows 14/15, at left (no dot) or right (dot). An unusual feature of this stamp is that there is an additional single box printed in orange beneath the

double box which is in black
1s.6d. None
**Marginal arrows (photo-etched):** "W" shaped, at top, bottom and sides
**Marginal rule:** At bottom of sheet
**Colour register marks:**
3d. None
1s.6d. Above and below vertical rows 1 and 6
**Autotron marks (solid):**
3d. Black, blue, orange opposite rows 5/6 at right (no dot) or left (dot)
1s.6d. None
**Colour designations (usually trimmed off):**
3d. G1 BROWN G2 BLUE G3 BLACK in right margin reading upwards opposite rows 8/5 on dot panes
1s.6d. None
**Traffic lights (boxed):**
3d. Black, blue, orange opposite R. 19/6
1s.6d. Black, blue, purple opposite R. 19/6

**Imprimaturs from the National Postal Museum Archives**

**A. Ordinary**
Nos. W77/78 imperforate, watermark Type W.24

| Watermark upright (set of 2) | £4500 |
|---|---|

**B. Phosphor**
Nos. WP77/78 imperforate, watermark Type W.24

| Watermark upright (set of 2) | £4500 |
|---|---|

**Quantities Issued**

|  | Ordinary | Phosphor |
|---|---|---|
| 3d. | 50,598,720 | 4,488,240 |
| 1s.6d. | 5,476,800 | 1,018,560 |

**Withdrawn:** 30.6.66

**W75**. Telecommunications Network

**W76**. Radio Waves and Switchboard

(Des. Andrew Restall)

**1965 (15 November). I.T.U. Centenary**
The aims of the Union created in 1865, then known as the International Telegraph Union, were to promote, maintain and extend international co-operation in telecommunications.
Types **W75/76**
**A. Ordinary**

| **W79** (=SG 683) |  | Mint | Used |
|---|---|---|---|
| 9d. | red, ultramarine, deep slate-violet, black and pink | 50 | 40 |
| ✓ a. | Watermark inverted | 25·00 | |

| **W80** (=SG 684) |  |  |  |
|---|---|---|---|
| 1s.6d. | red, greenish blue, indigo, black and light pink | 1·50 | 1·25 |
| a. | Light pink omitted | £4200 | |
| b. | Watermark inverted | £300 | |
| c. | Retouched arm (R. 1/4) | 20·00 | |

| First Day Cover (W79/80) | | 17·00 |
|---|---|---|

**B. Phosphor**
**WP79** (=SG 683p)

| 9d. | Three bands | 1·00 | 75 |
|---|---|---|---|
| a. | Watermark inverted | 90·00 | |
| b. | Error. Two bands | 70·00 | |
| c. | Narrow band at left (stamp with vert. margin) | 2·50 | |

**WP80** (=SG 684p)

| 1s.6d. | Three bands | 4·25 | 5·25 |
|---|---|---|---|
| a. | Error. Two bands | 30·00 | |
| b. | Narrow band at left (stamp with vert. margin) | 6·00 | |
| c. | Red pin with arm (R. 1/4) | 25·00 | |
| d. | Retouched | 20·00 | |

| First Day Cover (WP79/80) | | 20·00 |
|---|---|---|

Originally scheduled for issue on 17 May 1965, supplies from the Philatelic Bureau were sent in error to reach a dealer on that date and another dealer received his supply on 27 May. Ordinary and phosphor sets exist on cover postmarked Stretford on 18 May 1965.

WP80c                                   W80c, W80d

On the phosphor printing the red pin has a projecting arm at right; this was later retouched leaving faint traces of red on the pink background and it is known only in the retouched state on the ordinary printing.

**Cylinder Numbers** (Blocks of Six)

**(a) Ordinary**

| Cylinder Nos. (No dot) | Perforation Type F (P/E) |
|---|---|
| 9d. 1A (ultram.)–1B (red)–1C (violet)–1D (pink)–2E (black) | 4·50 |
| 1s.6d. 2A (blue)–1B (indigo)–1C (pink)–1D (red)–2E (black) | 12·00 |

**(b) Phosphor**

| | |
|---|---|
| 9d. 1A (ultram.)–1B (red)–C (violet)–1D (pink)–2E (black) | 8·00 |
| 1s.6d. 2A (blue)–1B (indigo)–1C (pink)–1D (red)–2E (black) | 28·00 |

The same black cylinder was used for both values.

**Minor Constant Flaws**

9d. and 1s.6d. Cyl. 2E
  2/4 Small white curl in hair behind Queen's ear (Th. C12), OP
  5/2 Small nick in diagonal stroke of first N of UNION, OP
9d. Cyls. 1A–1B–1C–1D–2E
  6/5 Small break in diagonal blue network line at right (Th. B8), OP
  9/5 Diagonal white scratch in blue background above ATIO of INTERNATIONAL (Th. E3), OP
  10/5 Damaged lower half of 1 of 1865, shows as white nick and white scratch, OP
  17/6 Small nick in right-hand stroke of first M of TELECOM-MUNICATION, OP
  20/5 Wavy scratch in background over OMMUNI of TEL-ECOMMUNICATION (Th. E79), OP
1s.6d. Cyls. 2A–1B–1C–1D–2E
  3/3 Retouches to background above first C of TELECOM-MUNICATION, P

**Sheet Details**
Sheet size: 120 (6 × 20). Single pane sheet-fed

**Sheet markings:**
**Cylinder numbers:** Opposite rows 18/19 at left, boxed
**Guide holes:** None
**Marginal arrows (photo-etched):** "W" shaped, at top, bottom and sides
**Marginal rule:** At bottom of sheet
**Colour register marks:** Above and below vertical rows 1/2 and 5/6
**Autotron marks:** None
**Colour designations:** None
**Traffic lights (boxed):**
9d. Ultramarine, red, violet, pink, black opposite rows 18/19 at right
1s.6d. Blue indigo, pink, red, black opposite rows 18/19 at right

**Imprimaturs from the National Postal Museum Archives**

**A. Ordinary**
Nos. W79/80 imperforate, watermark Type W.24

| Watermark upright (set of 2) | £4500 |
|---|---|

**B. Phosphor**
Nos. WP79/80 imperforate, watermark Type W.24

| Watermark upright (set of 2) | £4500 |
|---|---|

**Quantities Issued**

| | Ordinary | Phosphor |
|---|---|---|
| 9d. | 5,321,880 | 556,080 |
| 1s.6d. | 5,287,920 | 589,800 |

**Withdrawn:**
30.6.66 (1s.6d. phosphor sold out December 1965)

**W77**. Robert Burns (after Skirving chalk drawing)

**W78**. Robert Burns (after Nasmyth portrait)

(Des. Gordon F. Huntly)

## 1966 (25 January). Burns Commemoration

Robert Burns (1759–1796), Scotland's celebrated national poet, was born in Alloway, near Ayr.
Types **W77/78**

**A. Ordinary**
**W81** (=SG 685)

| | | | Mint | Used |
|---|---|---|---|---|
| W77 | 4d. | black, deep violet-blue and new blue | 15 | 15 |

**W82** (=SG 686)

| | | | | |
|---|---|---|---|---|
| W78 | 1s.3d. | black, slate-blue and yellow-orange | 40 | 70 |
| First Day Cover (W81/2) | | | | 4·00 |
| Presentation Pack (W81/2) | | | | 60·00 |

**B. Phosphor**
**WP81** (=SG 685p)

| | | | | |
|---|---|---|---|---|
| W77 | 4d. | Three bands | 25 | 50 |
| | | a. Narrow band at left or right (stamp with vert. margin) | 2·00 | |

**WP82** (=SG 686p)

| | | | | |
|---|---|---|---|---|
| W78 | 1s.3d. | Three bands | 2·25 | 2·25 |
| First Day Cover (WP81/2) | | | | 6·00 |

These are known postmarked 24 January 1966.

**Cylinder Numbers** (Blocks of Four)

**(a) Ordinary**

| Cylinder Nos. | *A (E/I)* No dot | *A (E/I)* Dot | *F (P/E)* No dot |
|---|---|---|---|
| | | *Perforation Types* | |
| 4d. 1A (violet-blue)–1B (black)–1C (new blue) | 1·25 | 1·25 | † |
| 1A–2B–1C | 1·25 | 1·25 | † |
| 1s.3d. 2A (slate-blue)–1B (black)–1C (orange) | † | † | 2·50 |

**(b) Phosphor**

| | | | |
|---|---|---|---|
| 4d. 1A (violet-blue)–1B (black)–1C (new blue) | 2·50 | 2·50 | † |
| 1s.3d. 2A (slate-blue)–1B (black)–1C (orange) | † | † | 11·00 |

**Minor Constant Flaws**

4d. Cyls. 1A–1B–1C dot and 1A–2B–1C dot
    9/4 Small white flaw at front of diadem (Th. A10), OP
    18/1 Coloured spot above Queen's upper lip (Th. C10), OP
    19/3 White flaw on Queen's neck above centre of collar (Th. E11), OP

4d. Cyls. 1A–2B–1C dot only
    15/1 White spot at back of Burns's hair by parting (Th. A5), OP

1s.3d. Cyls. 2A–1B–1C no dot
    2/6 Pale background flaw in front of Queen's neck (Th. D9), OP
    3/6 Grey spot on Burns's nose near his right eye (Th. C5), OP
    4/6 Grey diagonal line through white line to panel at lower right (Th. E8–G9), OP
    6/5 White patch to right of Queen's left eyebrow (Th. B11), OP
    9/4 Large dark retouch in Burns's hair left of parting (Th. B4), OP
    19/1 Flaw on Burns's right cheek (Th. D4), OP
    19/5 Dark flaw on Burns's shirt touching left lapel (Th. F5), OP

**Sheet Details**
Sheet size: 120 (6 × 20). 4d. double pane reel-fed: 1s.3d. single pane sheet-fed
Sheet marking:
**Cylinder numbers:** R. 19/1, boxed
**Guide holes:**
4d. In double "SON" box opposite rows 14/15, at left (no dot) or right (dot)
1s.3d. None
**Marginal arrows (photo-etched):** "W" shaped, at top, bottom and sides
**Marginal rule:** At bottom of sheet
**Colour register marks:**
4d. None
1s.3d. Above and below vertical rows 1 and 6
**Coloured crosses:**
4d. None
1s.3d. Above and below vertical row 2
**Autotron marks (solid):**
4d. Violet-blue, black, new blue opposite rows 5/6, at right (no dot) or left (dot)
1s.3d. None
**Colour designations:** None
**Traffic lights (boxed):**
4d. New blue, black, violet-blue opposite R. 19/6
1s.3d. Orange, black, slate-blue opposite R. 19/6

**Imprimaturs from the National Postal Museum Archives**

**A. Ordinary**
Nos. W81/82 imperforate, watermark Type W.24

| Watermark upright (*set of* 2) | £4500 |
|---|---|

**B. Phosphor**
Nos. WP81/82 imperforate, watermark Type W.24

| Watermark upright (*set of* 2) | £4500 |
|---|---|

**Quantities Sold:**

| | Ordinary | Phosphor |
|---|---|---|
| 4d. | 77,905,176 | 8,738,520 |
| 1s.3d. | 5,685,096 | 1,226,160 |
| Pack | 38,968 | — |

**Withdrawn:** 29.7.66 but later put on sale again in error for a short time at the Philatelic Counter in London, the Philatelic Bureau in Edinburgh and at the Edinburgh Festival.

**W79**. Westminster Abbey

(Des. Sheila Robinson)

**W80.** Fan Vaulting, Henry VII Chapel

(Des. and eng. Bradbury, Wilkinson)

---

**1966 (28 February). 900th Anniversary of Westminster Abbey**

Westminster Abbey, officially the Collegiate Church of St. Peter, Westminster, is the nation's Coronation Church and a mausoleum for England's greatest men and women.

The 2s.6d. is recess-printed on chalk-surfaced paper by Bradbury, Wilkinson and comb perf. 11 × 12.
Types **W79/80**
**A. Ordinary**

| W83 (=SG 687) | Mint | Used |
|---|---|---|
| 3d. black, red-brown and new blue | 15 | 20 |
| a. Diadem flaw (No dot, R.16/2) | 20·00 | |
| b. Retouch on Queen's cheek (Dot, R. 15/6) | 20·00 | |
| **W84 (=SG 688)** | | |
| 2s.6d. black | 55 | 80 |
| First Day Cover (WP83/4) | | 6·00 |
| Presentation Pack (WP83/4) | 55·00 | |

**B. Phosphor**
**WP83 (=SG 687p)**

| | Mint | Used |
|---|---|---|
| 3d. One band | 20 | 25 |
| a. Diadem flaw (No dot, R. 16/2) | 20·00 | |
| b. Retouch on Queen's cheek (Dot. R. 15/6) | 20·00 | |
| c. Error. Two bands | 11·00 | |
| First Day Cover (WP83) | | 14·00 |

W83a, WP83a

W83b, WP83b

**Cylinder and Plate Numbers** (Blocks of Four)

| Cylinder or Plate Nos. | Perforation Type A (E/I) | |
|---|---|---|
| | No dot | Dot |
| 3d. 2A (blue)–1B (black)–1C (brown). Ordinary | 1·25 | 1·25 |
| 2A–1B–1C. Phosphor | 3·50 | 3·50 |
| 2s.6d. Plate 1. Ordinary | 5·00 | † |
| Plate 1A | 7·00 | † |

**Minor Constant Flaws**
3d. Cyls. 2A–1B–1C no dot
   1/6 Vertical scratch to right of Queen's head and running through bottom frame of panel (Th. D–E12), OP
   15/1 Small white dots touching E and second A of ANNIVERSARY, OP

2s.6d. Plate 1
   2/2 Broken horizontal line in top margin over Y of ANNIVERSARY (Th. A1)
   6/1 Scratch in bottom margin below Y of ABBEY (Th. I13–14)
   10/2 Second 0 of 900 joined to t of th

2s.6d. Plate 1A
   5/3 Horizontal line in margin left of Y of ANNIVERSARY and vertical line in top margin at left (Th. A1 and A2)
   7/4 Scratch through Y of ANNIVERSARY

**Sheet Details**
**Sheet sizes:**
3d. 120 (6 × 20). Double pane reel-fed
2s.6d. 40 (4 × 10). Double pane sheet-fed

**Sheet markings:**
**Cylinder numbers:** 3d. R. 19/1, boxed
**Plate numbers:** 2s.6d. Bottom margin below vertical rows 3/4
**Guide holes:**
3d. In double "SON" box opposite rows 14/15, at left (no dot) or right (dot)
2s.6d. In circle opposite row 6, at left (Pl. 1) or right (Pl. 1A)
**Marginal arrows (photo-etched):** 3d. "W" shaped, at top, bottom and sides; 2s.6d. none
**Marginal rule:** 3d at bottom of sheet; 2s.6d. none.
**Colour register marks:** None
**Coloured cross (black):** 2s.6d. opposite row 6, at right (Pl. 1) or left (Pl. 1A)
**Autotron marks (solid):**
3d. Blue, black, red-brown opposite rows 6/7, at right (no dot) or left (dot); 2s.6d. none
**Colour designations:** None
**Traffic lights (boxed):**
3d. Blue, black, red-brown opposite R. 19/6

**Imprimaturs from the National Postal Museum Archives**

**A. Ordinary**
Nos. W83/84 imperforate, watermark Type W.24

| Watermark upright (set of 2) | £4500 |
|---|---|

**B. Phosphor**
No. WP83 imperforate, watermark Type W.24

| Watermark upright | £4500 |
|---|---|

**Quantities Sold:**

| | Ordinary | Phosphor |
|---|---|---|
| 3d. | 48,703,426 | 5,247,720 |
| 2s.6d. | 2,819,056 | — |
| Pack | 24,272 | — |

**Withdrawn:** 31.8.66 3d. (2s.6d. sold out in April 1966)
The 3d. was later put on sale again in error for a short time at the Philatelic Counter in London and at the Philatelic Bureau in Edinburgh.

---

**W81**. View near Hassocks, Sussex

**W82**. Antrim, Northern Ireland

**W83**. Harlech Castle, Wales

**W84**. Cairngorm Mountains, Scotland

(Des. Leonard Rosoman. Queen's portrait adapted by David Gentleman from coinage)

---

## 1966 (2 May). Landscapes

Britains first special pictorial stamps featuring scenes in England, Northern Ireland, Wales and Scotland.

The Queen's profile design on this, and following special issues to 1967 Christmas, was taken from the coinage design by Mrs. Mary Gillick and adapted by David Gentleman.
Types **W81/84**
A. Ordinary

| | | Mint | Used |
|---|---|---|---|
| **W85** (=SG 689) | | | |
| 4d. | black, yellow-green and new blue | 10 | 15 |
| | a. Dash before ENGLAND (No dot, R. 20/5) | 20·00 | |
| | b. Green flaw on tree trunk (Dot, R. 3/4) | 20·00 | |
| **W86** (=SG 690) | | | |
| 6d. | black, emerald and new blue | 15 | 20 |
| ✓ | a. Watermark inverted | 6·00 | |
| | b. AN for AND (R. 10/3) | 35·00 | |
| | c. Retouched, with misaligned D | 20·00 | |
| **W87** (=SG 691) | | | |
| 1s.3d. | black, greenish yellow and greenish blue | 25 | 35 |
| | a. Broken D (R. 14/2) | 20·00 | |
| **W88** (=SG 692) | | | |
| 1s.6d. | black, orange and Prussian blue | 40 | 35 |

| | | | |
|---|---|---|---|
| ✓ | a. Watermark inverted | 18·00 | |
| First Day Cover (W85/8) | | | 7·00 |

**B. Phosphor**

| | | | |
|---|---|---|---|
| **WP85** (=SG 689p) | | | |
| 4d. | Three bands | 10 | 15 |
| | a. Narrow band at left or right (stamp with vert. margin) | 2·00 | |
| | b. Green flaw on tree trunk (Dot. R. 3/4) | 20·00 | |
| **WP86** (=SG 690p) | | | |
| 6d. | Three bands | 15 | 20 |
| | a. Watermark inverted | £140 | |
| | b. AN for AND (R. 10/3) | 25·00 | |
| **WP87** (=SG 691p) | | | |
| 1s.3d. | Three bands | 25 | 35 |
| ✓ | a. Broken D (R. 14/2) | 20·00 | |
| **WP88** (=SG 692p) | | | |
| 1s.6d. | Three bands | 40 | 40 |
| First Day Cover (W85/8) | | | 8·50 |

These are known postmarked 26 April in Winchester.

No. W85 exists with Queen's head and value omitted, due to a paper fold, with the stamp above showing value only omitted. A vertical pair of No. W86 exists with the Queen's head and value omitted from the upper stamp and partial omission on the lower stamp, both due to a paper fold (*Price* £10,000).

W86b and WP86b. 40,000 sheets, including all the phosphor stamps, were printed before this was discovered and the D was then added to the cylinder, forming W86c.

W85a
(Later retouched)

W85b, WP85b

W87a, WP87a

**Cylinder Numbers** (Blocks of Four)

| (a) Ordinary | Perforation Type A (E/I) | |
|---|---|---|
| Cylinder Nos. | No dot | Dot |
| 4d. 2A (blue)–1B (black)–1C (yellow-green) | 1·25 | 1·25 |

| | No dot | |
|---|---|---|
| | Type F (P/E) | Type F(L) (I/E) |
| 6d. 1A (blue)–3B (black)–1C (green) | 1·25 | † |
| 1s.3d. 2A (blue)–2B (black)–1C* (yellow) | 2·50 | † |
| 1s.6d. 1A (blue)–1B (orange)–1C (black) | 3·00 | 3·00 |

## (b) Phosphor

| | A (E/I) No dot | A (E/I) Dot | F (P/E) No dot |
|---|---|---|---|
| 4d. 2A (blue)–1B (black)–1C (yellow-green) | 1·25 | 1·25 | † |
| 6d. 1A (blue)–3B (black)–1C (green) | † | † | 1·25 |
| 1s.3d. 2A (blue)–2B (black)–1C* (yellow) | † | † | 2·50 |
| 1s.6d. 1A (blue)–1B (orange)–1C (black) | † | † | 2·50 |

*Above columns under heading* Perforation Types

*The figure one of this cylinder is inverted

### Minor Constant Flaws

4d. Cyls. 2A–1B–1C no dot
 11/2 Pale area behind Queen's collar above value (Th. E–F12–13), OP
 14/5 Dark spot in green field at top left corner (Th. A1–2), OP

4d. Cyls. 2A–1B–1C dot
 2/4 Retouching in sky between clouds (Th. A2), OP

6d. Cyls. 1A–1B–1C no dot
 2/2 Horizontal blue line across Queen's neck, later retouched on ordinary (Th. D11), OP
 5/4 Green spot between N. and I, OP
 17/2 Curved green flaw on trees opposite Queen's chin (Th. D9), OP
 18/1 Blue mark in field left of cottage (Th. F5), OP
 19/2 Green line running across Queen's head (Th. B10–12), OP
 20/6 Diagonal black flaw below second R of HARRISON, OP

1s.3d. Cyls. 2A–2B–1C no dot
 6/1 Pale diagonal white line above ES of WALES, OP
 9/2 Pale area between 1 and 3 of value (Th. F11–12), OP
 19/1 Dot before M of ROSOMAN (Th. H2), OP

1s.6d. Cyls. 1A–1B–1C no dot
 1/6 Blurred area at back of Queen's hair (Th. B-C12), OP
 4/6 Several blemishes in background between mountains which appear as italic figures 20 (Th. A4–5), OP
 8/1 Retouch above d of value (Th. F13), OP
 13/4 Retouch behind Queen's neck (Th. D12), OP
 18/3 White spot between AN of SCOTLAND and foot of A is enlarged, OP

### Sheet Details
**Sheet size**: 120 (6 × 20). 4d. double pane reel-fed; others single pane sheet-fed

### Sheet markings:
**Cylinder numbers**: R. 19/1, boxed
**Guide holes**:
4d. In single "SON" box opposite rows 14/15, at left (no dot) or right (dot). The centre bar of the double box has been erased
**Others**: None
**Marginal arrows (photo-etched)**: "W" shaped, at top, bottom and sides
**Marginal rule**: At bottom of sheet
**Colour register marks**: 4d. None
**Others**: Above and below vertical rows 1/2 and 5/6
**Autotron marks (solid)**:
4d. Blue, black, yellow-green opposite rows 5/6, at right (no dot) or left (dot); others, none
**Colour designations**: None
**Traffic lights (boxed)**:
4d. Blue, black, yellow-green opposite R. 19/6
6d. Blue, black, green opposite R. 19/6
1s.3d. Blue, black, yellow opposite R. 19/6
1s.6d. Black, blue, orange opposite R. 19/6

### Imprimaturs from the National Postal Museum Archives

**A. Ordinary**
Nos. W85/88 imperforate, watermark Type W.24

| Watrmark upright (set of 4) | £9000 |
|---|---|

**B. Phosphor**
Nos. WP85/88 imperforate, watermark Type W.24

| Watermark upright (set of 4) | £9000 |
|---|---|

**Quantities Sold:**

| | Ordinary | Phosphor |
|---|---|---|
| 4d. | 80,326,440 | 11,283,720 |
| 6d. | 11,531,760 | 2,459,280 |
| 1s.3d. | 5,286,000 | 1,242,720 |
| 1s.6d. | 5,462,640 | 1,204,200 |

**Withdrawn**: 1.5.67 but 6d. phosphor was sold out in January

**W85.** Players with Ball   **W85.** Players with Ball

(Des. William Kempster)  (Des. David Gentleman)

**W87.** Goalkeeper saving Goal

(Des. David Caplan)

___

### 1966 (1 June). World Football Cup Championship

Sixteen countries took part in the final stages of the World Football Championship for the Jules Rimet Cup in England during July, 1966. See also No. W96.

Watermark sideways on 4d.

Types **W85/87**
#### A. Ordinary

**W89** (=SG 693)

| | | Mint | Used |
|---|---|---|---|
| 4d. | red, reddish purple, bright blue, flesh and black | 10 | 25 |
| a. | Patch on thigh (No dot, R. 3/20) | 20·00 | |
| b. | Broken shadow (No dot, R. 5/17) | 22·00 | |

**W90** (=SG 694)

| | | | |
|---|---|---|---|
| 6d. | black, sepia, red, apple-green and blue | 15 | 25 |
| a. | Black omitted | £200 | |
| b. | Apple-green omitted | £5500 | |
| c. | Red omitted | £1100 | |
| d. | Watermark inverted | 2·00 | |

**W91** (=SG 695)

| | | | |
|---|---|---|---|
| 1s.3d. | black, blue, yellow, red and light yellow-olive | 50 | 1·00 |
| a. | Blue omitted | £325 | |
| b. | Watermark inverted | £140 | |
| c. | Darned stocking (R. 19/2) | 20·00 | |

| First Day Cover (W89/91) | 20·00 |
|---|---|
| Presentation Pack (W89/91) | 15·00 |

#### B. Phosphor
**WP89** (=SG 693p)

| | | | |
|---|---|---|---|
| 4d. | Two bands | 10 | 25 |
| a. | Narrow band at left (stamp with vert. margin) | 2·00 | |
| b. | Error. Extra phosphor band at right | | |
| c. | Error. One broad band | 25·00 | |

| | | | |
|---|---|---|---|
| d. | Patch on thigh (No dot. R. 3/20) | 20·00 | |
| e. | Red patch below ball (No dot, R. 4/16) | 22·00 | |
| f. | Broken shadow (No dot, R. 5/17) | 22·00 | |

**WP90** (=SG 694p)

| | | | |
|---|---|---|---|
| 6d. | Three bands | 15 | 25 |
| a. | Black omitted | £2600 | |

**WP91** (=SG 695p)

| | | | |
|---|---|---|---|
| 1s.3d. | Three bands | 50 | 1·00 |
| a. | Watermark inverted | 1·25 | |
| b. | Darned stocking (R. 19/2) | 20·00 | |
| c. | Error. Two bands | 16·00 | |

| First Day Cover (WP89/91) | 22·00 |
|---|---|

The 4d. ordinary has been seen postmarked 31 May in Hereford.

W89a, WP89d, W96a       W89b, WP89f, W96c

WP89e, W96b              W91c, WP91b

#### Cylinder Numbers (Blocks of Six)

**(a) Ordinary**

| | | Perforation Type A (I/E) | |
|---|---|---|---|
| | Cylinder Nos. | No dot | Dot |
| 4d. | 1A (black)–1B (blue)–1C (red)–1D (purple)–1E (flesh)* | 1·50 | 1·50 |

| | | Perforation Types | |
|---|---|---|---|
| | | F (P/E) | F(L) (I/E) |
| | | No dot | No dot |
| 6d. | 1A (blue)–1B (green)–1C (red)–1D (sepia)–1E (black) | 1·50 | † |
| | 2A–1B–1C–1D–1E | 3·00 | † |
| 1s.3d. | 1A (black)–1B (yellow)–1C (yellow-olive)–1D (blue)–1E (red) | 7·00* | 8·50* |
| | 1A–1B–1C–1D–2E | 7·00* | 7·50* |

**(b) Phosphor**

| | | Perforation Types | | |
|---|---|---|---|---|
| | | A (I/E) | A (I/E) | F (P/E) |
| | | No dot | Dot | No dot |
| 4d. | 1A (black)–1B (blue)–1C (red)–1D (purple)–1E (flesh)* | 1·50 | 1·50 | † |
| 6d. | 1A (blue)–1B (green)–1C (red)–1D (sepia)–1E (black) | † | † | 1·50 |

1s.3d. 1A (black)–1B
(yellow)–1C (yellow-
olive)–1D (blue)–2E
✓ (red) † † 7·00*

*In the 4d. no dot pane the flesh cylinder is expressed in error
thus: "1E.".
For perforation Type A the 4d. is with sheet orientated showing
head to left.

**Minor Constant Flaws**
4d. Cyls. 1A–1B–1C–1D–1E no dot
3/1 Horizontal scratch through top of ball (Th. K1–2), OP
5/6 Blue patch below u of Cup, OP
6/18 Blue spots over T of LTD, OP
4d. Cyls. 1A–1B–1C–1D–1E dot
4/20 Red line joins head and left arm of player at left (Th.
F3), OP
5/10 Dark spot on ball (Th. K1), OP
5/17 Grey coloured spur to top of l of World, OP
6d. Cyls. 1B–1C–1D–1E in combination with blue cyls. 1A or
2A no dot
5/4 Diagonal scratch on barrier next to grass below crowd
(Th. G–57), OP
6d. Cyl. 1A no dot
17/4 Pale area around top of 1 of 1966, OP
1s.3d. Cyls. 1A–1B–1C–1D no dot in combination with red
cyls. 1E or 2E
1/3 Patch on sock of central player (Th. G2), OP
9/2 Black spur on head of right-hand player (Th. B7), OP
14/5 Break in black frame line around players opposite U
of CUP, OP
18/1 Black spot to right of stroke of 1/3; also black spot
below second R of HARRISON OP
20/1 Black spot below second A of CAPLAN, OP
1s.3d. Cyl. 2E no dot
1/6 Red scratch on face of central player, OP

**Sheet Details**
Sheet size:
4d. 120 (20 × 6). Double pane reel-fed
6d. and 1s.3d. 120 (6 × 20). Single pane sheet-fed

**Sheet markings:**
**Cylinder numbers:**
4d. Above vertical rows 2/3, boxed
6d. and 1s.3d. Opposite rows 18/19 at left, boxed
**Guide holes:**
4d. In single photo-etched box above vertical rows 6/7 (no dot)
or below (dot). On the no dot pane the box is now lettered "SN",
the "S" being on the left in the box (usually trimmed off), and
the "N" above the right line. On the dot pane the sequence is
reversed.
6d. and 1s.3d. None
**Marginal arrows (photo-etched):** "W" shaped, at top, bottom
and sides, except that early printings of the 6d. from cylinder
1A both ordinary and phosphor were without any arrow
markings in the margins.
These were later inserted by hand.
Minimum price for marginal strip showing arrow omitted: £15
Ordinary or phosphor
**Marginal rule:**
4d. At left of sheet
6d. and 1s.3d. At bottom of sheet
**Colour register marks:**
4d. Above vertical rows 3/4 and 18/19 (no dot) or below (dot)
6d. and 1s.3d. Above and below vertical rows 1/2 and 6
**Coloured crosses:**
4d. None
6d. Above and below vertical row 3
1s.3d. Above and below vertical rows 3/4
**Autotron marks (solid):**
4d. Red, purple, flesh, blue, black below vertical rows 15/18
(no dot) or above (dot)
6d. and 1s.3d. None

**Colour designations:**
4d. 5 BLACK G4 BLUE MAROON G3 G2 RED G1 LIGHT RED
below vertical rows 11/16 on dot panes only
6d. and 1s.3d. None
**Traffic lights (boxed):**
4d. Black, blue, red, purple, flesh reading left to right below
vertical rows 2/3
6d. Blue, green, red, sepia, black opposite rows 18/19 at right
1s.3d. Black, yellow, yellow-olive, blue, red opposite rows
18/19 at right

**Imprimaturs from the National Postal Museum Archives**

**A. Ordinary**
Nos. W89/91 imperforate, watermark Type W.24

| | |
|---|---|
| Watermark upright (6d., 1s.3d.) or sideways (4d.) (set of 3) | £6750 |

**B. Phosphor**
Nos. WP89/91 imperforate, watermark Type W.24

| | |
|---|---|
| Watermark upright (6d., 1s.3d.) or sideways (4d.) (set of 3) | £6750 |

**Quantities Sold:**

| | Ordinary | Phosphor |
|---|---|---|
| 4d. | 129,764,160 | 16,397,880 |
| 6d. | 17,086,680 | 3,357,480 |
| 1s.3d. | 7,026,240 | 1,761,240 |
| Pack | 48,732 | — |

**Withdrawn:** 31.5.67

**W88**. Black-headed Gull

**W89**. Blue Tit

**W90**. Robin

**W91**. Blackbird

(Des. J. Norris Wood)

## 1966 (8 August). British Birds

These were the first British stamps to be printed in eight colours. On the blackbird design the black was printed over the bistre.

Issued together in *se-tenant* blocks of four within the sheet Types **W88/91**

**A. Ordinary**
**W92** (=SG 696)

| | | Mint | Used |
|---|---|---|---|
| 4d. | grey, black, red, emerald-green, bright blue, greenish yellow and bistre | 20 | 20 |
| a. | Block of 4. Nos. W92/5 | 1·00 | 2·00 |
| | *Missing colours:* | | |
| c. | Black, bright blue, bistre and reddish brown | £4000 | |
| d. | Greenish yellow | £1100 | |
| e. | Red | £1100 | |
| f. | Emerald-green | £200 | |
| g. | Bright blue | £700 | |
| h. | Bistre | £200 | |
| i. | Black (only) | | |
| j. | HARRISO omitted (No dot R. 15/5)* Block of four | 40·00 | |
| k. | Watermark inverted | 4·00 | |

**W93** (=SG 697)

| | | Mint | Used |
|---|---|---|---|
| 4d. | black, greenish yellow, grey, emerald-green, bright blue and bistre | 20 | 20 |
| | *Missing colours:* | | |
| c. | Black, bright blue, bistre and reddish brown | £4000 | |
| d. | Greenish yellow | £1100 | |
| e. | Emerald-green | £200 | |
| f. | Bright blue | £700 | |
| g. | Bistre | £200 | |
| k. | Watermark inverted | 4·00 | |

**W94** (=SG 698)

| | | Mint | Used |
|---|---|---|---|
| 4d. | red, greenish yellow, black, grey, bistre, reddish brown and emerald-green | 20 | 20 |
| | *Missing colours:* | | |
| c. | Black, bright blue, bistre and reddish brown | £4000 | |
| d. | Greenish yellow | £1100 | |
| e. | Red | £1100 | |
| f. | Emerald-green | £200 | |
| g. | Bistre | £200 | |
| h. | Reddish brown | £125 | |
| i. | Black (only) | – | |
| k. | Watermark inverted | 4·00 | |

**W95** (=SG 699)

| | | Mint | Used |
|---|---|---|---|
| 4d. | black, reddish brown, greenish yellow, grey and bistre | 20 | 20 |
| | *Missing colours:* | | |
| c. | Black, bright blue, bistre and reddish brown | £4000 | |
| d. | Greenish yellow | £1100 | |
| e. | Reddish brown | £125 | |
| f. | Bistre | £200 | |
| k. | Watermark inverted | 4·00 | |

| | | |
|---|---|---|
| First Day Cover (W92/5) | | 8·00 |
| Presentation Pack (W92/5) | 11·00 | |

**B. Phosphor**
**WP92** (=SG 696p)

| | | Mint | Used |
|---|---|---|---|
| 4d. | Three bands | 20 | 20 |
| a. | Block of 4. Nos. WP92/5 | 75 | 2·00 |
| | *Missing colours:* | | |
| b. | Emerald-green | £200 | |
| c. | Bright blue | £6000 | |
| d. | Bistre | £2750 | |
| e. | Greenish yellow | £2000 | |
| i. | Watermark inverted | 20·00 | |

**WP93** (=SG 697p)

| | | Mint | Used |
|---|---|---|---|
| 4d. | Three bands | 20 | 20 |
| | *Missing colours:* | | |
| b. | Emerald-green | £200 | |
| c. | Bright blue | £6000 | |
| d. | Bistre | £2750 | |
| e. | Greenish yellow | £2000 | |
| i. | Watermark inverted | 20·00 | |

**WP94 (=SG 698p)**

| | | | |
|---|---|---|---|
| 4d. | Three bands | 20 | 20 |
| | *Missing colours:* | | |
| b. | Emerald-green | £200 | |
| c. | Bistre | £2750 | |
| d. | Reddish brown | £175 | |
| e. | Greenish yellow | £2000 | |

| | | |
|---|---|---|
| i. | Watermark inverted | 20·00 |

**WP95 (=SG 699p)**

| | | | |
|---|---|---|---|
| 4d. | Three bands | 20 | 20 |
| | *Missing colours:* | | |
| b. | Reddish brown | £175 | |
| c. | Bistre | £2750 | |
| e. | Greenish yellow | £2000 | |
| i. | Watermark inverted | 20·00 | |

First Day Cover (WP92/5) 8·00 Prices for missing colour errors and inverted watermarks in blocks of four:

| | Ordinary | Phosphor |
|---|---|---|
| Black, bright blue, bistre and reddish brown | £18000 | † |
| Greenish yellow | £4400 | £8000 |
| Red | £2200 | † |
| Emerald green | £600 | £600 |
| Bright blue | £1400 | £12000 |
| Bistre | £800 | £11000 |
| Reddish brown | £250 | £350 |
| Watermark inverted | 18·00 | 80·00 |

*"HARRISON" is omitted except for fragments of the N and on the stamp below (W94) the imprint is very faint, particularly "AND SO". The price is for a block containing both varieties. The damage was quickly discovered and repaired during the early stages of the printing.
Black only is not known in a block.
These are known postmarked at various places with dates from 17 July 1966 due to supplies prematurely released by the Philatelic Bureau.

**Cylinder Numbers (Blocks of Eight)**

| | Perforation Type F (P/E). No dot | |
|---|---|---|
| Cylinder Nos. | Ordinary | Phosphor |
| 2A (black)–1B (grey)–1C (yellow)–1D (red)–1E (green)–2F (blue)–2G (bistre)–1H (Brown) | ✓ 6·00 | 6·00 |
| 2A–1B–1C–1D–1E–2F–2G–2H | 15·00 | † |

**Minor Constant Flaws**

4d. Cyls. 2A–1B–1C–1D–1E–2F–2G with 1H or 2H no dot
1/2 Small brown dot under main twig (Th. B3), OP
4/3 Small brown dot to right of Robin's tail (Th. B7), OP
5/1 Small black dot in gull's wing (Th. D5), OP
6/2 Red spot between blackbird's claws (Th. F6), OP
7/1 Small black dot in gull's wing (Th. D6), OP
7/4 Extension to main twig at right (Th. A6), OP
9/6 Horizontal bistre line above main twig at left (Th. A–B3–4), O

**Sheet Details**
Sheet size: 120 (6 × 20). In se-tenant blocks of four, single pane sheet-fed

**Sheet markings:**
**Cylinder numbers:** Opposite rows 17/19 at left, boxed
**Guide holes:** None
**Marginal arrows (photo-etched):** "W" shaped, at top, bottom and sides
**Marginal rule:** At bottom of sheet
**Colour register marks:** Above and below vertical rows 1/3 and 5/6

**Coloured crosses:** Above and below vertical rows 3/4
**Autotron marks and Colour designations:** None
**Traffic lights (boxed):** In same order as cylinder numbers opposite rows 18/19 at right
A number of sheets from the end of the printing run showed part of the design in the left-hand margin by row 20. This was caused by incomplete masking of the multipositive; touched out before printing, but then wearing through.

**Imprimaturs from the National Postal Museum Archives**

**A. Ordinary**
Nos. W92/95 imperforate, watermark Type W.24

| | |
|---|---|
| Watermark upright (se-tenant block of 4) | £9000 |

**B. Phosphor**
Nos. WP92/95 imperforate, watermark Type W.24

| | |
|---|---|
| Watermark upright (se-tenant block of 4) | £9000 |

**Quantities Sold:**
Ordinary 88,047,742; phosphor 14,613,120; Pack (ordinary) 42,888

**Withdrawn:** 7.8.57

**W92.** Cup Winners

(Des. David Gentleman)

## 1966 (18 August). England's World Cup Football Victory

England won the World Cup Football Championship by defeating West Germany 4–2 at Wembley on 30 July 1966.
Watermark sideways
Type **W92**

**W96 (=SG 700)**

| | | Mint | Used |
|---|---|---|---|
| | 4d. red, reddish purple, bright blue, flesh and black | 30 | 30 |
| a. | Patch on thigh (No dot, R. 3/20) | 20·00 | |
| b. | Red patch below ball (No dot, R. 4/16) | 20·00 | |
| c. | Broken shadow (No dot, R. 5/17) | 20·00 | |

The above was only put on sale at post offices in England, the Channel Islands and the Isle of Man, and the Philatelic Bureau in London and also, on August 22, in Edinburgh on the occasion of the opening of the Edinburgh Festival as well as at Army post offices at home and abroad.
It was also pre-released on 17 August at an Army Camp P.O. in Great Britain.
An example of No. W89 with forged additional inscription on Edinburgh (22 August) first day cover is known.
For W96a, W96b and W96c. see illustrations after Nos. WP89/91.

**Cylinder Numbers** (Blocks of Six)

| | Perforation Type A (I/E) | |
|---|---|---|
| Cylinder Nos. | No dot | Dot |
| 4d 1A (black)–1B (blue)–1C (red)–1D (purple)–1E (flesh)* | √4·00 | 4·00 |

*In the no dot pane the flesh cylinder is expressed in error thus: "1E". and on the dot pane the black cylinder is shown as ."1A".

Perforation Type A is with sheet orientated showing head to left.

**Minor Constant Flaws**

4d. Cyls. 1A–1B–1C–1D–1E no dot
1/15 Black dot in second N of ENGLAND
2/9 Black spur on left player's right boot (Th. J–K5)
3/1 Horizontal scratch through top of ball (Th. K1–2)
5/6 Blue patch below u of Cup
6/13 White patch on heel of left player's left boot (Th. J3)
6/18 Blue spots over T of LTD

4d. Cyls. 1A–1B–1C–1D–1E dot
4/11 Black dot between W and I of WINNERS
5/10 Dark spot on ball (Th. K1)
5/17 Grey coloured spur to top of l of World

**Sheet Details**
Sheet size: 120 (20 × 6). Double pane reel-fed

**Sheet markings:**
**Cylinder numbers:** Above vertical rows 2/3, boxed
**Guide holes:** In single "S N" box above vertical rows 6/7 (no dot) or below (dot)
**Marginal arrows (photo-etched):** "W" shaped, at top, bottom and sides
**Marginal rule:** At left of sheet
**Colour register marks:** Above vertical rows 3/4 and 18/19 (no dot) or below (dot)
**Autotron marks (solid):** Red, purple, flesh, blue, black below vertical rows 15/18 (no dot) or
above (dot)
**Colour designations:** 5 BLACK G4 BLUE MAROON G3 G2 RED G1 LIGHT RED below vertical rows 11/16 on dot panes only
**Traffic lights (boxed):** Black, blue, red, purple, flesh reading left to right below vertical rows 2/3

**Imprimatur from the National Postal Museum Archives**
Ordinary paper
No. W96 imperforate, watermark Type W.24

| Watermark sideways | £2250 |
|---|---|

**Quantity Sold:** 12,452,640
Sold Out Soon after issue

**W93**. Jodrell Bank Radio Telescope

**W94**. British Motor-cars

(Des. David and A. Gillespie)

**W95**. SRN 6 Hovercraft

**W96**. Windscale Reactor

(Des. Andrew Restall)

**1966 (19 September). British Technology**

The designs represent British Technological achievements.
Types **W93/96**

**A. Ordinary**

| | | Mint | Used |
|---|---|---|---|
| **W97** (=SG 701) | | | |
| 4d. | black and lemon | 15 | 10 |
| a. | Struts flaw (No dot, R. 4/6) | 22·00 | |
| **W98** (=SG 702) | | | |
| 6d. | red, deep blue and orange | 25 | 20 |
| a. | Red (Mini-cars) omitted | £19000 | |
| b. | Blue (Jaguar and inscr.) omitted | £16000 | |
| c. | Broken D (R. 19/6) | 20·00 | |
| **W99** (=SG 703) | | | |
| 1s.3d. | black, orange-red, slate and light greenish blue | 50 | 40 |
| **W100** (=SG 704) | | | |
| 1s.6d. | black, yellow-green, bronze-green, lilac and deep blue | 50 | 60 |
| First Day Cover (W97/100) | | | 5·00 |
| Presentation Pack (W97/100) | | 12·00 | |

### B. Phosphor
**WP97** (=SG 701p)

| | | | |
|---|---|---|---|
| 4d. | Three bands | 10 | 10 |
| a. | Error. Pair, with and without phosphor | 24·00 | |
| b. | Narrow band at left or right (stamp with vert. margin) | 2·50 | |
| c. | Struts flaw (No dot, R. 4/6) | 20·00 | |

**WP98** (=SG 702p)

| | | | |
|---|---|---|---|
| 6d. | Three bands | 15 | 25 |
| a. | Narrow band at left or right (stamp with vert. margin) | 2·50 | |
| b. | Broken D (R. 19/6) | 20·00 | |

**WP99** (=SG 703p)

| | | | |
|---|---|---|---|
| 1s.3d. | Three bands | 35 | 40 |

**WP100** (=SG 704p)

| | | | |
|---|---|---|---|
| 1s.6d. | Three bands | 50 | 60 |
| a. | Narrow band at left or right (stamp with vert. margin) | 2·50 | |
| b. | Error. Two broad bands | 35·00 | |

| | |
|---|---|
| First Day Cover (WP97/100) | 5·00 |

W97a, WP97c
Strong retouch consisting of three strong black strokes in the form of an arrow

W98c, WP98b

### Cylinder Numbers (Blocks of Six)

#### (a) Ordinary

| Cyl. Nos. | Perforation Type A (E/I) | |
|---|---|---|
| | No dot | Dot |
| 4d. 1A (lemon)–1B (black) | 1·50 | 1·50 |
| 6d. 1A (orange)–1B (red)–1C (blue) | 2·00 | |
| 1s.3d. 1A (blue)–1B (slate)–1C (orange)–1D (black) | 4·50 | |
| 1s.6d. 1A (bronze-green)–1B (lilac)–1C (black)–1D (yellow-green)–1E (blue) | 4·50 | |

#### (b) Phosphor

| | | |
|---|---|---|
| 4d. 1A (lemon)–1B (black) | 5·00 | 3·00 |
| 6d. 1A (orange)–1B (red)–1C (blue) | 3·00 | |
| 1s.3d. 1A (blue)–1B (slate)–1C (orange)–1D (black) | 4·00 | |
| 1s.6d. 1A (bronze-green)–1B (lilac)–1C (black)–1D (yellow-green)–1E (blue) | 6·00 | |

### Minor Constant Flaws

4d. Cyls. 1A–1B no dot
    1/1 Lines of retouching above Queen's head resemble a thumb-print (Th. A9–12); also small pale area in left of telescope bowl (Th. C3–4), both OP
    1/2 Retouch to background right of value (Th. B3–4), OP
    1/6 Retouch to background top left corner of stamp (Th. A1), OP
    5/4 Retouch to background in front of Queen's neck (Th. E9), OP
    10/6 Horizontal line of retouching to background behind Queen's head (Th. D12–13), OP
    19/6 Horizontal white line above ON AND SONS of imprint, OP
    20/5 Horizontal white line below portrait (Th. F10–12), OP
    20/6 As 20/5 but stronger line, OP

4d. Cyls. 1A–1B dot
    3/3 Retouch to background in front of Queen's neck (Th. E10), OP
    5/5 White scratch in right of telescope bowl (Th. B6–7), OP
    9/3 Small white patch in background below portrait (Th. F–G12), OP
    9/5 Retouch to background at left of telescope bowl (Th. E–F1), OP
    13/4 Small white patch in background bottom left of portrait (Th. FG9), OP
    13/5 Pale patch in background to left of telescope bowl (Th. E–F2), OP
    14/6 Yellow spot in right of telescope bowl (Th. D6), OP

6d. Cyls. 1A–1B–1C no dot
    5/6 Retouch to background above Queen's head (Th. A10–11), OP
    10/3 Vertical blue line in Queen's portrait (Th. AC10), OP
    13/3 Pale area above value (Th. A2), OP
    17/4 Spur of first S of SONS, OP

1s.3d. Cyls. 1A–1B–1C–1D no dot
    1/1 Retouch in background behind Queen's head (Th. CD13), OP
    1/4 White spot below e of Hovercraft, OP
    1/6 Retouch in sea, bottom centre (Th. G7), OP
    12/6 Horizontal orange coloured line extends from sea to sheet margin (Th. G13–15), OP

1s.6d. Cyls. 1A–1B–1C–1D–1E no dot
    1/3 Retouch in sky in front of Queen's neck (Th. CD10), OP
    1/5 Grey coloured flaw in sky top right of Queen's head (Th. A13), OP
    2/2 Lower part of left stroke of n of Advanced is broken off, OP
    16/3 Vertical blue line in gutter between design edge and perforation (Th. D–G13), OP
    16/5 Wispy whitish line runs vertically above v of Advanced (Th. F–G2), OP
    20/1 Small white flaw in large door of building (Th. F6), OP

### Sheet Details
Sheet size: 120 (6 × 20). 4d. double pane reel-fed; others single pane reel-fed

**Sheet markings:**
**Cylinder numbers:**
4d., 6d., 1s.3d. Opposite R. 19/1, boxed
1s.6d. Opposite rows 18/19 at left, boxed
**Guide holes:**
4d. In single "S N" box opposite rows 14/15, at left (no dot) or right (dot)

Others. In single "S O N" box opposite rows 14/15, at both sides

**Marginal arrows (photo-etched):** "W" shaped, at top, bottom and sides

**Marginal rule:** None

**Colour register marks:**
4d. Opposite rows 1/2 and 20, at left (no dot) or right (dot)
6d., 1s.3d. Opposite rows 2/3 and 17/18, at both sides
1s.6d. Opposite rows 3/4 and 17/18, at both sides

**Autotron marks (solid):**
4d. Black, lemon, opposite row 5, at right (no dot) or left (dot)
6d. Blue, red, orange below vertical rows 1/3
1s.3d. Black, orange, blue, slate below vertical rows 1/3. Additional black below vertical row 3
1s.6d. Black, lilac, bronze-green, yellow-green, blue below vertical rows 1/3 and additionally black below vertical row 1. During printing the correct sequence, black, blue, bronze-green, lilac, yellow-green, was engraved below vertical rows 4/6

**Colour designations:**
4d. G1 YELLOW G2 BLACK in right margin reading upwards opposite rows 8/5 on dot panes only
6d. G2 RED G3 BLUE in right margin reading upwards opposite rows 7/6
1s.3d. G1 GREY G2 BLUE G3 RED G4 BLACK in right margin reading upwards opposite rows 7/4
1s.6d. G1 BLUE G2 YELLOW G3 GREEN G4 MAUVE G5 BLACK in right margin reading upwards opposite rows 9/5

**Traffic lights (boxed):**
4d. Lemon, black opposite R. 19/6
6d. Orange, red, blue opposite R. 19/6
1s.3d. Blue, slate, orange, black opposite rows 18/19 at right
1s.6d. Black, lilac, bronze-green, yellow-green, blue opposite rows 18/19 at right

**Imprimaturs from the National Postal Museum Archives**

**A. Ordinary**
Nos. W97/100 imperforate, watermark Type W.24

| Watermark upright (*set of* 4) | £9000 |
|---|---|

**B. Phosphor**
Nos. WP97/100 imperforate, watermark Type W.24

| Watermark upright (*set of* 4) | £9000 |
|---|---|

**Quantities Sold:**

| | Ordinary | Phosphor |
|---|---|---|
| 4d. | 79,112,278 | 12,737,520 |
| 6d. | 11,087,516 | 2,388,720 |
| 1s.3d. | 5,199,900 | 1,431,000 |
| 1s.6d. | 5,284,069 | 1,414,320 |
| Pack | 35,437 | — |

**Withdrawn:** 18.9.67 (6d. phosphor sold out earlier)

W97.

W98.

W99.

W100.

W101.

W102.

Types W97/102 show battle scenes and were issued together *se-tenant* in horizontal strips of six within the sheet

W103. Norman Ship

**W104**. Norman Horsemen attacking Harold's Troops

(Des. David Gentleman)
(Printed in photogravure with the Queen's head die-stamped in gold 6d., 1s.3d.)

●────────────

## 1966 (14 October). 900th Anniversary of Battle of Hastings

The scenes depicted are all reproduced from the celebrated Bayeux Tapestry which records the Norman invasion of England.

Watermark sideways on 1s.3d. (normal is top of crown pointing to left when stamps are viewed from the back)

Types **W97/104**

### A. Ordinary

**W101** (=SG 705)

| | | Mint | Used |
|---|---|---|---|
| 4d. | black, olive-green, bistre, deep blue, orange, magenta, green, blue and grey | 10 | 10 |
| a. | Strip of 6. Nos. W101/6 | 1·90 | 2·25 |
| ab. | Imperforate strip of six | £3500 | |
| | *Missing colours:* | | |
| b. | Olive-green | 65·00 | |
| c. | Bistre | 65·00 | |
| d. | Deep blue | 75·00 | |
| e. | Orange | 65·00 | |
| f. | Magenta | 65·00 | |
| g. | Green | 65·00 | |
| h. | Blue | 65·00 | |
| i. | Grey | 65·00 | |
| j. | Watermark inverted | 7·00 | |

**W102** (=SG 706)

| | | | |
|---|---|---|---|
| 4d. | black, olive-green, bistre, deep blue, orange, magenta, green, blue and grey | 10 | 10 |
| | *Missing colours:* | | |
| b. | Olive-green | 65·00 | |
| c. | Bistre | 65·00 | |
| d. | Deep blue | 75·00 | |
| e. | Orange | 65·00 | |
| f. | Magenta | 65·00 | |
| g. | Green | 65·00 | |
| h. | Blue | 65·00 | |
| i. | Grey | 65·00 | |
| j. | Watermark inverted | 7·00 | |

**W103** (=SG 707)

| | | | |
|---|---|---|---|
| 4d. | black, olive-green, bistre, deep blue, orange, magenta, green, blue and grey | 10 | 10 |
| | *Missing colours:* | | |
| b. | Olive-green | 65·00 | |
| c. | Bistre | 65·00 | |

| | | | |
|---|---|---|---|
| d. | Deep blue | 75·00 | |
| e. | Orange | 65·00 | |
| f. | Magenta | 65·00 | |
| g. | Green | 65·00 | |
| h. | Blue | 65·00 | |
| i. | Grey | 65·00 | |
| j. | Watermark inverted | 7·00 | |

**W104** (=SG 708)

| | | | |
|---|---|---|---|
| 4d. | black, olive-green, bistre, deep blue, magenta, green, blue and grey | 10 | 10 |
| | *Missing colours:* | | |
| b. | Olive-green | 65·00 | |
| c. | Bistre | 65·00 | |
| d. | Deep blue | 75·00 | |
| f. | Magenta | 65·00 | |
| g. | Green | 65·00 | |
| h. | Blue | 65·00 | |
| i. | Grey | 65·00 | |
| j. | Watermark inverted | 7·00 | |

**W105** (=SG 709)

| | | | |
|---|---|---|---|
| 4d. | black, olive-green, bistre, deep blue, orange, magenta, green, blue and grey | 10 | 10 |
| | *Missing colours:* | | |
| b. | Olive-green | 65·00 | |
| c. | Bistre | 65·00 | |
| d. | Deep blue | 75·00 | |
| e. | Orange | 65·00 | |
| f. | Magenta | 65·00 | |
| g. | Green | 65·00 | |
| h. | Blue | 65·00 | |
| i. | Grey | 65·00 | |
| j. | Watermark inverted | 7·00 | |

**W106** (=SG 710)

| | | | |
|---|---|---|---|
| 4d. | black, olive-green, bistre, deep blue, orange, magenta, green, blue and grey | 10 | 10 |
| | *Missing colours:* | | |
| b. | Olive-green | 65·00 | |
| c. | Bistre | 65·00 | |
| d. | Deep blue | 75·00 | |
| e. | Orange | 65·00 | |
| f. | Magenta | 65·00 | |
| g. | Green | 65·00 | |
| h. | Blue | 65·00 | |
| i. | Grey | 65·00 | |
| j. | Watermark inverted | 7·00 | |

**W107** (=SG 711)

| | | | |
|---|---|---|---|
| 6d. | black, olive-green, violet, blue, green and gold | 10 | 10 |
| a. | Watermark inverted | 42·00 | |
| b. | Yellowish gold | 1·00 | |

**W108** (=SG 712)

| | | | |
|---|---|---|---|
| 1s.3d. | black, lilac, bronze-green, rosine, bistre-brown and gold | 20 | 75 |
| a. | Lilac omitted | £5000 | |
| b. | Watermark sideways inverted (top of crown pointing to right) | 35·00 | |

| | | | |
|---|---|---|---|
| | c. Club flaw (R. 7/2) | 25·00 | |

| | |
|---|---|
| First Day Cover (W101/8) | 8·00 |

| | |
|---|---|
| Presentation Pack (W101/8) | 9·00 |

**B. Phosphor**
**WP101** (=SG 705p)

| | | | |
|---|---|---|---|
| 4d. | Three bands | 10 | 10 |
| a. | Strip of 6. Nos. WP101/6 | 1·90 | 6·00 |
| | *Missing colours:* | | |
| b. | Olive-green | 65·00 | |
| c. | Bistre | 65·00 | |
| d. | Deep blue | 75·00 | |
| e. | Orange | 65·00 | |
| f. | Magenta | 65·00 | |
| g. | Green | 65·00 | |
| h. | Blue | 65·00 | |
| i. | Grey | 65·00 | |
| j. | Magenta and green | 75·00 | |
| | | | |
| k. | Watermark inverted | 3·00 | |

**WP102** (=SG 706p)

| | | | |
|---|---|---|---|
| 4d. | Three bands | 10 | 10 |
| | *Missing colours:* | | |
| b. | Olive-green | 65·00 | |
| c. | Bistre | 65·00 | |
| d. | Deep blue | 75·00 | |
| e. | Orange | 65·00 | |
| f. | Magenta | 65·00 | |
| g. | Green | 65·00 | |
| h. | Blue | 65·00 | |
| i. | Grey | 65·00 | |
| j. | Magenta and green | 75·00 | |
| | | | |
| k. | Watermark inverted | 3·00 | |

**WP103** (=SG 707p)

| | | | |
|---|---|---|---|
| 4d. | Three bands | 10 | 10 |
| | *Missing colours:* | | |
| b. | Olive-green | 65·00 | |
| c. | Bistre | 65·00 | |
| d. | Deep blue | 75·00 | |
| e. | Orange | 65·00 | |
| f. | Magenta | 65·00 | |
| g. | Green | 65·00 | |
| h. | Blue | 65·00 | |
| i. | Grey | 65·00 | |
| j. | Magenta and green | 75·00 | |
| | | | |
| k. | Watermark inverted | 3·00 | |

**WP104** (=SG 708p)

| | | | |
|---|---|---|---|
| 4d | Three bands | 10 | 10 |
| | *Missing colours:* | | |
| b. | Olive-green | 65·00 | |
| c. | Bistre | 65·00 | |
| d. | Deep blue | 75·00 | |
| f. | Magenta | 65·00 | |
| g. | Green | 65·00 | |
| h. | Blue | 65·00 | |
| i. | Grey | 65·00 | |
| j. | Magenta and green | 75·00 | |
| | | | |
| k. | Watermark inverted | 3·00 | |

**WP105** (=SG 709p)

| | | | |
|---|---|---|---|
| 4d. | Three bands | 10 | 10 |
| | *Missing colours:* | | |
| b. | Olive-green | 65·00 | |
| c. | Bistre | 65·00 | |
| d. | Deep blue | 75·00 | |
| e. | Orange | 65·00 | |
| f. | Magenta | 65·00 | |
| g. | Green | 65·00 | |
| h. | Blue | 65·00 | |
| i. | Grey | 65·00 | |
| j. | Magenta and green | 75·00 | |
| k. | Watermark inverted | 3·00 | |

**WP106** (=SG 710p)

| | | | |
|---|---|---|---|
| 4d. | Three bands | 10 | 10 |
| | *Missing colours:* | | |
| b. | Olive-green | 65·00 | |
| c. | Bistre | 65·00 | |
| d. | Deep blue | 75·00 | |
| e. | Orange | 65·00 | |
| f. | Magenta | 65·00 | |
| g. | Green | 65·00 | |
| h. | Blue | 65·00 | |
| i. | Grey | 65·00 | |
| j. | Magenta and green | 75·00 | |
| | | | |
| k. | Watermark inverted | 3·00 | |

**WP107** (=SG 711p)

| | | | |
|---|---|---|---|
| 6d. | Three bands | 10 | 10 |
| a. | Watermark inverted | 55·00 | |
| b. | Yellowish gold | 1·00 | |

**WP108** (=SG 712p)

| | | | |
|---|---|---|---|
| 1s.3d. | Four bands | 20 | 75 |
| a. | Lilac omitted | £1250 | |
| b. | Error. Three bands | 8·00 | |
| c. | Watermark sideways inverted (top of crown pointing to right) | 35·00 | |
| ✓ d. | Club flaw (R. 7/2) | 25·00 | |

| | |
|---|---|
| First Day Cover (WP101/8) | 9·00 |

4d. Prices for missing colour errors and inverted watermarks in strips of six:

| | Ordinary | Phosphor |
|---|---|---|
| Olive-green | £390 | £390 |
| Bistre | £390 | £390 |
| Deep blue | £450 | £450 |
| Orange (on five stamps) | £325 | £325 |
| Magenta | £390 | £390 |
| Green | £390 | £390 |
| Blue | £390 | £390 |
| Grey | £390 | £390 |
| Magenta and green | † | £450 |
| Watermark inverted | 45·00 | 20·00 |

Nos. W101 and W105 with grey and blue omitted have been seen commercially used, posted from Middleton-in-Teesdale.

The 6d. and 1s.3d. were also issued with the die-stamped gold head omitted but as these can also be removed by chemical means we are not prepared to list them unless a way is found of distinguishing the genuine stamps from the fakes which will satisfy the Expert Committees. However, three examples of No. W108 in a right-hand top corner block of 10 (2 × 5) are known with the Queen's head omitted as a result of a double paper fold prior to die-stamping. The perforation is normal. Of the other seven stamps, four have the Queen's head misplaced and three are normal.

W108c, WP108d
The fallen knight has what appears to be a
large black club at his right hand

**Cylinder Numbers** (Blocks of Twenty-Four (4d.), Six (6d.), Eight
(1s.3d.))

| | | Perforation Types | |
| | | F (P/E) No dot | |
| Cylinder Nos | | Ordinary | Phosphor |
|---|---|---|---|
| 4d. | 1A (black)–1B (olive-green)–1C (bistre)–1D (deep blue)–1E (orange)–1F (magenta)–1G (green)–H (blue)–1J (grey) | 12·00 | 10·00 |
| | 2A–1B–1C–1D–1E–1F–1G–1H–1J | 10·00 | |

| | G (P/P) | | | |
| | Ordinary | | Phosphor | |
| | No dot | Dot | No dot | Dot |
|---|---|---|---|---|
| 6d. 1A (black)–1B (olive-green)–1C (violet)–1D (blue)–1E (green) | 1·00 | 1·00 | 1·00 | 1·00 |

| | A (T) (E/P) | |
| | No dot | |
| | Ordinary | Phosphor |
|---|---|---|
| 1s.3d. 1A (black)–1B (lilac)–1C (bronze-green)–1D (rosine)–1E (bistre-brown) | 30·00* | 30·00* |

**Minor Constant Flaws**

4d. Cyls. 1B–1C–1D–1E–1F–1G–1H–1J no dot in combination with black cyls. 1A or 2A
   3/4 Spur on second S of HASTINGS, OP
   4/1 Horizontal black line to left of Queen's forehead (Th.
   A10–11), OP (1A only)
   4/5 Black line under Queen's chin (Th. C11), OP (1A only)
   9/1 Right hind leg of dark horse is paler than normal (Th.
   F–G8), OP
   9/2 Second S of SONS pale and distorted, possibly hand
   drawn (OP) (1A only)
   19/4 White spot on horseman's leg (Th. F7), OP (1A only)
   20/3 LTD heavier than normal, OP (1A only)
   20/4 HARRISON AND heavier than normal, OP (1A only)

4d. Cyl. 2A no dot
   10/1 H of HARRISON is indistinct, O
   11/1 Hastings 1066 weaker than normal, O

6d. Cyls. 1A–1B–1C–1D–1E no dot
   1/1 Blue patch on hull due to lack of black shading (Th.
   F9), OP
   4/1 Small dot after final s of Hastings, OP
   6/1 Diagonal black line through figures in small boat (Th.
   C3–B5), OP
   8/4 Diagonal spur on first t of Battle, OP

6d. Cyls. 1A–1B–1C–1D–1E dot
   1/1 Partial break in main left-hand rigging of main vessel
   (Th. D3), OP
   3/1 Extra gold enlarges Queen's throat at both sides (Th.
   C–D12), P
   8/5 Horizontal black line in upper part of first 6 of 1966,
   OP
   8/6 Horizontal black line through HAR of HARRISON, OP

1s.3d. Cyls. 1A–1B–1C–1D–1E no dot
   6/2 Dot in g of Hastings, OP

   8/1 Diagonal hairline runs from bottom of red shield of
   second soldier through toes of right foot to bottom of
   stamp (Th. E–H12), O
   9/1 Line continues to right-hand arm of first soldier (Th.
   A12), O
   10/4 Bronze-green dot upper left of 1 of 1/3 (Th. F8), OP

**Sheet Details**
**Sheet sizes:**
4d. 120 (6 × 20). In se-tenant strips of six, single pane sheet-
fed
6d. 60 (6 × 10). Double pane sheet-fed
1s.3d. 60 (6 × 10). Single pane sheet-fed

**Sheet markings:**
**Cylinder numbers:**
4d. Opposite rows 17/19 at left, boxed
6d. Opposite rows 8/9 at left, boxed
1s.3d. Opposite rows 7/8 at left, boxed
**Guide holes:** None
**Marginal arrows (photo-etched):** "W" shaped, at top, bottom
and sides
**Marginal rule:** None
**Colour register marks:**
4d. Above and below vertical rows 1 and 5/6
6d. Above vertical rows 1 and 5/6 (no dot) or below them (dot)
1s.3d. Opposite rows 1/2 and 9/10, at both sides
**Coloured crosses:**
4d. Above and below vertical rows 3/4
6d. Above vertical rows 3/4 (no dot) or below them (dot)
1s.3d. Opposite rows 5/6, at both sides
**Autotron marks and Colour designations:** None
Traffic lights (boxed and in same order as cylinder numbers):
4d. Opposite rows 17/19 at right
6d. Opposite rows 8/9 at right
1s.3d. Opposite rows 7/8 at right

**Imprimaturs from the National Museum Archives**

**A. Ordinary**
Nos. W101/106 imperforate, watermark Type W.24

| Watermark upright (se-tenant strip of six) | £12500 |
|---|---|

Nos. W107/108 imperforate, watermark Type W.24

| Watermark upright (6d.) or sideways (1s.3d.) | (Each) £2250 |
|---|---|

**B. Phosphor**
Nos. WP101/106 imperforate, watermark Type W.24

| Watermark upright (se-tenant strip of six) | £12500 |
|---|---|

No. WP107 imperforate, watermark Type W.24

| Watermark upright (6d.) | £2250 |
|---|---|

**Quantities Sold:** Ordinary. 4d. 89,197,226; 6d. 12,012,328;
1s.3d. 5,721,426; Pack 51,332
Phosphor. 4d. 15,861,960; 6d. 2,820,360; 1s.3d. 1,646,280

**Withdrawn:** 13.10.67 (6d. phosphor sold out in September)

**W105**. King of the Orient
(Des. Miss Tasveer Shemza)

**W106**. Snowman
(Des. James Berry)

(Printed in photogravure with the Queen's head die-stamped in gold)

●━━━━━━━━━━

### 1966 (1 December). Christmas

These designs, executed by two six-year-old children, were chosen from nearly 5,000 entries in a Post Office competition for Britain's first adhesive Christmas stamps.
Watermark sideways on 3d.
Types **W105/6**
**A. Ordinary**

| W109 (=SG 713) | | *Mint* | *Used* |
|---|---|---|---|
| 3d. | black, blue, green, yellow, red and gold | 10 | 25 |
| a. | Queen's head double | £6000 | † |
| ab. | Queen's head double, one albino | £650 | |
| b. | Green omitted | | |
| c. | Missing T (No dot, R. 6/2) | 20·00 | |

| W110 (=SG 714) | | | |
|---|---|---|---|
| 1s.6d. | blue, red, pink, black and gold | 30 | 50 |
| a. | Pink (hat) omitted | £3800 | |
| b. | Watermark inverted | 15·00 | |

| First Day Cover (W109/10) | | 2·50 |
|---|---|---|
| Presentation Pack (W109/10) | | 12·00 |

The one phosphor band on No. WP109 was produced by printing broad phosphor bands across alternate vertical rows of perforations. Individual examples show the band at right or left (same prices either way).

**B. Phosphor**
**WP109 (=SG 713p)**

| | | | |
|---|---|---|---|
| 3d. | One band at left | 10 | 10 |
| a. | Band at right | 10 | 25 |
| ab. | Nos. WP109/a (horiz. pair) | 20 | 60 |
| ac. | Error. Pair, with and without phosphor | 18·00 | |
| b. | Missing T (No dot. R. 6/2) | 20·00 | |

| WP110 (=SG 714p) | | | |
|---|---|---|---|
| 1s.6d | Two bands | 30 | 50 |
| a. | Watermark inverted | 50·00 | |

| First Day Cover (WP109/10) | | 2·00 |
|---|---|---|

W109c, WP109b

Both values were also issued with the die-stamped gold head omitted but as these can also be removed by chemical means we are not prepared to list them unless a way is found of distinguishing the genuine stamps from the fakes which will satisfy the Expert Committees. However, the gold head and embossing omitted also occurred on the last vertical row of a sheet of the 3d. ordinary due to a major displacement to the left. Examples in horizontal marginal pairs can be considered to be genuine. Another example shows two gold head omissions, due to a paper fold, with three partial gold heads on the gummed side.

No. WP109 exists with a horizontal phosphor band across the top of the stamp. This was caused by phosphor spillage under the doctor blade and occurred on the top horizontal row of a sheet.

**Cylinder Numbers** (Blocks of Six)

| (a) Ordinary | | *Perforation Types* | |
|---|---|---|---|
| | | *A (I/E)* | *A (I/E)* |
| | *Cylinder Nos* | *No dot* | *Dot* |
| 3d. | 1A (blue)–1B (black)–1C (green)–1D (yellow)–1E (red) | 20·00 | 20·00 |
| | 1A–3B–1C–1D–1E | 1·00 | 1·00 |
| | 1A–4B–1C–1D–1E | 1·00 | 1·00 |
| | | *A (I/E)* | *A(T) (P/E)* |
| | | *No dot* | *No dot* |
| 1s.6d. | 1A (blue)–1B (black)–2C (red)–1D (pink) | 4·00 | 4·00 |

| (b) Phosphor | | *Perforation Types* | |
|---|---|---|---|
| | | *A (I/E)* | *A (I/E)* |
| | *Cylinder Nos* | *No dot* | *Dot* |
| 3d. | 1A (blue)–3B (black)–1C (green)–1D (yellow)–1E (red) | 1·00 | 1·00 |
| | 1A–4B–1C–1D–1E | 1·00 | 1·00 |
| | | *A (I/E)* | *A(T) (P/E)* |
| | | *No dot* | *No dot* |
| 1s.6d. | 1A (blue)–1B (black)–2C (red)–1D (pink) | 4·00 | 4·00 |

Perforation Types A and A(T) are with sheets orientated showing head to left.
In the dot panes of the 3d. the dot is missing after B in the black colour.

**Minor Constant Flaws**

3d. Cyls. 1A–1C–1D–1E no dot in combination with black cyls. 3B or 4B
2/1 During the course of printing a diagonal cut developed at base of Queen's neck and later the piece of gold foil separated and dropped downwards (Th. C–D5), OP
2/3 Blue dot in front of H of HARRISON, OP
2/8 A of AND in imprint shorter than normal, OP
3/4 White patch at top left corner of panel is larger than normal (Th. A1), OP
3/8 Extra stop after T. of T. SHEMZA, OP
7/1 Damaged top to A of AND, OP
8/8 Red dot under first leg of H of HARRISON, OP

3d. Cyls. 1A–1C–1D–1E dot in combination with black cyls. 3B or 4B
1/5 Two red dots in the yellow above red circle in crown (Th. F–G3), OP (3B only)
2/1 As for no dot cyls.

4/6 Background retouch between points of crown at right (Th. F5), OP
4/7 First S of SONS incomplete, OP
5/5 Red spot in white area below Queen's portrait (Th. D5), OP (3B only)
8/1 Top of S of HARRISON incomplete, OP

1s.6d. Cyls. 1A–1B–2C–1D no dot

3/1 White spot normally found in red scarf is filled in (Th. E4), OP
6/7 Dark blue spot inside 6 of 1/6, OP
8/2 Small blue projection into right-hand margin (Th. L7), OP
9/1 Second R of BERRY is damaged, OP

**Sheet Details**
Sheet size: 80 (8 × 10)
3d. double pane reel-fed, with dot pane above no dot pane
1s.6d. single pane sheet-fed

**Sheet markings:**
**Cylinder numbers:**
3d. Above vertical rows 2/3, boxed
1s.6d. Opposite R. 8/1, boxed
**Guide holes**: 3d. Boxed above vertical rows 6/7; 1s.6d. none
**Marginal arrows (photo-etched)**: "W" shaped, at top, bottom and sides
**Marginal rule**: None
**Colour register marks:**
3d. None; 1s.6d. above and below vertical rows 1/2 and 7/8
**Coloured crosses**: 3d. None; 1s.6d. above and below vertical rows 4/5
**Autotron marks (solid):**
3d. Green, yellow, red, black, blue opposite rows 8/10, left margin (dot); 1s.6d. none
Colour designations: None
**Traffic lights (boxed):**
3d. Black, blue, green, yellow, red below vertical rows 2/3
1s.6d. Blue, red, pink, black opposite R. 8/10

**Imprimaturs from the National Postal Museum Archives**

**A. Ordinary**
Nos. W109/110 imperforate, watermark Type W.24

| Watermark upright (1s.6d.) or sideways (3d.) (set of 2) | £4500 |
|---|---|

**B. Phosphor**
Nos. WP109/110 imperforate, watermark Type W.24

| Watermark upright (1s.6d.) or sideways (3d.) (set of 2) | £4500 |
|---|---|

**Quantities Sold:**

|  | Ordinary | Phosphor |
|---|---|---|
| 3d. | 153,318,160 | 20,774,000 |
| 1s.6d. | 8,756,960 | 2,109,280 |
| Pack | 33,672 | — |

**Withdrawn**: The 3d. phosphor was sold out in January, the 3d ordinary and 1s.6d. phosphor were sold out in October, and the 1s.6d. ordinary was withdrawn on 30.11.67

**W107**. Sea Freight

**W108**. Air Freight

(Des. Clive Abbott)

## 1967 (20 February). European Free Trade Association

Issued to commemorate the movement of trade between Austria, Denmark, Norway, Portugal, Sweden, Switzerland and the United Kingdom. Finland was an associate member.
Types **W107/8**
**A. Ordinary**

| **W111** (=SG 715) | | Mint | Used |
|---|---|---|---|
| 9d. | deep blue, red, lilac, green, brown, new blue, yellow and black | 25 | 20 |
| | *Missing colours:* | | |
| a. | Black (Queen's head), brown, new blue and yellow | £1250 | |
| b. | Lilac | £135 | |
| c. | Green | £135 | |
| d. | Brown (rail trucks) omitted | 95·00 | |
| e. | New blue | £135 | |
| f. | Yellow | £135 | |
| g. | Watermark inverted | 95·00 | |
| h. | Quay flaw (R. 8/3) | 20·00 | |

| **W112** (=SG 716) | | | |
|---|---|---|---|
| 1s.6d. | violet, red, deep blue, brown, green, blue-grey, new blue, yellow and black | 50 | 45 |
| | *Missing colours:* | | |
| a. | Red | | |
| b. | Deep blue | £550 | |
| c. | Brown | £135 | |
| d. | Blue-grey | £135 | |
| e. | New blue | £135 | |
| f. | Yellow | £135 | |
| g. | Green | | |
| h. | Broken ribbon (R. 11/3) | 20·00 | |
| i. | Broken strut (R. 13/6) | 25·00 | |
| j. | Break in frame (R. 20/1) | 20·00 | |

| First Day Cover (W111/12) | | | 3·00 |
|---|---|---|---|
| Presentation Pack (W111/12) | | | 3·50 |

## B. Phosphor (9d. applied flexo.; 1s.6d. applied typo.)
**WP111** (=SG 715P)

| | 9d. Three bands | 25 | 20 |
|---|---|---|---|
| | *Missing colours:* | | |
| a. | Lilac | £225 | |
| b. | Green | £135 | |
| c. | Brown (rail trucks) omitted | 95·00 | |
| d. | New blue | £135 | |
| e. | Yellow | £180 | |
| f. | Watermark inverted | 95·00 | |
| g. | Quay flaw (R. 8/3) | 20·00 | |

**WP112** (=SG 716p)

| | 1s.6d. Three bands | 25 | 40 |
|---|---|---|---|
| | *Missing colours:* | | |
| a. | Red | | |
| b. | Deep blue | £550 | |
| c. | Brown | 95·00 | |
| d. | Blue-grey | £135 | |
| e. | New blue | £135 | |
| f. | Watermark inverted | 30·00 | |
| g. | Broken ribbon (R. 11/3) | 20·00 | |
| h. | Broken strut (R. 13/6) | 25·00 | |
| j. | Break in frame (R. 20/1) | 20·00 | |
| k. | All over phosphor | | |

| First Day Cover (WP111/12) | 3·00 |
|---|---|

No. WP112k came from the first vertical column of a sheet. It was due to a weak mixture of the phosphor ink which leaked under the phosphor doctor blade.

W111h, WP111g    Normal    W112h, WP112g
Black protuberance on quay between trucks

W112i, WP112h
Broken strut below wing

W112j, WP112j
Break in the frame of Portuguese flag

### Cylinder Numbers (Blocks of Eight)

| | | Perforation Type | |
|---|---|---|---|
| | | F (P/E) | No dot |
| | Cylinder Nos | Ordinary | Phosphor |
| 9d. | 1A (deep blue)–B (red)–1C (lilac)–1D (green)–1E (brown)–1F (new blue)–1G (yellow)–1H (black) | 3·00 | 3·00 |
| 1s.6d. | 2A (violet)–1B (red)–1C (deep blue)–1D (green)–1E (brown)–1F (new blue)–1G (yellow)–2H (blue-grey)–2J (black) | 12·00* | 11·00* |

### Minor Constant Flaws
9d. Cyls. 1A–1B–1C–1D–1E–1F–1G–1H no dot
  6/5 Black colour on roof of bridge is smudged (Th. D8–9), OP
  11/5 Small blue dot in base of letter E (Th. B–C2), OP
  12/5 White spot in lilac superstructure (Th. E11), OP
1s.6d. Cyls. 2A–1B–1C–1D–1E–1F–1G–2H–2J no dot
  10/1 Small violet dot in top of letter E (Th. A2), OP
  19/1 White spur in 6 of 1/6, OP

### Sheet Details
Sheet size: 120 (6 × 20). Single pane sheet-fed

### Sheet markings:
**Cylinder numbers:**
9d. Opposite rows 17/19 at left, boxed
1s.6d. Opposite rows 17/20 at left, boxed
**Guide holes:** None
**Marginal arrows (photo-etched):** "W" shaped, at top, bottom and side.
**Marginal rule:** At bottom of sheet
**Colour register marks:** Above and below vertical rows 1/2 and 5/6
**Coloured crosses:** Above and below vertical rows 4/5
**Autotron marks and Colour designations:** None
**Traffic lights (boxed):**
9d. Opposite rows 17/19 at right, in same order as cylinder numbers
1s.6d. Violet, red, deep blue, brown, green, blue-grey, new blue, yellow, black opposite rows 17/19 at right

### Imprimaturs from the National Postal Museum Archives

**A. Ordinary**
Nos. W111/112 imperforate, watermark Type W.24

| Watermark upright (*set of* 2) | £4500 |
|---|---|

**B. Phosphor**
Nos. WP111/112 imperforate, watermark Type W.24

| Watermark upright (*set of* 2) | £4500 |
|---|---|

### Quantities Sold:

| | *Ordinary* | *Phosphor* |
|---|---|---|
| 9d. | 6,553,738 | 5,557,104 |
| 1s.6d. | 6,363,483 | 4,237,944 |
| Pack | 42,906 | — |

**Withdrawn:** 19.2.68

**W109**. Hawthorn and Bramble

**W110**. Larger Bindweed and Viper's Bugloss

**W111**. Ox-eye Daisy, Coltsfoot and Buttercup

**W112**. Bluebell, Red Campion and Wood Anemone

The above were issued together *se-tenant* in blocks of four within the sheet

(Des. Rev. W. Keble Martin)

**W113**. Dog Violet

**W114**. Primroses

(Des. Mary Grierson)

## 1967 (24 April). British Wild Flowers

Types **W109/14**

**A. Ordinary**

| W113 (=SG 717) | Mint | Used |
|---|---|---|
| 4d. grey, lemon, myrtle-green, red, agate and slate-purple | 20 | 20 |
| a. Block of 4. Nos. W113/16 | 80 | 2·25 |
| b. Grey double* | | |
| c. Red omitted | £5000 | |
| d. Watermark inverted | 2·00 | |
| e. Slate-purple omitted | £5500 | |

| W114 (=SG 718) | | |
|---|---|---|
| 4d. grey, lemon, myrtle-green, red, agate and violet | 20 | 20 |
| b. Grey double* | | |
| d. Watermark inverted | 2·00 | |

| W115 (=SG 719) | | |
|---|---|---|
| 4d. grey, lemon, myrtle-green, red and agate | 20 | 20 |
| b. Grey double* | | |
| d. Watermark inverted | 2·00 | |

| W116 (=SG 720) | | |
|---|---|---|
| 4d. grey, lemon, myrtle-green, reddish purple, agate and violet | 20 | 20 |
| b. Grey double* | | |
| c. Reddish purple omitted | £2000 | |
| d. Watermark inverted | 2·00 | |
| e. Value omitted (see note) | £10000 | |

| W117 (=SG 721) | | |
|---|---|---|
| 9d. lavender-grey, green, reddish violet and orange-yellow | 20 | 25 |
| a. Watermark inverted | 1·25 | |
| b. Notch in leaf (R. 20/2) | 20·00 | |

| W118 (=SG 722) | | |
|---|---|---|
| 1s.9d. lavender-grey, green, greenish yellow and orange | 25 | 35 |

| First Day Cover (W113/18) | 5·00 |
|---|---|

| Presentation Pack (W113/18) | 6·00 |
|---|---|

**B. Phosphor**

| WP113 (=SG 717p) | | |
|---|---|---|
| 4d. Three bands | 10 | 15 |
| a. Block of 4. Nos. WP113/16 | 50 | 2·00 |
| b. Agate omitted | £4500 | |
| c. Slate-purple omitted | £525 | |
| d. Watermark inverted | 2·00 | |

| WP114 (=SG 718p) | | |
|---|---|---|
| 4d. Three bands | 10 | 15 |
| b. Agate omitted | £4500 | |
| c. Violet omitted | | |
| d. Watermark inverted | 2·00 | |

| WP115 (=SG 719p) | | |
|---|---|---|
| 4d. Three bands | 10 | 15 |
| b. Agate omitted | £4500 | |
| c. Watermark inverted | 2·00 | |

| WP116 (=SG 720p) | | |
|---|---|---|
| 4d. Three bands | 10 | 15 |
| b. Agate omitted | £4500 | |
| c. Violet omitted | | |
| d. Watermark inverted | 2·00 | |

**WP117 (=SG 721p)**

| | | | |
|---|---|---|---|
| 9d. | Three bands | 15 | 25 |
| a. | Notch in leaf (R. 20/2) | 20·00 | |

**WP118 (=SG 722p)**

| | | |
|---|---|---|
| 1s.9d. | Three bands | 20 | 30 |

| | |
|---|---|
| First Day Cover (WP113/18) | 5·00 |

| | |
|---|---|
| Presentation Pack (WP113/18) | 6·00 |

4d. Prices for missing colour errors and inverted watermarks in blocks of four:

| | Ordinary | Phosphor |
|---|---|---|
| Red | £5000 | † |
| Reddish purple | £2000 | † |
| Agate | † | £18000 |
| Violet | † | |
| Slate purple | £5500 | £525 |
| Watermark inverted | 9·00 | 9·00 |
| Grey double | | † |

*The double impression of the grey printing affects the Queen's head, value and inscription.

The 1s.9d. is known postmarked 20 April in the Bristol area.

No. W116e (Bluebell etc.) was caused by something obscuring the face value on R. 14/6 during the printing of one sheet.

W117b, WP117a

**Cylinder Numbers** (Blocks of Eight (4d.) or Six (others))

| | Perforation Types | |
|---|---|---|
| | F (P/E) | No dot |
| Cylinder Nos. | Ordinary | Phosphor |
| 4d. 3A (grey)–1B (lemon)–2C (myrtle-green)–1D (reddish purple)–1E (red)–1F (agate)–2G (violet)–1H (slate-purple) | 3·25 | 3·00 |
| 3A–1B–3C–1D–1E–1F–2G–1H | | 22·00 |
| | A (E/I) | No dot |
| 9d. 2A (lavender-grey)–3B (green)–3C (reddish violet)–2D (orange-yellow) | 9·00* | 9·00* |
| 1s.9d. 2A (lavender-grey)–2B (green)–2C (greenish yellow)–2D (orange) | 2·50 | 2·25 |

**Minor Constant Flaws**

4d. Cyls. 3A–1B–2C–1D–1E–1F–2G–1H no dot
1/4 Green flaw in large leaf above flower (Th. A4), OP
4/6 Yellow spot by Queen's chin (Th. C10), P
8/6 Small spot by upper leaf of wood anemone (Th. A6), OP
10/2 Small green spot in lower wood anemone (Th. D9), OP
15/6 Style on left-hand flower of right-hand plant is incomplete (Th. A6), OP
16/2 Green spot at left of bluebell leaf (Th. E1), P

9d. Cyls. 2A–3B–3C–2D no dot
9/6 Diagonal hairline running down from small right-hand leaf (Th. F10), OP
13/5 Green spot between left leaf and centre violet flower (Th. D3), OP
14/1 Fine vertical yellow line at right of right-hand leaf on top left-hand stamen (Th. BC3), OP
20/6 Green spot in lower left-hand leaf (Th. G1), OP

1s.9d. Cyls. 2A–2B–2C–2D no dot
1/2 Diagonal yellow hairline in the white portion from Queen's neck to top of value (Th. CE11), OP

1/6 Retouch between top of stroke and 9 of value (Th. F12), OP
2/2 Retouch over 9 of value (Th. F13), OP
10/1 M of MARY is weak, OP
15/1 Line of green dots between two right-hand primroses (Th. E9), OP
19/4 Dotted green line projecting left from top left-hand leaf (Th. C–D1), OP
19/5 Horizontal green hairline on central primrose (Th. D4), OP
19/6 N of HARRISON is weak, OP
20/1 Break in outline of petals in topmost primrose (Th. B7), OP

**Sheet Details**
Sheet size: 120 (6 × 20)
4d. In se-tenant blocks of four, single pane sheet-fed
9d. and 1s.9d. Single pane reel-fed

**Sheet markings:**
**Cylinder numbers:**
4d. Opposite rows 17/19 at left, boxed
9d., 1s.9d. Opposite rows 18/19 at left, boxed
**Guide holes:**
4d. None
9d., 1s.9d. Opposite row 15 (boxed), at both sides
**Marginal arrows (photo-etched):** "W" shaped at top, bottom and sides
**Marginal rule:** At bottom of sheet
**Colour register marks:**
4d. Above and below vertical rows 1/2 and 5/6
9d., 1s.9d. Opposite rows 1/2 and 20, at both sides
**Coloured crosses:**
4d. Above and below vertical rows 3/4
9d., 1s.9d. None
**Autotron marks (solid):**
4d. None
9d. Lavender-grey, green, reddish violet, green over orange, below vertical rows 1/3
1s.9d. Lavender-grey, orange, green, greenish yellow, below vertical rows 1/3
**Colour designations:**
4d. None
9d. G1 GREEN G2 MAUVE G3 ORANGE G4 GREY in right margin reading upwards opposite rows 9/3
1s.9d. G1 YELLOW G2 GREEN G3 ORANGE G4 GREY in right margin reading upwards opposite rows 13/7
**Traffic lights (boxed and in same order as cylinder numbers):**
4d. Opposite rows 17/19 at right
9d., 1s.9d. Opposite rows 18/19 at right

**Imprimaturs from the National Postal Museum Archives**

**A. Ordinary**
Nos. W113/116 imperforate, watermark Type W.24

| | |
|---|---|
| Watermark upright (se-tenant block of four) | £9000 |

Nos. W117/118 imperforate, watermark Type W.24

| | |
|---|---|
| Watermark upright (2 values only) | (Each) £2250 |

**B. Phosphor**
Nos. WP113/116 imperforate, watermark Type W.24

| | |
|---|---|
| Watermark upright (se-tenant block of four) | £9000 |

Nos. WP 117/118 imperforate, watermark Type W.24

| | |
|---|---|
| Watermark upright (2 values only) | (Each) £2250 |

**Quantities Sold:**

| | Ordinary | Phosphor |
|---|---|---|
| 4d. | 78,331,778 | 37,133,952 |
| 9d. | 5,873,042 | 5,701,608 |
| 1s.9d. | 3,259,521 | 4,929,648 |
| Pack (including ordinary andphosphor) | 53,446 | |

**Withdrawn:** 23.4.68

**W115**. Master Lambton (Sir Thomas Lawrence)

**W116**. Mares and Foals in a Landscape (George Stubbs)

**W117**. Children Coming Out of School (L. S. Lowry)

(Des. Stuart Rose)

## 1967 (10 July). British Paintings

This is the first issue of British Paintings for which Harrisons made photographs from the originals.

No watermark. Two phosphor bands, applied by flexography

Types **W115/7**

**W119** (=SG 748)

| | Mint | Used |
|---|---|---|
| 4d. rose-red, lemon, brown, black, new blue and gold | 10 | 10 |
| a. Gold omitted (value and Queen's head) | £325 | |
| b. New blue omitted | £17000 | |
| c. Phosphor omitted | 7·00 | |

**W120** (=SG 749)

| | | |
|---|---|---|
| 9d. Venetian red, ochre, grey-black, new blue, greenish yellow and black | 15 | 15 |
| a. Black omitted (Queen's head and value) | £950 | |

| | |
|---|---|
| ab. Black (Queen's head only) omitted | £2200 |
| c. Phosphor omitted | £450 |
| d. Error. One broad band | 15·00 |

**W121** (=SG 750)

| | | |
|---|---|---|
| 1s.6d. greenish yellow, grey, rose, new blue, grey-black and gold | 25 | 35 |
| a. Gold omitted (Queen's head) | | |
| b. New blue omitted | £280 | |
| c. Grey (clouds and shading) omitted | £150 | |
| d. Phosphor omitted | £300 | |
| e. Error. One broad band | 8·00 | |
| f. Extra window (No dot, R. 9/1) | 20·00 | |

| | |
|---|---|
| First Day Cover (W119/21) | 4·00 |

| | |
|---|---|
| Presentation Pack (W119/21) | 8·00 |

No. W120ab with Queen's head only omitted, was due to a major colour shift. A similar shift caused the face value to be misplaced to the right of the Queen's head.

All values were put on sale in error on 30 June at the Lincoln head post office.

W121f

**Cylinder Numbers** (Blocks of Four (4d.) or Six (others))

| Cylinder Nos. | Perforation Type A(T) (I/E) | |
|---|---|---|
| | No dot | Dot |
| 4d. 3A (gold)–1B (lemon)–1C (rose-red)–1D (new blue)–1E (brown)–1F (black) | 1·00 | 1·00 |
| 3A–1B–2C–1D–1E–1F | 1·00 | 1·00 |
| 4A–1B–1C–1D–1E–1F | 1·00 | 1·00 |
| 4A–1B–2C–1D–1E–1F | 1·00 | 1·00 |
| 5A–1B–2C–1D–1E–1F | 1·00 | 1·00 |

| | Perforation Type A(T) (E/P) | |
|---|---|---|
| | No dot | Dot |
| 9d. 2A (black)–1B (greenish yellow)–1C (Venetian red)–1D (ochre)–1E (new blue)–3F (grey- black) | 2·00 | 2·00 |
| 1s.6d. 2A (grey-black)–1B (greenish yellow)–1C (rose)–1D (new blue)–1E (grey)–1F (gold) | 2·75 | 2·75 |

Perforation Type A(T) on the 4d. is with sheet orientated showing head to right. In the 4A dot pane the dot is omitted for the gold cylinder and it appears before the C in the rose-red cylinder.

In the 9d. the greenish yellow 1B is very faint in the dot pane and is sometimes almost invisible. Also in the dot pane the dot appears before the 2A.

In the 1s.6d. dot pane the dot appears before the 1F.

**Minor Constant Flaws**

4d. Cyls. 1B–2C–1D–1E–1F in combination with gold cyls. 3A, 4A or 5A no dot
2/1 Two small dots on boy's left leg (Th. K6, L6)

3/1 Gold dot on boys right collar (Th. F5)
5/4 Dark spot on right leg of boy's breeches (Th. 14)

4d. Cyls 1B–2C–1D–1E–1F in combination with gold cyls. 3A, 4A or 5A dot
1/11 Red spot in left gutter, sometimes lost in perforations (Th. JO)
2/11 Small red spot on boy's right collar (Th. E5)
3/4 Small spot in the V of boy's collar (Th. F5)
5/3 Dark spot on inside of boy's left elbow (Th. F7)

9d. Cyls. 2A–1B–1C–1D–1E–3F no dot
3/1 Break in first S of STUBBS
4/3 Dark spot in foliage of lower centre branch (Th. C5)
7/1 Dark spot between right-hand foal's forelegs (Th. G7) and another in the grass just below (Th. H7)

9d. Cyls. 2A–1B–1C–1D–1E–3F dot
2/5 Slight nick in upright stroke of d of value
9/3 Small retouch in sky above white horse (Th. D10)
10/1 Break in first R of HARRISON
11/1 Dark dot below horse's hind hoof in bottom left corner (Th. H1)

1s.6d. Cyls. 2A–1B–1C–1D–1E–1F no dot
1/1 Circular patch in building below 1 of value (Th. C2)
1/5 Small dot by leg of foreground figure left of centre (Th. I6)
9/4 Small spot above roof of small house in side street (Th. E9)

1s.6d. Cyls. 2A–B1–C1–D–1E–1F dot
1/1 Break in Y of LOWRY
1/4 Lack of colour on second red door from right (Th. F–G11)
12/1 Line of small dots in top gutter

**Sheet Details**
Sheet size: 4d. 60 (12 × 5), others (5 × 12). All double pane sheet-fed

**Sheet markings:**
**Cylinder numbers:**
4d. Opposite R. 4/1, boxed
Others, Opposite rows 10/11 at left, boxed
**Guide holes:** None
**Marginal arrows (photo-etched):** "W" shaped, at top and bottom (4d.) or at both sides (others)
**Marginal rule:** At bottom of sheet
**Colour register marks, coloured crosses, autotron marks and Colour designations:** None
Traffic lights (boxed and in same order as cylinder numbers):
4d. Opposite R. 4/12
Others. Opposite rows 10/11 at right

**Imprimaturs from the National Postal Museum Archives**
Nos. W119/121 imperforate

| | |
|---|---|
| No watermark (set of 3) | £6750 |

**Quantities Sold:**
4d. 102,443,229; 9d. 9,568,991; 1s.6d. 9,660,509; Pack 46,017

**Withdrawn:**
9.7.68 (4d. sold out October 1967, 9d. sold out January 1968)

**W118**. *Gipsy Moth IV*

(Des. Michael and Sylvia Goaman)

## 1967 (24 July). Sir Francis Chichester's World Voyage

Sir Francis Chichester voyaged single-handed from England to Australia and back in Gipsy Moth IV and was knighted by the Queen on his return.

No watermark. Three phosphor bands, applied by flexography

Type **W118**

**W122** (=SG 751)

| | | Mint | Used |
|---|---|---|---|
| 1s.9d. | black, brown-red, light emerald and blue | 20 | 20 |
| | a. Broken ribbon (R. 19/3) | 20·00 | |

| | | |
|---|---|---|
| First Day Cover (W122) | | 1·00 |

Normal          W122a

**Cylinder Numbers** (Blocks of Six)

| | | Perforation Type A (E/I) |
|---|---|---|
| | Cylinder. Nos. | No dot |
| 1s.9d. | 2A (black)–1B (light emerald)–1C (blue)–1D (brown-red) | 2·25 |

**Minor Constant Flaws**

1s.9d. Cyls. 2A–1B–1C–1D no dot
1/6 Dark flaw in Queen's hair below ribbon (Th. B12–13)
2/1 Grey flaw at top of main sail (Th. A7) and flaw in rear sail (Th. C8–9)
6/5 Diagonal line running across main sail (Th. D6–7)
13/1 Line of small blue dots in rear sail (Th. D–E8)
14/4 White flaw in figure 1 of value (Th. G12)
16/2 Break in rigging near main-mast (Th. D5)
17/6 Line of blue dots on hull below main sail (Th. E4–5)
18/5 Scratch through rear sail to grey clouds (Th. E8–D11)
18/6 Same scratch extends to foresail (Th. C1–B5)
19/1 Small spur protrudes from top right of rear sail (Th. B–C9)
20/1 Curved dotted blue line between rear sail and Queen's portrait (Th. C9)
20/2 Diagonal blue line in top gutter (Th. O–13 in gutter)
20/3 Vertical white line at bottom left of main sail (Th. D–E5)
20/4 Blue flaw at top of main sail (Th. A7)
20/6 Dot between ON of HARRISON

**Sheet Details**
Sheet size: 120 (6 × 20). Single pane reel-fed

**Sheet markings:**
**Cylinder numbers:** Opposite rows 18/19 at left, boxed
**Guide holes:** Boxed, opposite row 14, at both sides. Boxes without holes also appear opposite row 15, at both sides
**Marginal arrows (photo-etched):** "W" shaped, at top, bottom and sides
**Marginal rule:** At bottom of sheet
**Colour register marks:** Opposite rows 1/2 and 20, at both sides
**Autotron marks (solid):** Black, blue, emerald, brown-red, below vertical rows 1/3
**Coloured crosses and Colour designations:** None
**Traffic lights (boxed):** Blue, brown-red, black, emerald, opposite rows 18/19 at right

**Imprimatur from the National Postal Museum Archives**
No. W122 imperforate

| No watermark (single) | £2250 |
|---|---|

**Quantity Sold:** 10,060,867

**Withdrawn:** 23.7.68

**W119**. Radar Screen

**W120**. Penicillin Mould

(Des. Clive Abbott)

**W121**. VC-10 Jet Engines

**W122**.
Television Equipment

(Des. Negus and Sharland team)

## 1967 (19 September). British Discovery and Invention

Watermark Multiple Crowns, sideways on 1s.9d. This was the last commemorative issue to bear a watermark.

Three phosphor bands (4d.) or two phosphor bands (others)

Types **W119/22**

**W123** (=SG 752)

| | | Mint | Used |
|---|---|---|---|
| 4d. | greenish yellow, black and vermilion | 10 | 10 |
| | a. Phosphor omitted | 5·00 | |
| | b. Broken scale (R. 10/2) | 25·00 | |

**W124** (=SG 753)

| | | Mint | Used |
|---|---|---|---|
| 1s. | blue-green, light greenish blue, slate-purple and bluish violet | 10 | 20 |
| | a. Phosphor omitted | 10·00 | |
| | b. Watermark inverted | 20·00 | |

**W125** (=SG 754)

| | | Mint | Used |
|---|---|---|---|
| 1s.6d. | black, grey, royal blue, ochre and turquoise-blue | 20 | 25 |
| | a. Phosphor omitted | £500 | |
| | b. Watermark inverted | £225 | |
| | c. Cowling flaw (R. 1/2) | 20·00 | |

**W126** (=SG 755)

| | | Mint | Used |
|---|---|---|---|
| 1s.9d. | black, grey-blue, pale olive-grey, violet and orange | 20 | 30 |
| | a. Pale olive-grey omitted | | £4500 |
| | b. Orange (Queen's head) omitted | | |
| | c. Phosphor omitted | £500 | |
| | d. Error. One broad band | 50·00 | |

| First Day Cover (W123/6) | 2·00 |
|---|---|

| Presentation Pack (W123/6) | 4·00 |
|---|---|

All values are known on a special cover prepared by the Edinburgh G.P.O. Philatelic Bureau but postmarked 8 August 1967.

W123b

W125c

**Cylinder Numbers** (Blocks of Six)

| | Perforation Types | |
|---|---|---|
| Cyl. Nos. (No dot) | A (E/I) | F (P/E) |
| 4d. 1A (vermilion)–1B (greenish yellow)–1C (black) | 1·00 | |
| 1s. 1A (bluish violet)–1B (blue-green)–1C (light greenish blue)1D (slate-purple) | 1·00 | |
| 1s.6d. 1A (black)–1B (ochre)–1C (royal blue)–1D (grey)–1E (turquoise-blue) | 2·25 | |

|  | F (E/P) |
|---|---|
| 1s.9d. 1A (black)–1B (violet)–1C (pale olive-grey)–1D (grey-blue)–1E (orange) | 2·25 |

Perforation Type F on the 1s.9d. is with sheet orientated showing head to right.

**Minor Constant Flaws**

4d. Cyls. 1A–1B–1C
  2/2 Break in outer ring of radar screen at top centre (Th. A6)
  8/5 Break in scale division of radar screen just to left of centre bottom mark (Th. G5)
  14/5 Break in scale division of radar screen in centre left mark (Th. D3)

1s. Cyls. 1A–1B–1C–1D
  19/3 Retouch to background at right of value (Th. F12–13)
  19/6 Violet coloured flaw in bottom right of white outer ring (Th. G6)

1s.6d. Cyls. 1A–1B–1C–1D–1E
  12/3 Small break in outer frame-line to right of 1/6 (Th. G13)
  13/2 Pale area in background above first e of engine (Th. F8)
  19/5 White scratch to background extends to next stamp (Th. G3–10)
  19/6 White scratch to background extending from previous stamp (Th. G4–10)
  20/3 The small grey coloured projection of the tailplane at right of the engines is malformed (Th. C8)

1s.9d. Cyls. 1A–1B–1C–1D–1E
  1/18 Two of the holes of the disc at left are joined (Th. E1)
  5/1 One of the slits in grey-blue disc below portrait is joined to hub by white flaw (Th. E5)

**Sheet Details**
**Sheet sizes:**
4d. 120 (6 × 20). Single pane reel-fed
1s. and 1s.6d. 120 (6 × 20). Single pane sheet-fed
1s.9d. 120 (20 × 6). Single pane sheet-fed

**Sheet markings:**
**Cylinder numbers:**
4d. and 1s. Opposite R. 19/1, boxed
1s.6d. Opposite rows 18/19 at left, boxed
1s.9d. Opposite rows 5/6 at left, boxed
**Guide holes:**
4d. Opposite rows 14/15 (boxed), at both sides; others, none
**Marginal arrows (photo-etched):** "W" shaped, at top, bottom and sides
**Marginal rule:** At bottom of sheet
**Colour register marks:**
4d. Opposite rows 3/4 and 17/18, at both sides
1s. and 1s.6d. Above and below vertical rows 1 and 6
1s.9d. Opposite rows 1 and 6 bottom margin, at both sides
**Coloured crosses:**
4d. None
1s. and 1s.6d. Above and below vertical rows 2/3
1s.9d. Opposite rows 4/5, at both sides
**Autotron marks (solid):**
4d. Black, yellow, vermilion below vertical rows 1/3. An additional semi-solid mark in red appears below vertical row 1; others, none
**Colour designations:** None
**Traffic lights (boxed):**
4d. and 1s. In same order as cylinder numbers opposite R. 19/6
1s.6d. In reverse order to cylinder numbers opposite rows 18/19 at right
1s.9d. Violet, black, olive-grey, grey-blue, orange opposite rows 5/6 at right

**Imprimaturs from the National Postal Museum Archives**
Nos. W 123/126 imperforate, watermark Type W.24

| Watermark upright (4d., 1s., 1s.6d.) or sideways (1s.9d.) (set of 4) | £9000 |
|---|---|

**Quantities Sold:**
4d. 104,165,625; 1s. 10,718,389; 1s.6d. 10,380,413; 1s.9d. 7,469,585; Pack 59,117

**Withdrawn:** 18.9.68

NO WATERMARK. All commemorative stamps from here onwards were printed on paper without watermark

**W123**. The Adoration of the Shepherds (School of Seville)

**W124**. Madonna and Child (Murillo)

**W125**. The Adoration of the Shepherds (Louis Le Nain)

(Des. Stuart Rose)

## 1967. Christmas

The 4d. was issued on 18 October and the others were put on sale on 27 November.

One phosphor band (3d.) or two phosphor bands (others), applied by flexography
Types **W123/5**
**W127** (=SG 756)

| | | Mint | Used |
|---|---|---|---|
| 3d. | olive-yellow, rose, blue, black and gold | 10 | 15 |
| a. | Gold omitted (value and Queen's head) | £110 | |
| ab. | Gold (value only) omitted | £3000 | |
| ac. | Gold (Queen's head only) omitted | £4500 | |
| b. | Rose omitted | £3750 | |
| c. | Imperforate between stamp and left margin | £850 | |
| d. | Phosphor omitted | 1·00 | |
| e. | Printed on the gummed side | £600 | |
| f. | Olive-yellow omitted | — | £400 |

**W128** (=SG 757)

| | | | |
|---|---|---|---|
| 4d. | bright purple, greenish yellow, new blue, black and gold | 10 | 15 |
| a. | Gold (value and Queen's head) omitted | 80·00 | |
| b. | Gold ("4D" only) omitted | £2800 | |
| c. | Greenish yellow (Child, robe and Madonna's face) omitted | £7500 | |
| d. | Phosphor omitted | £125 | |
| da. | Error. Right-hand band omitted | | |
| ✓ e. | Error. One broad band | 38·00 | |
| f. | Brown flaw (Dot, R. 2/3) | 20·00 | |

g. Greenish yellow and gold omitted  £15000

**W129** (=SG 758)

| | | | |
|---|---|---|---|
| 1s.6d. | bright purple, bistre, lemon, black, orange-red, ultramarine, gold | 15 | 50 |
| a. | Gold omitted (value and Queen's head) | £5500 | |
| ab. | Gold (Queen's head only) omitted | £3000 | |
| b. | Ultramarine omitted | £750 | |
| c. | Lemon omitted | £20000 | |
| ✓ d. | Phosphor omitted | 12·00 | |
| e. | Error. One broad band | 45·00 | |

| First Day Covers (2) (W127/29) | 1·50 |
|---|---|

The original printing of the 4d. was double-pane and printed on the wood press (dot pane above no dot); cylinders 2A–1B–1C–1D–1E, 2A–2B–2C–2D–2E and 3A–2B–2C–2D–2E. The second printing was on the Thrissell press; cylinders 6A–3B–3C–3D–3E 8A–3B–3C–3D–3E.

There is a wide variation on shades of the 3d. and 4d. but they are not listed as there are a number of intermediate shades. For the 4d. value, stamps from one machine show a darker background and give the appearance of the greenish yellow being omitted, but this is not so and these should not be confused with the true missing greenish yellow, No. W128c.

The 3d. and 4d. are known with value omitted resulting from colour shifts. No. W128b comes from first vertical row of a sheet on which the gold cylinder was stopped so that it printed the head only.

No. W129 ab comes from stamps in the first vertical row of a sheet. No. W127 ab was caused by a paper fold.

No. W128f. This marked variety on the 4d. consists of a large brown area in the lower right corner (Th. J–K 8–9) which can be clearly seen by the naked eye, but which would not show up in an enlarged illustration. It occurs on cylinders 2B–2C–2D–2E dot in conjunction with gold cylinders 2A or 3A.

**Cylinder Numbers** (Blocks of Six)

| | | Perforation Types A (P/E) | |
|---|---|---|---|
| | Cylinder Nos. | No dot | Dot |
| 3d. | 1A (gold)–1B (olive-yellow)–1C (rose)–1D (blue)–1E (black) | 1·00 | |
| | 2A–1B–1C–1D–1E | 1·00 | |
| | | (I/E) | (I/E) |
| 4d. | 2A (gold)–1B (bright purple)–1C (new blue)–1D (greenish yellow)–1E (grey-black) | 1·00 | 1·00 |
| | 2A–2B–2C–2D–2E | 4·00 | 4·00 |
| | 3A–2B–2C–2D–2E | 1·00 | 1·00 |
| | 6A–3B–3C–3D–3E | 6·00 | |
| | 8A–3B–3C–3D–3E | 6·00 | |
| | | A(T) (E/P) No dot | |
| 1s.6d. | 2A (gold)–1B (ultramarine)–1C (bright purple)–1D (orange-red)–1E (lemon)–1F (bistre)–2G (black) | 4·00 | |

Perforation Type A on the 3d. and 4d. are with the sheet orientated showing the head to right.
The gold of the Queen's portrait and the value is normally further to the left on the 6A and 8A cylinders.

**Minor Constant Flaws**

3d. Cyls. 1B–1C–1D–1E in conjunction with gold cyls. 1A or 2A no dot
1/7 Black horizontal line across triangle of red above Mary's head (Th. E2–3)

3d. Cyls. 1A–1B–1C–1D–1E no dot
1/11 Break in upright wall of building shows against sky (Th. D6)

3d. Cyls. 2A–1B–1C–1D–1E no dot

3/10 Small black spot in Joseph's cloak (Th. D5)
4/9 Background retouch in left pillar (Th. D2)

4d. Cyls. 2B–2C–2D–2E in conjunction with gold cyls. 2A or 3A no dot
1/5 Prominent pale area in background at bottom right (Th. K–L 8–9)

4d. Cyls. 3A–2B–2C–2D–2E no dot
2/12 A cut at top of diagonal of 4 of value
7/5 Dark spot in Mother s right hand (Th. E5)

4d. Cyls. 2B–2C–2D–2E in conjunction with gold cyls. 2A or 3A dot
4/5 Line of pale dots over 4 of value (Th. J1)

4d. Cyls. 3A–2B–2C–2D–2E dot
2/12 Black dot over first R of HARRISON
3/6 Black dot on Child's forehead (Th. C6)
4/9 Spot on lower left margin of stamp (Th. K1)
7/2 Small spot just beyond little finger of Madonna's right hand (Th. E6)
7/12 Two small red dots over H of HARRISON

1s.6d. Cyls. 2A–1B–1C–1D–1E–1F–2G no dot
1/2 Background disturbance above ll of shilling
3/6 Curved green flaw left of cow's tail (Th. E1)
4/9 Background disturbance below n of One

**Sheet Details**
**Sheet sizes:**
3d. 120 (12 × 10). Single pane sheet-fed
4d. 120 (12 × 10). Double pane reel-fed for gold cyls. 2A and 3A and single pane reel-fed for gold cyls. 6A and 8A
1s.6d. 60 (10 × 6). Single pane sheet-fed

**Sheet markings:**
**Cylinder numbers:**
3d. Opposite R. 9/1, boxed
4d. (Thrissell) Below vertical column 11 and open boxed
4d. (Wood) Below vertical row 11, boxed
1s.6d. Opposite rows 4/5 at right, boxed
**Guide holes:**
3d. and 1s.6d None
4d. (Wood) Above and below vertical row 8
4d. (Thrissell Above and below vertical column 8 and open boxed
**Marginal arrows (photo etched):** "W" shaped, at top, bottom and sides
**Marginal rules:** None
**Colour register marks:**
3d. Above and below vertical rows 1/2 and 11/12
4d. (Wood) Above and below vertical rows 1/3 (dot) and 8/10 (no dot)
4d. (Thrissell) Above and below column 1 and column 12
1s.6d. Opposite rows 1/2 and 6, at both sides
**Coloured crosses:**
3d. Above and below vertical rows 3/4
4d. None
1s.6d. Next to cylinder numbers at left and traffic lights at right
**Autotron marks (solid):**
3d. and 1s.6d. None
4d. (Wood) Greenish yellow, bright purple, new blue, grey-black, gold opposite rows 6/8, right margin (dot) with the 3A–2B–2C–2D–2E cylinders but the order of the colours is reversed with the 2A–1B–1C–1D–1E cylinders
4d. (Thrissell) Opposite rows 7/8 right margin, yellow and red by row 7, blue and black by row 8 (there is no gold Autotron mark)
**Colour designations:**
3d. and 1s.6d. None
4d. (Wood) G1 YELLOW above vertical row 12 on the dot pane and G2 GREY G3 GREEN G4 RED G5 GOLD above vertical rows 1/4 on the no dot pane, the whole inscription being upside down.
The G3 GREEN is printed in blue
4d. (Thrissell) Above columns 1/6 and inverted. G1 YELLOW (Row 6) G2 RED G3 GREEN (printed in blue) G4 GREY and G5

GOLD (row 1/2)
**Traffic lights (boxed):**
3d. In the same order as the cylinder numbers opposite R. 9/12
4d. (both printings) Greenish yellow, bright purple, gold, new blue, grey-black above vertical rows 10/11
1s.6d. Lemon, bright purple, orange-red, ultramarine, black, bistre, gold opposite rows 4/5 at right
**Cut lines:** 4d. (Thrissell) Opposite row 9, right margin. Below column 9.

**Imprimaturs from the National Postal Museum Archives**
Nos. W127/129 imperforate

| No watermark (set of 3) | £6750 |
|---|---|

The 3d. (missing phosphor) and 4d. (normal and missing gold) are known imperforate and were not issued. Care should be taken not to confuse these with NPM imprimaturs.

**Quantities Sold:** 3d. 270,349,845; 4d. 287,827,440; 1s.6d. 17,913,209

**Withdrawn:** 3d. Sold out July 1968; 4d. 17.10.68; 1s.6d. 26.11.68

---

### 1967 (27 November). Gift Pack 1967

| WGP1 Comprising Nos. WP111/18 and W119/29 | 3·00 |
|---|---|

**Quantity Sold:** 105,577

---

PVA GUM. All commemorative issues from here onwards printed by Harrisons are on paper with PVA gum. For further particulars about this gum see notes at the beginning of Section UA on the Machin definitive issues.

**W126.** Tarr Steps, Exmoor

(Des. Jeffery Matthews)

**W127.** Aberfeldy Bridge

(Des. Andrew Restall)

**W128.** Menai Bridge

(Des. Leonard Rosoman)

**W129.** M4 Viaduct

(Des. Jeffery Matthews)

## 1968 (29 April). British Bridges

Two phosphor bands, applied by flexography (4d., 1s.9d.) or photogravure (others)
Type **W126/9**

**W130** (=SG 763)

| | | Mint | Used |
|---|---|---|---|
| 4d. | black, bluish violet, turquoise-blue and gold | 10 | 10 |
| a. | Printed on the gummed side | 32·00 | |
| b. | Phosphor omitted | | |
| c. | O retouch (R. 20/6) | 20·00 | |
| d. | No curve to slab (R. 10/6) | 20·00 | |

**W131** (=SG 764)

| | | | |
|---|---|---|---|
| 9d. | red-brown, myrtle-green, ultramarine, olive-brown, black and gold | 10 | 15 |
| a. | Gold (Queen's head) omitted | £225 | |
| b. | Ultramarine omitted | † | £7000 |

| | | | |
|---|---|---|---|
| c. | Phosphor omitted | 15·00 | |
| d. | Phosphor bands diagonal | 25·00 | |
| e. | Error. One broad band | 20·00 | |
| f. | HARRISON redrawn (R. 18/3) | 20·00 | |
| g. | RESTALL redrawn (R. 18/4) | 20·00 | |

**W132** (=SG 765)

| | | | |
|---|---|---|---|
| 1s.6d. | olive-brown, red-orange, bright green, turquoise- green and gold | 15 | 25 |
| a. | Gold (Queen's head) omitted | £350 | |
| b. | Red-orange omitted | £375 | |
| c. | Phosphor omitted | 50·00 | |
| d. | Broken corner stones (R. 15/1) | 20·00 | |

**W133** (=SG 766)

| | | | |
|---|---|---|---|
| 1s.9d. | olive-brown, greenish yellow, dull green, deep ultramarine and gold | 20 | 30 |
| a. | Gold (Queen's head) omitted | £350 | |
| b. | Gold (Queen's head) and phosphor omitted | | |
| c. | Phosphor omitted | 10·00 | |
| d. | Error. One broad band | | |

| First Day Cover (W130/3) | 1·50 |
|---|---|

| Presentation Pack (W130/3) | 3·00 |
|---|---|

No. W131b is only known on first day covers posted from Canterbury, Kent or the Philatelic Bureau, Edinburgh.
   Used examples of the 1s.6d. are known with both the gold and the phosphor omitted.

W130c

W130d
No curve at left to central slab

W132d

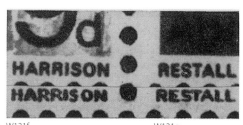

W131f                    W131g
Inscriptions redrawn by hand. Normal above varieties

**Cylinder Numbers** (Blocks of Eight)

|  | Perforation Type |
| Cylinder Nos. | F (P/E) No dot |
| 4d. 3A (black)–1B (turquoise-blue)–2C (bluish violet)–2D (gold) | 1·50 |
| 9d. 1A (black)–1B (red-brown)–1C (ultramarine)–1D (olive- brown)–1E (myrtle-green)–1F (gold) | 1·50 |
| 1s.6d. 2A (olive-brown)–1B (red-orange)–1C (bright green)–2D (turquoise-green)–3E (gold) | 2·50 |
| 1s.9d. 2A (olive-brown)–1B (gold)–1C (dull green)–1D (deep ultramarine)–1E (greenish yellow) | 3·00 |

**Minor Constant Flaws**

4d. Cyls. 3A–1B–2C–2D no dot
    4/1 Diagonal dotted line across top of bridge near far end (Th. C10)
    9/1 Lack of screening dots in left of pale green patch left of Tarr (Th G4–5)
    11/1 Similar variety but more pronounced (Th. G4–5)
    12/2 Broken tip to horizontal bar of T of Tarr
    14/2 Scratch across lower stones near far end of bridge (Th. D10–C12)
    17/2 Weakness behind and below hi of Prehistoric (Th. G11)
    19/4 Damaged H in HARRISON

9d. Cyls. 1A–1B–1C–1D–1E–1F no dot
    9/4 Break in olive-brown line at left of ultramarine area under main arch (Th. F6)
    20/4 Small dark spot under r of Bridge

1s.6d. Cyls. 2A–1B–1C–2D–3E no dot
    5/5 Two diagonal lines in sky at right (Th. B–C13)
    5/6 Diagonal line in sky extending to base of Queen's neck (extension of one of the lines in 5/5) (Th. C1)
    6/1 Small curved flaw in front of H of HARRISON
    6/2 White flaw in first arch beyond the far tower (Th. E12)
    14/5 Small white flaw at top right of near tower (Th. B8)
    19/1 Green spot on near tower above right-hand arch (Th. D7–8)

1s.9d. Cyls. 2A–1B–1C–1D–1E no dot
    2/5 Retouch in centre lane (Th. C–D8)
    10/4 Disturbance at right of pale green area below Queen (Th. D3–4)
14/5 Vertical line appears as radio mast above building on skyline (Th. A6)
    15/1 Retouch between buildings at bend in motorway (Th. C10)
    17/4 Break at foot of s in value

**Sheet Details**
Sheet size: 120 (6 × 20). Single pane sheet-fed

**Sheet markings:**
**Cylinder numbers:** Opposite rows 17/18 at left, boxed
**Guide holes:** None
**Marginal arrows (photo-etched):** "W" shaped, at top, bottom and sides

**Marginal rule:** At bottom of sheet
**Colour register marks:**
4d. and 1s.9d. Above and below vertical rows 1/2 and 6
9d. and 1s.6d. Above and below vertical rows 1 and 5/6
**Coloured crosses:**
4d. and 1s.6d. Above and below vertical row 3
9d. Above and below vertical rows 3/4
1s.9d. Above and below vertical rows 2/3
**Autotron marks and Colour designations:** None
**Traffic lights (boxed):**
4d. Gold, bluish violet turquoise-blue, black above vertical row 5
9d. Black, red-brown, ultramarine, myrtle-green, gold, olive-brown above vertical rows 4/5
1s.6d. Gold, turquoise-green, bright green, red-orange, olive-brown above vertical row 5
1s.9d. Gold, dull green, olive-brown, deep ultramarine, greenish yellow above vertical row 5

**Imprimaturs from the National Postal Museum Archives**
Nos. W130/133 imperforate

| No watermark (set of 4) | £9000 |

**Quantities Sold:**
4d. 97,458,120; 9d. 8,773,080; 1s.6d. 9,451,400; 1s.9d. 5,924,800; Pack 69,646

**Withdrawn:** 28.4.69

**W130**. "T U C" and Trade Unionists

**W131**. Mrs. Emmeline Pankhurst (statue)

**W132**. Sopwith Camel and Lightning Fighters

**W133**. Captain Cook's *Endeavour* and Signature

(Des. David Gentleman (4d.), Clive Abbott (others))

---

## 1968 (29 May). British Anniversaries

Four famous anniversaries, with the events described on the stamps.

Two phosphor bands, applied by flexography (1s., 1s.9d.) or photogravure (others)

Types **W130/3**

**W134** (=SG 767)

| | Mint | Used |
|---|---|---|
| 4d. emerald, olive, blue and black | 10 | 10 |
| a. Phosphor omitted* | 12·00 | |
| b. Retouch on large C (No dot, R. 3/2) | 20·00 | |

**W135** (=SG 768)

| | | |
|---|---|---|
| 9d. reddish violet, grey and black | 10 | 15 |
| a. Phosphor omitted | 7·00 | |
| b. Error. One broad band | 30·00 | |

**W136** (=SG 769)

| | | |
|---|---|---|
| 1s. olive-brown, blue, red, slate-blue and black | 15 | 15 |
| a. Phosphor omitted | 10·00 | |

**W137** (=SG 770)

| | | |
|---|---|---|
| 1s.9d. ochre, brownish ochre and blackish brown | 35 | 35 |
| a. Phosphor omitted | £180 | |

| | | |
|---|---|---|
| b. Broken bulwarks (R. 8/2) | 20·00 | |
| First Day Cover (W134/7) | 4·00 | |
| Presentation Pack (W134/7) | 3·00 | |

*The phosphor bands are normally faint and difficult to see and care is needed in identifying the phosphor omitted on the 4d. value.

The 1s.9d. is known with phosphor removed by chemical means. These can be detected, but care is needed in identifying genuine examples.

This issue is known postmarked at Netheravon, Salisbury, Wiltshire on 28 May.

W134b                    W137b

**Cylinder Numbers** (Blocks of Eight (4d., 1s.), Four (9d.), Six (1s.9d.))

| | Perforation Types | |
|---|---|---|
| | A (E/I) | A (E/I) |
| Cylinder Nos. | No dot | Dot |
| 4d. 1A (black)–1B (blue)–1C (olive)–1D (emerald) | 1·60 | 1·60 |
| | F (P/E) No dot | |
| 9d. 1A (black)–1B (reddish violet)–1C (grey) | 1·25 | |
| 1s. 1A (black)–1B (olive-brown)–1C (blue)–1D (slate-blue)–1E (red) | 2·00 | |
| 1s.9d. 2A (blackish brown)–1B (brownish ochre)–1C (ochre) | 4·00 | |

### Minor Constant Flaws

4d. Cyls. 1A–1B–1C–1D no dot
1/1 Small retouch in right cross bar of large T
2/2 Stop between Union and Congress
4/1 Retouch at top of large C (not as prominent as No. W134b)
10/6 Small retouch at top left of large U
11/3 Small flaw in 6 of 1968
11/6 Vertical green line from right cross bar of large T (Th. B–E3)

4d. Cyls. 1A–1B–1C–1D dot
2/6 Small spot right of 4 of value
4/5 Green spots by d of Trades (Th. F–G1)
5/5 Dotted line across back of Queen's hair (Th. B–C12)
19/1 Retouch on cheek of face shown in large T (Th. D1–2)
20/5 Two tiny dots above g of Congress

9d. Cyls. 1A–1B–1C no dot
9/4 Spur at top right of Queen's head (Th. A13)
14/6 Dark flaw on collar (Th. D10/11) and small flaw on left sleeve (Th. F11)

1s. Cyls. 1A–1B–1C–1D–1E no dot
3/1 Dot over O of ROYAL
4/4 Extension of wing joining it to last T of ABBOTT

1s.9d. Cyls. 2A–1B–1C no dot
10/3 Small flaws in background above Y of DISCOVERY level with value (Th. F10–11)
11/2 Small cut in Y of VOYAGE
13/2 Flaw in lower part of S of DISCOVERY
16/2 Sliced F in FIRST
20/5 Tail of 9 of 1968 slightly shortened

## Sheet Details
Sheet size: 120 (6 × 20). 4d. double pane reel-fed; others single pane sheet-fed

**Sheet markings:**
**Cylinder numbers:**
4d. and 1s. Opposite rows 17/18 at left, boxed
9d. Opposite R. 19/1, boxed
1s.9d. Opposite R. 18/1, boxed
**Guide holes:**
4d. In double "S O N" box opposite rows 14/15, at left (no dot) or right (dot)
**Others:** None
**Marginal arrows (photo-etched):** "W" shaped, at top, bottom and sides
**Marginal rule:** 4d. None; others at bottom of sheet
**Colour register marks:**
4d. Opposite rows 2/4 and 18/20 at left (no dot) or right (dot)
**Others:** Above and below vertical rows 1 and 6
**Coloured crosses:**
4d. None
9d. and 1s.9d. Above and below vertical row 3
1s. Above and below vertical rows 2/3
**Autotron marks (solid):**
4d. Black, blue, olive, emerald opposite rows 4/6, at right (no dot) or left (dot); others, none
**Colour designations:** None
**Traffic lights (boxed):**
4d. In same order as cylinder numbers opposite rows 1/2, at right
9d. Black, grey, reddish violet above vertical row 5
1s. Olive-brown, blue, slate-blue, red, black above vertical row 5
1s.9d. Brownish ochre, blackish brown, ochre above vertical row 5

**Imprimaturs from the National Postal Museum Archives**
Nos. W134/137 imperforate

| | |
|---|---|
| No watermark (set of 4) | £9000 |

**Quantities Sold:**
4d. 97,757,920; 9d. 9,135,240; 1s. 9,872,160; 1s.9d. 6,217,440; Pack 67,639

**Withdrawn:** 28.5.69

**W134**. Queen Elizabeth I (Unknown Artist)    **W135**. Pinkie (Sir Thomas Lawrence)

**W136**. Ruins of St. Mary Le Port (John Piper)

**W137**. The Hay Wain (John Constable)

(Des. Stuart Rose)

(Printed in photogravure with the Queen's head embossed in gold)

## 1968 (12 August). British Paintings

This is the second issue of British Paintings for which Harrisons made photographs from the originals.
    Two phosphor bands applied by photogravure (1s.9d.) or flexography (others)
Types **W134/7**
W138 (=SG 771)

| | | Mint | Used |
|---|---|---|---|
| 4d. | black, vermilion, greenish yellow, grey and gold | 10 | 10 |
| a. | Gold omitted (value and Queen's head) | £300 | |
| b. | Gold (value and Queen's head) and phosphor omitted | £3700 | |
| c. | Vermilion omitted* | £600 | |
| d. | Phosphor omitted | 1·50 | |
| e | Embossing omitted | 80·00 | |
| f. | Blister on hand (No dot, R. 2/8) | 20·00 | |

**W139** (=SG 772)

| | | | |
|---|---|---|---|
| 1s. | mauve, new blue, greenish yellow, black, magenta and gold | 10 | 20 |
| a. | Gold omitted (value and Queen's head) | £7000 | |
| b. | Gold (value and Queen's head), embossing and phosphor omitted | £600 | |
| c. | Embossing omitted | | |
| d. | Phosphor omitted | 7·00 | |

**W140** (−SG 773)

| | | | |
|---|---|---|---|
| 1s.6d. | slate, orange, black, mauve, greenish yellow, ultramarine, and gold | 20 | 25 |
| a. | Gold (value and Queen's head) omitted | £275 | |
| b. | Phosphor omitted | 10·00 | |
| c. | Embossing omitted | £300 | |

**W141** (=SG 774)

| | | | |
|---|---|---|---|
| 1s.9d. | greenish yellow, black, new blue, red and gold | 25 | 40 |
| a. | Gold (value and Queen's head), embossing and phosphor omitted | £850 | |
| b. | Red omitted | £13000 | |
| c. | Phosphor omitted | 20·00 | |
| d. | Embossing omitted | £140 | |

| | |
|---|---|
| First Day Cover (W138/41) | 2·00 |

| | |
|---|---|
| Presentation Pack (W138/41) | 3·50 |

Pack also exists with a Japanese insert card.

| | |
|---|---|
| Presentation Pack (German) (W138/41) | 12·00 |

*No. W138c shows the face and hands white, and there is more yellow and olive in the costume.

The 4d. also exists with the value only omitted resulting from a colour shift.

This issue is known pre-released on a first day cover postmarked 10 August from Vauxhall Bridge P.O., S.W.1.

W138f

**Cylinder Numbers** (Blocks of Six)

| | Perforation Type A(T) (I/E) | |
|---|---|---|
| Cylinder Nos. | No dot | Dot |
| 4d. 2A (gold)−1B (embossing)−3C (black)−2D (grey−3E (vermilion)−2F (greenish yellow) | 1·00 | 1·00 |
| 1s. 2A (gold)−1B (embossing)−2C (black)−2D (new blue)−2E (mauve)−2F (magenta)−2G (greenish yellow) | 1·25 | 1·25 |
| 2A−2B−2C−2D−2E−2F−2G | 1·25 | 1·25 |
| 1s.6d. 1A (gold)−1B (embossing)−1C (black)−1D (ultramarine)−1E (slate)−1F (mauve)−1G (orange)−1H (greenish yellow) | 1·75 | 1·75 |

| | Perforation Type A(T) (E/P) | |
|---|---|---|
| 1s.9d. 2A (gold)−1B (embossing)−1C (black)−1D (new blue)−1E (red)−1F (greenish yellow) | 3·00 | 3·00 |

Perforation Type A(T) on the 4d., 1s. and 1s.6d. are with sheet orientated showing head to right.

In each value the 1B cylinder number appears in colourless embossing; it is difficult to see but can often be discerned with the aid of a magnifying glass.

**Minor Constant Flaws**

4d. Cyls. 2A−1B−3C−2D−3E−2F no dot
6/8 Thick A in HARRISON

4d. Cyls. 2A−1B−3C−2D−3E−2F dot
4/2 Black flaw on dress above Queen's right hand (Th. J4−5)

1s. Cyls. 2A−1B−2C−2D−2E−2F−2G no dot
2/4 Diagonal black line across Pinkie's shoulder (Th. D4)
5/1 Black spur to A of HARRISON
6/1 Thin diagonal black line across dress (Th. H3−5)

1s.6d. Cyls. 1A−1B−1C−1D−1E−1F−1G−1H no dot
6/1 Dark coloured spot in top right corner of dark blue area (Th. A8−9)

1s.6d. Cyls. 1A−1B−1C−1D−1E−1F−1G−1H dot
1/8 ? shaped black flaw in doorway (Th. J5)
6/6 Extra patch at upper left corner of yellow wall (Th. E8)

1s.9d. Cyls. 2A−1B−1C−1D−1E−1F no dot
9/2 Blue spot after HARRISON
10/1 Green instead of brown bush in bottom left-hand corner

**Sheet Details**
Sheet size: 1s.9d. 60 (6×10), others 60 (10×6). All double pane sheet-fed

**Sheet markings:**
**Cylinder numbers:**
4d. Opposite row 5, left margin, boxed
1s. and 1s.6d. Opposite rows 4/5, left margin, boxed
1s.9d. Opposite rows 8/9, left margin, boxed
**Guide holes:** None
**Marginal arrows (photo-etched):** "W" shaped, at top, bottom and sides
**Marginal rule:** None
**Colour register marks:**
4d., 1s. and 1s.6d. Above vertical rows 1/2 and 9/10 (no dot) or below (dot)
1s.9d. Opposite rows 1/2 and 9/10, left margin (no dot) or right margin (dot)
**Coloured crosses:**
4d. and 1s. Above vertical rows 6/7 (no dot) or below (dot)
1s.6d. Above vertical rows 7/8 (no dot) or below (dot)
1s.9d. Opposite rows 7/8, left margin (no dot) or right margin (dot)
**Autotron marks, Colour designations:** None
**Traffic lights (boxed):**
4d., 1s. and 1s.6d. In same order as cylinder numbers, except that on the 1s.6d. the gold and embossing lights are transposed, reading left to right above vertical rows 8/9
1s.9d. In same order as cylinder numbers, except that the gold and embossing lights are transposed, reading left to right above vertical row 5

**Imprimaturs from the National Postal Museum Archives**
Nos. W138/141 imperforate

| | |
|---|---|
| No watermark (set of 4) | £9000 |

**Quantities Sold:**

| | |
|---|---|
| 4d. | 185,034,000 |
| 1s. | 17,953,440 |
| 1s.6d. | 8,878,440 |
| 1s.9d. | 5,739,000 |

| English Pack | 93,829 |
| German Pack | 7,880 |

**Withdrawn:** 11.8.69

---

## 1968 (16 September). Gift Pack 1968

| WGP2 Comprising Nos. W130/41 | 6·00 |
| a. German text | 38·00 |

**Quantities Sold:** Ordinary 41,308; German 1,650

---

## 1968 (16 September). Collectors Pack 1968

| WCP1 Comprising Nos. W123/41 | 7·00 |

**Quantity Sold:** 26,284

---

**W139**. Girl with Doll's House

**W138**. Boy and Girl with Rocking Horse

**W140**. Boy with Train Set

(Des. Rosalind Dease)

(Printed in photogravure with the Queen's head embossed in gold)

## 1968 (25 November). Christmas

The joy of giving is emphasised on this Christmas issue; all three designs show children playing with their Christmas toys. One centre phosphor band (4d.) or two phosphor bands (others), applied by flexography

Types **W138/40**

**W142** (=SG 775)

| | | | Mint | Used |
|---|---|---|---|---|
| 4d. | black, orange, vermilion, ultramarine, bistre and gold | | 10 | 15 |
| | a. Gold omitted | £8000 | | |
| | b. Vermilion omitted* | £550 | | |
| | c. Ultramarine and phosphor omitted | £450 | | |
| | d. Embossing omitted | 6·00 | | |
| ✓ | e. Phosphor omitted | 5·00 | | |
| | f. Retouched dapples (Cyl. 1A. R. 12/4) | 20·00 | | |
| | g. Bistre omitted | — | | |

**W143** (=SG 776)

| | | | | |
|---|---|---|---|---|
| 9d. | yellow-olive, black, brown, yellow, magenta, orange, turquoise-green and gold | | 15 | 25 |
| | a. Yellow omitted | £150 | | |
| | b. Turquoise-green (dress) omitted | £20000 | | |
| | c. Embossing and phosphor omitted | 10·00 | | |
| | d. Embossing omitted | 6·00 | | |
| | f. Phosphor omitted | 10·00 | | |

**W144** (=SG 777)

| | | | | |
|---|---|---|---|---|
| 1s.6d. | ultramarine, yellow-orange, bright purple, blue-green, black and gold | | 15 | 50 |
| | a. Embossing omitted | | | |
| | b. Phosphor omitted | 15·00 | | |

| First Day Cover (W142/4) | 1·00 |
|---|---|
| Presentation Pack (W142/4) | 5·00 |
| Presentation Pack (German) (W142/4) | 14·00 |

*The effect of the missing vermilion is shown on the rocking horse, saddle and faces which appear orange instead of red.

No. W142 is known pre-released on 24 November at Edinburgh.

A single used example of No. W142g has been seen with the bistre omitted from the mane of the rocking horse and the girl's hair. No. W142a also exists with a single complete omission and three partial gold heads on the gummed side due to a paper fold.

Two machines were used for printing the 4d. value:

Stamps from cylinders 1A–1B–2C–1D–1E in combination with 1F, 2F or 3F (gold) were printed entirely on the Rembrandt sheet-fed machine. They invariably have the Queen's head level with the top of the boy's head and the sheets are perforated through the left side margin (perforation type F).

Stamps from cylinders 2A–2B–3C–2D–2E in combination with 1F, 2F, 3F or 4F (gold) were printed on the reel-fed Thrissell machine in five colours (its maximum colour capacity) and subsequently sheet-fed on the Rembrandt machine for the gold Queen's head and the embossing. The position of the Queen's head is generally lower than on the stamps printed at one operation, but it varies in different parts of the sheet and is not, therefore, a sure indication for identifying single stamps. Another small difference is that the boy's grey pullover is noticeably "moth-eaten" in the Thrissell printings and is normal on the Rembrandt. The Thrissell printings are perforated through the top margin (perforation type A).

Marginal copies can usually be identified by the characteristics of the perforation (if any) in the sheet margin. Ideally, cylinder blocks of six are required to show examples of the two printing machines used.

Normal                    W142f

Grey dapples on the horse nearest to the boy and extending to the boy's belt and trousers, are heavily retouched

## Cylinder Numbers (Blocks of Six)

| A. Rembrandt only printings | Perforation Types | |
|---|---|---|
| Cylinder Nos. (No dot) | A (E/I) | F (P/E) |
| 4d. 1A (black)–1B (orange)–2C (vermilion)–1D (ultramarine)–1E (bistre)–1F (gold) | † | 2·00 |
| 1A–1B–2C–1D–1E–2F | † | 2·00 |
| 1A–1B–2C–1D–1E–3F | † | 3·00 |
| 1A–1B–2C–1D–1E–4F | † | – |
| | | (E/P) |
| 9d. 1A (black)–1B (brown)–1C (yellow)–2D (magenta)–1E (orange) 1F (turquoise-green)–1G (yellow-olive)–1H (gold) | † | 3·00 |
| 1s.6d. 1A (black)–1B (ultramarine)–1C (yellow-orange)–1D (bright purple)–1E (blue-green)–1F (gold) | † | 4·00 |

| B. Thrissell and Rembrandt printings | | |
|---|---|---|
| 4d. 2A (black)–2B (orange)–3C (vermilion)–2D (ultramarine)–2E (bistre)–1F (gold) | 2·00 | † |
| 2A–2B–3C–2D–2E–2F | 3·00 | † |
| 2A–2B–3C–2D–2E–3F | 5·00 | † |
| 2A–2B–3C–2D–2E–4F | 5·00 | † |

Perforation Type F on the 9d. and 1s.6d. are with sheet orientated showing head to right. The 1s.6d. has cyl. nos. 1B–1E unboxed.

### Minor Constant Flaws

4d. Cyls. 1A–1B–2C–1D–1E in combination with gold cyls. 1F, 2F, 3F, or 4F
   3/6 Small black flaw in m of Christmas
   12/5 Small nick on right edge of upright stroke of 4 of value

4d. Cyls. 2A–2B–3C–2D–2E in combination with gold cyls. 1F, 2F, 3F or 4F
   16/4 Small black flaw above horse's left foreleg by boy's waist (Th. D9)
   20/4 Break in outline at top centre of near rocker (Th. F4–5)

9d. Cyls. 1A1B1C2D1E1F1G1H
   4/3 Small black flaw between a and s of Christmas
   6/18 Break in middle of final s of Christmas

1s.6d. Cyls. 1A–1B–1C–1D–1E–1F
   2/18 Pale patch on boy's left shoulder (Th. F4)
   3/8 Thick horizontal spur on left of lower central purple slotted plate (Th. D–E4)
   5/2 Black flaws in background lower right of Queen's head (Th. C–D7)
   5/3 Two black dots between 1 and stroke of 1/6

   6/20 Purple coloured flaws in background below boy's foot (Th. J7)

## Sheet Details

| | Rembrandt | Thrissell/Rembrandt |
|---|---|---|
| **Sheet sizes:** | | |
| 4d. 120 (6 × 20) | Single pane sheet-fed | Single pane reel-fed for five colours, and then single pane sheet fed for the gold and embossing |
| 9d. and 1s.6d. 120 (20 × 6) | Single pane sheet-fed | |
| **Sheet markings:** | | |
| **Cylinder numbers:** | | |
| 4d. | Opposite rows 18/19, left margin, boxed | Opposite rows 18/19, left margin, boxed |
| 9d. and 1s.6d. | Opposite rows 4/5, left margin, boxed | |
| **Guide holes:** | | |
| 4d. | None | Opposite rows 14/15 (boxed), at both sides |
| 9d. and 1s.6d. | None | |
| **Marginal arrows (photo- etched):** | | |
| 4d. | "W" shaped, at top, bottom and sides | "W" shaped, at top, bottom and sides |
| 9d. and 1s.6d. | As 4d. | |
| **Marginal rule:** | | |
| | None | None |
| **Colour register marks:** | | |
| 4d. | Above and below vertical rows 1/2 and 6 | Opposite rows 2/3 and 19/20 at both sides |
| 9d. and 1s.6d. | Opposite rows 1/2 and 5/6 at both sides | |
| **Coloured crosses:** | | |
| 4d. | Above and below vertical row 3 | Gold only below vertical row 3 |
| 9d. and 1s.6d. | Opposite rows 3/4 at both sides | |
| **Autotron marks (solid):** | | |
| 4d. | None | Black, bistre, ultra-marine, vermilion, orange below verti-cal rows 4/6 |
| 9d. and 1s.6d. | None | |
| Colour designa-tions: | None | |
| | | None |
| **Traffic lights (boxed):** | | |
| 4d. | Orange, vermilion, ultramarine, bistre, black, gold, em-bossing opposite rows 18/19, right margin; also above vertical row 5 read-ing left to right | Orange, vermilion, ultramarine, bistre, black, gold, em-bossing opposite rows 18/19, right margin; also gold and embossing (unboxed) above vertical row 5 read-ing left to right |

| 9d. | Rembrandt | Thrissell/Rembrandt |
|---|---|---|
| | Gold, olive, green, orange, magenta, yellow, brown, black opposite rows 4/5, right margin; also embossing, gold, olive, green, orange, magenta, yellow, brown, black above vertical rows 17/19 reading left to right | |
| 1s.6d. | Embossing, gold, green, purple, orange, ultramarine, black opposite rows 4/5, at right; also gold, green, purple, orange, ultramarine, black, above vertical rows 18/19 reading left to right | |

Although the Traffic Light box in the right margin on the 9d. and the upper margin on the 1s.6d. were designed to accommodate an embossing light the space was not in fact used.

**Imprimaturs from the National Postal Museum Archives**
Nos. W142/144 imperforate

| No watermark (*set of* 3) | £6750 |
|---|---|

**Quantities Sold:**
4d. 326,078,360, 9d. 17,102,520, 1s.6d. 21,344,760, English Pack 72,474, German Pack 7,298
**Withdrawn:** 24.11.69

**W141**. R.M.S. *Queen Elizabeth 2*

**W142**. *Elizabethan Galleon*

**W143**. *East Indiaman*

**W144**. *Cutty Sark*

**W145**. *S.S. Great Britain*

**W146**. *R.M.S. Mauretania*

(Des. David Gentleman)

## 1969 (15 January). British Ships

Issued as a tribute to British shipbuilders and seamen, these stamps depict five famous ships of the past and the *Queen Elizabeth 2*, which sailed on her maiden voyage to New York on 2 May 1969.

The 9d. values were issued together *se-tenant* in strips of three throughout the sheet and the 1s. values were issued together *se-tenant* in pairs throughout the sheet.

Two phosphor bands at right (1s.), one horizontal phosphor band (5d.) or two phosphor bands (9d.), applied by flexography Types **W141/6**

**W145** (=SG 778)

| | | Mint | Used |
|---|---|---|---|
| 5d. black, grey, red and turquoise | | 10 | 15 |
| a. Black omitted (Queen's head, value, hull and inscr.) | | £2800 | |
| b. Grey omitted (decks, etc.) | | £225 | |
| c. Red (inscription) omitted | | £250 | |
| d. Red and phosphor omitted | | £225 | |
| e. Phosphor omitted | | 5·00 | |

**W146** (=SG 779)

| | | Mint | Used |
|---|---|---|---|
| 9d. red, blue, ochre, brown, black and grey | | 10 | 25 |
| a. Strip of 3. Nos. W146/48 | | 1·25 | 1·50 |
| b. Red, blue and phosphor omitted | | £3500 | |
| c. Blue omitted | | £3500 | |
| d. Phosphor omitted | | 12·00 | |
| da. Phosphor omitted. (strip of three) | | 40·00 | |

**W147** (=SG 780)

| | | Mint | Used |
|---|---|---|---|
| 9d. ochre, brown, black and grey | | 10 | 25 |
| b. Phosphor omitted | | 12·00 | |

**W148** (=SG 781)

| | | Mint | Used |
|---|---|---|---|
| 9d. ochre, brown, black and grey | | 10 | 25 |
| b. Phosphor omitted | | 12·00 | |

**W149** (=SG 782)

| | | | |
|---|---|---|---|
| 1s. | brown, black, grey, green and greenish yellow | 40 | 35 |
| a. | Pair, Nos. W149/50 | 1·25 | 1·50 |
| b. | Greenish yellow omitted | £4000 | |
| c. | Phosphor omitted | 28·00 | |
| ca. | Phosphor omitted. (pair) | 65·00 | |

**W150** (=SG 783)

| | | | |
|---|---|---|---|
| 1s. | red, black, brown, carmine and grey | 40 | 35 |
| a. | Carmine (hull overlay) omitted | £35000 | |
| b. | Red (funnels) omitted | £24000 | |
| c. | Carmine and red omitted | £24000 | |
| d. | Phosphor omitted | 30·00 | |

| | |
|---|---|
| First Day Cover (W145/50) | 5·00 |

| | |
|---|---|
| Presentation Pack (W145/50) | 4·50 |

Pack also exists with a Dutch or Japanese insert card

| | |
|---|---|
| Presentation Pack (W145/50) | 40·00 |

*In addition to the generally issued Presentation Pack (inscribed "RMS Queen Elizabeth 2... she sailed on her maiden voyage to New York on 17 January 1969") a further pack (inscribed "RMS Queen Elizabeth 2... she sails on her maiden voyage early in 1969") was issued for sale exclusively on board the Q.E.2 during her maiden voyage which had been postponed. (*Price* £8).

| | |
|---|---|
| 9d. Prices for missing colour errors in strips of three: | |
| Red, blue and phosphor | £3500 |
| Blue | £3500 |
| 1s. Price for missing colour error in pair: | |
| Greenish yellow | £4000 |

First Day covers are known postmarked 14 January, Buckley, Flintshire. The year date shown as 1968 instead of 1969 exists postmarked at Brighton, Sussex.

**Cylinder Numbers** (Blocks of Six (5d. and 1s.) or Twelve (9d.))

| | Perforation Types | |
|---|---|---|
| Cyl. Nos. (No dot) | A(T) (E/P) | F (P/E) |
| 5d. 1A (black)–1B (grey)–1C (red)–1D (turquoise) | 3·00 | † |
| 9d. 1A (black)–2B (brown)–1C (ochre)–1D (grey)–1E (red)–1F (blue) | † | 5·50 |
| 1s. 2A (black)–1B (grey)–1C (green)–1D (red)–1E (carmine)–1F (brown)–1G (yellow) | 7·00 | † |

**Minor Constant Flaws**

5d. Cyls. 1A–1B–1C–1D
    2/5 Disturbance in sea over liz of Elizabeth
    3/2 Blue flaw on superstructure halfway between funnel and stern (Th. E6) (later removed)
    4/5 Weak patch in hull directly below funnel (Th. F9)

9d. Cyls. 1A–2B–1C–1D–1E–1F
    16/2 Rope between second and third masts is broken (Th. D5)

1s. Cyls. 2A–1B–1C–1D–1E–1F–1G
    1/6 Small brown flaw lower right of stern mast (Th. D6)
    2/8 Curved black flaw just above third funnel (Th. C10)
    4/2 Weak patch in hull directly below foremast (Th. E17)
    10/1 Wispy black flaw in front of Queen's chin (Th. B–C17)

**Sheet Details**
**Sheet sizes:**
All single pane sheet-fed
5d. 72 (8 × 9)
9d. 120 (6 × 20). In se-tenant strips of three
1s. 80 (8 × 10). In se-tenant pairs

**Sheet markings:**
**Cylinder numbers:**
5d. Opposite rows 7/8, left margin, boxed
9d. Opposite rows 17/18, left margin, boxed
1s. Below vertical row 7, boxed
**Guide holes:** None
Marginal arrows (photo-etched); "W" shaped, at top and bottom (5d.); "W" shaped, at top, bottom and sides (others)
**Marginal rule:** None
**Colour register marks:**
5d. Opposite rows 1/2 and 8/9 at both sides
9d. Above and below vertical rows 1 and 6
1s. Opposite rows 1/2 and 10 at both sides
**Coloured crosses:**
5d. Opposite rows 5/6 at both sides
9d. Above and below vertical rows 3/4
1s. Opposite rows 5/7 at both sides
**Autotron marks,Colour designations:** None
**Traffic lights (boxed):**
5d. In same order as cylinder numbers opposite rows 7/8, right margin; also above vertical row 7 reading left to right
9d. In same order as cylinder numbers opposite rows 18/19, right margin; also above vertical rows 5/6 but in reverse order to cylinder numbers reading left to right
1s. In reverse order to cylinder numbers opposite rows 8/9, right margin; also above vertical row 8 in reverse order to cylinder numbers reading left to right

**Imprimaturs from the National Postal Museum Archives**
Imperforate, no watermark

| | |
|---|---|
| No W145 single | £2250 |
| Nos. W146/8 se-tenant strip of three | £6750 |
| Nos. W149/50 se-tenant pair | £4500 |

**Quantities Sold:**
5d. 67,584,528, 9d. 14,351,160, 1s. 10,784,480, English Pack 116,526, German Pack 4.416

**Withdrawn:** 14.1.70

**W147**. Concorde in Flight

(Des. Michael and Sylvia Goaman)

**W148**. Plan and Elevation Views

**W149**. Concorde's Nose and Tail

(Des. David Gentleman)

## 1969 (3 March). First Flight of Concorde

Issued to commemorate the first flight of the "Concorde" supersonic airliner developed and produced jointly by Britain and France.
Two phosphor bands
Types **W147/9**
**W151** (=SG 784)

| | | Mint | Used |
|---|---|---|---|
| 4d. | yellow-orange, violet, greenish blue, blue-green and pale green | 25 | 25 |
| a. | Violet omitted (value, etc.) | £600 | |
| b. | Yellow-orange and phosphor omitted | £600 | |
| c. | Yellow-orange omitted | £600 | |
| d. | Phosphor omitted | 1·00 | |
| e. | Error. Left-hand band omitted | 55·00 | |
| f. | Oil slick flaw (R. 13/2) | 20·00 | |

**W152** (=SG 785)

| | | | |
|---|---|---|---|
| 9d. | ultramarine, emerald, red and grey-blue | 55 | 75 |
| a. | Phosphor omitted | £100 | |
| b. | Grey-blue (Face value and inscr. omitted) | £40000 | |

**W153** (=SG 786)

| | | | |
|---|---|---|---|
| 1s.6d. | deep blue, silver-grey and light blue | 75 | 1·00 |
| a. | Silver-grey omitted* | £600 | |
| b. | Phosphor omitted | 9·00 | |

| | |
|---|---|
| First Day Cover (W151/3) | 4·00 |

| | |
|---|---|
| Presentation Pack (W151/3) | 12·00 |

Pack also exists with a Dutch or Japanese insert card

| | |
|---|---|
| Presentation Pack (German)(W151/3) | 40·00 |

*No. W153a affects the Queen's head which appears in the light blue colour.

**This exists as a complete sheet with guide marks and sheet markings in grey-blue affecting the remaining five stamps of top row.

A cover with all three values is known postmarked 2 March, at Hindon, Salisbury.

W151f
Dark flaw in Atlantic Ocean appears as an oil slick

### Cylinder Numbers (Blocks of Six)

| Cyl. Nos. (No dot) | Perforation Type F (P/E at left and I/E at right) |
|---|---|
| 4d. 1A (violet)–1B (orange)–1C (greenish blue)–1D (pale green)–1E (blue-green) | 3·00 |
| 9d. 2A (grey-blue)–1B (red)–1C (emerald)–1D (ultramarine) | 5·50 |
| 1s.6d. 1A (deep blue)–1B (silver-grey)–3C (light blue) | 7·00 |

In this issue cylinder blocks exist at the left or right of the sheets.

**Minor Constant Flaws**
4d. Cyls. 1A–1B–1C–1D–1E
    1/2 Disturbance in background below tail (Th. F–G11)
    2/2 Disturbance in background below tail (Th. F–G12)
9d. Cyls. 2A–1B–1C–1D
    11/2 Flaw on Queen's hair below ribbons (Th. B13)
1s.6d. Cyls. 1A–1B–3C
    18/2 Small white patch below tip of Concorde's nose (Th.F13)

**Sheet Details**
Sheet size: 120 (6 × 20). Single pane sheet-fed

**Sheet markings:**
**Cylinder numbers:**
4d. Opposite rows 1/2 and 18/19, at both sides, boxed
9d. Opposite rows 2/3 and 18/19, at both sides, boxed
1s.6d. Opposite rows 2 and 19, at both sides, boxed
**Guide holes:** None
**Marginal arrows (photo-etched):** "W" shaped, at top, bottom and sides
**Marginal rule:** At bottom of sheet
**Colour register marks:**
4d. Above and below vertical rows 1/2 and 6
9d. Above and below vertical rows 1 and 5/6
1s.6d. Above and below vertical rows 1/2 and 6
**Coloured crosses:** Above and below vertical rows 2/3
**Autotron marks,Colour designations:** None
**Traffic lights (boxed):**
4d. Blue-green, orange, violet, greenish blue, pale green reading left to right above vertical row 5
9d. Ultramarine, emerald, red, grey-blue reading left to right above vertical row 5
1s.6d. Deep blue, light blue, silver-grey reading left to right above vertical row 5

**Imprimaturs from the National Postal Museum Archives**
Nos. W151/153 imperforate

| | |
|---|---|
| No watermark (set of 3) | £6750 |

**Quantities Sold:**

| | |
|---|---|
| 4d. | 91,551,720 |
| 9d. | 9,488,520 |
| 1s.6d. | 9,874,560 |
| English Pack | 100,608 |
| German Pack | 2,827 |

**Withdrawn:** 2.3.70

**W150**. Page from *Daily Mail* and Vickers Vimy Aircraft

(Des. Philip Sharland)

**W151**. Europa and CEPT Emblems

(Des. Michael and Sylvia Goaman)

**W152**. ILO Emblem

(Des. Philip Sharland)

**W153**. Flags of NATO Countries

(Des. Philip Sharland)

**W154**. Vickers Vimy Aircraft and Globe showing Flight

(Des. Michael and Sylvia Goaman)

### 1969 (2 April). Notable Anniversaries

Five famous anniversaries, with the events described on the stamps.
  Two phosphor bands, applied by photogravure (5d.) or flexography (others)
Types **W150/4**
**W154** (=SG 791)

|  | | Mint | Used |
|---|---|---|---|
| 5d. | black, pale sage-green, chestnut and new blue | 10 | 15 |
| | a. Phosphor omitted | | |
| ✓ | b. Missing windshield (R. 3/4) | 20·00 | |

**W155** (=SG 792)

|  | | | |
|---|---|---|---|
| 9d. | pale turquoise, deep blue, light emerald-green and black | 15 | 25 |
| | a. Uncoated paper* | £1800 | |
| | b. Phosphor omitted | 18·00 | |

**W156** (=SG 793)

|  | | | |
|---|---|---|---|
| 1s. | bright purple, deep blue and lilac | 15 | 25 |
| | a. Phosphor omitted | 10·00 | |

**W157** (=SG 794)

|  | | | |
|---|---|---|---|
| 1s.6d. | red, royal blue, yellow-green, black, lemon and new blue | 15 | 30 |
| | a. Black omitted | £120 | |
| | b. Yellow-green (from flags) omitted | 85·00 | |
| | c. Yellow-green and phosphor omitted | 95·00 | |
| | d. Phosphor omitted | 9·00 | |
| | e. Shadow variety (R. 18/6) | 20·00 | |
| | f. Lemon (from flags) omitted | † | £4500 |

**W158** (=SG 795)

|  | | | |
|---|---|---|---|
| 1s.9d. | yellow-olive, greenish yellow and pale turquoise- green | 20 | 40 |
| | a. Uncoated paper* | £275 | |
| | b. Phosphor omitted | 6·00 | |

| First Day Cover (W154/8) | | 3·00 |
|---|---|---|

| Presentation Pack (W154/8) | 3·50 | |
|---|---|---|

Pack also exists with a Japanese insert

| Presentation Pack (German)(W154/8) | 65·00 | |
|---|---|---|

*Uncoated paper see General Notes for Section UA also below Nos. W159/64.
No. W154 is known postmarked 1 April.
No. W157f is only known used on a first day cover from Liverpool.

Normal

W154b

W157e
Deficient shading in shadow by fold

**Cylinder Numbers** (Blocks of Six (5d., 1s., 1s.9d.) or Eight (9d., 1s.6d.))

| | | Perforation Types | |
|---|---|---|---|
| Cylinder Nos. (No dot) | | A (E/I) | F (P/E) |
| 5d. | 1A (blue)–1B (chestnut)–1C (sage-green)–1D (black) | 1·75 | † |
| 9d. | 1A (blue)–1B (green)–1C (black)–1D (turquoise) | † | 2·75 |
| 1s. | 1A (blue)1B (purple)1C (lilac) | † | 2·50 |

| 1s.6d. | 1A (new blue)–1B (lemon)–1C (red)–1D (royal blue)–1E (black)–1F (green) | † | 4·00 |
|---|---|---|---|
| 1s.9d. | 2A (yellow-olive)–2B (green)–1C (yellow) | † | 4·50 |

## Minor Constant Flaws

5d. Cyls. 1A–1B–1C–1D
3/4 Black horizontal line extending through the engine and fuselage (Th. E9–12)
4/6 Vertical black scratch top left of photograph of Alcock (Th. A–B3)
15/3 Retouch to base of engine (Th. E10)
15/5 White flaw on Brown's cap (Th. B6). Later retouched

9d. Cyls. 1A–1B–1C–1D
14/1 Retouch to background below O of EUROPA (Th. FG4)
15/3 Weak patch in background to left of CEPT symbol (Th. E11)
19/3 Retouch to background below EU of EUROPA (Th. F2)
20/2 Weak patch in background above O of EUROPA (Th. B–C4)

1s. Cyls. 1A–1B–1C
19/1 Dark patch in upper jaw of spanner (Th. F1)

1s.9d. Cyls. 2A–2B–1C
17/4 Horizontal scratch through value (Th. A1–3)
20/6 Pale patch in East Asia on globe (Th. B12)

## Sheet Details
Sheet size: 120 (6 × 20). 5d. single pane reel-fed; others single pane sheet-fed

## Sheet markings:
**Cylinder numbers:**
5d. Opposite rows 18/19, left margin, boxed
9d. Opposite rows 17/18, left margin, boxed
1s. Opposite row 18, left margin, boxed
1s.6d. Opposite rows 17/18, left margin, boxed
1s.9d. Opposite row 18, left margin, boxed
**Guide holes:**
5d. Opposite rows 14/15 (boxed), at both sides

**Others**: None
**Marginal arrows (photo-etched)**: "W" shaped, at top, bottom and sides
**Marginal rule**: None
**Colour register marks:**
5d. Opposite rows 1/2 and 19/20 at both sides
Others: Above and below vertical rows 1 and 6
**Coloured crosses:**
5d. None
9d., 1s. and 1s.9d. Above and below vertical row 3
1s.6d. Above and below vertical rows 3/4
**Autotron marks (solid):**
5d. Black, sage-green, blue, chestnut below vertical rows 1/3
Others: None
**Colour designations:**
5d. G1 BROWN G2 BLUE G3 (blank) G4 BLACK in right margin reading upwards opposite rows 14/9
Others: None
**Sheet values**: Opposite rows 4/7 and 14/17 reading upwards in left margin and downwards in right margin
**Traffic lights (boxed):**
5d. Black, sage-green, blue, chestnut opposite rows 18/19, right margin; also in same order opposite rows 1/2, left margin
9d. Black, green, blue, turquoise opposite rows 17/18, right margin; also in reverse order reading left to right above vertical row 5
1s. In same order as cylinder numbers opposite row 18, right margin; also in reverse order reading left to right above vertical row 5
1s.6d. In same order as cylinder numbers opposite rows 17/18, right margin; also in reverse order reading left to right above vertical row 5
1s.9d. In same order as cylinder numbers opposite row 18, right

margin; also in reverse order reading left to right above vertical row 5

**Imprimaturs from the National Postal Museum Archives**
Nos. W154/158 imperforate

| No watermark (*set of* 5) | £11250 |
|---|---|

**Quantities Sold:**

| | |
|---|---|
| 5d. | 82,285,680 |
| 9d. | 9,823,200 |
| 1s. | 10,302,360 |
| 1s.6d. | 10,512,480 |
| 1s.9d. | 6,155,760 |
| English Pack | 90,282 |
| German Pack | 4,539 |

**Withdrawn**: 1.4.70

**W155**. Durham Cathedral

**W156**. York Minster

**W157**. St. Giles', Edinburgh

**W158**. Canterbury Cathedral

**W159**. St. Paul's Cathedral

**W160**. Liverpool Metropolitan Cathedral

(Des. Peter Gauld)

## 1969 (28 May). British Architecture (Cathedrals)

The designs show six famous British Cathedrals dating from medieval times to the present, the Liverpool Metropolitan Cathedral being completed in 1967.

The 5d. values were issued together *se-tenant* in blocks of four throughout the sheet

Two phosphor bands, applied by flexography (5d.) or photogravure (others)

Types **W155/60**

**W159** (=SG 796)

| | | Mint | Used |
|---|---|---|---|
| 5d. | grey-black, orange, pale bluish violet and black | 10 | 10 |
| a. | Block of 4. Nos. W159/62 | 1·10 | 1·25 |
| ac. | Uncoated paper* (block of four) | £1000 | |
| b. | Pale bluish violet omitted | £15000 | |
| c. | Uncoated paper* | £250 | |
| d. | Missing d | £500 | |

**W160** (=SG 797)

| | | | |
|---|---|---|---|
| 5d. | grey-black, pale bluish violet, new blue and black | 10 | 10 |
| b. | Pale bluish violet omitted | £15000 | |
| c. | Uncoated paper* | £250 | |

**W161** (=SG 798)

| | | | |
|---|---|---|---|
| 5d. | grey-black, purple, green and black | 10 | 10 |
| b. | Green omitted* | £100 | |
| c. | Uncoated paper* | £250 | |
| d. | Missing d | £600 | |

**W162** (=SG 799)

| | | | |
|---|---|---|---|
| 5d. | grey-black, green, new blue and black | 10 | 10 |
| c. | Uncoated paper* | £250 | |

**W163** (=SG 800)

| | | | |
|---|---|---|---|
| 9d. | grey-black, ochre, pale drab, violet and black | 25 | 30 |
| a. | Black (value) omitted. | £250 | |
| b. | Black (value) and phosphor omitted | £300 | |
| c. | Phosphor omitted | 45·00 | |

**W164** (=SG 801)

| | | | | |
|---|---|---|---|---|
| W160 | 1s.6d. | grey-black, pale turquoise-blue, pale reddish violet, pale yellow-olive and black | 25 | 30 |
| | a. | Black (value) omitted | £4700 | |
| | b. | Black (value) double | £4000 | |
| | c. | Phosphor omitted | 20·00 | |
| | ca. | Error. Phosphor omitted and one stamp with diagonal phosphor band (pair) | 50·00 | |

| | |
|---|---|
| First Day Cover (W159/64) | 3·00 |

| | |
|---|---|
| Presentation Pack (W159/64) | 3·25 |

Pack also exists with a Dutch or Japanese insert card

| | |
|---|---|
| Presentation Pack (German)(W159/64) | 30·00 |

*__Uncoated paper.__ This does not respond to the chalky paper test, and may be further distinguished from the normal chalk-surfaced paper by the fibres which clearly show on the surface, resulting in the printing impression being rougher, and by the screening dots which are not so evident.

For this issue hand stamped "Cancelled" see Special Issues–Notes, "Specimen".

5d. Prices for missing colour errors in blocks of four:

| | |
|---|---|
| Pale bluish violet | £30000 |
| Green | £100 |

*The missing green on the roof top is known on R. 2/5, R. 8/5 and R. 10/5 but all from different sheets and it only occurred in part of the printing, being "probably caused by a batter on the impression cylinder". Examples are known with the green partly omitted.

Nos. W159d and W161d missing d affects stamps R. 1/1 and R. 2/1 in a block; the stamps at right were normal.

**Cylinder Numbers** (Blocks of Eight (5d.) or Six (9d., 1s.6d.))

| | Perforation Types | | |
|---|---|---|---|
| | A (E/I) | A (E/I) | F (P/E) |
| Cylinder. Nos. | No dot | Dot | No dot |
| **5d.** 1A (black)–1B (purple)–1C (blue)–1D (orange)–2E (green)–2F (grey-black)–1G (violet)* | 3·00 | 3·00 | † |
| 1A–1B–2C–1D–2E–2F–1G* | 3·00 | 3·00 | † |
| **9d.** 1A (black)–1B (grey-black)–2C (violet)–1D (drab)–1E (ochre)** | † | † | 4·00 |
| **1s.6d.** 1A (black)–1B (violet)–1C (turquoise-blue)–1D (yellow-olive)–1E (grey-black) | † | † | 4·00 |

*In the 5d. dot panes the violet cylinder is expressed in error thus: "1.G" and the black cylinder "1.A".
**In the 9d. the violet 2C often appears battered, the 2 sometimes being hardly discernible.

## Minor Constant Flaws

5d. Cyls. 1A–1B–1D–2E–2F no dot in combination with blue cyls. 1C or 2C no dot
　1–2/4 Thin diagonal green line joins portrait to inset design (Th. C-E2)

5d. Cyls. 1A–1B–1D–2E–2F dot in combination with blue cyls. 1C or 2C dot
　14/3 Green coloured scratch extends from bottom of third stamp in row 1 to top of third stamp in row 4. (Most noticeable in the sky of R. 3/3)
　4/1 Damaged first S of ST. GILES'
　10/3 Grey-black coloured spur at right of angel (Th. F13)

9d. Cyls. 1A–1B–2C–1D–1E
　8/5 Dark spot in window on first floor just to right of centre of St. Paul's (Th. F7)
　9/1 Dot left of ground floor window next to entrance columns (Th. G3)

1s.6d. Cyls. 1A–1B–1C–1D–1E
　1/1 Retouch on Queen's head (Th. A11)
　15/1 Spur at left of third spike of central tower (Th. A5); also dot before C of CATHEDRAL

## Sheet Details
**Sheet sizes**:
5d. 72 (6 × 12). In se-tenant blocks of four, double pane reel-fed, with dot pane above no dot pane
9d. and 1s.6d. 120 (6 × 20). Single pane sheet-fed

**Sheet markings**:
**Cylinder numbers**:
5d. Opposite rows 10/11, left margin, boxed
9d. and 1s.6d. Opposite rows 18/19, left margin, boxed
**Guide holes**:
5d. Opposite rows 6/7 (boxed), at both sides
Others: None Marginal arrows (photo-etched): "W" shaped, at top, bottom and sides
**Marginal rule**: None
**Colour register marks**:
5d. Opposite rows 10/12, left margin, although usually trimmed off
9d. and 1s.6d. Above and below vertical rows 1 and 6
**Coloured crosses**:
5d. None 9d. and 1s.6d. Above and below vertical rows 3/4
**Autotron marks**:
5d. Normally trimmed off
9d. and 1s.6d. None
**Colour designations**: None
**Sheet values**:
5d. Opposite rows 2/5 and 8/11 reading upwards in left margin and downwards in right margin
9d. and 1s.6d. Opposite rows 5/6 and 15/16 reading upwards in left margin and downwards in right margin
**Traffic lights (boxed)**:

5d. In same order as cylinder numbers opposite rows 10/11, right margin; also in same order reading left to right above vertical rows 4/5
9d. In reverse order to cylinder numbers opposite rows 18/19, right margin; also above vertical row 5 but in same order as cylinder numbers reading left to right
1s.6d. Black, yellow-olive, turquoise-blue, violet, grey-black opposite rows 18/19, right margin; also grey-black, yellow-olive, turquoise-blue, violet and black reading left to right above vertical row 5

**Imprimaturs from the National Postal Museum Archives**
Imperforate, no watermark

| | |
|---|---|
| Nos. W159/62 se-tenant block of four | £9000 |
| Nos. W163 single | £2250 |
| Nos. W164 single | £2250 |

**Quantities Sold**:

| | |
|---|---|
| 5d. | 65,344,176 |
| 9d. | 11,065,920 |
| 1s.6d. | 11,414,280 |
| English Pack | 119,828 |
| German Pack | 7,200 |

**Withdrawn**: 27.5.70

**W161**. The King's Gate, Caernarvon Castle　**W162**. The Eagle Tower, Caernarvon Castle

**W163**. Queen Eleanor's Gate, Caernarvon Castle

Types W161/63 were issued together *se-tenant* in horizontal strips of three within the sheet

**W164**. Celtic Cross, Margam Abbey

**W165**. H.R.H. The Prince of Wales (after photograph by G. Argent)

(Des. David Gentleman)

## 1969 (1 JULY). Investiture of H.R.H. The Prince of Wales

The ceremony of Investiture dates back to 1284 when King Edward I presented his son to the people of Caernarvon as the first Prince of Wales.

Two phosphor bands, applied by flexography, the phosphor being printed between two groups of colour units.

Types **W161/5**

**W165** (=SG 802)

| | | Mint | Used |
|---|---|---|---|
| 5d. | deep olive-grey, light olive-grey, deep grey, light grey, red, pale turquoise-green, black and silver | 10 | 15 |
| a. | Strip of 3. Nos. W165/7 | 50 | 1·00 |
| b. | Black (value and inscr.) omitted | £650 | |
| c. | Red omitted* | £1250 | |
| d. | Deep grey omitted** | £475 | |
| e. | Pale turquoise-green omitted | £1100 | |
| f. | Light grey omitted (see footnote) | £12000 | |
| g. | Phosphor omitted | 5·00 | |
| ga. | Phosphor omitted (strip of three) | 15·00 | |

**W166** (=SG 803)

| | | | |
|---|---|---|---|
| 5d. | deep olive-grey, light olive-grey, deep grey, light grey, red, pale turquoise-green, black and silver | 10 | 15 |
| b. | Black (value and inscr.) omitted | £650 | |
| c. | Red omitted* | £1250 | |
| d. | Deep grey omitted** | £475 | |
| e. | Pale turquoise-green omitted | £1100 | |
| f. | Light grey omitted (see footnote) | £12000 | £8000 |
| g. | Phosphor omitted | 5·00 | |

**W167** (=SG 804)

| | | | |
|---|---|---|---|
| 5d. | deep olive-grey, light olive-grey, deep grey, light grey, red, pale turquoise-green, black and silver | 10 | 15 |
| b. | Black (value and inscr.) omitted | £650 | |
| c. | Red omitted* | £1250 | |
| d. | Deep grey omitted** | £475 | |
| e. | Pale turquoise-green omitted | £1100 | |
| f. | Light grey omitted (see footnote) | £12000 | |
| g. | Phosphor omitted | 5·00 | |

**W168** (=SG 805)

| | | | |
|---|---|---|---|
| 9d. | deep grey, light grey, black and gold | 15 | 30 |

| | | | |
|---|---|---|---|
| a. | Phosphor omitted | 22·00 | |
| b. | Error. One broad band | 45·00 | |

**W169** (=SG 806)

| | | | |
|---|---|---|---|
| 1s. | blackish yellow-olive and gold | 15 | 30 |
| a. | Phosphor omitted | 15·00 | |
| b. | Error. One broad band | 40·00 | |
| c. | Error. Diagonal broad band | 50·00 | |

| First Day Cover (W165/9) | 1·50 |
|---|---|

| Presentation Pack (W165/9) | 3·00 |
|---|---|

Pack also exists with a Dutch or Japanese insert card.

| First Day Cover (German) (W165/9) | 30·00 |
|---|---|

5d. Prices for missing colour errors in strips of three:

| Black | £1950 |
|---|---|
| Pale turquoise-green | £3300 |
| Red | £3750 |
| Light grey | £36000 |
| Deep grey | £1425 |

The light grey (marks on walls, window frames, etc) omitted is unique in a mint strip of three and one. No. W166f commercially used on cover.

*The 5d. is also known with the red misplaced downwards and where this occurs the red printing does not take very well on the silver background and in some cases is so faint that it could be mistaken for a missing red. However, the red can be seen under a magnifying glass and caution should therefore be exercised when purchasing examples of W165/7c.

**The deep grey affects the dark portions of the windows and doorways.

In addition to the generally issued Presentation Pack a further pack in different colours and with all texts printed in both English and Welsh was made available exclusively through Education Authorities for free distribution to all schoolchildren in Wales and Monmouthshire. (*Price £16*).

First Day Covers are known postmarked in error "1 JUL 1968" at London N.W.1.

**Cylinder Numbers** (Blocks of Nine (5d.) or Four (9d., 1s.))

| | | | Perforation Type | | | |
|---|---|---|---|---|---|---|
| | | | F (E left margin) | | | |
| | Cylinder Nos. | | No dot | | | |
| 5d. | 1A (black)–1B (red)–1C (silver)–1D (green)–1E (deep olive- grey)–1F (light olive-grey)–1G (deep grey)–1H (light grey) | | 3·00 | | | |
| | | | A (P/E) No dot | A (P/E) Dot | A(T) (I/E) No dot | A(T) (I/E) Dot |
| 9d. | 1A (black)–1B (gold)–1C (deep grey)–1D (light grey) | | 2·50 | 2·50 | † | † |
| 1s. | 1A (gold)–2B (blackish yellow-olive) | | 2·50 | 2·50 | † | † |

The above are with sheets orientated showing head to right.

**Minor Constant Flaws**

9d. Cyls. 1A–1B–1C–1D dot
5/9 yw of Tywysog are joined together

1s. 1A–2B no dot
1/10 Retouch to right of Prince's lower lip (Th. J-K6)

3/4 Small retouch below Prince's left eye (Th. G6)
1A–2B dot
3/9 R Dark patch below Prince's left eye (Th. G6)

**Sheet Details**
**Sheet sizes**:
5d. 72 (12 × 6). In se-tenant strips of three, single pane sheet-fed
9d. and 1s. 60 (10 × 6). Double pane sheet-fed, with no dot pane above dot pane

**Sheet markings**:
**Cylinder numbers**:
5d. Opposite rows 4/5, left margin, boxed
9d. and 1s. Opposite row 6, left margin, boxed
**Guide holes**: None
Marginal arrows (photo-etched):
5d. None
9d. and 1s. "W" shaped, at top, bottom and sides
**Marginal rule**: None
**Colour register marks**:
5d. Opposite rows 1 and 6, at both sides
9d. Above (no dot) or below (dot) vertical rows 1/2 and 10
1s. Above (no dot) or below (dot) vertical rows 1/2 and 9/10
**Coloured crosses**:
5d. Opposite rows 3/4, at both sides
9d. and 1s. Above (no dot) or below (dot) vertical row 4
**Autotron marks,Colour designations**: None
**Sheet values**:
5d. Above and below vertical rows 2/5 and 8/11 reading left to right in top margin and right to left (upside-down) in bottom margin
9d. and 1s. Opposite rows 1/3 and 4/6 reading upwards in left margin and downwards in right margin
**Traffic lights (boxed)**:
5d. In same order as cylinder numbers opposite rows 4/5, right margin; also in same order reading left to right above vertical rows 10/11
9d. In same order as cylinder numbers opposite row 6, right margin; also in same order reading left to right above vertical row 9
1s. In reverse order to cylinder numbers opposite row 6, right margin; also in reverse order reading left to right above vertical row 9

**Imprimaturs from the National Postal Museum Archives**
Imperforate, no watermark

| | |
|---|---|
| Nos. W165/7 se-tenant strip of three | £6750 |
| Nos. W168 and W169 | (Each) £2250 |

**Quantities Sold**:
5d. 99,467,496; 9d. 13,384,380; 1s. 12,972,720; English Pack 256,709; German Pack 9,360;
Welsh Schoolchildren s Pack 146,958

**Withdrawn**: 30.6.70

**W166**. Mahatma Gandhi

(Des. Biman Mullick)

## 1969 (13 August). Gandhi Centenary Year

This stamp marking the Gandhi Centenary Year was also the first United Kingdom postage stamp to commemorate an overseas leader and the first to be designed by an overseas artist.

Two phosphor bands, applied by flexography

Type **W166**

**W170** (=SG 807)

| | | | |
|---|---|---|---|
| | 1s.6d. black, green, red-orange and grey | 30 | 30 |
| a. | Printed on the gummed side | £1400 | |
| b. | Phosphor omitted | 4·00 | |
| c. | Tooth Flaw (R. 20/3) | 20·00 | |

| | |
|---|---|
| First Day Cover (W170) | 1·00 |

The above is known pre-released on 12 August at Penyfai (Bridgend), Glamorgan and also postmarked Paisley, Renfrewshire 13 July 1969, the latter being due to the use of an incorrect date-stamp on a first day cover.

W170c

White patch in Gandhi's mouth appears as tooth. Later retouched to near normal

**Cylinder Numbers** (Blocks of Six)

| | | Perforation Type |
|---|---|---|
| | *Cyl. Nos. (No dot)* | *F (P/E)* |
| 1s.6d. | 2A (black)–1B (grey)–2C (green)–1D (orange) | 5·00 |

**Minor Constant Flaws**
1s.6d. Cyls. 2A–1B–2C–1D
1/6 Second white spot in Gandhi's right eye (Th. D6). Later retouched; also small nick in left arm of Y of Year
3/4 Dark patch on arm of spectacles (Th. C4)
3/5 Retouch on Gandhi's nose (Th. E6)
5/3 Dark spot in front of Gandhi's right ear (Th. D3)
8/2 Dark spot on Gandhi's temple (Th. C4). Later retouched
12/4 White patch on Gandhi's right lapel (Th. G2)
16/1 Retouched G of Gandhi

**Sheet Details**
Sheet size: 120 (6 × 20). Single pane sheet-fed

**Sheet markings**:
**Cylinder numbers**: Opposite rows 18/19, left margin, boxed
**Guide holes**: None
**Marginal arrows (photo-etched)**: "W" shaped, at top, bottom and sides

**Marginal rule:** None

**Colour register marks:** Above and below vertical rows 1 and 6

**Coloured crosses:** Above and below vertical row 3

**Autotron marks and Colour designations:** None

**Sheet values:** Opposite rows 4/7 and 14/17 reading upwards in left margin and downwards in right margin

**Traffic lights (boxed):** Black, grey, green, orange opposite rows 19/20, right margin; also in reverse order reading left to right above vertical row 5

**Imprimatur from the National Postal Museum Archives**
No. W170 imperforate

| No watermark (single) | £2250 |
|---|---|

**Quantity Sold:** 10,804,920

**Withdrawn:** 12.8.70

---

## 1969 (15 September). Collectors Pack

| WCP2 | Comprising Nos. W142/70 | 25·00 |
|---|---|---|

This pack also exists with a German or Japanese insert card.
**Quantity Sold:** 63,890

---

**W167.** National Giro
"G" Symbol

**W168.** Telecommunications—
International Subscriber Dialling

**W169.** Telecommunications— Pulse Code Modulation

**W170.** Postal Mechanisation— Automatic Sorting

(Des. David Gentleman)

(Lithography by De La Rue)

## 1969 (1 October). **Post Office Technology Commemoration**

Issued on the day the Post Office became a public corporation, these stamps depict some of its technological achievements. This issue in itself was a technical departure for the Post Office being the first British stamps to be printed by lithography.

Comb perforation 13½ × 14. Two phosphor bands applied by typography

Types **W167/70**

**W171** (=SG 808)

|  |  | Mint | Used |
|---|---|---|---|
| 5d. | new blue, greenish blue, pale lavender and black | 10 | 10 |
| | a. Phosphor omitted | 5·00 | |
| | b. Error. One broad band | 15·00 | |

**W172** (=SG 809)

|  |  | Mint | Used |
|---|---|---|---|
| 9d. | emerald, violet-blue and black | 20 | 20 |
| | a. Error. One broad band | 15·00 | |

**W173** (=SG 810)

|  |  | Mint | Used |
|---|---|---|---|
| 1s. | emerald, lavender and black | 20 | 20 |
| | a. Phosphor omitted | £300 | |
| | b. Error. One broad band | 15·00 | |

**W174** (=SG 811)

|  |  | Mint | Used |
|---|---|---|---|
| 1s.6d. | bright purple, light turquoise-blue, grey-blue and black | 15 | 35 |
| | a. Error. One broad band | 18·00 | |

| First Day Cover (W171/4) | 1·50 |
|---|---|

| Presentation Pack (W171/4) | 3·00 |
|---|---|

Pack also exists with a Dutch, German or Japanese insert card

No. W171a can be found with or without a dry impression of the typography plate.

The 1s. is known postmarked at Gloucester on 29 September and the 1s.6d. at Gutcher Yell (Shetland Isles) on 26 September.

For examples with "Cancelled" handstamp, see Special Issues—Notes, "Specimens".

**Plate Numbers** (Blocks of Four)

|  | Plate Nos. (all Dot) | Perforation Type F (L) (I/E) |
|---|---|---|
| 5d. | 2A (new blue)–2B (greenish blue)–2C (lavender)–2D (black) | 1·25 |
| | 2A–3B–2C–2D | 1·00 |
| | 2A–3B–2C–3D | 1·00 |
| | 3A–4B–3C–4D | 1·50 |
| 9d. | 2A (emerald)–2B (violet-blue)–2C (black) | 1·50 |
| 1s. | 1A (emerald)–1B (lavender)–1C (black) | 3·00 |
| | 1A–1B–2C | 2·50 |
| | 1A–1B–3C | 2·50 |
| 1s.6d. | 1A (purple)–1B (light turquoise-blue)–1C (grey-blue)–1D (black) | 3·00 |

Although all the plate numbers are followed by a dot they were in fact only printed in single panes.

**Minor Constant Flaws**

Numerous minor flaws caused by specks of dust settling on the printing plate and preventing the ink from reaching the area appear as white inkless rings and are known as litho ring flaws. Minor flecks of colour are similarly caused. As such flaws only affect part of a printing and cannot be regarded as constant we have decided not to record them.

**Sheet Details**

Sheet size: 120 (10 × 12). Single pane sheet-fed

**Sheet markings:**

**Plate numbers:** Opposite rows 1/2, left margin, unboxed

**Guide holes:** Above and below vertical row 6 in crossed box. Reserve guide-hole boxes appear above and below vertical row 4 but these were not used

**Marginal arrows (solid):** "W" shaped, at top, bottom and sides

**Marginal rule:** None

**Colour register marks:**

5d., 9d. and 1s. Below vertical rows 1 and 10 and opposite rows 1 and 12, at both sides

1s.6d. Above and below vertical rows 1 and 10 and opposite rows 1 and 12, at both sides

**Coloured crosses, Autotron marks, Colour designations:** None

**Sheet values:** Above and below vertical rows 2/4 and 7/9 reading left to right in top margin and right to left (upside-down) in bottom margin

**Traffic lights (unboxed):**

5d. Opposite rows 8/10, right margin

9d. and 1s. Opposite rows 9/10, right margin

1s.6d. Opposite rows 9/11, right margin

**Encapulated stamp card:**

On pale green card, 3¾ × 5¾ encapsulated in perspex

**Imprimaturs from the National Postal Museum Archives**

Nos. W171/174 imperforate

| No watermark (set of 4) | £9000 |
|---|---|

**Quantities Sold:** 5d. 72,405,720; 9d. 8,472,000; 1s. 10,296,120; 1s.6d. 10,757,040; Pack 104,230

**Withdrawn:** 30.9.70

**W171**. Herald Angel

**W172**. The Three Shepherds

**W173**. The Three Kings

(Des. Fritz Wegner)

(Printed in photogravure with the Queen's head (and stars 4d., 5d. and scroll-work 1s.6d. embossed in gold)

## 1969 (26 November). Christmas

Traditional religious themes are featured on these stamps by Austrian-born designer Fritz Wegner.

One 7 to 8 mm. centre phosphor band (4d.) or two phosphor bands (others), applied by photo-gravure (W175b) or flexography (others)

Types **W171/3**

**W175** (=SG 812)

| | | Mint | Used |
|---|---|---|---|
| 4d. | vermilion, new blue, orange, bright purple, light green, bluish violet, blackish brown and gold | 10 | 10 |
| a. | Gold (Queen's head etc.) omitted | £11000 | |
| b. | Centre band 3·5 mm | 30 | 20 |
| c. | Phosphor omitted | | |

**W176** (=SG 813)

| | | | |
|---|---|---|---|
| 5d. | magenta, light blue, royal blue, olive-brown, green, greenish yellow, red and gold | 15 | 15 |
| a. | Light blue (sheep, etc.) omitted | £110 | |
| b. | Red omitted* | £2500 | |
| c. | Gold (Queen's head etc.) omitted | £1000 | |
| d. | Green omitted | £450 | |
| e. | Olive-brown, red, gold and phosphor omitted | £15000 | |
| f. | Embossing omitted | 22·00 | |
| g. | Phosphor omitted | 5·00 | |

**W177** (=SG 814)

| | | | |
|---|---|---|---|
| 1s.6d. | greenish yellow, bright purple, bluish violet, deep slate, orange, green, new blue and gold | 20 | 20 |
| a. | Gold (Queen's head etc.) omitted | £170 | |
| b. | Deep slate (value) omitted | £475 | |
| c. | Greenish yellow omitted | £450 | |
| e. | New blue omitted | £120 | |
| f. | Embossing omitted | 10·00 | |
| g. | Embossing and phosphor omitted | 10·00 | |
| h. | Phosphor omitted | 6·00 | |
| i. | Broken arch (R. 1/6) | 20·00 | |

| First Day Cover (W159/64) | 1·00 |
|---|---|

| Presentation Pack (W159/64) | 3·00 |
|---|---|

*The effect of the missing red is shown on the hat, leggings and purse which appear as dull orange.

The 4d. is known postmarked at Dudley, Worcs. on 25 November.

No. W175 has one centre band 8 mm. wide but this was of no practical use in the automatic facing machines and after about three-quarters of the stamps had been printed the remainder were printed with a 3·5 mm. band (No. W175b). The wide band is sometimes difficult to see. Stamps have also been seen with a very wide phantom band measuring about 20 mm. which only reacts very faintly under the lamp and with a clear 3·5 mm. band over it.

No. W176e was caused by a paper fold.

No. W177d bluish violet has been deleted as examples showed only a partial omission.

W 177i

Break in the arch above the crown of King at right

**Cylinder Numbers** (Blocks of Six (4d.) or Eight (5d., 1s.6d.))

| Cyl. Nos. | Perforation Types A (E/I) | | | |
|---|---|---|---|---|
| | 7–8 mm. band | | 3·5 mm. band | |
| | No dot | Dot | No dot | Dot |
| **4d.** 1A (brown)–1B (vermilion)–2C (orange)–1D (purple)–1E (new blue)–1F (green)–1G (violet)–1H (gold) | 2·00 | 2·00 | † | † |
| 1A–1B–2C–1D–1E– 2F–1G–1H | 4·00 | 4·00 | 4·00 | 4·00 |
| | F (P/E) No dot | | F(L) (I/E) No dot | |
| **5d.** 1A (royal blue)– 1B (yellow)–1C (magenta)–1D (green)–2E (brown)–1F (light blue)–1G (red)–1H (gold) | 3·00 | | 15·00 | |
| **1s.6d.** 3A (slate)–1C (gold)–1D (blue)– 1E (yellow)–1F (green)–1G (violet)–1H (purple)–1J (orange) | 5·00 | | † | |

On the 4d. cylinder numbers 1A and 1H often appear as 1A1 and 1H1 on the dot and no dot panes respectively; the 1B and 1E have what appear to be small letters "IN" in place of dot, whilst the 2C is an alteration from 1C, all on the dot panes.

**Minor Constant Flaws**

4d. Cyls. 1A –1B–2C–1D–1E–2F–1G–1H dot
  5/3 White flaw in hem of angel's gown (later corrected) (Th. E1)
  11/1 A break in the pattern of the pillar on the right (Th. E13)
  11/4 White flaw in the pattern of the arch over the Queen's head (Th. A11)

**Sheet Details**
**Sheet sizes:**
4d. 72 (6 × 12). Double pane reel-fed (one pane above the other) for four colours and phosphor, and then single pane sheet-fed for remaining four colours and embossing
5d. and 1s.6d. 120 (6 × 20). Single pane sheet-fed

**Sheet markings:**
**Cylinder numbers:**
4d. Opposite rows 10/12, left margin, boxed
5d. and 1s.6d. Opposite rows 17/19, left margin, boxed
**Guide holes:**
4d. Opposite rows 6/7 (boxed), at both sides
5d. and 1s.6d. None
**Marginal arrows (photo-etched):** "W" shaped, at top, bottom and sides
**Marginal rule:** None
**Colour register marks:**
4d. None
5d. and 1s.6d. Above and below vertical rows 1/2 and 5/6
**Coloured crosses:**
4d. Usually trimmed off
5d. and 1s.6d. Above and below vertical rows 3/4
**Autotron marks, Colour designations:** None
**Sheet values:**
4d. Opposite rows 3/4 and 9/10 reading upwards in left margin and downwards in right margin
5d. Opposite rows 4/7 and 14/17 reading upwards in left margin and downwards in right margin
1s.6d. Opposite rows 5/6 and 15/16 reading upwards in left margin and downwards in right margin

**Traffic lights (boxed):**
4d. Vermilion, orange, purple, new blue, green, brown, violet, gold and embossing opposite rows 9/11, right margin; also in same order reading left to right above vertical rows 4/5
5d. Embossing and then as cylinder numbers but in reverse order opposite rows 17/19, right margin; also in same order as cylinder numbers followed by embossing above vertical rows 4/5
1s.6d. Embossing, gold, blue, yellow, slate, green, violet, purple and orange opposite rows 17/19, right margin; also in reverse order reading left to right above vertical rows 4/5

**Encapsulated Stamp Card:**
**Imprimaturs from the National Postal Museum Archives**
Nos. W175/177 imperforate

| | |
|---|---|
| No watermark (set of 3) | £6750 |

**Quantities Sold:** 4d. 271,244,808; 5d. 139,845,600; 1s.6d. 19,136,520; Pack 121,454

**Withdrawn:** 25.11.70

**W174**. Fife Harling

**W175**. Cotswold Limestone

(Des. David Gentleman)

**W176**. Welsh Stucco

**W177**. Ulster Thatch

(Des. Sheila Robinson)

## 1970 (11 February). British Rural Architecture

The designs feature typical cottage architecture in Scotland, England, Wales and Northern Ireland respectively.

Two phosphor bands

Types **W1747**

**W178** (=SG 815)

| | | Mint | Used |
|---|---|---|---|
| 5d. | grey, grey-black, black, lemon, greenish blue, orange-brown, ultramarine and green | 10 | 10 |
| a. | Lemon omitted | £150 | |
| b. | Lemon omitted from chimney at left (R. 12/2) | 20·00 | |
| c. | Grey (Queen's head and cottage shading) omitted | | |
| d. | Greenish blue (door) omitted | † | £4500 |
| e. | Grey-black (insciption and face value) omitted | £18000 | |
| ea. | Grey-black (face value only) omitted | £17000 | |
| eb. | Green (cobblestones) omitted | | |
| f. | Phosphor omitted | 2·00 | |
| g. | Nick in hair (R. 15/6) | 20·00 | |

**W179** (=SG 816)

| | | | |
|---|---|---|---|
| 9d. | orange-brown, olive-yellow, bright green, black, grey-black and grey | 10 | 25 |
| a. | Phosphor omitted | 10·00 | |

**W180** = S.G. 817)

| | | | |
|---|---|---|---|
| 1s. | deep blue, reddish lilac, drab and new blue | 15 | 25 |
| a. | New blue omitted | £130 | |
| b. | Phosphor omitted | 15·00 | |
| c. | Error. One broad band | | |

**W181** (=SG 818)

| | | | |
|---|---|---|---|
| 1s.6d. | greenish yellow, black, turquoise-blue and lilac | 20 | 40 |
| a. | Turquoise-blue | £18000 | |
| b. | Phosphor omitted | 5·00 | |
| c. | Broken panes in middle window (No dot, R. 3/2) | 10·00 | |

| | | |
|---|---|---|
| First Day Cover (W178/81) | | 1·50 |

| | | |
|---|---|---|
| Presentation Pack (W159/64) | 4·00 | |

Pack also exists with a Dutch, German or Japanese insert card

Examples showing "Fife harling" (No. W178) omitted were due to a partial omission of the grey-black (Price mint £475). The listed example of No.W178d is used and tied on piece, with the greenish blue colour omitted. No. W178e is a total omission and should only be purchased with certificate.

Misdated First Day covers are known postmarked 11 January (Doncaster) or 1969 (Farnham).

No. W178b. The lemon is omitted from the chimney at left once in every sheet (later added to cylinder and appearing normal).

W178g

W181c

**Cylinder Numbers** (Blocks of Eight (5d.), Six (9d.), Four (1s., 1s.6d.))

| | | Perforation Types | | |
|---|---|---|---|---|
| | | F (P/E) | A(T) (E/P) | |
| | Cylinder Nos. | No dot | No dot | Dot |
| 5d. | 1A (black)–1B (grey-black)1C (brown)–1D (ultramarine)–1E (greenish blue)–1F (green)–1G (grey)–1H (lemon) | 2·00 | † | † |
| 9d. | 1A (grey-black)–1B (yellow)–1C (brown)–1D (black)–IE (green)–1F (grey) | 3·00 | † | † |
| 1s. | 1A (deep blue)–2B (lilac)–1C (new blue)–1D (drab) | † | 4·00 | 4·00 |
| 1s.6d. | 1A (black)–1B (yellow)–1C (turquoise-blue)–1D (lilac) | † | 5·00 | 5·00 |

**Minor Constant Flaws**

5d. Cyls. 1A–1B–1C–1D–1E–1F–1G–1H no dot
4/2 Right leg of h of harling is broken
9/6 Pale patch on wall above left-hand first-floor window of building at right (Th. D8)
20/6 Pale patch on wall by top of upright at the bottom of the banisters and similar patch with grey spot in it just above (Th. F1); coloured spur to centre chimney (Th. A7); and orange-brown flaw below F of Fife (Th. A2)

9d. Cyls. 1A–1B–1C–1D–1E–1F no dot
19/1 Dark flaw on gate at left (Th. G2)

1s.6d. Cyls. 1A–1B–1C–1D no dot
2/3 Pale flaw on left stroke of U of ULSTER and two yellow dots in front of Queen's neck

1s.6d. Cyls. 1A–1B–1C–1D dot
5/5 White flaw to right of sixth brick from bottom (Th. G7)

**Sheet Details**

**Sheet sizes:**
5d. and 9d. 120 (6 × 20). Single pane sheet-fed
1s. and 1s.6d. 60 (6 × 10). Double pane sheet-fed (etched sideways on the cylinder)

**Sheet markings:**
**Cylinder numbers:**
5d. Opposite rows 17/19, left margin, boxed
9d. Opposite rows 18/19, left margin, boxed
1s. and 1s.6d. Opposite rows 9/10, left margin, boxed
**Guide holes:** None
**Marginal arrows (photo-etched):** "W" shaped, at top, bottom and sides
**Marginal rule:** None
**Colour register marks:**
5d. and 9d. Above and below vertical rows 1/2 and 6
1s. Opposite rows 1/2 and 6, at left (no dot) or right (dot)
1s.6d. Opposite rows 1 and 6, at left (no dot) or right (dot)
**Coloured crosses:**
5d. and 9d. Above and below vertical rows 3/4
1s. Opposite row 7, at left (no dot) or right (dot)
1s.6d. Opposite rows 6/7, at left (no dot) or right (dot)
**Autotron marks, Colour designations:** None
**Sheet values:**
5d. and 9d. Opposite rows 4/7 and 14/17 reading upwards in left margin and downwards in right
margin 1s. Opposite row 2/4 and 7/9 reading upwards in left margin and downwards in right margin
1s.6d. As 1s. but reading downwards in left margin and upwards in right margin
**Traffic lights (boxed):**
5d. In same order as cylinder numbers opposite rows 18/19, right margin; also in reverse order reading left to right above vertical rows 4/6
9d. In reverse order to cylinder numbers opposite rows 18/19;

also in same order as cylinder numbers above vertical row 5

1s. In same order as cylinder numbers opposite rows 6/7, right margin; also in same order reading left to right above vertical row 5

1s.6d. In same order as cylinder numbers opposite rows 7/8 at both sides; also in reverse order above vertical row 5

**Imprimaturs from the National Postal Museum Archives**
Nos. W178/181 imperforate

| | |
|---|---|
| No watermark (*set of* 4) | £9000 |

**Quantities Sold**: 5d. 81,581,880; 9d. 11,723,160; 1s. 10,258,320; 1s.6d. 8,969,280; Pack 116,983

**Withdrawn**: 10.2.71

---

**Sales quantities.** The figures quoted for quantities actually sold of the 1970 issues are according to the best estimates available from the Post Office, as exact records of unsold returns could not be made in the circumstances following the postal strike, and the change to decimal issues. In particular the estimates for the Philympia and Christmas issues cannot be guaranteed.

**W178**. Signing the Declaration of Arbroath

**W179**. Florence Nightingale attending Patients

(Des. Fritz Wegner)

**W180**. Signing the International Co-operative Alliance

(Des. Marjorie Saynor)

**W181**. Pilgrims and *Mayflower*

(Des. Fritz Wegner)

**W182**. Sir William Herschel, Francis Baily, Sir John Herschel and Telescope

(Des. Marjorie Saynor)

(Printed in photogravure with the Queen's head embossed in gold)

---

**1970 (1 April). General Anniversaries**

Five famous anniversaries, with the events described on the stamps.

An additional feature of this issue was the introduction of cylinder numbers for the cylinders printing the phosphor bands. They are not easy to see but are printed below the ordinary cylinder numbers.

Two phosphor bands

Types **W178/82**

**W182** (=SG 819)

| | | Mint | Used |
|---|---|---|---|
| 5d. | black, yellow-olive, blue, emerald, greenish yellow, rose-red, gold and orange-red | 10 | 10 |
| a. | Gold (Queen's head) omitted | £3500 | |
| b. | Emerald omitted | £500 | |
| c. | Phosphor omitted | £350 | |
| d. | White flaw in desk (R. 2/6) | 20·00 | |
| e. | White spot in hem (R. 5/5) | 20·00 | |
| f. | Missing portions of desk and foot (R. 20/4) | 20·00 | |

**W183** (=SG 820)

| | | | |
|---|---|---|---|
| 9d. | ochre, deep blue, carmine, black, blue-green, yellow-olive, gold and blue | 15 | 15 |
| a. | Ochre omitted | £500 | |
| b. | Embossing omitted | 15·00 | |
| c. | Phosphor omitted | 5·00 | |

**W184** (=SG 821)

| | | | |
|---|---|---|---|
| 1s. | green, greenish yellow, brown, black, cerise, gold and light blue | 20 | 25 |
| a. | Gold (Queen's head) omitted | 90·00 | |
| b. | Green and embossing omitted | £160 | |
| c. | Green omitted | £160 | |
| d. | Brown and phosphor omitted | £300 | |
| e. | Brown omitted | £300 | |
| f. | Embossing and phosphor omitted | 22·00 | |
| g. | Embossing omitted | 12·00 | |
| h. | Phosphor omitted | 5·00 | |

**W185** (=SG 822)

| | | | |
|---|---|---|---|
| 1s.6d. | greenish yellow, carmine, deep yellow-olive, emerald, black, blue, gold and sage-green | 20 | 30 |
| a. | Gold (Queen's head) omitted | £300 | |
| b. | Emerald omitted | £160 | |
| c. | Embossing omitted | 6·00 | |
| d. | Phosphor omitted | 5·00 | |

| | | |
|---|---:|---:|
| e. Flag flaw (R. 20/5) | 20·00 | |

**W186** (=SG 823)

| | | |
|---|---:|---:|
| 1s.9d. black, slate, lemon, gold and bright purple | 25 | 30 |
| a. Lemon (trousers and document) omitted | £9000 | |
| b. Phosphor omitted | 5·00 | |
| c. Embossing omitted | 75·00 | |
| d. Error. One broad band | 9·00 | |

| | |
|---|---:|
| First Day Cover (W186/6) | 2·00 |

| | |
|---|---:|
| Presentation Pack (W182/6) | 3·00 |

Pack also exists With a Dutch, German or Japanese insert card.

The 5d. is known with the gold partly omitted, possibly due to under-inking. Of a complete sheet seen the cylinder number did not show, the traffic lights appeared smaller and the back of the Queen's head on every stamp was rounded with no ribbons.

The 1s.9d. (No. W186a) is also known used on first day cover postmarked London WC.

Nos. W182/6 were pre-released at Dorking on 25 March.

Two dies were used to emboss the presentation pack coat of arms. The designers name was spelt as "Majorie" instead of "Marjorie", used on the later version.

W182d

W182e

Amount of white varies with the registration of colours

W182f

Large part of base of desk and front of shoe missing

All the above are multipositive flaws which appear on no dot and dot panes

W185e

Portion of blue in bottom right-hand corner of Union Jack is missing

**Cylinder Numbers** (Blocks of Eight (5d., 9d., 1s., 1s.6d.) or Six (1s.9d.))

| | Perforation Types | | | |
|---|---|---|---|---|
| | A (T) (E/P) | | F (P/E) | F(L) (I/E) |
| Cylinder Nos. | No dot | Dot | No dot | No dot |
| 5d. 1A (black)–1B (gold)–1C (blue)–1D (emerald)–IE (olive)–1F (rose-red)–1G (yellow)–1H (orange-red)– P1 (phosphor) | 2·00 | 2·00 | † | † |
| 9d. 2A (blue)–1B (ochre)–1C (deep blue)–1D (green)–1E (gold)–2F (black)–1G (olive)–1H (carmine)–P2 (phosphor) | † | † | 3·00 | † |
| 1s. 1A (black)–1B (blue)–1C (yellow)–1D (brown)–IE (gold)–2F (cerise)–1G (green)–P2 (phosphor) | † | † | 4·00 | 20·00 |
| 1s.6d. 1A (black)–1B (sage-green)–1C (yellow)–1D (carmine)–1E (gold)–2F (blue)–1G (deep yellow- olive)–1H (emerald)–P2 (phosphor) | † | | 6·00 | † |
| 1s.9d. 1A (black)–1E (gold)–1B (slate)–1C (lemon)–2D (bright purple)–P2 (phosphor) | † | | 6·00 | † |

The phosphor cylinder numbers appear below the ordinary cylinder numbers opposite R. 20/1.

In the 5d. the P1 is indented into the phosphor band but in the other values the P2 is to the left of the phosphor band.

In the 5d. the 1 of 1C and the bar below it are sometimes missing.

The 9d. is known without phosphor cylinder number.

In the 1s.9d. the cylinder numbers are always out of sequence.

**Minor Constant Flaws**

5d. Cyls. 1A–1B–1C–1D–1E–1F–1G–1H–P1 no dot
    2/1 Weak patches in background below r and t of Declaration
    6/1 Vertical scratch in background, through and below th of Arbroath (Th. A10 to C11)
    7/1 As 6/1

9d. Cyls. 2A–1B–1C–1D–1E–2F–1G–1H–P2 no dot
    8/6 Pale area surrounds final e of Florence
    19/4 Dark patch in background below second g of Nightingale

1s. Cyls. 1A–1B–1C–1D–1E–2F–1G–P2 no dot
    3/4 Missing top to t in Co-operative
    8/3 Dark flaw by top of first I of Alliance

1s.6d. Cyls. 1A–1B–1C–1D–1E–2F–1G–1H–P2 no dot
    8/3 Letters flo of Mayflower have hazy appearance

1s.9d. Cyls 1A–1E–1B–1C–2D–P2 no dot
    2/3 Pale patch in background above on of Astronomical
    2/6 Small break in t of Astronomical
    19/1 Dark patch on left leg of figure at right (Th. F6)
    19/5 Bright purple coloured flaw on left sleeve of man at
        left due to lack of screening dots on black cylinder
        (Th. D3)
    20/4 Black dot on e of Society

**Sheet Details**
**Sheet sizes**: 120 (6 × 20). 5d. double pane reel-fed with no dot
pane above dot pane; others single pane sheet-fed

**Sheet markings:**
**Cylinder numbers:**
1s.9d. Opposite rows 18/19, left margin, boxed.
Others: Opposite rows 17/19, left margin, boxed.
**Guide holes**: 5d. Opposite rows 6/7 (boxed), at both sides.
Others: None
**Marginal arrows (photo-etched)**: "W" shaped, at top, bottom
and sides
**Marginal rule**: None
**Colour register marks**:
5d. Opposite rows 9/12 at right (no dot) or left (dot).
Others: Above and below vertical rows 1
and 6
**Coloured crosses**: 5d. None.
Others: Above and below vertical rows 3/4
**Autotron marks (solid)**:
5d. Gold, black, blue, emerald, olive, rose-red, yellow, orange-
red above left margin and above vertical rows 1/4.
Others: None
**Colour designations**: None
**Sheet values**:
1s. Opposite rows 5/6 and 15/16 reading upwards in left
margin and downwards in right margin
Others: Opposite rows 4/7 and 14/17 reading upwards in left
margin and downwards in right margin
**Traffic lights (boxed)**:
5d. Embossing, gold, black, blue, emerald, olive, rose-red, yellow and orange-red opposite rows 16/18, right margin; also in
same order reading left to right above vertical rows 4/5
9d. Blue, ochre, deep blue, green, gold, embossing, black,
olive and carmine opposite rows 17/19, right margin; also in
reverse order reading left to right above vertical rows 4/5
1s. Green, black, cerise, gold, embossing, brown, yellow and
blue opposite rows 18/19, right margin; also blue, yellow,
embossing, gold, brown, cerise, black and green reading left
to right above vertical rows 4/5
1s.6d. Sage-green, yellow, carmine, blue, gold, embossing,
deep yellow-olive, black and emerald opposite rows 17/19,
right margin; also in reverse order reading left to right above
vertical rows 4/5
1s.9d. Black, gold, embossing, slate, lemon and bright purple
opposite rows 18/19, right margin; also embossing, gold,
black, slate, lemon and bright purple reading left to right
above vertical  row 5

**Imprimaturs from the National Postal Museum Archives**
Nos. W182/186 imperforate

| | |
|---|---|
| No watermark (set of 5) | £11250 |

**Quantities Sold**: 5d. 71,259,000; 9d. 10,590,120; 1s. 10,287,840;
1s.6d. 11,388,960; 1s.9d. 6,120,600;
Pack 120,564

**Withdrawn**: 31.3.71

**W183**. Mr. Pickwick and Sam   **W184**. Mr. and Mrs. Micawber
Weller    (*Pickwick Papers*)    (*David Copperfield*)

**W185**. David Copperfield and   **W186**. Oliver asking for
Betsy Trotwood    more (*Oliver Twist*)
(*David Copperfield*)

**W187**. Grasmere
(from engraving by J. Farington, R.A.)

(Des. Rosalind Dease. 5d. based on etchings
by Phiz and George Cruickshank)

(Printed in photogravure with the Queen's head
embossed in gold)

## 1970 (3 June). Literary Anniversaries

The four 5d. stamps, commemorating the death centenary of Charles Dickens, feature popular characters from his novels. The 1s.6d. stamp commemorates the birth bicentenary of Lakeland poet William Wordsworth.

The 5d. values were issued together *se-tenant* in blocks of four throughout the sheet.

Two phosphor bands

Types W**183/7**

**W187** (= S.G.824)

| | | Mint | Used |
|---|---|---|---|
| 5d. | black, orange, silver, gold and magenta | 10 | 25 |
| a. | Block of 4. Nos. W187/90 | 75 | 1·50 |
| ab. | Imperf. (block of four) | £2000 | |
| ac. | Silver (inscr) omitted (block of four) | £40000 | |
| ad. | Error. One broad band (block of four) | 30·00 | |

**W188** (=SG 825)

| | | | |
|---|---|---|---|
| 5d. | black, magenta, silver, gold and orange | 10 | 25 |

**W189** (=SG 826)

| | | | |
|---|---|---|---|
| 5d. | black, light greenish blue, silver, gold and yellow-bistre | 10 | 25 |
| b. | Yellow-bistre (value) omitted | £8500 | |

**W190** (=SG 827)

| | | | |
|---|---|---|---|
| 5d. | black, yellow-bistre, silver, gold and light greenish blue | 10 | 25 |
| b. | Yellow-bistre (background) omitted | £20000 | |
| c. | Light greenish blue (value) omitted* | £800 | |
| d. | Light-greenish blue and silver (inscription at foot) omitted | £30000 | |

**W191** (=SG 828)

| | | | |
|---|---|---|---|
| 1s.6d. | light yellow-olive, black, silver, gold and bright blue | 25 | 50 |
| a. | Gold (Queen's head) omitted | £6000 | |
| b. | Silver (Grasmere) omitted | £225 | |
| c. | Bright blue (value) omitted | £20000 | |
| d. | Embossing and phosphor omitted | 22·00 | |
| e. | Embossing omitted | 6·00 | |
| f. | Phosphor omitted | 5·00 | |
| g. | Retouch in slope (R. 1/18) | 20·00 | |
| h. | Extra road (R. 6/8) | 20·00 | |
| i. | Bright blue and silver omitted | £25000 | |

| | |
|---|---|
| First Day Cover (W187/91) | 2·00 |

| | |
|---|---|
| Presentation Pack (W187/91) | 3·00 |

Pack also exists with a Dutch, German or Japanese insert card

*No. W190c (unlike No. W189b) results from a partial missing colour. Although it is completely missing on No. W190, it is only partially omitted on No. W189.

5d. Prices for missing colour errors in blocks of four:

| | |
|---|---|
| Yellow-bistre | £20000 |
| Light greenish blue | £800 |
| Light greenish blue and silver | £30000 |

The light greenish blue and silver error in block of four is unique.

**W191**g
Retouch consists of diagonal black lines over triangular green patch N.E. of Grasmere

Normal
Green line gives the impression of an extra road leading up the foothill

**W191**h

**Cylinder Numbers** (Blocks of Eight (5d.) or Four (1s.6d.))

| | | Perforation Types | | |
|---|---|---|---|---|
| | | A (P/E) | | F (E/P) |
| | Cylinder Nos. | No dot | Dot | No dot |
| 5d. | 1A (orange)–1B (magenta)–3C (bistre)–1D (blue)–1E (black)–1F (silver)–1G (gold)–P4 (phosphor) | 3·00 | 3·00 | † |
| 1s.6d. | 1A (blue)–1B (gold)–1C (silver)–1D (black)–1E (olive)–P3 (phosphor) | † | † | 3·50 |

Perforation Type A on 5d. have the sheets orientated showing head to right.
In the 5d. the 1F is printed over a figure 2 in both panes.

**Minor Constant Flaws**

5d. Cyls. 1A–1B–3C–1D–1E–1F–1G dot
5/17 Extra button on Sam's coat under armpit (Th. B6)
5/19 Dot by 7 of 1870 level with centre of 8

**Sheet Details**
Sheet size: 120 (20 × 6)
5d. In se-tenant blocks of four, double pane reel-fed with no dot pane above dot pane
1s.6d. Single pane sheet-fed

**Sheet markings:**
**Cylinder numbers:**
5d. above vertical rows 1/3, boxed
1s.6d. Opposite row 5, left margin, boxed
**Guide holes:**
5d. In single box above and below vertical rows 14/15
1s.6d. None
**Marginal arrows (photo-etched):** "W" shaped, at top, bottom and sides
**Marginal rule:** None
**Colour register marks:**
5d. None
1s.6d. Opposite rows 1 and 6 at both sides
**Coloured crosses:**
5d. None

1s.6d. Opposite rows 3/4 at both sides
**Autotron marks (solid):**
5d. Opposite rows 1/4 at right on no dot pane only
1s.6d. None
**Sheet values:** Above and below vertical rows 4/7 and 14/17
**Traffic lights (boxed):**
5d. Embossing, gold, silver. blue, bistre, magenta, orange and black opposite rows 5/6, right margin; also in reverse order below vertical rows 3/4
1s.6d. Embossing, gold, silver, blue, black and olive opposite row 5, right margin; also in same order above vertical rows 18/19

**Essays.** Nos. W187/90 exist as a block of four, each design 22½ × 38½ mm. (larger than issued). The Queen's head is printed in silver and the Copperfield stamps are in olive-green. The four inscriptions read: Mr. Pickwick & Sam, Mr. & Mrs. Micawber, David Copperfield & Aunt Trotwood and Oliver asks for more.

**Encapsulated Stamp Card:** On black card 4¼×6 in, encapsulated in perspex

**Imprimaturs from the National Postal Museum Archives**
Imperforate, no watermark

| | |
|---|---|
| Nos. W187/90 se-tenant block of four | £9000 |
| Nos. W191 single | £2250 |

**Quantities Sold:** 5d. 83,472,440; 1s.6d. 10,913,360; Pack 113,770

**Withdrawn**: 3.6.71

**W188**. Runners

**W189**. Swimmers

**W190**. Cyclists

(Des. Andrew Restall)
(Lithography by De La Rue)

**1970 (15 July). British Commonwealth Games**

These were issued on the eve of the Ninth British Commonwealth Games which were held in Edinburgh. Like the Post Office Technology issue these were printed in lithography by De La Rue.
   Comb perforation 13½ × 14. Two phosphor bands applied by typography
Type **W188/90**

**W192** (=S.G 832)

| | | Mint | Used |
|---|---|---|---|
| 5d. | pink, emerald, greenish yellow and deep yellow- green | 25 | 25 |
| a. | Greenish yellow omitted | £20000 | |
| b. | Phosphor omitted | £200 | |
| c. | Error. One diagonal broad band at right | 55·00 | |

**W193** (=SG 833)

| | | | |
|---|---|---|---|
| 1s.6d. | light greenish blue, lilac, bistre-brown and Prussian blue | 50 | 50 |
| a. | Phosphor omitted | 60·00 | |

**W194** (=SG 834)

| | | | |
|---|---|---|---|
| 1s.9d. | yellow-orange, lilac, salmon and deep red-brown | 50 | 50 |

| | |
|---|---|
| First Day Cover (W192/4) | 1·20 |

| | |
|---|---|
| Presentation Pack (W192/4) | 3·00 |

Pack also exists with a Dutch, German or Japanese insert card

**Plate Numbers** (Blocks of Four)

| Plate Nos. | Perforation Type F (L) (I/E) | |
|---|---|---|
| | No dot | Dot |
| 5d. 1A (yellow)–1B (emerald)–1C (pink)–1D (green) | 2·50 | 2·50 |
| 2A–1B–1C–1D | 2·50 | 2·50 |
| 1s.6d. 1A (bistre-brown)–1B (greenish blue)–1C (lilac)–1D (indigo) | 3·00 | 3·00 |
| 2A–2B–2C–2D | 3·00 | – |
| 1s.9d. 1A (salmon)–1B (lilac)–1C (yellow-orange)1D (red brown) | 3·00 | 3·00 |
| 1A–2B–1C–1D | 3·00 | 3·00 |

**Minor Constant Flaws**
The notes relating to minor flaws in lithographed stamps under the 1969 Post Office Technology issue also apply here.

**Sheet Details**
**Sheet size:** 120 (10 × 12). Double pane sheet-fed with no dot pane at top and dot pane below

**Sheet markings:**
**Plate numbers:** Opposite rows 1/2, left margin, unboxed
**Guide holes:** Above and below vertical row 4 in crossed box on no dot pane and below vertical row 4 in crossed box on dot pane; the reserve box in top margin was not used. In addition reserve guide-hole boxes appear above and below vertical row 6 in both panes but these were not used
**Marginal arrows (solid):** "W" shaped, at top, bottom and sides
**Marginal rule:** None
**Colour register marks:** Below vertical rows 1 and 12 and in right-hand margin opposite rows 1 and 12 in both panes; in addition, they occur in the left-hand margin opposite row 12 in the no dot pane
**Coloured crosses, Autotron marks, Colour designations:** None
**Sheet values:** Above and below vertical rows 2/4 and 7/9 reading left to right in top margin and right to left (upside down) in bottom margin
**Traffic lights (unboxed):** Opposite rows 9/10, right margin in same order as plate numbers

**Encapsulated Stamp Card:** On black card 4¼×6in, encapsulated in perspex

**Imprimaturs from the National Postal Museum Archives**
Nos. W192/194 imperforate

| No watermark (set of 3) | £6750 |
|---|---|

**Quantities Sold:** 5d. 75,255,440; 1s.6d. 10,909,760; 1s.9d. 6,303,800; Pack 114,209

**Withdrawn:** 15.7.71

## 1970 (14 September). Collectors Pack 1970

| WCP3 | Comprises Nos. W171/94 | 20·00 |
|---|---|---|

This pack also exists with a German or Japanese insert card.

**Quantity Sold:** 54,768

**Withdrawn:** 13.9.71

1840 first engraved issue
**W191.** 1d. Black (1840)

1847 first embossed issue
**W192.** 1s. Green (1847)

1855 first surface printed issue
**W193.** 4d. Carmine (1855)

(Des. David Gentleman)

## 1970 (18 September). Philympia 70 Stamp Exhibition

Issued for the opening of the International Philatelic Exhibition held at the Olympia Exhibition Hall, London. The 5d. depicts the first adhesive postage stamp ever issued, the famous Penny Black. This is shown with the check letters "P" and "L" for Philympia and London. The 9d. and 1s.6d. show the first Great Britain stamps using the embossed and surface-printed processes respectively.

Two phosphor bands

Types **W191/3**

**W195** (=SG 835)

| | Mint | Used |
|---|---|---|
| 5d. grey-black, brownish bistre, black and dull purple | 25 | 10 |
| a. Grey-black (Queen's head) omitted | £20000 | |
| b. Phosphor omitted* | 5·00 | |
| c. Error. One broad phosphor band | 25·00 | |
| d. White blob (No dot, R. 5/6) | 20·00 | |
| e. Weak entry (Dot, R. 1/2) | 20·00 | |

**W196** (=SG 836)

| | Mint | Used |
|---|---|---|
| 9d. light drab, bluish green, stone, black and dull purple | 25 | 30 |
| a. Phosphor omitted | 11·00 | |

**W197** (=SG 837)

| | Mint | Used |
|---|---|---|
| 1s.6d. carmine, light drab, black and dull purple | 25 | 45 |
| a. Phosphor omitted | 4·00 | |
| b. Missing dot over i (R. 6/12) | 20·00 | |

| First Day Cover (W195/7) | 1·50 |
|---|---|

Presentation Pack (W195/7)                    3·00

Pack also exists with a Dutch, German or Japanese insert card

The 5d. is known postmarked at Boughton, King's Lynn on 17 September.

*The phosphor is sometimes difficult to see on the 5d. due to dry prints so care is needed in identifying true missing phosphors.

W195d                                W195e
Large white blob between "OS"        Weak entry of frameline in top
of "POSTAGE" (later retouched)       left corner

In No. W197b the dot is missing over the "i" of "printed"

**Cylinder Numbers** (Blocks of Four)

| | Perforation Types | | |
|---|---|---|---|
| | A (T) | (I/E) | A (P/E) |
| Cylinder Nos. | No dot | Dot | No dot |
| 5d. 1A (black)–1B (dull purple)–1C (brownish bistre)–1D (grey-black)–P6 (phosphor) | 2·00 | 2·00 | † |
| 9d. 1A (black)–1B (stone)–2C (bluish green)–1D (dull purple)–1E (light drab)– P10 (phosphor) | † | 2·00 | |
| 1s.6d. 1A (black)–1B (light drab)–1C (dull purple)–1D (carmine)–P5 (phosphor) | † | 2·00 | |

Perforation Types A and A (T) of the above are with sheets orientated showing head to right.

**Minor Constant Flaw**
1s.6d. Cyls. 1A–1B–1C–1D–P5 no dot 1/1 Frame flaw below N of PENCE

**Sheet Details**
Sheet size: 120 (12 × 10). 5d. double pane reel-fed with no dot pane above dot pane; others single pane sheet-fed

**Sheet markings:**
**Cylinder numbers:** Opposite row 9, left margin, boxed but the phosphor number is opposite row 10, left margin
**Guide holes:** 5d. Above and below vertical row 6 (boxed). Others: None
**Marginal arrows (photo-etched):** "W" shaped, at top, bottom and sides
**Marginal rule:** None
**Colour register marks:**
5d. None.
Others: Above and below vertical rows 1 and 10/11
**Coloured crosses:** 5d. None.
Others: Above and below vertical rows 3/4
**Autotron marks and Colour designations:** None
**Sheet values:** Opposite rows 2/4 and 7/9 at both sides, reading up at left and down at right
**Traffic lights (boxed):**
5d. Dull purple, black, brownish bistre, grey-black opposite row 10 right margin; also in same order reading from left to right above vertical rows 11/12
9d. Bluish green, stone, dull purple, black, light drab opposite row 10 right margin; also in same order reading from left to

right above vertical rows 11/12
1s.6d. Light drab, dull purple; carmine, black opposite 9/10 right margin; also in reverse order reading from left to right above vertical row 12
**Encapsulated Stamp Card:** On black card 3⅞ × 5¾ in, encapsulated in perspex

**Imprimaturs from the National Postal Museum Archives**
Nos. W195/197 imperforate

| No watermark (set of 3) | £6750 |
|---|---|

**Quantities Sold:** 5d. 72,211,000; 9d. 16,330,000; 1s.6d. 15,203,836

**Withdrawn:** 18.9.71

**W194**. Shepherds and        **W195**. Mary, Joseph and Christ
Apparition of the Angel         in the Manger

**W196**. The Wise Men bearing Gifts

(Des. Sally Stiff)

(Printed in photogravure with the Queen's head in gold and then embossed)

## 1970 (25 November). Christmas

The designs depict traditional Nativity scenes taken from the De Lisle Psalter in the Arundel Collection at the British Museum.

The 4d. stamps were printed by the Wood machine which has a capacity for ten cylinders. Eight were used for the colours and the others for simultaneous application of the embossing and phosphor bands.

One central 4 mm. phosphor band (4d.) or two phosphor bands (others)
Types **W194/6**
**W198** (=SG 838)

| | | Mint | Used |
|---|---|---|---|
| 4d | brown-red, blue, turquoise-green, pale chestnut, brown, grey-black, gold and vermilion | 15 | 10 |
| | a. Embossing omitted | 50·00 | |

| | | |
|---|---|---|
| b. | Phosphor omitted | 60·00 |
| c. | Error. Two side bands | |
| ca | Error. Band at left | |
| d. | Imperf, between stamp and left margin | £250 |
| e. | Thinned frame (No dot, R. 4/6) | 20·00 |

**W199** (=SG 839)

| | | | |
|---|---|---|---|
| 5d. | emerald, gold, blue, brown-red, ochre, grey-black and violet | 15 | 15 |
| a. | Gold (Queen's head) omitted | † | £3500 |
| b. | Emerald omitted | | £130 |
| c. | Imperforate (pair) | | £450 |
| d. | Embossing omitted | | 15·00 |
| e. | Phosphor omitted | | 5·00 |

**W200** (=SG 840)

| | | | |
|---|---|---|---|
| 1s.6d. | gold, grey-black, pale turquoise-green, salmon, ultramarine, ochre, red and yellow-green | 25 | 30 |
| a. | Salmon omitted | | £200 |
| b. | Ochre omitted | | £120 |
| c. | Embossing and phosphor omitted | | |
| d. | Embossing omitted | | 35·00 |
| e. | Phosphor omitted | | 5·00 |
| f. | Error. One broad band | | |

| | |
|---|---|
| First Day Cover (W199/200) | 1·00 |

| | |
|---|---|
| Presentation Pack (W199/200) | 2·75 |

Pack also exists with a Dutch, German or Japanese insert card

A red slip-in wallet bearing the Royal Arms and inscribed "Christmas 1970" was issued with the "Scandinavia 71" special pack produced for sale during a visit to six cities in Denmark, Sweden and Norway by a mobile display unit between 15 April and 20 May 1971. Due to the moratorium on commemoratives at the time of the introduction of decimal issues, these 1970 £.s.d. Christmas stamps were the only recent commemoratives on sale at Special counters etc. which could be offered for sale in Scandinavia alonside the decimal definitives.

W198e

Gold frame at right by shepherd's arm is thinned and has been strengthened by two parallel chesnut lines

**Cylinder Numbers** (4d. Blocks of Ten; Others Blocks of Six)

| | Perforation Type A (P/E) | |
|---|---|---|
| Cylinder Nos. | No dot | Dot |
| 4d. 1A (vermilion)–1B (grey-black)–1C (brown)–1D (brown-red)–1E (turquoise-green)–1F (blue)–1G (pale chestnut)–1J (gold)–P9 (phosphor) | 2·75 | 2·75 |
| 5d. 1A (violet)–1B (brown-red)–1C (blue)–1D (ochre)–3E (grey-black)–1F (emerald)–1G (gold)–P7 (phosphor) | 1·50 | † |
| 1s.6d. 1A (yellow-green)–1B (grey-black)–1D (red)–1E (salmon)–1F (pale turquoise-green)–1G (gold)–1J (ochre)–1C (ultramarine)–P7 (phosphor) | 4·50 | † |

Perforation Type A on the above are with sheets orientated showing head to right.

On some sheets of the 4d. the J is completely omitted.

**Minor Constant Flaws**
4d. Cyls. 1A–1B–1C–1D–1E–1F–1G–1J–P9 no dot
5/5     Dotted line across central shepherd's temple and through hair (Th. G6–7)

5d. Cyls. 1A–1B–1C–1D–3E–1F–1G–P7 no dot
8/8     Diagonal line over Mary's left hand (Th. J3)

1s.6d. Cyls. 1A–1B–1D–1E–1F–1G–1J–1C–P7 no dot
1/12    Horizontal scratch across cloaks of Three Wise Men (Th. K2–6)

The Thirkell Position Finder readings are taken with the finder over the perforations.

**Sheet Details**
Sheet size: 120 (12 × 10). 4d. double pane reel-fed with no dot pane above dot pane; others single pane sheet-fed

**Sheet markings:**
**Cylinder numbers:**
4d. Bottom margin, unboxed, reading down below vertical rows 5/2
5d. Opposite rows 8/9, left margin, boxed but the phosphor number is opposite row 10, left margin
1s.6d. Opposite rows 8/10, left margin, boxed. The 1C was added at the bottom opposite row 10
**Guide holes**: 4d. Above and below vertical row 6 (boxed). Others: None
**Marginal arrows (photo-etched)**: "W" shaped, at top, bottom and sides
**Marginal rule**: None
**Colour register marks:**
4d. Above and below vertical rows 2/5.
Others: Above and below vertical rows 1/2 and 12
**Autotron marks and Colour designations**: None
**Coloured crosses:** 4d. None.
Others: Above and below vertical rows 3/4
**Sheet values**: Opposite rows 2/4 at both sides and rows 7/8 at left and 7/9 at right, reading up at left and down at right
**Traffic lights (boxed):**
4d. Vermilion, grey-black, brown, brown-red, turquoise-green, blue, pale chestnut, gold, embossing* opposite rows 9/10 right margin; also in same order reading from left to right above vertical rows 11/12
5d. Violet, brown-red, blue, ochre, grey-black, emerald, gold, embossing opposite rows 9/10 right margin; also in same order reading from left to right above vertical rows 10/11
1s.6d. Yellow-green, grey-black, ultramarine; red, salmon, pale turquoise-green, gold, ochre, embossing; also in same order reading from left to right above vertical rows 9/11
*The embossing is usually very faint on the 4d. traffic lights.

**Postal Notice**: On black card 4 × 5¼ in, encapsulated in perspex

**Imprimaturs from the National Postal Museum Archives**
Nos. W198/200 imperforate

| | |
|---|---|
| No watermark (set of 3) | £6750 |

**Quantities Sold**: 4d. 360,016,216; 5d. 181,161,720; 1s.6d. 22,598,520

**Withdrawn**: 25.11.71

# SECTION XA
Regional £.s.d. Issues
1958–70. Photogravure

## General Notes

**Introduction.** On 18 August 1958 the first Great Britain Regional issues were put on sale for use in Northern Ireland, Scotland and Wales including Monmouthshire and in the islands of Guernsey, Jersey and the Isle of Man. The ordinary postage stamps of Great Britain in the same values are not on sale at post offices in these regions except at the Philatelic Counters in Belfast, Cardiff, Edinburgh and Glasgow, apart from Monmouthshire where the Welsh Regionals and Great Britain postage stamps were on sale concurrently.

Although specifically issued for regional use, these issues were initially valid for use throughout Great Britain. However, they ceased to be valid in Guernsey and Jersey from 1 October 1969 when these islands each established their own independent postal administrations and introduced their own stamps. Guernsey and Jersey Regionals were withdrawn locally on 30 September 1969 but remained on sale at British Philatelic Counters until 30 September 1970.

Following the practice set by Great Britain, these issues do not bear the names of the regions, these being indicated by various devices and symbols which relate to them. The three island issues are inscribed Postage only and have no usage as revenue stamps as they have their own Parliaments.

The portrait used is by Dorothy Wilding, Ltd.

**Printers.** All the Regional issues were printed in photogravure by Harrison & Sons on continuous reels of paper on the web. The 3d., 4d. and 5d. values of Northern Ireland, Scotland and Wales and Monmouthshire were printed in double pane width, i.e. 480 stamps consisting of two panes (no dot and dot) each of 240 stamps arranged in twenty rows of twelve stamps, the panes being guillotined before issue. All the island issues and the 6d., 9d., 1s.3d. and 1s.6d. values from the other regions were made from single cylinders printing sheets of 240 stamps (i.e. no dot panes only).

**Paper and watermark.** As with the Wilding definitives, for the first few years the Regional issues were printed on a creamy paper but starting in February 1962 a whiter paper was gradually introduced as new printings were made. See the General Notes for Section S for further information. Exceptionally, a chalk-surfaced paper was used for a printing of the Isle of Man 3d. in 1963.

Crowns
W.24

Only the Crowns watermark, type W.24 was used for the Regional issues. From 1967 new printings of a number of values were on the chalk-surfaced paper without watermark, as used for the Machin definitives.

**Gum.** Gum arabic was used from 1958 to 1968 after which PVA gum was introduced. The distinction between gum arabic and PVA gum is explained in the General Notes to Section U. It is worth noting that gum arabic was used on the creamy, white and unwatermarked chalk-surfaced papers but that PVA gum exists only on the last of these.

**Perforation.** Harrisons used the same 15 × 14 comb perforation as for the Wilding definitives. A number of different perforators were used and these are described and illustrated in Appendix G. The following listings include abbreviations for the side and horizontal margins of the listed block so that the first letter refers to the left margin and the second to the bottom margin. See page 2 under Notes in Section S.

**Phosphor bands.** See the General Notes for Section S for a detailed description of these. In the Regional issues it is sufficient to state that these were applied as follows:
Blue 8 mm. bands: 1963–64
Violet 8 mm. bands: 1965–66
Violet 9·5 mm. bands: 1967–70
The one centre band stamps in the violet period were always 4 mm. bands.
Phosphor omitted. A number of values have appeared with the phosphor bands omitted in error and these are listed separately. All values are believed to have the bands applied in photogravure.

**Misplaced Bands.** The instances of misplaced bands in the regionals is unusual. One broad (9·5mm.) instead of two bands are listed and one (No. XG8b) with horizontal band is recorded under Guernsey.

**Dates of issue.** Conflicting dates of issue have been announced for some of the issues, partly explained by their being released on different dates by the Philatelic Bureau in Edinburgh or the Philatelic Counter in London and in the regions. We give the earliest date, since once released the stamps could have been used anywhere in the U.K.

**First Day Covers.** Prices for these are only quoted where there was a specific service provided by the Post Office. These are listed at the end of each region.

**Presentation Packs.** The pack containing stamps from the six regions is listed after Wales and Monmouthshire. The other packs are listed at the end of each region.

**Sheet Markings.** Reference should be made to the descriptions of sheet markings given in the General Notes for Sections S and U, as most of them apply to this Section and the information given there is not repeated here. Additional information is given below.

**Cylinder Numbers.** In the Regional issues these appear in the left-hand margin opposite Row 18 No. 1 (R. 18/1) in the style as illustrated in Section S.

**Phosphor Cylinder Numbers.** The notes in the General Notes for Section U £.s.d. Low Values also apply here but they are only found on the Scottish 5d. No. XS15 and Welsh 5d. No. XW10.

**Marginal Arrows.** In the Regional issues these are "W" shaped (photo-etched) at top, bottom and sides, except for the Jersey and Isle of Man 3d. and the Northern Ireland, Scotland and Wales and Monmouthshire 3d., 6d. and 1s.3d. which are all "V" shaped (hand engraved) at top and bottom of the sheet and "W" shaped (photo-etched) at both sides (only cyl. 4 Scotland 1s.3d.).

**Perforation Guide Holes.** Perforation guide holes which relate to the perforator employed appear in the sheet margins. Refer to the descriptions given for Section U at the end of the General Notes where an illustration of the box associated with perforator type F(L)* appears. Perforator types are given under Cylinder Block listings and further details will be found under Appendix G.

**Cancelled Overprint.** No. XW5 exists overprinted "CANCELLED" as part of the test programme carried out by the Forensic Department of the Post Office.

**Withdrawal Dates.** All £.s.d. Regional issues, not previously withdrawn, were taken off sale at the Post Office Philatelic Counters on 25 November 1971 and were invalidated as from 1 March 1972.

**\*Prices for Cylinder Blocks with Asterisks**
These denote cylinder blocks containing a listed variety and the price includes the variety.

# GUERNSEY

XG1             XG2

(Des. E. A. Piprell)

## ■ 2½d. Type XG1 (1964)

### 1964 (8 June). 2½d. Watermark crowns

XG1 (=SG 6)

|  |  |  | Mint | Used |
|---|---|---|---|---|
| 2½d. | (1) | Pale rose-red (Cyl. 1) | 1·50 | 1·50 |
| . | (2) | Rose-red (Cyl. 3) | 35 | 40 |

**Cylinder Numbers (Blocks of Six)**
Single pane cylinders. Perforation Type F (L) (I/E)

| Cylinder No. | No Dot | Dot |
|---|---|---|
| 1 | 12·00 |  |
| 3 | 4·00 |  |

**Minor Constant Flaws**

| Cyl. 1 | 1/4 | Small retouch over TA |
|---|---|---|
|  | 1/5 | White patch over left part of diadem to left of central cross (Th. A3) |
|  | 17/12 | Background disturbance in top loop of left-hand ribboning (Th. B1) |
|  | 19/2 | White patch below left leg of R |
| Cyl. 3 | 17/5 | Dark spot under topmost tip of ribboning at right (Th. B6) |
|  | 17/12 | and 19/2. As on cyl. 1 (multipositive flaws) |

**Quantity Sold:** 3,485,760 including 10,100 on First Day Covers

**Withdrawn:** 31.8.66

## ■ 3d. Type XG2 (1958-62)

### 1958 (18 August). 3d. Watermark crowns

**A. Cream Paper**
XG2

| | Mint | Used |
|---|---|---|
| 3d.  Deep lilac | 1·50 | 50 |

**B. White Paper (5 July 1962)**
XG3 (=SG 7)

| | | |
|---|---|---|
| . 3d.  Deep lilac | 30 | 30 |

**Cylinder Numbers (Blocks of Six)**

**Cream Paper (No XG2)**

| | | Perforation Types | |
|---|---|---|---|
| Cylinder No. | No Dot | B(I/P) | C (E/P) |
| 4 | | 15·00 | 15·00 |

**Whiter Paper (No XG3)**

| | | Perforation Types | | |
|---|---|---|---|---|
| Cylinder No. | No Dot | B(I/P) | C (E/P) | F(L)(I/E) |
| 4 | | 4·50 | 4·50 | 4·50 |
| 5 | | † | † | 4·25 |

**Minor Constant Flaws**

| Cyl. 5 | 4/1 | Background scratch above right-hand petal (Th. C–D2) |
|---|---|---|
| | 7/10 | Dark spot in left-hand margin (opposite Th. C1) |
| | 9/10 | Pale scratch in background from petal at far right down to Queen's chin (Th. D–E3) |
| | 11/11 | Diagonal background scratch from base of lily's stem to base of Queen's neck (Th. F3–E4) |
| | 13/1 | Flaw in background above centre stamen of lily (Th. C2) |
| | 18/6 | Smudge in background near Queen's mouth (Th. D3) |

**Quantity Sold:** 25,812,360

**Sold Out:** 6.3.68

### 1967 (24 May). 3d. One centre phosphor band reacting violet. Watermark crowns

XG4 (=SG 7p)

| | Mint | Used |
|---|---|---|
| ·  3d.  (1) Deep lilac | 15 | 20 |
| (2) Deep reddish lilac | 60 | 30 |

**Cylinder Number (Block of Six)**
Single pane cylinder. Perforation Type F (L) (I/E)

| Cylinder No. | No Dot | Dot |
|---|---|---|
| 5 | 2·25 | |

**Minor Constant Flaws**
As for flaws on Cyl. 5 of No. XG3

**Sold Out:** 11.68

## ■ 4d. Type XG2 (1966-69)

### 1966 (7 February). 4d. Watermark crowns

XG5 (=SG 8)

| | Mint | Used |
|---|---|---|
| .  4d.  Ultramarine | 25 | 30 |
| a. Stem flaw (R. 12/8) | 25·00 | |

Coloured line across top of stem

XG5a, XG6a, XG7b, XG8c

**Cylinder Number (Block of Six)**
Single pane cylinder. Perforation Type F (L) (I/E)

| Cylinder No. | No Dot | Dot |
|---|---|---|
| 1 | 3·50 | |

**Minor Constant Flaws**

| Cyl. 1 | 1/1 | Small spot above centre stamen of lily (Th. C2) |
|---|---|---|
| | 9/5 | White dot between two stamens on left-hand side (Th. D2) |
| | 13/4 | White spot on right-hand petal (Th. D3) |
| | 20/12 | Pale flaw in background to right of central diadem (Th. A5) |

These are generally more marked on later issues from this cylinder.

**Quantity Sold:** 4,415,040 including 12,350 on First Day Covers

**Sold Out:** 6.3.68

### 1967 (2 October4). 4d. Two 9·5 mm. phosphor bands reacting violet. Watermark crowns

XG6 (=SG 8p)

| | Mint | Used |
|---|---|---|
| 4d.  Ultramarine | 15 | 20 |
| a. Stem flaw (R. 12/8) | 25·00 | |

For illustration of No. XG6a, see No. XG5a.

**Cylinder Number (Block of Six)**
Single pane cylinder. Perforation Type F (L) (I/E)

| Cylinder No. | No Dot | Dot |
|---|---|---|
| 1 | 2·25 | |

**Minor Constant Flaws**

| Cyl. 1 | 5/10 | Circular background retouch below Queen's chin (Th. E4) |
|---|---|---|
| | 16/12 | Break in centre stamen (Th. C–D2) |
| | 17/10 | Break in second stamen from left (Th. C2) |

**Others:** As on No. XG5

**Sold Out:** 10.68

## 1968 (16 April*). 4d. No watermark. Chalky paper. PVA Gum. Two 9·5 mm phosphor bands reacting violet

**XG7** (=SG 9)

|  |  | Mint | Used |
|---|---|---:|---:|
| 4d. | Pale ultramarine | 10 | 20 |
| a. | Phosphor omitted | 45·00 | |
| b. | Stem flaw (R. 12/8) | 25·00 | |

*This was not issued in Guernsey until 22 April. For illustration of No. XG7b, see No. XG5a.

**Cylinder Number (Block of Six)**
Single pane cylinder. Perforation Type F (L) (I/E)

| Cylinder No. | No Dot | Dot |
|---|---|---|
| 1 | 1·90 | |

**Minor Constant Flaws**

Cyl. 1    2/8 Weak patch in background at upper left (Th. A1)
19/6 Small retouch between A and G

Others: As on Nos. XG5 and XG6

**Sold Out**: 3.69

## 1968 (4 September). 4d. Change of colour. No wate mark. Chalky paper. PVA Gum. One centre phosphor band reacting violet

**XG8** (=SG 10)

|  |  | Mint | Used |
|---|---|---:|---:|
| 4d. | Olive-sepia | 10 | 15 |
| a. | Phosphor omitted | 45·00 | |
| b. | Error. Phosphor horizontal | £120 | |
| c. | Stem flaw (R. 12/8) | 22·00 | |
| d. | Retouched 4 (R. 16/10) | 22·00 | |

For illustration of No. XG8c, see No. XG5a.

Spot over "4" has been retouched
Corrected on No. XG9

XG8d

**Cylinder Number (Block of Six)**
Single pane cylinder. Perforation Type F (L) (I/E)

| Cylinder No. | No Dot | Dot |
|---|---|---|
| 1 | 1·90 | |

**Minor Constant Flaws**
As for No. XG7 except that flaw on R. 5/10 does not show

**Withdrawn**: 30.9.70

## 1969 (26 February). 4d. Further change of colour. No watermark. Chalky paper. PVA gum. One centre phosphor band reacting violet

**XG9** (=SG 11)

|  |  | Mint | Used |
|---|---|---:|---:|
| 4d. | Bright vermilion | 20 | 25 |
| a. | Stem flaw retouched (R. 12/8) | 22·00 | |

The stem flaw has been retouched but still shows as a smudge to right of stem

XG9a

**Cylinder Number (Block of Six)**
Single pane cylinder. Perforation Type F (L) (I/E)

| Cylinder No. | No Dot | Dot |
|---|---|---|
| 1 | 2·75 | |

**Minor Constant Flaws:** As for No. XG8

**Withdrawn**: 30.9.70

## ■ 5d. Type XG2 (1968)

**1968 (4 September). 5d. No watermark. Chalky paper. PVA gum. Two 9·5 mm. phosphor bands reacting violet**

**XG10** (=SG 12)

|  |  | Mint | Used |
|---|---|---|---|
| 5d. | Royal blue | 20 | 30 |
| a. | Stamen flaw (R. 12/1) | 25·00 | |
| b. | Retouched | 25·00 | |

XG10a

XG10b
Still visible after retouch on late printing

**Cylinder Number (Block of Six)**
Single pane cylinder. Perforation Type F (L) (I/E)

| Cylinder No. | No Dot | Dot |
|---|---|---|
| 1 | 2·75 | |

**Minor Constant Flaw**

| Cyl. 1 | 12/6 | Small white flaw to left of Queen's mouth (Th. D3) |
|---|---|---|

**Withdrawn:** 30.9.70

**First Day Covers**

| XGFC1 | | | | |
|---|---|---|---|---|
| (8.6.64) | 10,100 posted | 2½d. | | 30·00 |
| XGFC2 | | | | |
| (7.2.66) | 12,350 posted | 4d. Ultramarine | | 8·00 |
| XGFC3 | | | | |
| (4.9.68) | 52,449 posted | 4d. Olive-sepia, 5d. | | 3·00 |

**INVALIDATION.** The regional issues for Guernsey were invalidated for use in Guernsey and Jersey on 30 September 1969 but remained valid for use in the rest of the United Kingdom. Those still current remained on sale at philatelic sales counters until 30 September 1970.

●———————

## JERSEY

XJ1

XJ2

(Des. Edmund Blampied)　　(Des. William M. Gardner)

## ■ 2½d. Type XJ1 (1964)

**1964 (8 June). 2½d. Watermark crowns**

**XJ1** (=SG 9) .

|  |  | Mint | Used |
|---|---|---|---|
| 2½d | Carmine-red | 30 | 45 |
| a. | Imperf. three sides (pair) | £3000 | |
| b. | Thin POSTAGE (R. 18/1) | 20·00 | |

Normal

XJ1b

Letters of "POSTAGE" are thinner, resulting in more white showing in the "O" and "G"

**Cylinder Number (Block of Six)**
Single pane cylinder. Perforation Type F (L) (I/E)

| Cylinder No. | No Dot | Dot |
|---|---|---|
| 1 | 14·00* | |

**Minor Constant Flaws**

| Cyl. 1 | 11/1 | Two tiny dots on Queen's nose |
|---|---|---|
| | 18/2 | Spot to right of mace level with O of POSTAGE |

**Quantity Sold:** 4,770,000 including 12,800 on First Day Covers

**Withdrawn:** 31.8.66

●———————

## 3d. Type XJ2 (1958-67)

### 1958 (18 August). 3d. Watermark crowns

**A. Cream Paper**
XJ2

| | | Mint | Used |
|---|---|---|---|
| 3d. | Deep lilac | 1·50 | 40 |
| a. | Joined tomato (Cyl. 1, R. 19/9) | 22·00 | |
| b. | Halberd flaw (Cyl. 1, R. 20/3) | 22·00 | |

**B. Whiter Paper (23 September 1962)**
XJ3 (=SG 10)

| | | Mint | Used |
|---|---|---|---|
| 3d. | Deep lilac | 30 | 25 |
| a. | Scratched collar (Cyl. 2, R. 9/8) | 25·00 | |

XJ2a XJ2b

Both these varieties were later retouched to normal

XJ3a, XJ4a

**Cylinder Numbers (Blocks of Six)**

**Cream Paper (No XJ2)**

| | | Perforation Types | |
|---|---|---|---|
| Cylinder No. | No Dot | B(I/P) | C (E/P) |
| 1 | | 15·00 | 15·00 |

**Whiter Paper (No XJ3)**

| | | Perforation Types | | |
|---|---|---|---|---|
| Cylinder No. | No Dot | B(I/P) | C (E/P) | F(L)(I/E) |
| 4 | | 4·25 | 4·25 | 4·25 |
| 5 | | † | † | 27·00 |

**Minor Constant Flaws**

Cyl. 1    20/4 Short white line extends below left of D

Cyl. 2    3/7 Weak background below left-hand berry of middle pair on right-hand plant (Th. E5)
14/12 Dot in left-hand margin (Opposite Th. D1)
16/1 Dot on top left leaf of right-hand plant (Th. C5–6)
16/12 Dot in top margin (Above Th. A4)
20/3 Dot in top margin (Above Th. A4)

**Quantity Sold**: 35,169,720

**Sold Out**: 10.67

### 1967 (9 June). 3d. One centre phosphor band reacting violet. Watermark crowns

XJ4 (=SG 10p)

| | | Mint | Used |
|---|---|---|---|
| 3d. | (1) Deep lilac | 15 | 15 |
| | (2) Dull reddish lilac | 45 | 30 |
| a. | (2) Scratched collar (Cyl. 2, R. 9/8) | 25·00 | |

For illustration of No. XJ4a, see No. XJ3a.

**Cylinder Numbers (Blocks of Six)**
Single pane cylinder. Perforation Type F (L) (I/E)

**Deep Lilac No XJ4 (1)**

| Cylinder No. | No Dot | Dot |
|---|---|---|
| 2 | 2·75 | |

**Dull reddish lilac No. XJ4 (2)**

| | | |
|---|---|---|
| 2 | 6·00 | |

**Minor Constant Flaws:** As for flaws on Cyl. 2 of No. XJ3
**Sold Out:** 10.68

## ▍ 4d. Type XJ2 (1966-69)

### 1966 (7 February). 4d. Watermark crowns

XJ5 (=SG 11)

| | Mint | Used |
|---|---|---|
| 4d. Ultramarine | 25 | 30 |
| ✓ a. Leaf flaw (R. 3/6) | 25·00 | |
| b. Neck flaw (R. 18/9) | 25·00 | |

XJ5a
Arrow like flaw over top leaf at left. Later retouched and only exists retouched on phosphor issues

XJ5b, XJ6a, XJ7b, XJ8a

**Cylinder Number (Block of Six)**
Single pane cylinder. Perforation Type F (L) (I/E)

| Cylinder No. | No Dot | Dot |
|---|---|---|
| 1 | 3·50 | |

**Minor Constant Flaws**

| Cyl. 1 | 3/4 | Diagonal scratch under Queen's chin (Th. E2–3) |
|---|---|---|
| | 3/11 | Spot in top margin (close to perf. hole) (Above Th. A4) |
| | 9/10 | Slight dent in left-hand frame line (Opposite Th. D–E1) |
| | 11/10 | White flaw in background behind Queen's hair (Th. C5) |
| | 15/1 | Dark patch in background to left of top leaf on left-hand side of sceptre (Th. D1). This varies in intensity and is particularly strong on No. XJ7. |
| | 15/12 | Two small white flaws in front of Queen's collar (Th. F2–3) |
| | 18/8 | Break in top frame line (Above Th. A5) |
| | 20/8 | Diagonal scratch to right of Queen's left eye (Th. C3–4) |

**Quantity Sold:** 6,623,040 including 14,487 on First Day Covers

**Sold Out:** 11.67

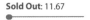

### 1967 (5 September). 4d. Two 9·5 mm. phosphor bands reacting violet. Watermark crowns

XJ6 (=SG 11p)

| | Mint | Used |
|---|---|---|
| 4d. Ultramarine | 15 | 25 |
| a. Neck flaw (R. 18/9) | 25·00 | |

For illustration of No. XJ6a, see No. XJ5b.

**Cylinder Number (Block of Six)**
Single pane cylinder. Perforation Type F (L) (I/E)

| Cylinder No. | No Dot | Dot |
|---|---|---|
| 1 | 2·50 | |

**Minor Constant Flaws:** As for No. XJ5

**Sold Out:** 10.68

### 1968 (4 September). 4d. Change of colour. No watermark. Chalky paper. PVA Gum. One centre phosphor band reacting violet

XJ7 (=SG 12)

| | Mint | Used |
|---|---|---|
| 4d. Olive-sepia | 15 | 25 |
| a. Phosphor omitted | £1000 | |
| b. Neck flaw (R. 18/9) | 25·00 | |

For illustration of No. XJ7b, see No. XJ5b.

**Cylinder Number (Block of Six)**
Single pane cylinder. Perforation Type F (L) (I/E)

| Cylinder No. | No Dot | Dot |
|---|---|---|
| 1 | 2·50 | |

**Minor Constant Flaws:** As for No. XJ5

**Withdrawn:** 30.9.70

### 1969 (26 February). 4d. Further change of colour. No watermark. Chalky paper. PVA Gum. One centre phosphor band reacting violet

XJ8 (=SG 13)

| | Mint | Used |
|---|---|---|
| 4d. Bright vermilion | 15 | 25 |
| a. Neck flaw (R. 18/9) | 22·00 | |

For illustration of No. XJ8a, see No. XJ5b.

**Cylinder Number (Block of Six)**
Single pane cylinder. Perforation Type F (L) (I/E)

| Cylinder No. | No Dot | Dot |
|---|---|---|
| 1 | 2·50 | |

**Minor Constant Flaws:** As for No. XJ5

**Withdrawn:** 30.9.70

## ■ **5d. Type XJ2 (1968)**

**1968 (4 September). 5d. No watermark. Chalky paper. PVA Gum. Two 9·5 mm. phosphor bands reacting violet**

**XJ9** (=SG 14)

|  |  | Mint | Used |
|---|---|---|---|
| 5d. | Royal blue | 15 | 50 |
| a. | Leaf dot (R. 16/6) | 25·00 | |
| b. | Shield flaw (R. 19/12) | 22·00 | |

XJ9a
White dot above lowest leaf

XJ9b
Leaf joined to shield

**Cylinder Number** (Block of Six)
Single pane cylinder. Perforation Type F (L) (I/E)

| Cylinder No. | No Dot | Dot |
|---|---|---|
| 1 | 2·50 | |

**Minor Constant Flaws**

| Cyl. 1 | 5/1 | Dot in top margin (Above Th. A2) |
|---|---|---|
| | 6/5 | White scratch from back of Queen's collar to back of neck (Th. E–F4) |
| | 9/11 | Flaw in background above middle right-hand jewel of sceptre (Th. A2) |
| | 10/4 | White scratch extending from Queen's chin to top of P |
| | 11/1 | Tiny break in left-hand frame line (Th. C1) |
| | 14/12 | Small white flaw on Queen's collar (Th. F3–4) |
| | 17/12 | Dotted line extending from right of top leaf below flower at right of sceptre across Queen's face and plant at right (Th. E2–6) |

**Withdrawn:** 30.9.70

**First Day Covers**

| XJFC1 | | | | |
|---|---|---|---|---|
| (8.6.64) | 12,800 posted | 2½d. | | 30·00 |
| XJFC2 | | | | |
| (7.2.66) | 14,487 posted | 4d. | Ultramarine | 10·00 |
| XJFC3 | | | | |
| (4.9.68) | 57,500 posted | 4d. | Olive-sepia, 5d. | 3·00 |

**Invalidation.** The regional issues for Jersey were invalidated for use in Jersey or Guernsey on 30 September 1969 but remained valid for use in the rest of the United Kingdom. Those still current remained on sale at philatelic sales counters until 30 September 1970.

## **ISLE OF MAN**

XM1                                    XM2

(Des. J. H. Nicholson)

## ■ **2½d. Type XM1 (1964)**

**1964 (8 June). 2½d. Watermark crowns**

**XM1** (=SG 1)

|  |  | Mint | Used |
|---|---|---|---|
| 2½d. | Carmine-red | 50 | 1·25 |

**Cylinder Number** (Block of Six)
Single pane cylinder. Perforation Type F (L) (I/E)

| Cylinder No. | No Dot | Dot |
|---|---|---|
| 1 | 7·50 | |

**Minor Constant Flaw**
Cyl. 1 11/1 Red dot to right of lower cross of crown (Th. C5)

**Quantity Sold:** 4,298,160 including 9,237 on First Day Covers

**Withdrawn:** 31.8.66

## ◼ 3d. Type XM2 (1958-68)

### 1958 (18 August). 3d. Watermark crowns

**A. Cream Paper**
XM2

| | Mint | Used |
|---|---|---|
| 3d. Deep lilac | 1·50 | 35 |

**B. Chalky Paper (17 May 1963)**
XM3 (=SG 2a)

| | | |
|---|---|---|
| 3d. Deep lilac | 12·00 | 12·00 |

**C. Whiter Paper (1963)**
XM4 (=SG 2)

| | | |
|---|---|---|
| 3d. Deep lilac | 50 | 20 |

No. XM3 was released in London sometime after 17 May 1963.
The paper used for No. XM3 was the residue of the heavy chalk-surfaced paper remaining from the 1961 Post Office Savings Bank Centenary issue.

**Cylinder Numbers (Blocks of Six)**

**Cream paper No. XM2**

| | | Perforation Types | |
|---|---|---|---|
| Cylinder No. | No Dot | B(I/P) | C (E/P) |
| 1 | | 15·00 | 15·00 |

**Chalky paper No. XM3**

| | | Perforation Types |
|---|---|---|
| Cylinder No. | No Dot | J(I/P) |
| 1 | | £125 |

**Whiter paper No. XM4**

| | | Perforation Types |
|---|---|---|
| Cylinder No. | No Dot | F (L) (I/E) |
| 1 | | 7·50 |

**Minor Constant Flaw**

Cyl. 1  19/6  Fine curved line to right of second link from bottom at left (Th. G1)

**Imprimatur from the National Postal Museum Archives**
Cream paper. Imperforate, watermark Type W.24

| | |
|---|---|
| Watermark upright | £2000 |

**Quantity Sold**: 35,959,420 up to 31.3.68 and including 1,080,000 on chalky paper (No. XM3)

**Sold Out**: 12.68

### 1968 (27 June). 3d. One centre phosphor band reacting violet. Watermark crowns

XM5 (=SG 2p)

| | Mint | Used |
|---|---|---|
| 3d. Deep lilac | 20 | 50 |

This issue is known postmarked at Douglas, Isle of Man, on 19 June 1968.

**Cylinder Number (Block of Six)**
Single Pane cylinder. Perforation Type F (L) (I/E)

| Cylinder No. | No Dot | Dot |
|---|---|---|
| 1 | 2·75 | |

**Minor Constant Flaws:** As for Nos. XM2/4

**Sold Out:** 4.69

## ◼ 4d. Type XM2 (1966-69)

### 1966 (7 February). 4d. Watermark crowns

XM6 (=SG 3)

| | Mint | Used |
|---|---|---|
| 4d. Ultramarine | 1·50 | 1·50 |

**Cylinder Number (Block of Six)**
Single pane cylinder. Perforation Type F (L) (I/E)

| Cylinder No. | No Dot | Dot |
|---|---|---|
| 1 | 15·00 | |

**Minor Constant Flaws**

Cyl. 1  7/12  Fine line from top of diadem to inner frame at right (Th. B−35)
        8/7  Coloured dot left of inner frame line at right (Th. C5−6)
        17/1  Coloured scratches below Queen's left eye (Th. D3−4)
        19/1  Coloured scratch behind Queen's neck (Th. F5)

**Quantity Sold**: 4,353,840 including 7,553 on First Day Covers

**Sold Out**: 11.67

### 1967 (5 July). 4d. Two 9·5 mm. phosphor bands reacting violet. Watermark crowns

XM7 (=SG 3p)

| | Mint | Used |
|---|---|---|
| 4d. Ultramarine | 20 | 30 |

**Cylinder Number (Block of Six)**
Single pane cylinder. Perforation Type F (L) (I/E)

| Cylinder No. | No Dot | Dot |
|---|---|---|
| 1 | 2·75 | |

**Minor Constant Flaws:** As for No. XM6

**Sold Out**: 12.68

### 1968 (24 June). 4d. No watermark. Chalky paper. PVA gum. Two 9·5 mm. phosphor bands reacting violet

XM8 (=SG 4)

| | Mint | Used |
|---|---|---|
| 4d. Blue | 25 | 30 |

**Cylinder Number (Block of Six)**
Single pane cylinder Perforation Type F (L) (I/E)

| Cylinder No. | No Dot | Dot |
|---|---|---|
| 1 | 3·50 | |

**Minor Constant Flaws**

Cyl. 1  6/7  Flaw behind lower cross of diadem (Th. D5)
        14/2  White background spot just above Queen's right eye (Th. C−D2)

Others as for No. XM6

**Sold Out**: 16.7.69

## 1968 (4 September). 4d. Change of colour. No watermark. Chalky paper. PVA Gum. One centre phosphor band reacting violet

**XM9** (=SG 5)

|  | Mint | Used |
|---|---|---|
| 4d. Olive-sepia | 25 | 40 |
| a. Phosphor omitted | 22·00 | |

**Cylinder Number (Block of Six)**
Single pane cylinder. Perforation Type F (L) (I/E)

| Cylinder No. | No Dot | Dot |
|---|---|---|
| 1 | 2·75 | |

**Minor Constant Flaws:** As for No. XM8

---

## 1969 (26 February). 4d. Further change of colour. No watermark. Chalky paper. PVA gum. One centre phosphor band reacting violet

**XM10** (=SG 6)

|  | Mint | Used |
|---|---|---|
| 4d. Bright vermilion | 45 | 75 |

**Cylinder Number (Block of Six)**
Single pane cylinder. Perforation Type F (L) (I/E)

| Cylinder No. | No Dot | Dot |
|---|---|---|
| 1 | 2·75 | |

**Minor Constant Flaws**
As for No. XM8

---

## ■ 5d. Type XM2 (1968)

### 1968 (4 September). 5d. No watermark. Chalky paper. PVA gum. Two 9·5 mm. phosphor bands reacting violet

**XM11** (=SG 7)

|  | Mint | Used |
|---|---|---|
| 5d. Royal blue | 45 | 75 |
| a. Phosphor omitted | £175 | |
| b. Error. Single broad band | 45·00 | |
| c. Frame flaw (top right) (R. 20/1) | 20·00 | |
| d. Frame flaw (bottom left) (R. 20/12) | 20·00 | |

XM11c        XM11d

**Cylinder Number (Block of Six)**
Single pane cylinder. Perforation Type F (L) (I/E)

| Cylinder No. | No Dot | Dot |
|---|---|---|
| 1 | 11·00* | |

**First Day Covers**

| | | | | |
|---|---|---|---|---|
| XMFC1 (8.6.64) | 9,237 posted | 2½d. | | 45·00 |
| XMFC2 (7.2.66) | 7,553 posted | 4d. Ultramarine | | 15·00 |
| XMFC3 (4.9.68) | 42,910 posted | 4d.. Olive-sepia, 5d | | 4·00 |

---

## NORTHERN IRELAND

XN1          XN2          XN3

(Des. W. Hollywood)   (Des. L. Pilton)   (Des. T. Collins)

### ■ 3d. Type XN1 (1958–67)

### 1958 (18 August). 3d. Watermark crowns

**A. Cream paper**
**XN1**

|  | Mint | Used |
|---|---|---|
| 3d. Deep lilac | 1·50 | 25 |

**B. Whiter Paper (21 May 1962)**
**XN2 (=SG NI1)**

| | Mint | Used |
|---|---|---|
| 3d. Deep lilac | 15 | 10 |

**Cylinder Numbers (Blocks of Six)**

**Cream Paper No. XN1**
Perforation Type A (E/I)

| Cylinder No. | No Dot | Dot |
|---|---|---|
| 3 | 15·00 | 15·00 |

**Whiter Paper No. XN2**
Perforation Type A (E/I)

| Cylinder No. | No Dot | Dot |
|---|---|---|
| 3 | 2·50 | 2·50 |

Perforation Type F (L)* )

| Cylinder No. | No Dot (I/E) | Dot (P/E) |
|---|---|---|
| 3** | — | — |

** This is probably No XN3 with the phosphor omitted.

**Minor Constant Flaw**
Cyl. 3 4/9     White flaw on edge of lowest flax flower (Th. G2)

**Imprimatur from the National Postal Museum Archives**
Cream paper. Imperforate, watermark Type W.24

| Watermark upright | £2000 |
|---|---|

**Quantity Sold:** 375,417,400

**Sold Out:** 10.67

---

### 1967 (9 June). 3d. One centre phosphor band reacting violet. Watermark crowns

XN3 (=SG NI1p)

|  | Mint | Used |
|---|---|---|
| 3d. Deep lilac | 15 | 15 |

**Cylinder Numbers (Blocks of Six)**

| Cylinder No. | No Dot | Dot |
|---|---|---|
| Perforation Type A (E/I) | | |
| 3 | 2·50 | 2·50 |
| Perforation Type F (L)* | | |
| Cylinder No. | No Dot (I/E) | Dot (P/E) |
| 3 | 2·50 | 2·50 |

**Minor Constant Flaws:** As for flaw on Nos. XN1/2

## ■ **4d. Type XN1 (1966-69)**

### **1966 (7 February). 4d. Watermark crowns**

XN4 (=SG NI2)

| | | Mint | Used |
|---|---|---|---|
| 4d. | Ultramarine | 15 | 15 |
| a. | Dot on leaf (No dot, R. 3/12) | 25·00 | |
| b. | Flower flaw (No dot, R. 7/7) | 25·00 | |
| c. | Dot under S of POSTAGE (Dot R. 2/4) | 25·00 | |

XN4a, XN5a, XN6a, XN7a, XN8b
White dot on leaf of plant.
Retouched on No. XN9

XN4b
White spot on top flower. The above only exists on No. XN4. It was retouched and shows as a dark patch on Nos. XN5b, XN6b, XN7b, XN8c and XN9b

XN4c
White dot under "S" of "POSTAGE".
Retouched on No. XN5.

### **Cylinder Numbers (Blocks of Six)**
Perforation Type A (E/I)

| Cylinder No. | No Dot | Dot |
|---|---|---|
| 1 | 2·50 | 2·50 |

**Cylinder number:** Opposite R.18/1. In addition, early printings of both no dot and dot panes bore a trace of cylinder numbers reading 1A and 1A. with two sides of a box opposite R.19/1. These had been inserted in error. Attempts to remove them were only partially successful, so that they exist in varying degrees of faintness.

### **Minor Constant Flaws**

| Cyl. 1 | 16/5 | Small white spot to right of second leaf down on upright flax plant (Th. B6) |
|---|---|---|
| Cyl. 1. | 2/1 | Small coloured projection above upper frame line (Th. A2) |
| | 3/12 | Small white dot below lower right leaf of flax plant (Th. G4) |
| | 10/6 | Coloured flaw in lower left of badge (Th. E1) |
| | 12/1 | Pale patch below P of POSTAGE (Th. F1) |

**Quantity Sold:** 61,449,360

**Sold Out:** 11.7.68

### **1967 (2 October). 4d. Two 9·5 mm. phosphor bands reacting violet. Watermark crowns**

XN5 (=SG NI2p)

| | | Mint | Used |
|---|---|---|---|
| 4d. | Ultramarine | 15 | 15 |
| a. | Dot on leaf (No dot, R. 3/12) | 25·00 | |
| b. | Flower flaw retouch (No dot, R. 7/7) | 25·00 | |

For illustration of No. XN5a and for description of No. XN5b, see Nos. XN4a/b.

### **Cylinder Numbers (Blocks of Six)**
Perforation Type F (L)*

| Cylinder No. | No Dot (I/E) | Dot (P/E) |
|---|---|---|
| 1 | 2·50 | 2·50 |

### **Minor Constant Flaws**

| Cyl. 1 | 16/5 | Small white spot to right of second leaf down on upright flax plant (Th. B6) |
|---|---|---|
| Cyl. 1. | 2/1 | Small coloured projection above upper frame line (Th. A2) |
| | 2/4 | Dark patch below S of POSTAGE where former white dot, No. XN4a, existed (Th. F2) |
| | 3/12 | Small white dot below lower right leaf of flax plant (Th. G4) |
| | 10/6 | Coloured flaw in lower left of badge (Th. E1) |
| | 12/1 | Pale patch below P of POSTAGE (Th. F1) |

**Sold Out:** 1.70

### **1968 (27 June). 4d. No watermark. Chalky paper. Two 9·5 mm. phosphor bands reacting violet**

**A. Gum Arabic**
XN6 (=SG NI7)

| | | Mint | Used |
|---|---|---|---|
| 4d. | Ultramarine | 15 | 15 |
| a. | Dot on leaf (No dot, R. 3/12) | 25·00 | |
| b. | Flower flaw retouch (No dot, R. 7/7) | 25·00 | |

**B. PVA Gum* (23 October 1968)**
XN7 (=SG NI7Ev)

| | | Mint | |
|---|---|---|---|
| ✓ | 4d. Ultramarine | 13·00 | |
| a. | Dot on leaf (No dot, R. 3/12) | 40·00 | |
| b. | Flower flaw retouch (No dot, R. 7/7) | 40·00 | |

For illustration of Nos. XN6a and XN7a and for description of Nos. XN6b and XN7b, see Nos. XN4a/b respectively.

*No. XN7 was never issued in Northern Ireland. After No. XN6 (gum arabic) had been withdrawn from Northern Ireland but whilst still on sale at the philatelic counters elsewhere, about fifty sheets with PVA gum were sold over the London Philatelic counter on 23 October 1968, and some were also on sale at the British Philatelic Exhibition Post Office.

### **Cylinder Numbers (Blocks of Six)**

**Gum Arabic No XN6**
Perforation Type A (E/I)

| Cylinder No. | No Dot | Dot |
|---|---|---|
| 1 | 2·50 | 2·50 |

**PVA Gum No XN7**
Perforation Type A (E/I)

| Cylinder No. | No Dot | Dot |
|---|---|---|
| 1 | £125 | † |

### **Minor Constant Flaws**

| Cyl. 1 | 16/5 | Small white spot to right of second leaf down on upright flax plant (Th. B6) |
|---|---|---|

Cyl. 1.
| | | |
|---|---|---|
| | 2/1 | Small coloured projection above upper frame line (Th. A2) |
| | 2/4 | Dark patch below S of POSTAGE where former white dot, No. XN4a, existed (Th. F2) |
| | 3/12 | Small white dot below lower right leaf of flax plant (Th. G4) |
| | 6/12 | Small coloured flaws on leaf above NU of REVENUE |
| | 10/6 | Coloured flaw in lower left of badge (Th. E1) |
| | 12/1 | Pale patch below P of POSTAGE (Th. F1) |

**Sold Out:** No. XN6, 4.70

**Withdrawn:** No. XN7 on the same day as released

●────────────

### 1968 (4 September). 4d. Change of colour. No watermark. Chalky paper. PVA gum. One centre phosphor band reacting violet

**XN8** (=SG NI8)

| | | Mint | Used |
|---|---|---|---|
| 4d. | Olive-sepia | 15 | 15 |
| a. | Phosphor omitted | | |
| b. | Dot on leaf (No dot, R. 3/12) | 25·00 | |
| c. | Flower flaw retouch (No dot, R. 7/7) | 25·00 | |

For illustration of No. XN8b and for description of No. XN8c, see Nos. XN4a/b respectively.

**Cylinder Numbers (Blocks of Six)**
Perforation Type A (E/I)

| Cylinder No. | No Dot | Dot |
|---|---|---|
| 1 | 2·50 | 2·50 |

**Cylinder number:** Opposite R.18/1. In addition both no dot and dot panes bear traces of cylinder numbers reading 1A and 1A. with two sides of a box opposite R. 19/1. These exist in varying degrees of faintness.

**Minor Constant Flaws:** As for Nos. XN6/7

●────────────

### 1969 (26 February). 4d. Further change of colour. No watermark. Chalky paper. PVA gum. One centre phosphor band reactin+ violet

**XN9** (=SG NI9)

| | | Mint | Used |
|---|---|---|---|
| 4d. | Bright vermilion | 20 | 20 |
| a. | Phosphor omitted | 4·50 | |
| b. | Flower flaw retouch (No dot, R. 7/7) | 25·00 | |

For description of No. XN9b, see No. XN4b.

**Cylinder Numbers (Blocks of Six)**
Perforation Type A (E/I)

| Cylinder No. | No Dot | Dot |
|---|---|---|
| 1 | 2·75 | 2·75 |

Cylinder number: Opposite R. 18/1. In addition both no dot and dot panes bear traces of cylinder numbers reading 1A and 1A. with two sides of a box opposite R. 19/1. These exist in varying degrees of faintness.

**Minor Constant Flaws**

Cyl. 1.
| | | |
|---|---|---|
| | 2/4 | Dark patch below S of POSTAGE where former white dot, No. XN4a, existed (Th. F2) |
| | 6/12 | Small coloured flaws on leaf above NU of REVENUE |
| | 10/6 | Coloured flaw in lower left of badge (Th. E1) |
| | 12/1 | Pale patch below P of POSTAGE (Th. F1) |

### 5d. Type XN1 (1968)

### 1968 (4 September). 5d. No watermark. Chalky paper. PVA gum. Two 9·5 mm. phosphor bands reacting violet

**XN10** (=SG NI10)

| | | Mint | Used |
|---|---|---|---|
| 5d. | Royal blue | 20 | 20 |
| a. | Phosphor omitted | 25·00 | |
| b. | Extra leaf (No dot, R. 13/2) | 25·00 | |

XN10b

**Cylinder Numbers (Blocks of Six)**
Perforation Type A (E/I)

| Cylinder No. | No Dot | Dot |
|---|---|---|
| 1 | 2·75 | 2·75 |

●────────────

## ■ 6d. Type XN2 (1958-62)

### 1958 (29 September). 6d. Watermark crowns
XN11

| A. Cream Paper | Mint | Used |
|---|---|---|
| 6d. Deep claret | 2·25 | 50 |

**B. Whiter Paper (4 June 1962)**
XN12 (−SG NI3)

| | Mint | Used |
|---|---|---|
| 6d. Deep claret | 30 | 30 |

**Cylinder Numbers (Blocks of Six)**

Cream Paper (No XN11)

| | | Perforation Types | |
|---|---|---|---|
| Cylinder No. | No Dot | B(I/P) | C (E/P) |
| 1 | | 30·00 | 30·00 |

Whiter Paper (No XN12)

| | | Perforation Types | | |
|---|---|---|---|---|
| Cylinder No. | No Dot | B(I/P) | C (E/P) | F(L)(I/E) |
| 1 | | 4·00 | 4·00 | 2·75 |

**Minor Constant Flaws**

| Cyl. 1 | 1/12 | Flaw in background to right of diadem (Th. A4) |
|---|---|---|
| | 2/11 | White coloured spur on lowest leaf of left flax plant (Th. F1) |
| | 3/9 | Dot in diamond to right of 6D (Th. F4); also similar dot in diamond to right of Queen's collar (Th. E–F5) |
| | 3/10 | Ring on little finger of hand at left (Th. F2) |
| | 3/12 | Dark spot in centre of central cross of diadem (Th. B3) |
| | 4/2 | Coloured line in background to right of 6D (Th. G4) |
| | 10/2 | White bulge half way down stalk at left (Th. D1) |
| | 12/2 | Coloured spot in background to right of Queen's hair (Th. D5) |

**Imprimatur from the National Postal Museum Archives**
Cream paper. Imperforate, watermark Type W.24

| Watermark upright | £2000 |
|---|---|

**Quantity Sold:** 28,531,180 up to 31.3.68

**Sold Out:** 11.68

## ■ 9d. Type XN2 (1967)

### 1967 (1 March). 9d. Watermark crowns. Two 9·5 mm. phosphor bands reacting violet
XN13 (=SG NI4)

| | Mint | Used |
|---|---|---|
| 9d. Bronze-green | 30 | 70 |

**Cylinder Number (Block of Six)**
Single pane cylinder. Perforation Type F (L) (I/E)

| Cylinder No. | No Dot | Dot |
|---|---|---|
| 1 | 4·25 | |

**Imprimatur from the National Postal Museum Archives**
Imperforate, watermark Type W.24

| Watermark upright | £2000 |
|---|---|

## ■ 1s.3d. Type XN3 (1958-62)

### 1958 (29 September). 1s.3d. Watermark crowns

**A. Cream Paper**
**XN14**

| | Mint | Used |
|---|---|---|
| 1s.3d. Green | 5·00 | 1·25 |

**B. Whiter Paper (9 November 1962)**
**XN15 (=SG NI5)**

| | | |
|---|---|---|
| 1s.3d. Green | 30 | 70 |

**Cylinder Numbers (Blocks of Six)**

**Cream Paper (No XN14)**

| | | Perforation Types | |
|---|---|---|---|
| Cylinder No. | No Dot | B(I/P) | C (E/P) |
| 1 | | 30·00 | 30·00 |

**Whiter Paper (No XN15)**

| | | Perforation Types | | |
|---|---|---|---|---|
| Cylinder No. | No Dot | B(I/P) | C (E/P) | F(L)(I/E) |
| 1 | | 4·00 | 4·00 | 2·75 |

**Minor Constant Flaws**

Cyl. 1   1/1   White dot in upper loop of S of POSTAGE; also small area of retouching above emblems in diadem (Th. A4)

       3/7   White spur to O of POSTAGE (Th. E1)

**Imprimatur from the National Postal Museum Archives**
Cream paper. Imperforate, watermark Type W.24

| | |
|---|---|
| Watermark upright | £2000 |

**Quantity Sold**: 14,060,520 up to 31.3.68

## ■ 1s.6d. Type XN3 (1967–69)

### 1967 (1 March). 1s.6d. Watermark crowns. Two 9·5 mm. phosphor bands reacting violet

**XN16** (=SG NI6)

| | Mint | Used |
|---|---|---|
| 1s.6d. Grey-blue | 30 | 70 |
| a. Phosphor omitted | £200 | |

**Cylinder Number (Block of Six)**
Single pane cylinder. Perforation Type F (L) (I/E)

| Cylinder No. | No Dot | Dot |
|---|---|---|
| 1 | 4·50 | |

**Minor Constant Flaws**

Cyl. 1   4/12   Small area of retouching behind Queen's head. Consists of several small dark coloured dots (Th. E5)

       14/1   Dark coloured spot on Queen's cheek (Th. D4)

       15/12   A multitude of tiny coloured spots over the Queen's face, neck and collar, and in the background behind her neck

       17/8   Coloured spot to right of Queen's left eye (Th. D3–4)

**Imprimatur from the National Postal Museum Archives**
Imperforate, watermark Type W.24

| | |
|---|---|
| Watermark upright | £2000 |

### 1969 (20 May). 1s.6d. No watermark. Chalky paper. PVA Gum. Two 9·5 mm. phosphor bands reacting violet

**XN17** (=SG NI11)

| | Mint | Used |
|---|---|---|
| 1s.6d. Grey-blue | 2·25 | 2·50 |
| a. Phosphor omitted | £500 | |

It is believed that only three examples exist of No. XN17a.

**Cylinder Number (Block of Six)**
Single pane cylinder. Perforation Type F (L) (I/E)

| Cylinder No. | No Dot | Dot |
|---|---|---|
| 1 | 30·00 | |

**Minor Constant Flaws**

Cyl. 1   4/12   Small area of retouching behind Queen's head. Consists of several small dark coloured dots (Th. E5)

       11/12   Small dark coloured flaw on Queen's neck, just above necklace (Th. E4)

       14/1   Small dark coloured flaw on Queen's cheek (Th. D4)

       15/12   A multitude of tiny dark coloured spots over the Queen's face, neck and collar, and in the background behind her neck

       17/8   Area of retouching to right of Queen's left eye (Th. D3–4)

**Imprimatur from the National Postal Museum Archives**
Chalky paper, imperforate

| | |
|---|---|
| No watermark | £2000 |

**Presentation Pack**

| | | | |
|---|---|---|---|
| XNPP1 | (9.12.70) | Seven stamps | 3·50 |

Comprises Nos. XN3, 8/10, 13, and 15/16

**Quantity Sold:** 28,944

**Withdrawn:** 25.11.71

**First Day Covers**

| | | |
|---|---|---|
| XNFC1 (1.3.67) | 9d., 1s.6d. | 4·00 |
| XNFC2 (4.9.68) | 4d., 5d. | 3·00 |

## SCOTLAND

XS1
(Des. Gordon F. Huntly)

XS2
(Des. J. B. Fleming)

XS3
(Des. A. B. Imrie)

### 3d. Type XS1 (1958-68)

**1958 (18 August). 3d. Watermark crowns**

**A. Cream Paper**
**XS1**

| | | Mint | Used |
|---|---|---|---|
| 3d. | Deep lilac | 70 | 35 |
| a. | Spot on U of REVENUE (Cyl. 3 No dot, R. 19/8) | 25·00 | |
| b. | Dot in d of 3d (Cyl. 3 Dot, R. 20/12) | 20·00 | |

**B. Whiter Paper (9 July 1962)**
**XS2** (=SG S1)

| | | | |
|---|---|---|---|
| 3d. | Deep lilac | 15 | 15 |
| a. | Spot after last E of REVENUE (Cyl. 5 No dot, R. 20/2) | 20·00 | |

XS1a

XS1b Later retouched

XS2a, XS3a, XS4b, XS5b, XS7b XS8b

**Cylinder Numbers (Blocks of Six)**

**Cream Paper (No XS1)**
Perforation Type A (E/I)

| Cylinder No. | No Dot | Dot |
|---|---|---|
| 4 | 10·00 | 10·00 |
| 5 | 10·00 | 10·00 |

## Whiter Paper (No XS2)
Perforation Type A (E/I)

| Cylinder No. | No Dot | Dot |
|---|---|---|
| 4 | 2·75 | 2·75 |
| 5 | 2·75 | 6·00 |

**Same price as perforation type A with extension holes in left margin.

**Imprimatur from the National Postal Museum Archives**
Cream paper. Imperforate, watermark Type W.24
Watermark upright.

**Quantity Sold:** 1,487,481,480
**Sold Out:** 18.3.68

**1962 Miniature Sheet.** On the occasion of "Scotex" the 1962 Scottish Stamp Exhibition, a miniature sheet, size 105 × 60 mm., was produced comprising Types XS1/3 printed *se-tenant* in black, imperforate and surrounded by a decorative frame and inscription in blue on white chalk-surfaced gummed paper watermarked HARRISON AND SONS LTD sideways. The sheet was printed by Harrison & Sons with the use of actual stamp positives. It had no franking value. 15,000 printed.

## 1963 (29 January). 3d. phosphor bands reacting blue. Watermark crowns

| A. Two 8 mm. Bands | Mint | Used |
|---|---|---|
| **XS3** (=SG S1p) | | |
| 3d. Deep lilac | 13·00 | 2·75 |
| a. Spot after last E of REVENUE (Cyl. 5 Dot, R. 20/2) | 40·00 | |

**B. One Side Band*** (30 April 1965)
**XS4**

| | Mint | Used |
|---|---|---|
| 3d. Deep lilac (band at left) | 4·00 | 70 |
| a. Band at right | 4·00 | 70 |
| ab. Nos. XS4/a (horiz. pair) | 8·00 | |
| b. Spot after last E of REVENUE (Cyl. 5 Dot, R. 20/2) | 20·00 | |

*The one side band stamps were produced by an 8 mm. band applied down alternate vertical rows of the sheets over the perforations so that alternate stamps have the band at left (No. XS4) or right (No. XS4a). In theory the width of the band on a single stamp should be 4 mm. but this will vary if the bands have not been perfectly positioned.
For illustration of Nos. XS3a and XS4b, see No. XS2a.

**Cylinder Numbers (Blocks of Six)**

**Two Bands No. XS3**
Perforation Type A (E/I)

| Cylinder No. | No Dot | Dot |
|---|---|---|
| 4 | £130 | £130 |
| 5 | £130 | £150* |

**One Side Band No. XS4**
Perforation Type A (E/I)

| | | |
|---|---|---|
| 5 | 35·00 | 50·00* |

**Imprimatur from the National Postal Museum Archives**
Imperforate, watermark Type W.24. Two 8 mm. bands

| Watermark upright | £2000 |
|---|---|

**Sold Out:** No. XS3, 1968

## 1965 (December 16). 3d. phosphor bands reacting violet. Watermark crowns

| A. One Side Band* | Mint | Used |
|---|---|---|
| **XS5** (=SG S1pb) | | |
| 3d. Deep lilac (band at left) | 20 | 25 |
| a. Band at right | 20 | 25 |
| ab. Nos. XS5/a (horiz. pair) | 50 | |
| b. Spot after last E of REVENUE (Cyl. 5 Dot, R. 20/2) | 20·00 | |

**B. One 4 mm. Centre Band** (9 November 1967)
**XS6** (=SG S1pd)

| 3d. Deep lilac | 15 | 15 |
|---|---|---|

*The note re one side band stamps after No. XS4b also applies here.
For illustration of No. XS5b, see No. XS2a.

**Cylinder Numbers (Blocks of Six)**

**One Side Band No. XS5**
Perforation Type A (E/I)

| Cylinder No. | No Dot | Dot |
|---|---|---|
| 5 | 2·75 | 22·00* |

**One Centre Band No. XS6**
Perforation Type A (E/I)

| Cylinder No. | No Dot | Dot |
|---|---|---|
| 4 | 2·50 | 7·50 |

**Sold Out:** No. XS5, 15.7.68; No. XS6, 11.68

## 1968 (16 May). 3d. No watermark. Chalky paper. One centre phosphor band reacting violet

**XS7** (=SG S7)

| A. Gum Arabic | Mint | Used |
|---|---|---|
| 3d. Deep lilac | 10 | 15 |
| a. Phosphor omitted | 7·00 | |
| b. Spot after last E of REVENUE (Cyl. 5 Dot, R. 20/2) | 20·00 | |

**B. PVA Gum** (11 July 1968)
**XS8** (=SG S7Ev)

| | | |
|---|---|---|
| 3d. Deep lilac | 10 | |
| a. Phosphor omitted | 4·00 | |
| b. Spot after last E of REVENUE (Cyl. 5 Dot, R. 20/2) | 20·00 | |

For illustration of Nos. XS7b and XS8b, see No. XS2a.

**Cylinder Numbers (Blocks of Six)**

**Gum Arabic No. XS7**
Perforation Type F (LI)*

| Cylinder No. | No Dot (I/E) | Dot (P/E) |
|---|---|---|
| 5 | 1·90 | 22·00* |

**PVA Gum No. XS8**
Perforation Type F (LI)*

| Cylinder No. | No Dot (I/E) | Dot (P/E) |
|---|---|---|
| 5 | 1·90 | 22·00* |

**Minor Constant Flaws**

| Cyl. 5 | 8/6 | Retouching on Queen's forehead, nose and around lips (Th. B–D3) |
|---|---|---|
| | 13/3 | Pale patch on Queen's collar (Th. E–F4) |
| | 15/3 | Small dark flaw surrounded by white area on right side of thistle (Th. G6) |

17/7 Area of retouching on Queen's neck
(Th. E4–5)

18/1 Horizontal coloured line through G of
POSTAGE

■ **4d. Type XS1 (1966–69)**

**1966 (7 February). 4d. Watermark crowns**

XS9 (= S.G.S2)

| | | Mint | Used |
|---|---|---|---|
| 4d. Ultramarine | | 15 | 15 |
| a. Dot before second E of REVENUE (Dot, R. 10/9) | | 25·00 | |
| b. Spot on T (Dot, R. 4/4) | | 25·00 | |

XS9a, XS10a               XS9b, XS10b
Later retouched on No. XS10

**Cylinder Numbers (Blocks of Six)**
Perforation Type A (E/I)

| Cylinder No. | No Dot | Dot |
|---|---|---|
| 2 | 2·50 | 2·50 |

**Minor Constant Flaws**

| Cyl. 2 | 7/11 | White spot to left of crown at right (Th. F5) |
|---|---|---|
| | 8/6 | Small blue flaw on top left-hand leaf of thistle (Th. F5) |
| | 20/5 | Small dark flaw in background to right of d of 4d (Th. F4–5) |
| Cyl. 2. | 8/12 | Blue spot below Queen's left eye (Th. C3) |
| | 11/7 | Small blue spot on Queen's forehead (Th. B2) |
| | 12/8 | Small dark flaw in background to left of EV of REVENUE (Th. B5); also retouching on Queen's temple and cheek (Th. C3–4) |
| | 20/3 | Small coloured flaw above Queen's left eye (Th. B3); also small blue spot on top left-hand leaf of thistle (Th. F5) |

**Sold Out:** 7.70.

**1966 (7 February). 4d. Two 8 mm. phosphor bands reacting violet. Watermark crowns**

XS10 (=SG S2p)

| | | Mint | Used |
|---|---|---|---|
| 4d. Ultramarine | | 15 | 15 |
| a. Dot before second E of REVENUE (Dot, R.10/9) | | 25·00 | |
| b. Spot on T (Dot, R. 4/4) | | 25·00 | |

For illustrations of Nos. XS10a/b, see Nos. XS9a/b.

**Cylinder Numbers (Blocks of Six)**
Perforation Type A (E/I)

| Cylinder No. | No Dot | Dot |
|---|---|---|
| 2 | 2·50 | 2·50 |

**Minor Constant Flaws**

| Cyl. 2 | As for flaws on No. XS9 except that flaw on R. 20/5 was later retouched |
|---|---|
| Cyl. 2. | As for flaws on No. XS9 |

**Sold Out:** 7.70.

## 1967 (28 November). 4d. No watermark. Chalky paper. Two 9·5 mm. phosphor bands reacting violet

### A. Gum Arabic
**XS11** (=SG S8)

|  |  | Mint | Used |
|---|---|---|---|
| 4d. | Ultramarine | 10 | 15 |
| a. | Phosphor omitted | 10·00 | |

### B. PVA Gum (25 July 1968)
**XS12** (= S.G.S8Ev)

|  |  |  |
|---|---|---|
| 4d. | Ultramarine | 10 |

### Cylinder Numbers (Blocks of Six)

**Gum Arabic No. XS11**
Perforation Type F (LI)*

| Cylinder No. | No Dot (I/E) | Dot (P/E) |
|---|---|---|
| 2 | 2·00 | 2·00 |

**PVA Gum No. XS12**
Perforation Type A (E/I)

| Cylinder No. | No Dot (I/E) | Dot (P/E) |
|---|---|---|
| 2 | 2·00 | 2·00 |

### Minor Constant Flaws

| | | |
|---|---|---|
| Cyl. 2 | 1/7 | Retouch on Queen's forehead (Th. B3). PVA only |
| | 3/7 | Retouch on Queen's collar (Th. E4–5). PVA only |
| | 5/10 | White patches on Queen's nose and forehead |
| | 8/6 | Small blue flaw on top left-hand leaf of thistle (Th. F5) |
| | 10/11 | Retouch to right of Queen's mouth (Th. D3). PVA only |
| | 12/12 | White spot at rear tip of diadem (Th. C5) |
| | 14/10 | Retouch on Queen's forehead (Th. B3). Less pronounced on PVA |
| | 15/4 | Retouch on Queen's cheek (Th. C–D3) |
| | 19/7 | White spot on Queen's cheek (Th. C3). Retouched on PVA where it shows as three dark spots |
| | 20/5 | Small dark flaw in background to right of d of 4d (Th. F4–5). Less pronounced on PVA but can be confirmed by additional retouches on Queen's nose and forehead (Th. C2 and B3) |
| | 20/6 | Small blue flaw on Queen's cheek (Th. C3). On PVA there is an additional white flaw on Queen's right cheek (Th. C2) |
| Cyl. 2. | 1/5 | Coloured spot above Queen's left eye (Th. B3). |
| | 2/6 | Retouch on Queen's collar (Th. E4) |
| | 6/11 | White spot on Queen's cheek (Th. C–D3). Retouched on PVA where it shows as a dark spot |
| | 8/12 | White spot below Queen's left eye where former blue spot appeared (Th. C3). Further retouched on PVA |
| | 11/7 | Small blue spot on Queen's forehead (Th. B2) |
| | 12/8 | Small dark flaw in background to left of EV of REVENUE (Th. B5); also retouching on Queen's temple and cheek, the latter much more pronounced on PVA (Th. C3–4) |
| | 15/1 | Small retouch on Queen's temple (Th. C3–4). PVA only |
| | 15/2 | Small retouch on Queen's forehead (Th. B2). PVA only |
| | 18/4 | Weak patches on Queen's chin (Th. D2–3). |

| | | |
|---|---|---|
| | 18/6 | Blue spot on Queen's collar (Th. E4). Retouched on PVA but a scratch now appears across Queen's neck and collar (Th. E4) |
| | 19/3 | White spot on Queen's left cheek (Th. D3). Shows larger on PVA |
| | 20/3 | Small coloured flaw above Queen's left eye (Th. B3); also small blue spot on top left-hand leaf of thistle (Th. F5) |
| | 20/4 | Coloured spots around Queen's eyes and nose (Th. C2–3) |

## 1968 (4 September). 4d. Change of colour. No watermark. Chalky paper. PVA gum. One centre phosphor band reacting violet

**XS13** (=SG S9)

|  |  | Mint | Used |
|---|---|---|---|
| 4d. | olive-sepia | 10 | 10 |
| a. | Phosphor omitted | 3·00 | |

### Cylinder Numbers (Blocks of Six)
Perforation Type A (E/I)

| Cylinder No. | No Dot | Dot |
|---|---|---|
| 2 | 2·00 | 2·00 |

### Minor Constant Flaws

| | | |
|---|---|---|
| Cyl. 2 | 12/12 | White spot at rear tip of diadem (Th. C5) |
| Cyl. 2. | 1/5 | Coloured spot above Queen's left eye (Th. B3) |
| | 2/6 | Retouch on Queen's collar (Th. E4) |
| | 6/11 | Retouch on Queen's cheek (Th. C–D3) |
| | 8/12 | Retouch below Queen's left eye (Th. C3) |
| | 11/7 | Coloured spot on Queen's forehead (Th. B2) |
| | 12/8 | Small dark flaw in background to left of EV of REVENUE (Th. B5); also retouching on Queen's temple and cheek (Th. C3–4) |
| | 15/1 | Small retouch on Queen's temple (Th. C3–4) |
| | 15/2 | Small retouch on Queen's forehead (Th. B2) |
| | 18/4 | Weak patches on Queen's chin (Th. D2–4) |
| | 18/6 | Retouch on Queen's collar and also scratch across her neck and collar (Th. E4) |
| | 19/3 | Large white spot on Queen's left cheek (Th. D3) |
| | 20/3 | Small coloured flaw above Queen's left eye (Th. B3); also small coloured spot on top left-hand leaf of thistle (Th. F5) |
| | 20/4 | Coloured spots around Queen's eyes and nose (Th. C2–3) |

## 1969 (26 February). 4d. Further change of colour. No watermark. Chalky paper. PVA gum. One centre phosphor band reacting violet

**XS14** (=SG S10)

|  |  | Mint | Used |
|---|---|---|---|
| 4d. | Bright vermilion | 10 | 10 |
| a. | Phosphor omitted | 2·50 | |

### Cylinder Numbers (Blocks of Six)

| Cylinder No. | No Dot | Dot |
|---|---|---|
| 2 | 2·00 | 2·00 |
| 4 | 2·00 | 2·00 |

**Minor Constant Flaws**

Cyl. 2
| | |
|---|---|
| 1/7 | Retouch on Queen's forehead (Th. B3) |
| 3/7 | Retouch on Queen's collar (Th. E4–5) |
| 5/10 | Retouching on Queen's nose and forehead where former white patches appeared |
| 8/11 | Retouch by Queen's ear (Th. C–D4) |
| 12/12 | White spot at rear tip of diadem (Th. C5) |
| 10/11 | Retouch to right of Queen's mouth (Th. D3) |
| 14/10 | Heavy retouching on Queen's forehead (Th. B3) |
| 15/4 | Retouch on Queen's cheek (Th. C–D3) |
| 19/7 | Retouch on Queen's cheek where former white spot appeared (Th. C3) |
| 20/5 | Retouches on Queen's nose and forehead (Th. C2 and B3). Small dark flaw in background to right of d of 4d now hardly shows (Th. F4–5) |
| 20/6 | Retouches on both of the Queen's cheeks where former flaws appeared (Th. C2–3) |

Cyl. 2.
| | |
|---|---|
| 1/5 | Coloured spot above Queen's left eye (Th. B3) |
| 2/6 | Retouch on Queen's collar (Th. E4) |
| 6/11 | Heavy area of retouching on Queen's cheek (Th. C–D3) |
| 8/12 | Retouch below Queen's left eye (Th. C3) |
| 10/5 | Extensive area of retouching on Queen's temple and cheek (Th. B3 and C3–4) |
| 11/7 | Area of retouching on Queen's forehead where former coloured spot appeared (Th. B2) |
| 12/8 | Small dark flaw in background to left of EV of REVENUE (Th. B5) is now less noticeable but retouches on Queen's temple and cheek remain (Th. C34) |
| 15/1 | Small retouch on Queen's temple (Th. C3–4) |
| 15/2 | Small retouch on Queen's forehead (Th. B2) |
| 18/4 | Weak patches on Queen's chin (Th. D–24) |
| 18/6 | Retouch on Queen's collar and also scratch across her neck and collar (Th. E4) |
| 20/3 | Small coloured flaw above Queen's left eye (Th. B3); also small coloured spot on top left-hand leaf of thistle (Th. F5) |
| 20/4 | Coloured spots around Queen's eyes and nose (Th. C2–3) |

## ■ **5d. Type XS1 (1968)**

**1968 (4 September). 5d. No watermark. Chalky paper. PVA gum. Two 9·5 mm. phosphor bands reacting violet**

**XS15** (=SG S11)

| | | Mint | Used |
|---|---|---|---|
| 5d. | Royal blue | 20 | 10 |
| a. | Phosphor omitted | 55·00 | |
| b. | Shoulder retouch (Cyl. 2., R. 16/6) | 25·00 | |

XS15b
Large retouch on Queen's shoulder

**Cylinder Numbers (Blocks of Six)**
Perforation Type A (E/I)

| Cylinder No. | No Dot | Dot |
|---|---|---|
| 2 | 2·75 | 2·75 |
| 3 | 10·00 | 10·00 |

**Phosphor Cylinder number:** Ph 1 found on cyl. 3 dot, right margin

## ■ 6d. Type XS2 (1958–66)

### 1958 (29 September). 6d. Watermark crowns

**A. Cream Paper**
**XS16**

|  | Mint | Used |
|---|---|---|
| 6d. Reddish purple | 2·75 | 90 |
| a. Broken V of REVENUE (Cyl. 1, R. 11/12) | 28·00 | |
| b. Curled leaf (Cyl. 1, R. 7/7) | 25·00 | |

**B. Whiter Paper (28 May 1962)**
**XS17 (=SG S3)**

|  | Mint | Used |
|---|---|---|
| 6d. Deep reddish purple | 20 | 15 |
| a. Broken V of REVENUE (Cyl. 1, R. 11/12) | 25·00 | |
| b. Curled leaf (Cyl. 1, R. 7/7) | 25·00 | |
| c. Cut leaf (Cyl. 4, R. 2/10) | 25·00 | |

XS16a, XS17a
This is a multipositive flaw. It was later retouched on Cyl 1. On Cyls. 2 and 4 it is only known retouched and it shows as a much thicker "V" than normal

XS16b, XS17b
Later reouched

XS17c, XS18a
Leaf half-way down at right has V-shaped cut in solid colour

### Cylinder Numbers (Blocks of Six)

**Cream Paper (No XS16)**

| | | Perforation Types | |
|---|---|---|---|
| Cylinder No. | No Dot | B(I/P) | C (E/P) |
| 1 | | 35·00 | 35·00 |

**Whiter Paper (No XS17)**

| | | Perforation Types | | |
|---|---|---|---|---|
| Cylinder No. | No Dot | B(I/P) | C (E/P) | F(L)(I/E) |
| 1 | | † | † | † |
| 2 | | 2·75 | 2·75 | † |
| 4 | | † | † | 2·75 |

**Marginal rule:**
**Cylinder 1:** Instead of the usual stamp width rule below each stamp in the bottom row the rules on this cylinder are shorter (approx. 17 mm.) and are arranged alternately with a 1 mm.

wide rectangular rule, the latter being perforated through. The rules below vertical rows 9/12 are damaged.
**Cylinders 2 and 4:** As given in General Notes

### Minor Constant Flaws

| Cyl. 1 | 5/8 | Small white flaw by left thistle just outside oval frame (Th. B2) |
|---|---|---|
| Cyl. 2 | 11/12 | V of REVENUE retouched. It is thicker than normal and has a fuzzy appearance |
| Cyl. 4 | 11/12 | As for Cyl. 2 |

**Imprimatur from the National Postal Museum Archives**
Cream paper. Imperforate, watermark Type W.24

| Watermark upright | £2000 |
|---|---|

### 1963 (29 January). 6d. Two 8 mm. phosphor bands reacting blue. Watermark crowns
**XS18**

|  | Mint | Used |
|---|---|---|
| 6d. Deep reddish purple | 2·75 | 90 |
| a. Cut leaf (Cyl. 4, R. 2/10) | 25·00 | |

### Cylinder Number (Block of Six)
Single pane cylinder. Perforation Type F (L) (I/E)

| Cylinder No. | No Dot | Dot |
|---|---|---|
| 4 | 35·00 | |

### Minor Constant Flaw
Cyl. 4 11/12 V of REVENUE retouched. It is thicker than normal and has a fuzzy appearance

**Imprimatur from the National Postal Museum Archives**
Imperforate, watermark Type W.24

| Watermark upright | £2000 |
|---|---|

### 1966 (2 February). 6d. Two 8mm. phosphor bands reacting violet. Watermark crowns

**XS19 (=SG S3p)**

|  | Mint | Used |
|---|---|---|
| 6d. Deep reddish purple | 20 | 20 |

### Cylinder Number (Block of Six)
Single pane cylinder. Perforation Type F (L) (I/E)

| Cylinder No. | No Dot | Dot |
|---|---|---|
| 4 | 3·00 | |

**Quantity Sold:** 26,758,320 (including No. XS18) up to 31.3.68
**Sold Out:** 10.68

## 9d. Type XS2 (1967–70)

### 1967 (1 March). 9d. Watermark crowns. Two 9·5 mm. phosphor bands reacting violet
XS20 (=SG S4)

| | Mint | Used |
|---|---|---|
| 9d. Bronze-green | 35 | 40 |

**Cylinder Number (Block of Six)**
Single pane cylinder. Perforation Type F (L) (I/E)

| Cylinder No. | No Dot | Dot |
|---|---|---|
| 1 | 4·00 | |

**Imprimatur from the National Postal Museum Archives**
Imperforate, watermark Type W.24

| Watermark upright | £2000 |
|---|---|

### 1970 (28 September). 9d. No watermark. Chalky paper. PVA gum. Two 9·5 mm. phosphor bands reacting violet
XS21 (= S.G. S12)

| | Mint | Used |
|---|---|---|
| 9d. bronze-green | 6·00 | 6·00 |
| a. Phosphor omitted | £250 | |

**Cylinder Number (Block of Six)**
Single pane cylinder. Perforation Type F (L) (I/E)

| Cylinder No. | No Dot | Dot |
|---|---|---|
| 1 | 50·00 | |

**Imprimatur from the National Postal Museum Archives**
Chalky paper, imperforate

| No watermark | £2000 |
|---|---|

## 1s.3d. Type XS3 (1958-65)

### 1958 (29 September). 1s.3d. Watermark crowns

**A. Cream Paper**
XS22

| | Mint | Used |
|---|---|---|
| 1s.3d. Green | 4·50 | 90 |
| a. Broken oblique in value (Cyl. 4, R. 15/2) | 25·00 | |
| b. Broken hinge (Cyl. 4, R. 19/2) | 20·00 | |

**B. Whiter Paper (31 July 1962)**
XS23 (=SG S5)

| 1s.3d. Green | 40 | 40 |
|---|---|---|
| a. Broken oblique in value (Cyl. 4, R. 15/2) | 25·00 | |
| b. Broken hinge (Cyl. 4, R. 19/2) | 20·00 | |

XS22a, XS23a, XS24a, XS25a

XS22b, XS23b, XS24b, XS25b
Lowest "hinge" of the flag is incomplete. A multipositive flaw, (Cyls 4 and 8, R.19/2

**Cylinder Numbers (Blocks of Six)**

**Cream Paper (No XS22)**

| | | Perforation Types | |
|---|---|---|---|
| Cylinder No. | No Dot | B(I/P) | C (E/P) |
| 4 | | 45·00* | 45·00* |

**Whiter Paper (No XS23)**

| | | Perforation Types | | |
|---|---|---|---|---|
| Cylinder No. | No Dot | B(I/P) | C (E/P) | F(L)(I/E) |
| 4 | | 24·00* | 24·00* | 24·00* |

**Marginal arrows**: "V" shaped, hand engraved at top and bottom; "W" shaped, photo-etched at both sides. Early printings have the arrows omitted from the top and bottom of the sheet. *Price for marginal strip of 7 stamps* £60.

**Minor Constant Flaws**

| Cyl. 4 | 3/7 | Green spot on shoulder of right-hand unicorn (Th. D6) |
|---|---|---|
| | 11/12 | Small break in inner frame line at right of value tablet (Th. G4) |
| | 15/2 | Hind leg of lion on standard is severed (Th. B1) |

**Imprimatur from the National Postal Museum Archives**
Cream paper. Imperforate, watermark Type W.24

| Watermark upright | £2000 |
|---|---|

**1963 (29 January). 1s.3d. Two 8mm. phosphor bands reacting blue. Watermark crowns**

XS24

|  | | Mint | Used |
|---|---|---|---|
| 1s.3d. | Green | 4·50 | 90 |
| a. | Broken oblique in value (Cyl. 4. R. 15/2) | 28·00 | |
| b. | Broken hinge (Cyl. 4, R. 19/2) | 20·00 | |

For illustration of Nos. XS24a/b, see Nos. XS22a/b.

**Cylinder Number (Block of Six)**
Single pane cylinder. Perforation Type F (L) (I/E)

| Cylinder No. | No Dot | Dot |
|---|---|---|
| 4 | 50·00* | |

**Minor Constant Flaws**
As for Nos. XS22/3

**Imprimatur from the National Postal Museum Archives**
Imperforate, watermark Type W.24

| Watermark upright | £2000 |
|---|---|

●────────────

**1965 (26 November). 1s.3d. Two 8mm. phosphor bands reacting violet. Watermark crowns**

XS25 (=SG S5p)

|  | | Mint | Used |
|---|---|---|---|
| 1s.3d. | Green | 40 | 40 |
| a. | Broken oblique in value (Cyl. 4, R. 15/2) | 25·00 | |
| b. | Broken hinge (Cyls. 4, 8, R. 19/2) | 20·00 | |

For illustration of Nos. XS25a/b, see Nos. XS22a/b.

**Cylinder Numbers (Blocks of Six)**
Single pane cylinders. Perforation Type F (L) (I/E)

| Cylinder No. | No Dot | Dot |
|---|---|---|
| 4 | 24·00* | |
| 8 | 30·00* | |

**Minor Constant Flaws:** Cyl. 4 As for Nos. XS22/3

●────────────

**■ 1s.6d. Type XS3 (1967–68)**

**1967 (1 March). 1s.6d. Watermark crowns. Two 9·5 mm. phosphor bands reacting violet**

XS26 (=SG S6)

|  | | Mint | Used |
|---|---|---|---|
| 1s.6d. | Grey-blue | 45 | 50 |

**Cylinder Number (Block of Six)**
Single pane cylinder. Perforation Type F (L) (I/E)

| Cylinder No. | No Dot | Dot |
|---|---|---|
| 1 | 6·00 | |

**Minor Constant Flaw**
Cyl. 1 1/11 Coloured spot in background to right of Queen's neck, below her hair (Th. E4)

**Imprimatur from the National Postal Museum Archives**
Imperforate, watermark Type W.24

| Watermark upright | £2000 |
|---|---|

●────────────

**1968 (12 December). 1s.6d. No watermark. Chalky paper. PVA gum. Two 9·5 mm. phosphor bands reacting violet**

XS27 (=SG S13)

|  | | Mint | Used |
|---|---|---|---|
| 1s.6d. | Grey-blue | 1·75 | 1·50 |
| a. | Phosphor omitted | £125 | |

**Cylinder Number (Block of Six)**
Single pane cylinder. Perforation Type F (L) (I/E)

| Cylinder No. | No Dot | Dot |
|---|---|---|
| 1 | 20·00 | |

**Minor Constant Flaw:** As for No. XS26

**Imprimatur from the National Postal Museum Archives**
Chalky paper, imperforate

| No watermark | £2000 |
|---|---|

**Presentation Pack**

| XSPP1 | (9.12.70) | Eight stamps | 8·00 |
|---|---|---|---|

Comprises Nos. XS8, 13/15, 17, 21, 25 and 27.

**Quantity Sold:** 31,476

**Withdrawn:** 25.11.71

**First Day Covers**

| XSFC1 | (1.3.67) | 9d., 1s.6d. | 6·00 |
|---|---|---|---|
| XSFC2 | (4.9.68) | 4d., 5d. | 3·00 |

●────────────

## WALES AND MONMOUTHSHIRE

XW1          XW2          XW3

(Des. Reynolds Stone)

### 3d. Type XW1 (1958-67)

**1958 (18 August). 3d. Watermark crowns**

**A. Cream Paper**
**XW1**

|  | Mint | Used |
|---|---|---|
| 3d. Deep lilac | 70 | 35 |
| a. Bulge on oval value tablet (Cyl. 1 No dot, R. 6/3) | 25·00 | |
| b. Wing-tail flaw (Cyl. 2 No dot, R. 16/1) | 25·00 | |

**B. Whiter Paper (30 April 1962)**
**XW2** (=SG W1)

|  | Mint | Used |
|---|---|---|
| 3d. Deep lilac | 15 | 15 |
| a. Wing-tail flaw (Cyl. 2, No dot, R. 16/1) | 25·00 | |

XW1a
Later retouched

XW1b, XW2a
White flaw joins spine of dragon's wing to its tail

**Cylinder Numbers (Blocks of Six)**

**Cream Paper (No XW1)**
Perforation Type A (E/I)

| Cylinder No. | No Dot | Dot |
|---|---|---|
| 1 | 32·00 | 32·00 |
| 2 | 9·00 | 9·00 |

**Whiter Paper (No XW2)**
Perforation Type  A (E/I)

| Cylinder No. | No Dot | Dot |
|---|---|---|
| 2 | 2·50 | 2·50 |
| 3 | 2·50 | 2·50 |

**Minor Constant Flaws**
Multipositive flaws

| No dot | 1/12 | Small coloured flaw on dragon's neck (Th. F–G3) |
|---|---|---|
| | 17/10 | Known in three states: Cyl. 1 Two pale coloured dots on back of Queen's neck just below hair (Th. D4) Cyl. 2 Cylinder retouched to almost normal |

| Cyl. 1 | 15/7 | Cyl. 3 Cylinder retouched but still leaving one coloured dot on back of neck White flaw in middle of central cross of diadem (Th. A3) |
|---|---|---|
| Cyl. 2 | 6/11 | White spot on end of top horizontal bar of first E of REVENUE |

**Imprimatur from the National Postal Museum Archives**
Cream paper. Imperforate, watermark Type W.24

| Watermark upright | £2000 |
|---|---|

**Quantity Sold**: 902,289,240

**Sold Out**: 12.67

**1967 (16 May). 3d. One centre phosphor band reacting violet. Watermark crowns**

XW3 (=SG W1p)

|  | Mint | Used |
|---|---|---|
| 3d. Deep lilac | 20 | 15 |

**Cylinder Numbers (Blocks of Six)**
Perforation Type A (E/I)

| Cylinder No. | No Dot | Dot |
|---|---|---|
| 3 | 3·00 | 3·00 |

**Minor Constant Flaws**
Multipositive flaws

| No dot | 1/12 | Small coloured flaw on dragons neck (Th. FG3) |
|---|---|---|
| | 17/10 | Pale coloured dot on back of Queen's neck just below hair (Th. D4) |
| Cyl. 3 | 1/7 | Coloured spot on oval frame line opposite R of REVENUE (Th. A5) |
| | 1/8 | Small coloured flaw just inside oval frame opposite G of POSTAGE (Th. E2) |
| | 7/11 | Small coloured flaw on Queen's collar (Th. E5) |
| | 10/11 | Small dot on leaf to right of final E of REVENUE (Th. E6) |
| | 11/10 | Small dot on leaf to left of second E of REVENUE (Th. C6) |
| Cyl. 3. | 1/6 | Small retouch to right of Queen's mouth (Th. D3) |
| | 1/8 | Retouch on Queen's cheek (Th. C–D4) |
| | 3/5 | Small dot on leaf above E of POSTAGE (Th. E1) |
| | 3/9 | Coloured flaw on Queen's neck just above collar (Th. E4) |
| | 4/9 | Coloured diagonal flaw in front of Queen's neck (Th. E3) |
| | 5/9 | Coloured spot inside lower loop of 3 of right-hand 3d |
| | 8/1 | Two white flaws on dragon's front left foot (Th. G–H2) |
| | 10/2 | Coloured spot on Queen's collar (Th. E4) |
| | 11/6 | Small retouch on back of Queen's collar (Th. E4–5) |
| | 18/10 | Retouch to background within oval to right of O of POSTAGE (Th. A–B2) |
| | 18/11 | Small dot on leaf to right of T of POSTAGE (Th. C1–2) |
| | 20/6 | Pale patch on Queen's shoulder (Th. E4) |

**Sold Out** :1.68

## 1967 (6 December). 3d. No watermark. Chalky paper. One centre phosphor band reacting violet

**XW4** (=SG W7)

|  | Mint | Used |
|---|---|---|
| 3d.  Deep lilac | 20 | 10 |
| a.  Phosphor omitted | 60·00 | |

**Cylinder Numbers (Blocks of Six)**
Perforation Type F (L)*

| Cylinder No. | No Dot (I/E) | Dot (P/E) |
|---|---|---|
| 3 | 3·00 | 3·00 |

**Minor Constant Flaws**
As for multipositive and cylinder flaws on No. XW3 with the addition of the following cylinder flaws:

| Cyl. 3 | 5/9 | Retouch on Queen's cheek (Th. D3–4) |
|---|---|---|
| Cyl. 3. | 5/8 | Retouch on Queen's chin (Th. D3) |
| | 14/1 | Retouch on Queen's cheek (Th. D4) |
| | 20/5 | Retouch on Queen's chin (Th. D3–4) and several dark spots on her forehead, cheek and neck |

## ▐ 4d. Type XW1 (1966–69)

## 1966 (7 February). 4d. Watermark crowns

**XW5** (=SG W2)

|  | Mint | Used |
|---|---|---|
| 4d.  Ultramarine | 20 | 15 |

**Cylinder Numbers (Blocks of Six)**
Perforation Type A (E/I)

| Cylinder No. | No Dot | Dot |
|---|---|---|
| 1 | 3.00 | 3·00 |

**Quantity Sold:** 148,137,600

**Sold Out:** 7.2.68

## 1967 (October). 4d. Two 9·5 mm. phosphor bands reacting violet. Watermark crowns

**XW6** (=SG W2p)

|  | Mint | Used |
|---|---|---|
| 4d.  Ultramarine | 20 | 15 |

**Cylinder Numbers (Blocks of Six)**
Perforation Type F (L)*

| Cylinder No. | No Dot (I/E) | Dot (P/E) |
|---|---|---|
| 1 | 3.00 | 3·00 |

**Sold Out:** 4.70

## 1968 (June 21). 4d. No watermark. Chalky paper. PVA Gum. Two 9·5 mm. phosphor bands reacting violet

**XW7** (=SG W8)

|  | Mint | Used |
|---|---|---|
| 4d.  Ultramarine | 10 | 15 |
| a.  White spot before E of POSTAGE (No dot, R. 17/12) | 25·00 | |
| b.  White spot after E of POSTAGE (No dot, R. 18/10) | 25·00 | |
| c.  Bump on dragon's head (No dot, R. 19/2) | 20·00 | |
| d.  White spot above dragon's hind leg (No dot, R. 20/1) | 20·00 | |

XW7a, XW8a
Later retouched on No. XW8

XW7b, XW8b
Later retouched on No. XW8

XW7c, XW8c, XW9b     XW7d, XW8c
Retouched on No. XW9

**Cylinder Numbers (Blocks of Six)**
Perforation Type A (E/I)

| Cylinder No. | No Dot | Dot |
|---|---|---|
| 2 | 22·00* | 3·00 |

**Minor Constant Flaws**

| | | |
|---|---|---|
| Cyl. 2 | 6/9 | Small dot on leaf to left of second E of REVENUE (Th. C6) |
| | 12/6 | Coloured flaw on Queen's left eye-brow (Th. C4) |
| | 13/2 | Small dot on leaf above U of REVENUE (Th. D6) |
| | 18/5 | Coloured spots over Queen's face and background |
| | 20/12 | Coloured flaw over d of left-hand 4d. |
| Cyl. 2. | 1/6 | Small dot on leaf above U of REVENUE (Th. D6) |
| | 3/12 | Small dot on leaf to left of N of REVENUE (Th. D6) |
| | 4/3 | Small dot on leaf to right of T of POSTAGE (Th. C1–2) |
| | 4/6 | White spot in background of oval frame opposite R of REVENUE (Th. A4) |
| | 4/9 | White spot on right-hand frame line by first E of REVENUE (Th. B67) |
| | 7/2 | Small dot on leaf to right of E of POSTAGE (Th. E2) |
| | 7/11 | Small coloured flaw in background of oval frame opposite VE of REVENUE (Th. C5) |
| | 8/6 | Small white flaw to right of dragon's left hind foot (Th. H5) |
| | 11/7 | Coloured spot in left-hand margin opposite P of POSTAGE (opposite Th. A1) |
| | 12/2 | Retouch on Queen's chin (Th. D3) |
| | 12/6 | White flaw over Queen's upper lip (Th. D3) |
| | 16/10 | Small coloured flaw on Queen's shoulder just above collar (Th. E4) |

**Sold Out:** 4.70

**1968 (4 September). 4d. Change of colour. No watermark. Chalky paper. PVA gum. One centre phosphor band reacting violet**

XW8 (=SG W9)

| | | Mint | Used |
|---|---|---|---|
| 4d. | Olive-sepia | 15 | 15 |
| a. | White spot before E of POSTAGE (No dot, R. 17/12) | 25·00 | |
| b. | White spot after E of POSTAGE (No dot, R. 18/10) | 25·00 | |
| c. | Bump on dragon's head (No dot, R. 19/2) | 20·00 | |
| d. | White spot above dragon's hind leg (No dot, R. 20/1) | 20·00 | |

For illustrations of Nos. XW8a/d, see Nos. XW7a/d.
Note. Varieties XW8a/b were later retouched.

**Cylinder Numbers (Blocks of Six)**
Perforation Type A (E/I)

| Cylinder No. | No Dot | Dot |
|---|---|---|
| 2 | 22·00* | 3·00 |

**Minor Constant Flaws:** As for No. XW7

**1969 (26 February). 4d. Further change of colour. No watermark. Chalky paper. PVA Gum. One centre phosphor band reacting violet**

XW9 (=SG W10)

| | | Mint | Used |
|---|---|---|---|
| 4d. | Bright vermilion | 15 | 15 |
| ✓ a. | Phosphor omitted | 2·00 | |
| b. | Bump on dragon's head (No dot, R. 19/2) | 20·00 | |

**Cylinder Numbers (Blocks of Six)**
Perforation Type A (E/I)

| Cylinder No. | No Dot | Dot |
|---|---|---|
| 2 | 22·00* | 3·00 |

**Minor Constant Flaws**
Cyl. 2 As for flaws on No. XW7 except that flaw on R. 13/2 has been retouched
Cyl. 2. As for flaws on No. XW7 except that the following were retouched, R. 7/2, 8/6 and 12/6

## ■ **5d. Type XW1 (1968)**

## ■ **6d. Type XW2 (1958–62)**

**1968 (4 September). 5d. No watermark. Chalky paper. PVA Gum. Two 9·5 mm. phosphor bands reacting violet**

**XW10** (=SG W11)

|  | Mint | Used |
|---|---|---|
| 5d. Royal blue | 15 | 15 |
| a. Phosphor omitted | 3·00 | |

**Cylinder Numbers (Blocks of Six)**
Perforation Type A (E/I)

| Cylinder No. | No Dot | Dot |
|---|---|---|
| 2 | 3·00 | 3·00 |

**Phosphor Cylinder number**: Ph 1 found on cyl. 2 dot, right margin

**Minor Constant Flaws**

| Cyl. 2 | 2/3 | Coloured spot in background of oval frame just above central cross of diadem (Th. A3) |
|---|---|---|
| | 16/5 | Coloured flaws in background of oval frame to left of Queen's nose (Th. C–D2) |
| | 20/4 | White flaw on bottom frame line below dragon's left hind foot (Th. H4) |

**1958 (29 September). 6d. Watermark crowns**

**A. Cream Paper**
**XW11**

|  | Mint | Used |
|---|---|---|
| 6d. Deep claret | 1·75 | 70 |

**B. Whiter Paper (18 July 1962)**
**XW12** (=SG W3)

|  | | |
|---|---|---|
| 6d. Reddish purple | 35 | 30 |

**Cylinder Numbers (Blocks of Six)**

**Cream Paper (No XW11)**

|  |  | Perforation Types | |
|---|---|---|---|
| Cylinder No. | No Dot | B(I/P) | C (E/P) |
| 2 | | 16·00 | 16·00 |

**Whiter Paper (No XW12)**

|  |  | Perforation Types | | |
|---|---|---|---|---|
| Cylinder No. | No Dot | B(I/P) | C (E/P) | F(L)(I/E) |
| 3 | | 6·00 | 6·00 | 6·00 |

**Minor Constant Flaw**
Cyl. 3 16/4 Coloured spot on dragon's tail (Th. F5)

**Imprimatur from the National Postal Museum Archives**
Cream paper. Imperforate, watermark Type W.24

| Watermark upright | £2000 |
|---|---|

**Quantity Sold**: 66,754,200

**Sold Out**: 3.68

■ **9d. Type XW2 (1967)**

**1967 (1 March). 9d. Watermark crowns. Two 9·5 mm. phosphor bands reacting violet**

XW13 (=SG W4)

|  | Mint | Used |
|---|---|---|
| 9d.  Bronze-green | 40 | 35 |
| a.  Phosphor omitted | £350 | |

**Cylinder Number (Block of Six)**
Single pane cylinder. Perforation Type F (L) (I/E)

| Cylinder No. | No Dot | Dot |
|---|---|---|
| 1 | 4·75 | |

**Imprimatur from the National Postal Museum Archives**
Imperforate, watermark Type W.24

| Watermark upright | £2000 |
|---|---|

●━━━━━━━━━━━━━

■ **1s.3d. Type XW3 (1958-64)**

**1958 (29 September). 1s.3d. Watermark crowns**

**A. Cream Paper**
XW15

|  | Mint | Used |
|---|---|---|
| 1s.3d.  Green | 5·00 | 1·75 |

**B. Whiter Paper (11 May 1964)**
XW15 (=SG W5)

|  | Mint | Used |
|---|---|---|
| 1s.3d.  (1) Myrtle-green | 5·00 | 90 |
| (2) Deep dull green | 40 | 40 |
| (3) Deep myrtle-green | 2·00 | 75 |

**Cylinder Numbers (Blocks of Six)**

**Cream Paper (No XW14)**
Perforation Type A (E/I)

| Cylinder No. | No Dot B (I/P) | Dot C (E/P) |
|---|---|---|
| 1 | 45·00 | 45·00 |

**Whiter Paper (No XW15)**
Perforation Type A (E/I)

| Cylinder No. | No Dot F (L)(I/E) | Dot |
|---|---|---|
| 2 | 10·00 | |
| 3 | 4·75 | |

**Imprimatur from the National Postal Museum Archives**
Cream paper. Imperforate, watermark Type W.24

| Watermark upright | £2000 |
|---|---|

**Sold Out:** 7.70.

●━━━━━━━━━━━━━

## ■ 1s.6d. Type XW3 (1967-69)

### 1967 (1 March). 1s.6d. Watermark crowns. Two 9·5 mm. phosphor bands reacting violet

**XW16** (=SG W6)

|  | Mint | Used |
|---|---|---|
| 1s.6d. Grey-blue | 40 | 40 |
| a. Phosphor omitted | 50·00 | |

**Cylinder Number (Block of Six)**
Single pane cylinder. Perforation Type F (L) (I/E)

| Cylinder No. | No Dot | Dot |
|---|---|---|
| 1 | 4·75 | |

**Minor Constant Flaws**

| Cyl. 1 | 3/11 | Small dot in top of left fork of V of REVENUE |
|---|---|---|
| | 6/7 | Coloured flaw in base of second E of REVENUE |
| | 10/1 | Small dot on upper right-hand leaf of leek (Th. F6) |
| | 10/3 | Small coloured flaw on Queen's neck (Th. D4) |
| | 15/9 | Retouch on Queen's shoulder just above collar (Th. E4) |

**Imprimatur from the National Postal Museum Archives**
Imperforate, watermark Type W.24
Watermark upright

### 1969 (August 1). 1s.6d. No Watermark. Chalky paper. PVA Gum. Two 9·5 mm. phosphor bands reacting violet

**XW17** (=SG W12)

|  | Mint | Used |
|---|---|---|
| 1s.6d. Grey-blue | 3·50 | 3·50 |

**Cylinder Number (Block of Six)**
Single pane cylinder. Perforation Type F (L) (1/E)

| Cylinder No. | No Dot | Dot |
|---|---|---|
| 1 | 40·00 | |

**Minor Constant Flaws:** As for No. XW16

**Imprimatur from the National Postal Museum Archives**
Chalky paper, imperforate

| No watermark | £2000 |
|---|---|

### Presentation Pack

| XWPP1 | (9.12.70) | Six stamps | 4·00 |
|---|---|---|---|

Comprises Nos. XW4, 8/10, 13 and 16.

**Quantity Sold:** 32,964

**Withdrawn:** 25.11.71

### First Day Covers

| XWFC1 | (1.3.67) | 9d., 1s.6d. | 4·00 |
|---|---|---|---|
| XWFC2 | (4.9.68) | 4d., 5d. | 3·00 |

### Presentation Pack (Six Regions)

| XPP1 | (Issued 1960) | Twelve values | £100 |
|---|---|---|---|

The issued pack contained one each of the ordinary 3d., 6d. and 1s.3d. stamps from Northern Ireland, Scotland and Wales and Monmouthshire and one each of the ordinary 3d. stamps from Guernsey, Jersey and the Isle of Man together with 6-page printed leaflet describing the stamps.
Two forms of the pack exist:
(a)     Inscribed 7s. 3d. for sale in the U.K. and
(b)     Inscribed $1.20 for sale in the U.S.A.

# SECTION ZA

Postage Due Stamps
1954-69 (Typographed) and 1968-1971 (Gravure)

## General Notes

**Introduction.** These stamps generally fulfilled two functions: the lower values, inscribed POSTAGE DUE, were affixed to understamped and unstamped correspondence by the Post Office, to indicate to the postman and to the addressee the amount which was to be collected on delivery (usually twice the excess). The higher values, inscribed TO PAY, were affixed to mail from abroad for the collection of customs charges. The same basic stamp design was in continual use from 1914 until 1971.

**Printers.** All the Postage Due stamps were typographed by Harrison & Sons with the exception of the 4d. and 8d. values of 1969 and 1968 respectively which were printed in photogravure.

They were printed on sheet-fed machines in single panes of 240 each arranged in twelve rows of twenty stamps and this applies to both printing processes.

**Paper.** As with the Wilding definitives, for about the first ten years the Postage Due stamps were printed on a creamy paper but starting in 1964 a whiter paper was gradually introduced as new printings were made. See the General Notes for Section S for further information. Exceptionally, the 2s.6d. to £1 values were always printed on a yellow paper which did not change its appearance.

From 1968 unwatermarked chalk-surfaced paper, as used for the Machin definitives, was introduced for a number of values.

**Watermarks.** These were used as follows:

| | |
|---|---|
| W.22 Tudor Crown | Nos. Z1/6 (1954–55) |
| W.23 St. Edward's Crown | Nos. Z7/16 (1955–57) |
| W.24 Crowns | Nos. Z17/37 (1959–64) |
| No watermark | No. Z38 onwards (1968–69) |

See the General Notes for Section S for illustrations of these.

The watermarks are *always* sideways and *when seen from the front of the stamp* the normal watermark has the top of the Crowns pointing to left. In cases where the sheets were fed into the press the wrong way round (sideways inverted), the watermark appears as sideways with the Crowns pointing to right *when seen from the front of the stamp.*

**Gum.** This was used as follows:

| | |
|---|---|
| Gum Arabic | Nos. Z1/39 (1954–68) |
| PVA Gum | No. Z40 onwards (1968–69) |

The distinction between gum arabic and PVA gum is explained in the General Notes relating to Section UA.

**Perforation.** All values are comb perforated 14 × 15. The perforation types used are given following each issue, and are described and illustrated in Appendix G. In the photogravure-printed values the cylinder numbers are listed and priced according to the type of perforator used. The typographed issues do not have plate numbers.

**Date of issue.** The dates given are those on which the stamps were first issued by the Supplies Dept. to postmasters except in the case of dates for changes to chalky paper or to PVA gum when we have usually quoted dates of release by the Philatelic Bureaux.

**Sheet markings.** Compared with other stamps the Postage Due stamps show very few markings.

**Cylinder Numbers.** These only occur on the photogravure-printed stamps, opposite Row 11 No. 1 (4d.) or opposite Row 10 No. 1 (8d.). They are similar in style to the illustration in Section S.

**Marginal Arrows.** These are "W" shaped at top and bottom of the sheet only. They appear solid (typographed issues) or photo-etched (photogravure issues) as illustrated in Section S.

**Marginal Rule.** This occurs on all four sheet margins in the typographed issues only. It is similar in style to the Narrow Rule illustration in Section S. In the 1½d., 6d., 5s., 10s. and £1 values an additional 1 mm. square appears at each corner of the sheet thus giving a neater appearance.

Morse Code marking                    Cross

**Other Markings.** On the typographed issues Morse Code markings as illustrated appear opposite rows 6/7 at both sides of the sheet. These are possibly allied to the way in which the printing plate is fixed to the press.

In photogravure issues the Morse Code markings are replaced by a cross as illustrated. These are often trimmed off.

> **Watermarks.** The normal sideways watermark *when seen from the front of the stamp* has the top of the Crowns pointing to left.

**Z1**. POSTAGE DUE

**Z2**. TO PAY

---

**1954-55. Type Z1 and Z2 (2s.6d.). Typographed. Watermark Tudor crown, Type W.22, sideways**

**Z1** (=SG D40)

|  | Mint | Used |
|---|---|---|
| ½d.  Bright Orange (8.6.55) | 7·00 | 5·25 |
| a.  Wmk. Crown to right | 12·00 | |

**Z2** (=SG D41)

| 2d.  Agate (28.7.55) | 26·00 | 23·00 |
|---|---|---|
| a.  Wmk. Crown to right | | |

**Z3** (=SG D42)

| 3d.  Violet (4.5.55) | 75·00 | 60·00 |
|---|---|---|

**Z4** (=SG D43)

| 4d.  Blue (14.7.55) | 26·00 | 32·00 |
|---|---|---|
| a.  Imperf. (pair) | £250 | |

**Z5** (=SG D44)

| 5d.  Yellow-brown (19.5.55) | 20·00 | 20·00 |
|---|---|---|

**Z6** (=SG D45)

| 2s.6d.  Purple/yellow (.11.54) | £150 | 5·75 |
|---|---|---|
| a.  Wmk. Crown to right | | |

**Perforation Type**
Type A, all values

**Imprimaturs from the National Postal Museum Archives**

| Imperforate, watermark Type W.22 (sideways) | |
|---|---|
| ½d., 2d., 3d., 4d., 5d. | £2000 each |
| Perf. 14 × 15, watermark Type W.22 (sideways) 2s.6d. | £2000 |

---

**1955-57. Type Z1 and Z2 (2s.6d., 5s.). Typographed, Watermark St. Edward's Crown, Type W.23, sideways**

**Z7** (=SG D46)

|  | Mint | Used |
|---|---|---|
| ½d.  Orange (16.7.56) | 2·75 | 3·25 |
| a.  Wmk. Crown to right | 12·00 | |

**Z8** (=SG D47)

| 1d.  Violet-blue (7.6.56) | 5·00 | 1·50 |
|---|---|---|

**Z9** (=SG D48)

| 1½d.  Green (13.2.56) | 8·50 | 7·00 |
|---|---|---|
| a.  Wmk. Crown to right | 15·00 | |
| b.  Stop after THREE (Row 1) | 15·00 | |

**Z10** (=SG D49)

| 2d.  Agate (22.5.56) | 45·00 | 3·50 |
|---|---|---|

**Z11** (=SG D50)

| 3d.  Violet (5.3.56) | 6·00 | 1·50 |
|---|---|---|
| a.  Wmk. Crown to right | 30·00 | |

**Z12** (=SG D51)

| 4d.  Blue (24.4.56) | 25·00 | 6·00 |
|---|---|---|
| a.  Wmk. Crown to right | 35·00 | |

**Z13** (=SG D52)

| 5d.  Brown-ochre (23.3.56) | 26·00 | 20·00 |
|---|---|---|

**Z14** (=SG D53)

| 1s.  Ochre (22.11.55) | 65·00 | 2·25 |
|---|---|---|
| a.  Wmk. Crown to right | | |

**Z15** (=SG D54)

| 2s.6d.  Purple/yellow (28.6.57) | £200 | 8·25 |
|---|---|---|
| a.  Wmk. Crown to right | | |

**Z16** (=SG D55)

| 5s.  Scarlet/yellow (25.11.55) | £150 | 32·00 |
|---|---|---|
| a.  Wmk. Crown to right | | |

Stamps from the above issue are known bisected and used for half their face value at the following sorting offices:

| 1d. | Huddersfield (1956), London S.E.D.O. (1957), Beswick, Manchester (1958) |
|---|---|
| 2d. | Eynsham, Oxford (1956), Garelochhead, Helensburgh (1956), Harpenden (1956), Hull (1956), Kingston on Thames (1956), Leicester Square, London W.C. (1956), London W.C. (1956) |
| 3d. | London S.E. (1957) |
| 4d. | Poplar, London E. (1958) |

Z9b Z19a
Stop after THREE. Occurs on most stamps in Row 1

**Perforation Types**
Type A, all values, except that in the case of the 5s. the left-hand sheet margin is perforated through, possibly due to the use of a wider comb-head

**Imprimaturs from the National Postal Museum Archives**

| Imperforate, watermark Type W.23 (sideways) | |
|---|---|
| ½d., 1d., 1½d., 2d., 3d., 4d., 5d., 1s., 2s.6d., 5s. | £2000 each |

---

**1959-70. Type Z1 And Z2 (2s.6d. to £1). Typographed. Watermark crowns, Type W.24, sideways**

**A. Cream Paper**
**Z17** (=SG D56)

|  | Mint | Used |
|---|---|---|
| ½d.  Orange (18.10.61) | 50 | 80 |

**Z18** (=SG D57)

| 1d.  Violet-blue (9.5.60) | 50 | 20 |
|---|---|---|

**Z19** (=SG D58)

| 1½d.  Green (5.10.60) | 2·50 | 2·50 |
|---|---|---|
| a.  Stop after THREE (Row 1) | 12·00 | |

**Z20** (=SG D59)

| 2d.  Agate (14.9.59) | 2·75 | 1·00 |
|---|---|---|

**Z21** (=SG D60)

| 3d.  Violet (24.3.59) | 75 | 25 |
|---|---|---|

**Z22** (=SG D61)

| 4d.  Blue (17.12.59) | 75 | 30 |
|---|---|---|

**Z23** (=SG D62)

| | | | |
|---|---|---|---|
| 5d. | Yellow-brown (6.11.61) | 90 | ·0 |
| a. | Wmk. Crown to right | 28·00 | |

**Z24** (=SG D63)

| | | | |
|---|---|---|---|
| 6d. | Purple (29.3.62) | 1·00 | 1·25 |

**Z25** (=SG D64)

| | | | |
|---|---|---|---|
| 1s. | Ochre (11.4.60) | 3·00 | 50 |

**Z26** (=SG D65)

| | | | |
|---|---|---|---|
| 2s.6d. | Purple/yellow (11.5.61) | 3·00 | 50 |
| a. | Wmk. Crown to right | 9·00 | |

**Z27** (=SG D66)

| | | | |
|---|---|---|---|
| 5s. | Scarlet/yellow (8.5.61) | 8·25 | 1·00 |
| a. | Wmk. Crown to right | 15·00 | |

**Z28** (=SG D67)

| | | | |
|---|---|---|---|
| 10s. | Blue/yellow (2.9.63) | 11·00 | 5·75 |
| a. | Wmk. Crown to right (4.70) | 35·00 | |

**Z29** (=SG D68)

| | | | |
|---|---|---|---|
| £1 | Black/yellow (2.9.63) | 45·00 | 8·25 |

Whilst the 2s.6d. and 5s. already existed with watermark Crown to right further printings were issued in 1970, as also of the 10s., on highly fluorescent paper and with watermark Crown to right. These can only be distinguished by the use of a. u.v. lamp and so are not listed separately.

**B. Whiter Paper**

**Z30** (=SG D56)

| | | | |
|---|---|---|---|
| ½d. | Orange (22.9.64) | 15 | 1·25 |
| a. | Wmk. Crown to right | 2·00 | |

**Z31** (=SG D57)

| | | | |
|---|---|---|---|
| 1d. | Violet-blue (1.3.65) | 15 | 50 |
| a. | Wmk. Crown to right | 16·00 | |

**Z32** (=SG D59)

| | | | |
|---|---|---|---|
| 2d. | Agate (1.3.65) | 1·10 | 50 |
| a. | Wmk. Crown to right | 50·00 | |

**Z33** (=SG D60)

| | | | |
|---|---|---|---|
| 3d. | Violet (1.6.64) | 30 | 30 |
| a. | Wmk. Crown to right | 12·00 | |

**Z34** (=SG D61)

| | | | |
|---|---|---|---|
| 4d. | Blue (3.3.64) | 30 | 30 |
| a. | Wmk. Crown to right | 35·00 | |

**Z35** (=SG D62)

| | | | |
|---|---|---|---|
| 5d. | Yellow-brown (9.6.64) | 45 | 60 |
| a. | Wmk. Crown to right | 5·00 | |

**Z36** (=SG D63)

| | | | |
|---|---|---|---|
| 6d. | Purple (30.1.64) | 50 | 30 |
| a. | Wmk. Crown to right | 45·00 | |

**Z37** (=SG D64)

| | | | |
|---|---|---|---|
| 1s. | Ochre (28.8.64) | 90 | 30 |
| a. | Wmk. Crown to right | 10·00 | |

Stamps from the above issue are known bisected and used for half their face value at the following sorting offices:

| | |
|---|---|
| 1d. | Chieveley, Newbury (December 1962, March 1963), Henlan, Llandyssil (1961), Mayfield (1962), St. Albans (1964) |
| 2d. | Doncaster (?) |

For illustration of No. Z19a, see No. Z9b.

**Perforation Types**
Type A, all values; 2s.6d. also Type A (T).

**Imprimaturs from the National Postal Museum Archives**

Imperforate, watermark Type W.24 (sideways)
Cream paper
½d., 1d., 1½d., 2d., 3d., 4d., 5d., 6d., 1s., 2s.6d.,
5s., 10s., £1                                    £2000 each

**Sold Out:** 1s. 11.68; 2d. 1.69; 4d. 11.69; 3d. 9.71; 6d. 10.71

**Withdrawn.:** The 1½d. was withdrawn from sale to the public on 26.4.65. It had ceased to be issued on 31.1.65 but post offices continued to use existing stocks until exhausted.

●————————

**1968-69. Type Z1. Typographed. No Watermark. Chalky paper**

**A. Gum Arabic**
**Z38** (=SG D69)

| | | Mint | Used |
|---|---|---|---|
| 2d. | Agate (11.4.68) | 75 | 1·00 |

**Z39** (=SG D71)

| | | | |
|---|---|---|---|
| 4dr | Blue (25.4.68) | 1·00 | 1·00 |

**B. PVA Gum**
**Z40** (=SG D69Ev)

| | | | |
|---|---|---|---|
| 2d. | Agate (26.11.68) | 75 | |

**Z41** (=SG D70)

| | | | |
|---|---|---|---|
| 3d. | Violet (5.9.68) | 1·00 | 1·00 |

**Z42** (=SG D71Ev)

| | | | |
|---|---|---|---|
| 4d. | Blue (See footnote) | £1800 | |

**Z43** (=SG D72)

| | | | |
|---|---|---|---|
| 5d. | Orange-brown (3.1.69) | 8·00 | 11·00 |

**Z44** (=SG D73)

| | | | |
|---|---|---|---|
| 6d. | Purple (5.9.68) | 2·25 | 1·75 |

**Z45** (=SG D74)

| | | | |
|---|---|---|---|
| 1s. | Ochre (19.11.68) | 4·00 | 2·50 |

A copy of No. Z42 has been confirmed using infra-red attenuated total reflection spectroscopy, there is no date of issue.

**Perforation Types**
4d., 6d. Type A; other values Type A (T), except that in the case of the 2d. the right-hand sheet margin is perforated through and in the 4d. the left-hand sheet margin is perforated through, both possibly due to the use of a wider comb-head

**1968-69. Type Z1. Smaller format. 21½ × 17½ mm. Photogravure. No watermark. Chalky paper. PVA gum**

**Z46** (=SG D75)

| | | | |
|---|---|---|---|
| 4d. | Blue (12.6.69) | 7·00 | 6·75 |

**Z47** (=SG D76)

| | | | |
|---|---|---|---|
| 8d. | Red (3.10.68) | 50 | 1·00 |

**Cylinder Numbers** (Block of Four (4d.) or Six (8d.))
Perforation Type A (T) (E/P)

| | Cylinder No. | No dot |
|---|---|---|
| 4d. | 1 | 35·00 |
| 8d. | 1 | 5·00 |

On the 8d. the cylinder number appears as I.

**Imprimaturs from the National Postal Museum Archives**

| | |
|---|---|
| Chalky paper, imperforate. No watermark | |
| 2d., 3d., 4d., 5d., 6d., 8d., 1s. | £2000 each |

Stamps from the above issue are known bisected and used for half their face value at the following sorting offices:

| | |
|---|---|
| 4d. | Northampton (1970) |
| 6d. | Kilburn, London N.W. (1968) |

# APPENDIX G
Perforators

## General Notes

**Introduction.** Basically, two kinds of perforating machines were used for British stamps listed in this catalogue, 1952–70: sheet-fed and reel-fed. The sheet-fed machines generally employ a two-row comb and the reel-fed machines a three-row or four–row comb. Both kinds are full width, i.e. they are able to perforate two panes side by side.

Types A to H and J are the different sheet perforation types recorded in this catalogue, produced either by the sheet-fed or the reel-fed machines but they should not be regarded as representing the use of ten different machines, rather they are ten different sheet perforation types produced by various perforating machines.

Types E, E (½v) (from sheets), I, Ie, I (½v), AP, AP(2E) and P relate to booklet panes.

**Guide Holes.** Perforation guide holes can be an indication of the type of perforator used and these are recorded, where known, following the sheet perforation characteristics for each type. For reasons unknown these may not always appear in the sheet margins.

**ORDER.** This Appendix is divided into four sections:

1. Low Value Definitive Stamps (including Regionals and Postage Due Stamps)
2. High Value Definitive Stamps
3. Special Issues
4. Booklet Panes

**Illustrations.** The illustrations are all from definitive stamps but they are equally representative of the High Value and Special issues where the same types occur.

**Table of Perforation Types.** The useful tabulated list of Perforation Types at the end of this Appendix is primarily designed to be used for Special issues, although, the first part may also be used in conjunction with the Low and High Value definitive stamps for Types A, A (T), B, C, E (no dot panes only).

## 1. Low Value Definitive Stamps

This section deals with the small size Wilding and Machin definitives, the Regionals and the Postage Due Stamps.

**Type A.** Horizontal two-row comb. Sheet-fed.

No dot and dot panes

| | |
|---|---|
| Top margin | Perforated through |
| Bottom margin | Imperforate |
| Left margin | A single extension hole |
| Right margin | A single extension hole |
| Guide holes | Opposite rows 14/15, at left (no dot panes) or right (dot panes) |

In this machine an appropriate number of sheets (usually six to eight) are impaled through the guide holes and they go forward together under the comb. The imperf. margin (at the bottom) indicates the point of entry.

**Type A (T).** Horizontal two-row comb. Sheet-fed.

Single pane printing

| | |
|---|---|
| Top margin | Imperforate |
| Bottom margin | Perforated through |
| Left margin | A single extension hole |
| Right margin | A single extension hole |
| Guide holes | None |

This is simply a top (T) instead of a bottom feed of Type A. In the definitive stamps it only occurs in the Postage Due Stamps. Cylinder blocks are identical in appearance with Type C.

**Types B and C.** Horizontal three-row comb. Reel-fed.

Type B. No dot panes

| | |
|---|---|
| Top margin | Perforated through |
| Bottom margin | Perforated through |
| Left margin | Imperforate |
| Right margin | A single extension hole |
| Guide holes | Usually opposite rows 1, 7/8 and 14/15 at both sides of pane |

Type C. No dot and dot panes

| | |
|---|---|
| Top margin | Perforated through |
| Bottom margin | Perforated through |
| Left margin | A single extension hole |
| Right margin | Imperforate |
| Guide holes | As Type B, above |

Type B is the left and Type C the right halves of the same reel-fed perforator. The outer ends of the comb are without extension pins, there being only single extension pins in the interpane margin. In this machine the continuous web of paper advances under the comb in a single thickness and without interruption, hence both top and bottom margins are perforated through.

It often happened that two narrow reels were perforated together by placing them side by side on the machine so that single pane printings (i.e. no dot panes only) occur perforated with Type B and also Type C. It is only when double pane printings are perforated on this machine that no dot panes will always be Type B and dot panes will always be Type C, except that in the Special issues, the 4d. Scout Jamboree stamp from Cyl. 1 dot is known with perforation Type B and Type C.

**Type E.** Horizontal two-row comb. Sheet-fed.

| No dot panes | Top margin | Perforated through |
|---|---|---|
| | Bottom margin | Imperforate |
| | Left margin | A single extension hole on alternate rows only |
| | Right margin | A single extension hole |
| | Guide hole | Opposite rows 14/15, at left |
| Dot panes | Top margin | Perforated through |
| | Bottom margin | Imperforate |
| | Left margin | A single extension hole |
| | Right margin | A single extension hole on alternate rows only |
| | Guide hole | Opposite rows 14/15, at right |

This is a simple variation of Type A (q.v.) that may result from the removal of a perforating pin or a repair to a comb-head. Therefore, no dot cylinder blocks are as Type A but left margin has the single extension hole missing on alternate rows.

Cylinder blocks from the dot pane would be indistinguishable from Type A, hence only no dot cylinder blocks are recorded with Type E.

**Type F (L).** Vertical two-row comb. Sheet-fed.

| No dot panes | Top margin | A single extension hole |
|---|---|---|
| | Bottom margin | A single extension hole |
| | Left margin | Imperforate |
| | Right margin | Perforated through |
| | Guide holes | Through marginal arrow above vertical rows 6/7 and below vertical row 10 |

This type perforates from the left (L) through to the right side of the sheet. In this catalogue the use of this type has been restricted to single pane printings (i.e. no dot panes only).

**Type F (L)\*.** Vertical two-row comb. Sheet-fed.

| No dot panes | Top margin | A single extension hole |
|---|---|---|
| | Bottom margin | A single extension hole |
| | Left margin | Imperforate |
| | Right margin | Perforated through |
| | Guide holes | Above and below eighth vertical row |
| Dot panes | Top margin | A single extension hole |
| | Bottom margin | A single extension hole |
| | Left margin | Perforated through |
| | Right margin | Perforated through |
| | Guide holes | None (occur on no dot panes only) |

This is the same perforator as used for Type F (L) and it is given in this catalogue when double pane printings (i.e. no dot and dot panes) have been perforated together prior to their being guillotined into single sheets. This gives no dot cylinder blocks exactly as Type F (L) but because the vertical comb has perforated horizontally from left to right across both panes the interpane margin is also perforated and, therefore, the dot cylinder blocks are perforated through the left margin.

**Type H.** Horizontal two-row comb. Sheet-fed.

| No dot panes | Top margin | Perforated through |
|---|---|---|
| | Bottom margin | Imperforate |
| | Left margin | A single extension hole |
| | Right margin | Perforated through |
| | Guide hole | Opposite rows 14/15, at left |
| Dot panes | Top margin | Perforated through |
| | Bottom margin | Imperforate |
| | Left margin | Perforated through |
| | Right margin | A single extension hole |
| | Guide hole | Opposite rows 14/15, at right |

This is a further variation of Type A (q.v.) differing by the fact that the interpane margin is perforated through instead of there being single extension holes at the end of every row at right on the no dot pane and at the end of every row at left on the dot pane. Therefore, dot cylinder blocks are as Type A but left margin is perforated through. Cylinder blocks from the no dot pane would be indistinguishable from Type A, hence only dot cylinder blocks are recorded with Type H.

**Type J.** Vertical two-row comb. Sheet-fed.

| Single pane printing | Top margin | A single extension hole |
|---|---|---|
| | Bottom margin | Perforated through |
| | Left margin | Imperforate |
| | Right margin | Perforated through |
| | Guide holes | Through marginal arrow above vertical rows 6/7 and below vertical row 10 |

This is similar to Type F (L) (q.v.), except that the bottom sheet margin is perforated through instead of there being only a single extension hole at the end of every row. Cylinder blocks are identical in appearance with Type B.

Type A No Dot and Dot panes

Type SB and J Left or No Dot pane

Types F(L) and F(L)* (no dot panes)

Types C and A (T) Right or Dot pane

Type F(L)* (dot panes) and Type F (no dot panes)

## 2. High Value Definitive Stamps

This section deals with the Wilding and Machin High Value stamps.

### Wilding High Values

Perforation Type A, as described at the beginning of this Appendix, was used exclusively for these stamps. Waterlow and De La Rue both used a single-row comb and Bradbury, Wilkinson a two-row comb.

The guide holes appear opposite row 6, at left on left-hand panes and at right on right-hand panes.

For diagram showing printers guide marks see the General Notes for Section T.

### Machin £.s.d. High Values

The printer's sheet was perforated with Type A prior to being guillotined into four panes, so that the characteristics of each individual Post Office pane are different and this has, therefore, been described as perforation Type A*. The description of Type A, given at the beginning of this Appendix, applies equally to Type A*, except that Bradbury, Wilkinson used a single-row comb.

For diagram showing the printer's sheet, the method of perforation and the position of plate numbers and guide holes see the General Notes for Section UC.

## 3. Special Issues

**Type A.** In the special issues this type is exactly as described at the beginning of this Appendix except that with single pane printings (i.e. no dot panes only) the guide holes are opposite rows 14/15, at both sides of the sheet.

**Type A (T).** In the special issues this type is exactly as described at the beginning of this Appendix and it applies equally to both no dot and dot panes. Guide holes very rarely appear in the sheet margins but where they do this is given under Sheet Details in Section W.

**Types B and C.** In the special issues these types are exactly as described in the first part of this Appendix.

**Type E.** Horizontal two-row comb. Sheet-fed.

| | | |
|---|---|---|
| Right-hand panes | *Top margin* | Perforated through |
| | *Bottom margin* | Imperforate |
| | *Left margin* | A single extension hole on alternate rows only |
| | *Right margin* | A single extension hole |
| | *Guide hole* | Opposite rows 14/15, at right |

This is a variation of Type A that may result from the removal of a perforating pin or a repair to a comb-head. Therefore, cylinder blocks are as Type A but left margin has the single extension hole missing on alternate rows.

This type is only known on the 1s.3d. Freedom from Hunger and the 3d. Red Cross on the right-hand panes only (i.e. dot cylinder pane of 3d. Red Cross). The left-hand panes in both cases are believed to be Type A.

Perforation Type E did not affect the cylinder blocks of the 1s.3d. Freedom from Hunger issue as the cylinder numbers were placed at bottom right corner of each pane, at the opposite side of the left margin perforated with alternate extension holes.

**Types F and F (L).** Vertical single-row comb. Sheet-fed. Single pane printings.

| | | |
|---|---|---|
| Type F. Right feed | *Top margin* | A single extension hole |
| | *Bottom margin* | A single extension hole |
| | *Left margin* | Perforated through |
| | *Right margin* | Imperforate |
| Type F (L). Left feed | *Top margin* | A single extension hole |
| | *Bottom margin* | A single extension hole |
| | *Left margin* | Imperforate |
| | *Right margin* | Perforated through |

Type F perforates from the right through to the left side of the sheet and Type F (L) perforates from the left through to the right side of the sheet. Both types are used for single pane printings (i.e. no dot panes only). Guide holes very rarely appear in the sheet margins but where they do this is given under Sheet Details in Section W.

**Type G.** Vertical single-row comb. Sheet-fed.

| | | |
|---|---|---|
| No dot and dot panes | *Top margin* | Perforated through |
| | *Bottom margin* | Perforated through |
| | *Left margin* | Perforated through |
| | *Right margin* | Imperforate |
| | *Guide holes* | None |

This was a special perforator used exclusively for the 6d. Battle of Hastings issue. The cylinder block is perforated through in both the bottom and left margins.

## Table of Special Issue Perforation Types

The table below combines a list of the different sheet perforation types recorded in Section W, together with the characteristics of the four sheet margins. Following the basic perforation type the characteristics given relate to the sheet viewed with the stamps the right way up.

The identification of a particular perforation type from a cylinder block (or any corner block) can easily be established by referring to this table in conjunction with the recorded types under Cylinder Numbers in Section W.

Whilst this table is mainly designed to be used for the special stamps, the first part may also be used in conjunction with the Low and High Value definitive stamps for Types A, A (T), B, C, E (no dot panes only) and F (L).

### I. Horizontal Format Stamps

| Perforation Type | Top margin | Bottom margin | Left margin | Right margin |
|---|---|---|---|---|
| **Type A** (bottom feed) | Perforated through | Imperforate | Single extension hole | Single extension hole |
| **Type A (T)** (top feed) | Imperforate | Perforated through | Single extension hole | Single extension hole |
| **Type B** | Perforated through | Perforated through | Imperforate | Single extension hole |
| **Type C** | Perforated through | Perforated through | Single extension hole | Imperforate |
| **Type E** | Perforated through | Imperforate | Single extension hole alternate rows only | Single extension hole |
| **Type F** (right feed) | Single extension hole | Single extension hole | Perforated through | Imperforate |
| **Type F (L)** (left feed) | Single extension hole | Single extension hole | Imperforate | Perforated through |
| **Type G** | Perforated through | Perforated through | Perforated through | Imperforate |

### II. Vertical Format Stamps*

| Perforation Type | Top margin | Bottom margin | Left margin | Right margin |
|---|---|---|---|---|
| **Type A** (head to right) | Single extension hole | Single extension hole | Perforated through | Imperforate |
| **Type A** (head to left) | Single extension hole | Single extension hole | Imperforate | Perforated through |
| **Type A (T)** (head to right) | Single extension hole | Single extension hole | Imperforate | Perforated through |
| **Type A (T)** (head to left) | Single extension hole | Single extension hole | Perforated through | Imperforate |
| **Type B** (head to right) | Single extension hole | Imperforate | Perforated through | Perforated through |
| **Type C** (head to right) | Imperforate | Single extension hole | Perforated through | Perforated through |
| **Type F** (head to right) | Imperforate | Perforated through | Single extension hole | Single extension hole |

*The position of the head on vertical format stamps is determined by viewing the sheet with the marginal rule (normally on a short side) at the bottom. In most instances the head (or top of the stamp) is to the right; the head to the left occurring on the 3d. Post Office Tower, 4d. World Football Cup, 4d. World Cup Victory and the 3d. and 1s.6d. 1966 Christmas issue, although the latter does not in fact bear marginal rules but it should be regarded as being head to left.

From the 1966 Christmas issue onwards many sheets did not bear marginal rules. Where this is the case with vertical format designs the correct orientation of the sheets to determine the perforation type is given below the Cylinder Numbers in the listings.

Exceptionally, the 1967 British Paintings 4d. and the British Discovery and Inventions 1s.9d. show the marginal rule on a long side and this should be orientated to the left-hand side to show perforation Types A (T) (head to right) and F (head to right) respectively.

## 4. Booklet Panes

### (a) Panes of Four

Type I

Type I(½v)

Type AP

Type P

| | |
|---|---|
| **Type I.** | Margin imperforate |
| **Type I(½v).** | Ditto but with slanting cut at left or right (left illustrated) |
| **Type AP.** | Margin perforated through but alternate rows imperforate |
| **Type AP(2E)** | Margin perforated alternate rows, but two extension holes only |
| **Type P.** | Margin fully perforated through every row |

In order to facilitate access to the bottom selvedge of sheets with sideways watermark panes (and a side selvedge for Holiday Booklet (NR1/1a), which was torn off by hand, a slanting scissor cut was made in the imperforate trimmed margin. This pane is termed I(½v). The vertical perforations below the cut must be torn, and not guillotined, for the pane to be authentic.

Panes of four with Type AP(2E) occur in the majority of issues with sideways watermark. This was caused by the main perforator having a pin missing from the bottom line of the comb in the margin adjacent to stamps in column 12 of the sheet, resulting in Type AP(2E) perforations on 12 panes in each sheet.

### (b) Panes of Six

Type I

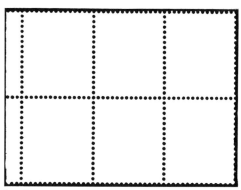

Type P

**Type I.**  Margin imperforate
**Type Ie.**  Margin with extnsion hole set wide
**Type P.**  Margin every row perforated through

Generally, all panes of six were rotary printed in double sheets and perforated in the web, resulting in Type I and Ie. Exceptionally, UB3 and UB4 were printed in single sheets and sheet perforated, UB3 in Type I, later changed to type P and UB4 in Type P' only.

Both the 20-row and the 21-row sheets perforated with Type I come with an extension holes in the margin between the no dot and dot row. The 20-row sheets, giving rise to Type Ie. were perforated with a three-row comb, so that panes can be found with traces of the inter-pane extension hole at the top, in the middle or at the bottom of the binding margin. After the change to 21-row sheets a four-row comb was used and on these panes the extension hole can be found at the top or at the bottom of the margin only. As an aid to identification, all dot cylinder panes should have traces of the extension hole. We do not distinguish these sub-types of perforation.

On 21-row sheets the perforated web is cut at every 20th row to make sheets of 480 (two panes of 240 (20 × 12)). Consequently on successive sheets the cylinder number appears one row lower so that a pane can have it adjoining the top or bottom row. In the listing of cylinder panes the letter "T" after the cylinder number indicates that it is a pane with the cylinder number adjoining the top row.

**(c) Panes of Fifteen**
These come from the £1 Stamps for Cooks booklet and are all perforated Type I.

**(d) Panes of Two**

Type E(½v)

**Type E.**  Extension hole in the margin in each row
**Type E(½v).**  Ditto but with slanting cut at top or bottom (bottom illustrated)
**Type I.**  Margin imperforate
**Type I(½v).**  Ditto but with slanting cut at top or bottom

The panes of two stamps were made up from columns 1 and 2 of counter sheets. The vertical sheet margin was guillotined leaving a narrow binding margin which was either imperforate or showed an extension hole at the top and bottom of the

binding margin. In addition, both types exist with the slanting scissor cut already described under section (a) of these notes. Panes with this form of separation show torn and not guillotined perforations below the cut.

# APPENDIX HA
Post Office Booklets of Stamps

## General Notes

This appendix is divided into the following sections:

A. Wilding Issues in Non-pictorial Types of Booklet Covers (1953-68)
B. Machin Pre-decimal Issues with Violet Phosphor Bands. Non-pictorial and Pictorial Covers (1968-70)

The booklets are listed in value and date order except for the 2 shilling booklets for Holiday Resorts (1963/64) and Christmas Cards (1965) which follow the ordinary 2s. booklets. The £1 booklet Stamps for Cooks containing Machin issues is at the end of the section. All booklets, except No. ZP1 which was stapled, had stitched panes. Most of the £1 booklets were stitched and these are listed under No. ZP1a.

**Booklet sheet arrangement.** Booklets are made up from specially printed sheets which are differently arranged from Post Office counter sheets in order to facilitate manufacture, with the binding margin on the left, so that all booklets open at the right. The arrangement of the sheet varies according to the size and format of the booklet pane required. For example, in the case of booklet panes of six, the printers sheet of 480 stamps, consisting of two panes (no dot and dot) each of 240 stamps arranged in twenty rows of twelve stamps, has additional gutters provided between the 6th and 7th vertical rows in both panes, and the stamps in the 4th, 5th and 6th, and 10th, 11th and 12th vertical rows in both panes are inverted in relation to the others (i.e. *tête-bêche*). Two horizontal rows of the sheet (producing eight booklets) would be arranged thus:

| NO DOT PANE | | DOT PANE | |
|---|---|---|---|
| ↑ 1239S↓ | GUTTER 1239S↓ | 1239S↓ | GUTTER 1239S↓ ← |
| Watermark 456ε21 | GUTTER 456ε21 | 456ε21 | GUTTER 456ε21 ← |

↑ ↑ ↑ ↑ ↑ ↑ ↑

The sheets of stamps, interleaving sheets and covers are stitched vertically, once at the two outer edges of the double pane and twice in each of the gutters as shown by the vertical rules in the diagram. Finally, the booklets are guillotined both horizontally and vertically as indicated by the arrows. This stitching and quilotining of the mass of booklets is done after the sheet has been divided into the no dot and dot panes, resulting in 40 complete booklets at a time.

**Inverted watermarks.** From the diagram it is easy to see how 50% of Wilding booklet stamps have inverted watermarks.

**Watermark positions.** Although 50% of booklet panes of six have the watermark inverted, in describing the contents of the booklets reference is made to the catalogue numbers in section SA of the stamps with upright watermark throughout the list. This is to avoid continual reference to the catalogue numbers of the inverted watermarks. Also this applies to some booklets with oanes of four and similarly, for panes of four with sideways watermark, reference is made only to the stamp with watermark sideways to the left.

**Whiter paper.** During the changeover period cream and whiter paper stamps could occur in the same booklet and we make no attempt to distinguish these.

***Tête-bêche* errors.** These occur in booklets due to faulty manufacture, usually the result of a corner of the sheet being folded over.

**Errors of make-up.** Such errors exist but we do not list them as it is not difficult to break up booklets and remake them to agree with known errors.

**Booklet covers.** All covers are printed in black except where otherwise stated.

**Booklet cylinder numbers.** These occur in the left-hand margin of both panes (i.e no dot and dot) similar to Post Office counter sheets. They are illustrated in Section S except that they always have prefix letters, e.g. E4, F5, G3, but the letters are liable to be partly or completely trimmed off.

All booklet panes of six printed from 20-row cylinders have the cylinder number adjoining the bottom row of stamps but in the case of 21-row cylinders, the perforated web is cut at every 20th row to make sheets of 480. Consequently, on successive sheets the cylinder number appears one row lower and thus a pane can have it adjoining the top or bottom row.

Booklet panes of four with sideways watermark invariably show the cylinder numbers trimmed, while panes of two (from counter sheets) show cylinder numbers.

Booklet panes of four with upright watermark and Machin panes of four and fifteen have the cylinder numbers trimmed off completely.

**Dates.** The month and year dates are those found printed on the booklets, either on the outer back cover or on the white interleaves. No dates are given on the 1s. booklets, the 2s. booklets Nos. N1/3, the 5s. Philympia booklet No. HP34 and the £1 booklet No. ZP1. The dates of issue of every booklet in a new cover design or composition are given in brackets where known.

**Quantities.** The quantities given are of the numbers manufactured, but some of the figures are shared by two or more booklets and this is indicated in the listing.

**Pattern books.** These were dummy books, including the postal rates panel dated December 1952, with SPACE AVAILABLE FOR COMMERCIAL ADVERTISING printed on the reverse of the front cover, reverse of second end leaf and on both sides of the back cover. The panes of stamps were represented by perforated and gummed labels. In the 2s.6d. booklet the third pane had the three labels in the upper row inscribed 1d. and SPACE AVAILABLE FOR COMMERCIAL ADVERTISING printed in the lower row. The panes in the 2s.6d. book were unwatermarked but those in the 5s. booklet had a large Crown multiple watermark.

The books exist with a red handstamp panel at the top of the front cover stating "This is the pattern (Book A) (Book B)..." inserted in manuscript for the 2s.6d. and 5s. books respectively and they exist without the handstamp, presumably being unsued examples. On the handstamp 5s. booklets the stamp contents were changed in manuscript to the new contents for issues from January 1953.

These pattern books were produced prior to the re-introduction of commercial advertising and were distributed to potential advertising contractors so that they could tender for the appointment as the Post Office advertising contractor for stamp books. This resulted in the appointment of J. Weiner Ltd., who were at the time the advertising contractor for Post Office telephone directories.

**Paste-up books.** The contractor was responsible for selling the advertising space and for the provision of copy to the printer. The commercial printed material was submitted to the Post Office Supplies Department in galley form for approval. These proofs were then used to prepare paste-up examples of each edition, so that the make-up could be checked. If the contractor failed to attract sufficient advertising for an edition, numerous official notices (apart from postal rate information) couold be used to fill up interleaves and covers.

Paste-up books were prepared using a previous advertiser voucher copy by marking the front cover with the new edition date, pasting in proofs of new commercial advertisements and annotating pages with any other changes. Four copies of each paste-up were prepared, three of which were sent to the Post Office Supplies Department, who forwarded one to the printer, Harrison and Sons Ltd. it appears that an additional copy, marked "Duplicate" was prepared by J. Weiner Ltd., making two copies for their records.

Many paste-up books are similar, with new or repeat commercial advertisements. Of particular interest are new series or booklets showing changes in postal rates or changes in the number of interleaves, where previous editions needed to be changed on the front cover or split and stapled with additional copy. This occurred on the changes from the 2s.6d. to the 3s. series (1957/8), the 3s.9d. to the 4s.6d. series (1957) and the 4s.6d. to the 6s. series (1965). Of further interest are paste-up books showing dates that were never issued due to a lack of sales, resulting in cancellation or a change in postal rates or impending decimalisation in February 1971. These more interesting editions are identified in the listings and priced separately. The listing commences with February 1956 as earlier editions are not know. If they exist, earlier editions will be included in future listings

**Advertiser's voucher copy books.** With the re-introduction of commercial qadvertising in September 1953 the Post office advertising contractor began to supply a voucher copy of each edition to the firms whose advertisements appeared in them.

In 1953, the 2s.6d. September, October and November issued books, together with the 5s. September book, were supplied as voucher copies with the stamps torn out. From November 1953, nearly all editions, including the £1 (sewn and without black binding) were made up as voucher copies without the stamp panes. All 1s. And 2s. Holiday and Christmas books had no commercial advertising anda few other editions have not been found as voucher copies.

Of particular interest are the 2s.6d. booklets containing the *se-tenant* pane of three 1d. stamps and three labels. From January 1954 to January 1955 voucher copies of these booklets come with these se-tenant labels shown, but not the stamps. In the January 1954 edition the labels were printed on unwatermarked, ungummed paper, imperforate, but in subsequent editions they are perforated on gummed paper with the Harrison "house" watermark.

Also, the January 1954 edition comes in three types, with the se-tenant pane on medium cream paper or thin buff paper and as a normal voucher copy without the pane. These dummy se-tenant panes are all specific to the voucher copies and do not have proof status.

The scarcer advertisers' voucher copy editions are listed and priced separately and the other editions are listed and priced at the end of each series, in each case being abbreviated to AVC.

**Publicity proofs for pictorial covers.** From March 1968, the Post Office adopted a policy of pictorial covers for all booklets other than the 2s. slot machine editions. In order to publicise this policy, a distribution of 15 designs was made to the press and visitors to the Post Office stand at Stampex held at Central Hall, Westminster, in March 1968. The distribution comprised four 4s.6d. designs, six 6s. designs and five 10s. designs on coloured card relevant to each booklet value and on white glazed art paper, which assisted press reproducing. Generally, these publicity proofs were booklet size, but four art paper proofs were on paper 10cm square.

During the course of production of booklets with pictorial covers from 1968 to 1970, the printers, Harrison and Sons Ltd., produced a variety of booklet cover proofs in advance of booklet issues which show the evolution of the covers. Many of these proofs were provided to the Post Office advertising contractor, J. Weiner Ltd., but were not distributed generally to the press or the public as occurred in March 1968.

Following the loss of the Post Office contract by J. Weiner Ltd., in 1971 and the cessation of commercial advertising in booklets in 1975, this proof material became surplus to requirements and has been dispersed through the philatelic trade. As the material is widely available and collected by booklet specialists, a complete listing of the publicity proofs and related material is provided after the listing of 10s. booklets.

**£1 "Stamps for Cooks" pattern books.** On 31 March 1969, a meeting was held at Postal Headquarters to plan a "bigger" stamp book and Post Office design director, Stuart Rose, was instructed to prepare dummy pattern books for J. Weiner Ltd., the Post Office advertising contractor to use for marketing to prospective advertisers. The pattern books were prepared by Post Office studios on the theme of "Cookery".

They comprised hand-painted front and back card covers, two illustrative stamp panes, two illustrative interleaves and five or six plain interleaves, all to indicate the contents of the proposed book. The front showed cooking ingredients in a label and is inscribed "Stamps for cooks" and "20s." and the back showed a prepared meal. Stamp panes had simulated stamps and text. The pattern books were stapled. At least seven books were produced, all slightly different, some remaining complete and some subsequently exploded for display.

The Milk Marketing Board accepted the proposal using recipes extracted from their Dairy Book of *Home Cookery*. The "Stamms for Cooks" £1 Book was experimental and was first in the series later to become termed "prestige" books.

**Catalogue numbers.** In order to avoid confusion we have used the same booklet numbers as in the Concise Catalogue. Many of these booklets bear the same prefix letters as other stamps listed in the Great Britain Specialised Catalogues so that when quoting numbers in this Appendix it should be made clear that booklets are being referred to.

Varieties shown thus (a) are those listed in the Great Britain Specialised Catalogues only.

**Illustrations.** The illustrations of the covers are ¾ size except where otherwise stated.

> **BOOKLET PRICES.** Prices in this Appendix are for booklets containing panes with "average" perforations (i.e. full perforations on two edges of the pane only). Booklets containing panes with complete perforations are worth more.

**Non-pictorial types of booklet covers**

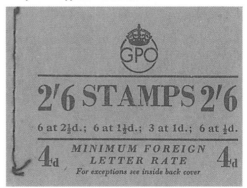

Type A  Circular GPO Cypher

Type B  Oval Type GPO Cypher

Type C  Oval Type GPO Cypher 15 mm wide

Type D  Larger Oval GPO Cypher 17 mm wide

## Section A.
## Wilding Issues

### ◼ 1s. Booklets for use in slot machines

**Booklet Series D**
**Contents:** 4 × 1½d., 4 × 1d., 4 × ½d. in panes of two
I. White Unprinted Cover. Not interleaved. For use in experimental machines
Watermark Tudor Crown (Nos. S1, S13, S25)

| | | |
|---|---|---|
| E1 No date (issued 2.9.53) | 56,650 | 9·25 |

Watermark St. Edward's Crown (Nos. S2, S14, S26)

| | | |
|---|---|---|
| E2 No date (issued 11.57) | 7,180 | 50·00 |
| E2a Ditto Stitched back to front | | £100 |

These booklets were made up from columns 1 and 2 from sheets and so do not have inverted watermarks. D booklet machines were withdrawn in November 1960.

**Booklet Series E**
**Contents:** 4 × 1½d., 4 × 1d., 4 × ½d. in panes of four
II. White Printed Cover as Type B. Not interleaved. For use in F1 machines.

**Watermark Tudor Crown (Nos. S1, S13, S25)**

| | | | |
|---|---|---|---|
| K1 | No date (Back cover MINIMUM FOREIGN LETTER RATE FOUR PENCE) (issued 22.7.54) | 180,360 | 8·00 |
| K1a | No date (Back cover MONEY BY POST) (issued 11.54) | 572,900 | 8·00 |

**Watermark St. Edward's Crown (Nos. S2, S14, S26)**

| | | | |
|---|---|---|---|
| K2 | No date (Back cover £5 only). (issued 5.7.56) | 373,000 | 8·00 |
| K2a | No date (Back cover £10 only. Inland letter rate 2½d.) (issued 6.57) | 532,000 | 8·00 |
| K2b | No date (Back cover £10 only. Inland letter rate 3d.) (issued 8.58) | 541,000 | 8·00 |

**Watermark Crowns (Nos. S4, S16, S28)**

| | | | |
|---|---|---|---|
| K3 | No date (Back cover £10 only. Overseas letter rate 6d.) (issued 13.8.59) | 623,500 | 8·00 |
| K3a | No date (Back cover £10 only. Overseas letter rate 4d.) (issued 10.60) | 250,000 | 9·50 |

1s. booklets continued to be available until 1964. The machines were then converted to issue the thicker 2s. booklets.

## 2s. Booklets for use in slot machines

**Contents:** 4 × 3d., 4 × 1½d., 4 × 1d., 4 × ½d. in panes of four

**I. Salmon Cover as Type B. Fully interleaved**
**Watermark St. Edward's Crown (Nos. S2, S14, S26, S68)**

| | | | |
|---|---|---:|---:|
| N1 | No date (issued 22.4.59) | 452,470 | 9·00 |

**II. Salmon Cover as Type C. Fully interleaved**
**Watermark Crowns (upright) (Nos. S4, S16, S28, S70)**

| | | | |
|---|---|---:|---:|
| N2 | No date (issued 2.11.60) | 300,500 | 10·50 |

**III. Lemon Cover as Type C. Fully interleaved**
**Watermark Crowns (upright) (Nos. S4, S16, S28, S70)**

| | | | |
|---|---|---:|---:|
| N3 | No date (issued 9.2.61) | 1,330,750 | 10·50 |

**Watermark Crowns (sideways)**
(Nos. S4d or S5a, S16e or S17a, S28a or S29a, S70d or S71a) or blue phosphor (Nos. S10b or S11a, S21b or S22a, S33b or S34a, S75b or S76a)

| | | | | |
|---|---|---|---:|---:|
| N 4 | | Apr 1961 (issued 26.5.61) | 1,381,440 | 38·00 |
| | p. | With blue phosphor bands (issued 14.7.61) | 171,400 | 80·00 |
| N 5 | | Sept 1961 | 889,000 | 60·00 |
| N 6 | | Jan 1962 | 911,600 | 55·00 |
| N 7 | | Apr 1962 | 958,600 | 65·00 |
| N 8 | | July 1962 | 935,600 | 60·00 |
| | p. | With blue phosphor bands | 51,600 | £110 |
| N 9 | | Nov 1962 | 975,000 | 80·00 |
| | p. | With blue phosphor bands | 56,000 | £120 |
| N10 | | Jan 1963 | 1,105,400 | 60·00 |
| | p. | With blue phosphor bands | 58,390 | £160 |
| N11 | | Mar 1963 | 1,090,800 | 60·00 |
| N12 | | June 1963 | 1,014,800 | 60·00 |
| | p. | With blue phosphor bands | 57,800 | 95·00 |
| N13 | | Aug 1963 | 989,000 | 60·00 |
| | p. | With blue phosphor bands | 56,400 | 95·00 |
| N14 | | Oct 1963 | 1,018,800 | 60·00 |
| | p. | With blue phosphor bands | 11,200 | £160 |
| N15 | | Feb 1964 | 1,122,400 | 60·00 |
| N 4 | p. | With blue phosphor bands | 76,600 | 95·00 |
| N16 | | June 1964 | 386,570 | 60·00 |
| | p. | With blue phosphor bands | 63,400 | £130 |
| N17 | | Aug 1964 | 122,300 | 80·00 |
| | p. | With blue phosphor bands | 58,800 | £130 |
| N18 | | Oct 1964 | 1,179,800 | 60·00 |
| | p. | With blue phosphor bands | 94,200 | 85·00 |
| N19 | | Dec 1964 | 109,170 | 70·00 |
| | p. | With blue phosphor bands | 34,000 | 85·00 |
| N20 | | Apr 1965 | 1,435,400 | 60·00 |
| | p. | With blue phosphor bands | 40,800 | 80·00 |

2s. booklets in this composition were withdrawn from sale on 31 August 1965
Paste-up books N4 to N20 each £100
AVC books N1 to N20 each 8·00
**Contents changed:** 4 × 4d. in pane of four, 2 × 1d. and 2 × 3d. in pane of four arranged *se-tenant* horizontally
Orange-Yellow Cover as Type C. Printed in black. Fully interleaved

**Watermark Crowns (sideways)**
(Nos. S17a, S71a, S85d) and blue or violet phosphor with one band on 3d. (Nos. S22a, S23d, or S24b; S77b or S78c; S90c, S91b or S92b)

| | | | |
|---|---|---:|---:|
| N21p. | July 1965 (issued 16.8.65) | 2,671,800 | 5·00 |
| | With blue phosphor bands (issued 16.8.65) | 109,600 | 18·00 |
| N22p. | Oct 1965 | 1,852,800 | 5·25 |

| | | | |
|---|---|---:|---:|
| | (a) With blue phosphor bands | } 223,200 | 30·00 |
| | (b) With violet 8 mm. phosphor bands) | | 18·00 |
| N23p. | Jan 1966 | 1,633,200 | 8·50 |
| | (a) With blue phosphor bands. | } 350,600 | 30·00 |
| | (b) With violet 8 mm. phosphor bands) | | 26·00 |
| N24p. | Apr 1966 | 2,125,200 | 8·00 |
| | With violet 8 mm. phosphor bands | 240,000 | 12·00 |
| N25p. | July 1966 | 1,981,800 | 6·00 |
| | With violet 8 mm. phosphor bands | 97,400 | 70·00 |
| N26p. | Oct 1966 | 1,787,400 | 8·00 |
| | With violet 8 mm. phosphor bands | 471,400 | 16·00 |
| N27p. | Jan 1967 | 644,200 | 9·00 |
| | With violet 8 mm. phosphor bands | 2,100,400 | 8·00 |
| N28p | Apr 1967 | | |
| | (a) With violet 8 mm. phosphor bands | } 2,330,200 | 10·00 |
| | (b) With violet 9·5 mm. phosphor bands) | | — |
| N29p | July 1967. With violet 8 mm. phosphor bands | 3,209,800 | 6·75 |
| N30p | Oct 1967 (issued 15.9.67) | | |
| | (a) With violet 8 mm. phosphor bands. | } 3,924,600 | 6·75 |
| | (b) With violet 9·5 mm. phosphor bands | | 40·00 |

For illustration showing how the *se-tenant* stamps with one phosphor band on the 3d. are printed, see listing of No. SB45/8.

**Watermark Crowns (sideways), 3d. with two violet phosphor bands (Nos. S23d or S24b; S78c or S80; S91b or S92b)**

| | | | |
|---|---|---:|---:|
| N31p | Jan 1968 (issued early 11.67) | | |
| | (a) Violet 9·5 mm. | | 4·00 |
| | (b) 8 mm. bands on 4d. pane | } 1,864,800 | 25·00 |
| | (c) 8 mm. bands on *se-tenant* pane/ | | 25·00 |
| N32p | Mar 1968 (issued mid 1.68) | | |
| | (a) Violet 9·5 mm. | | 4·50 |
| | (b) 8 mm. bands on 4d. pane | } 3,078,800 | 25·00 |
| | (c) 8 mm. bands on *se-tenant* pane | | 25·00 |

Paste-up books N21 to N32 each £100
AVC books N21 to N32 each 8·00
Nos. N31p(c) and N32p(c) have one band on 3d.
2s. booklets were withdrawn on 11 February 1971 prior to decimalisation on 15 February.

## 2s. Booklets for Holiday Resorts

**Contents**: 8 × 2½d. in panes of four and 3 × ½d. and 1 × 2½d. in pane of four arranged *se-tenant*
Lemon Cover as Type C. Printed in red. Fully interleaved
Watermark Crowns. Chalky paper (Nos. S6, S58)

**A. Black stitching**

| | | |
|---|---|---|
| NR1 No date (issued 15.7.63) | 415,000 | 5·00 |

**B. White stitching**

| | | |
|---|---|---|
| NR1a No date (issued 3.9.63) | 50,000 | 5·50 |

**Contents changed**: 8 × ½d. and 8 × 2½d. in panes of four arranged *se-tenant* vertically.
Lemon Cover as Type C. Printed in red. Fully interleaved
Watermark Crowns (sideways) (No. S5a/b, S57b/c)

| | | |
|---|---|---|
| NR2 1964 (issued 1.7.64) | 827,800 | 2·25 |

These replaced the normal 2s. booklets in the resort towns to which they were issued.

## 2s. Booklet for Christmas Cards

**Contents**: 8 × 3d. in two panes of four Orange-yellow Cover as Type C. Printed in red. Fully interleaved
Watermark Crowns (sideways) (No. S71a)

| | | | |
|---|---|---|---|
| NX1 | 1965 (issued 6.12.65) | 1,208,000 | 1·00 |

The above was withdrawn on 3.1.66 but reissued on 16.5.66 as a holiday resort booklet.

## ■ 2s.6d. Booklets

Contents: 6 × 2½d., 6 × 1½d., 3 × 1d. (page completed by
three perforated labels), 6 × ½d. in panes of six
**Pattern Book A.** Dec 1952 (see Notes)
(a) with red handstamp on cover £750
(b) without handstamp on cover £750

| LABELS. | |
|---|---|
| The wording printed on the labels differs as follows: | |
| "PPR" | "MINIMUM INLAND PRINTED PAPER RATE 1½d." Two types exist: (a) 17 mm. high. Printed in photogravure (b) 15 mm. high. Printed by typography |
| "SHORTHAND" | "SHORTHAND IN 1 WEEK" (covering all three labels) |
| "POST EARLY" | "PLEASE POST EARLY IN THE DAY" |
| "PAP" | "PACK YOUR PARCELS SECURELY" (1st label), "ADDRESS YOUR LETTERS CORRECTLY" (2nd label) "AND POST EARLY IN THE DAY" (3rd label) |

**I. Composite Booklets containing Stamps of
King George VI and Queen Elizabeth II**

**A. Green Cover as Type A. Not interleaved**
K.G. VI ½d. (No. Q3), 1d. (No. Q6) and Q.E. II 1½d. (No. S25),
2½d. (No. S51)

| F 1 | May 1953 | PPR 17 mm. | 2,272,000 | 32·00 |
|---|---|---|---|---|
| | b. Date error May 195 for May 1953 | | | 35·00 |
| F 2 | June 1953 | PPR 17 mm. | 2,751,000 | 35·00 |
| F 3 | July 1953 | PPR 17 mm. | 2,199,000 | 42·00 |
| F 4 | Aug 1953 | PPR 17 mm. | 2,464,000 | 38·00 |

**B. Green Cover as Type A, but with the addition of two
interleaving pages, one at each end**
K.G. VI ½d. (No. Q3), 1d. (No. Q6) and Q.E. II 1½d. (No. S25),
2½d. (No. S51)

| F 5 | Sept 1953 | PPR 17 mm. | } 2,386,000 | £200 |
|---|---|---|---|---|
| F 6 | Sept 1953 | PPR 15 mm. | | £140 |

**C. Green Cover as Type B. Contents as Nos. F 5/6**
K.G. VI ½d. (No. Q3), 1d. (No. Q6) and Q.E. II 1½d. (No. S25),
2½d. (No. S51)

| F 7 | Oct 1953 | PPR 17 mm. | } 2,532,000 | 55·00 |
|---|---|---|---|---|
| F 8 | Oct 1953 | PPR 15 mm. | | £120 |
| F 9 | Nov 1953 | PPR 17 mm. | 4,308,000* | 60·00 |
| | AVC book | | | 50·00 |
| F10 | Nov 1953 | PPR 15 mm. | | £200 |
| F11 | Dec 1953 | PPR 17 mm. | 2,918,000 | 60·00 |
| | AVC book | | | 50·00 |
| F12 | Jan 1954 | SHORT-HAND | 2,199,000 | 90·00 |
| | AVC book (without label pane) | | | £600 |
| | AVC book (with printed label pane) | | | 80·00 |
| F13 | Feb 1954 | SHORT-HAND | 2,202,000 | 95·00 |
| | AVC book (withprinted label pane) | | | £600 |

*The quantity given for F9 includes F10.

**D. Green Cover as Type B with contents as Nos. F 5/6 but Q.E.
II ½d. in place of K.G. VI ½d.**
K.G. VI 1d. (No. Q6) and Q.E. II ½d. (No. S1), 1½d. (No. S25), 2½d.

(No. S51)

| F14 | Mar 1954 | PPR 17 mm. | 139,000 | £550 |
|---|---|---|---|---|
| F14a | Mar 1954 | SHORTHAND | | |

## II. Booklets containing only Queen Elizabeth II Stamps

Green Cover as Type B.
Watermark Tudor Crown (Nos. S1, S13, S25, S51)

### A. Two interleaving pages, one at each end

| | | | | |
|---|---|---|---|---|
| F15 | Mar 1954 | PPR 15 mm. | 2,085,000 | £325 |
| | AVC book (with printed label pane) | | | £600 |
| F16 | Apr 1954 | POST EARLY | 3,176,000 | 50·00 |
| F17 | May 1954 | POST EARLY | 2,435,000 | 50·00 |
| F18 | June 1954 | POST EARLY | 2,419,000 | 50·00 |
| F19 | July 1954 | POST EARLY | 2,876,000 | 50·00 |
| F20 | Aug 1954 | POST EARLY | 2,871,000 | 55·00 |
| F21 | Sept 1954 | POST EARLY | 2,799,000 | 50·00 |
| F22 | Oct 1954 | POST EARLY | 2,803,000 | 50·00 |
| F23 | Nov 1954 | POST EARLY | 3,739,000 | 50·00 |
| F24 | Dec 1954 | POST EARLY | 2,813,000 | 50·00 |
| | AVC books F16 to F24 (with printed label pane) each | | | £250 |

### B. Fully interleaved

| | | | | |
|---|---|---|---|---|
| F25 | Jan 1955 | POST EARLY | | |
| | (a) (original setting) | | } 2,551,000 | 60·00 |
| | (b) (modified setting) | | | |
| | AVC book F25(a) (with printed label pane) | | | £400 |
| F26 | Jan 1955 | PAP | 160,000 | £140 |
| F27 | Feb 1955 | PAP | 2,694,000 | 55·00 |
| F28 | Mar 1955 | PAP | 2,530,000 | 55·00 |
| F29 | Apr 1955 | PAP | 2,522,000 | 55·00 |
| F30 | May 1955 | PAP | 2,530,000 | 55·00 |
| F31 | June 1955 | PAP | 2,522,000 | 55·00 |
| F32 | July 1955 | PAP | 2,431,000 | 55·00 |

In the modified setting the distance between IN THE is 1 mm. and this is only found on the majority of the Jan. 1955 edition (Booklet F25). The normal spacing is 1½ mm.

> **MIXED WATERMARKS.**
> See notes above No. F34. The mixed watermarks here are indicated by the code letters "E" (Edward) and "C" (Crowns) starting with the first pane of the booklet, i.e. 3d., 1½d., 1d., ½d. We only quote one price for each booklet and this is the minimum price. Some combinations are scarcer and worth more.

Tudor Crown, St. Edward's Crown and mixed watermarks. All have PAP labels.

| | | | | |
|---|---|---|---|---|
| F33 | Aug 1955 PAP (TTTT) | | | |
| | (a) Combination TTET | | } 2,563,000 | 55·00 |
| | (b) Combination TEET | | | |
| F34 | Sept 1955 (TTTT) | | | |
| | (a) Combination TTET | | | |
| | (b) Combination TEET | | | |
| | (c) Combination TEEE | | } 2,275,000 | 60·00 |
| | (d) Combination ETET | | | |
| | (e) Combination EEET | | | |
| | (f) Combination EEEE | | | |
| F35 | Oct 1955 (TTTT) | | | |
| | (a) Combination TEET | | | |
| | (b) Combination EEET | | } 2,289,000 | 40·00 |
| | (c) Combination TEEE | | | |
| | (d) Combination EEEE | | | |
| F36 | Nov 1955 (TTTT) | | | |
| | (a) Combination TEEE | | | |
| | (b) Combination EEET | | 4,125,000 | 40·00 |
| | (c) Combination EEEE | | | |
| | AVC books F27 to F36 each | | | 30·00 |

Watermark St. Edward's Crown (Nos. S2, S14, S26, S53). All have PAP labels

| | | | | |
|---|---|---|---|---|
| F37 | Dec 1955 | | | |
| | (a) Combination TEET | | } 2,789,000 | 40·00 |
| | (b) Combination EEET | | | |
| F38 | Jan 1956 | | | |
| | (a) Combination EEET | | } 2,001,000 | 40·00 |
| F39 | Feb 1956 | | 2,031,000 | 40·00 |
| F40 | Mar 1956 | | 2,289,000 | 40·00 |
| F41 | Apr 1956 | | 2,283,000 | 50·00 |
| F42 | May 1956 | | | |
| | (a) Combination EEET | | } 2,275,000 | 40·00 |
| | (b) Combination TEEE | | | |
| F43 | June 1956 | | | |
| | (a) Combination EEET | | } 2,293,000 | 45·00 |
| | (b) Combination TEEE | | | |
| F44 | July 1956 | | 2,279,400 | 40·00 |
| F45 | Aug 1956 | | 2,264,400 | 30·00 |

Paste-up books F39 to F52 each £150

| | | | | |
|---|---|---|---|---|
| F46 | Sept 1956 | | 2,533,000 | 48·00 |
| F47 | Oct 1956 | | 2,536,000 | 40·00 |
| F48 | Nov 1956 | | 4,165,800 | 40·00 |
| F49 | Dec 1956 | | 2,724,600 | 40·00 |
| F50 | Jan 1957 | | 2,212,800 | 40·00 |
| F51 | Feb 1957 | | 2,772,790 | 30·00 |
| F52 | Mar 1957 | | 2,497,800 | 40·00 |

**Contents changed:** 6 × 2½d., 6 × 2d., 6 × ½d. in panes of six
Watermark St. Edward's Crown (Nos. S2, S38, S53)

| | | | | |
|---|---|---|---|---|
| F53 | Apr 1957 | | 2,451,800 | 40·00 |
| F54 | May 1957 | | 2,062,400 | 35·00 |
| F55 | June 1957 | | 1,843,000 | 35·00 |
| F56 | July 1957 | | 2,305,000 | 35·00 |
| F57 | Aug 1957 | | 2,265,000 | 35·00 |
| F58 | Sept 1957 | | 2,482,200 | 35·00 |
| F59 | Oct 1957 | | 2,505,600 | 35·00 |
| F60 | Nov 1957 | | 3,085,600 | 28·00 |
| F61 | Dec 1957 | | 281,000 | 48·00 |

Paste-up books F53 to F61 each £150
AVC books F37 to F61 each 15·00
The 2s.6d. booklets were withdrawn from sale on 27 July 1958.

## ■ 3s. Booklets

**Contents:** 6 × 3d., 6 × 1½d., 6 × 1d., 6 × ½d. in panes of six
I. Red Cover as Type B. Fully interleaved

**Watermark St. Edward's Crown (Nos. S2, S14, S26, S68)**

| | | | |
|---|---|---|---|
| M1 | Jan 1958 | 1,815,000 | 28·00 |
| M2 | Feb 1958 | 2,224,000 | 28·00 |
| M3 | Mar 1958 | 2,271,000 | 28·00 |
| M4 | Apr 1958 | 2,654,000 | 28·00 |
| M5 | May 1958 | 2,146,000 | 28·00 |
| M6 | June 1958 | 2,222,000 | 28·00 |
| M7 | July 1958 | 885,000 | 28·00 |
| M8 | Aug 1958 | 896,000 | 32·00 |
| M9 | Nov 1958 | | |
| | (a) Combination EEEC | | |
| | (b) Combination EECE | | |
| | (c) Combination EECC | 1,367,000 | 32·00 |
| | (d) Combination CECE | | |
| | (e) Combination CCCE | | |

> **MIXED WATERMARKS**
> See notes above No. F33. The mixed watermarks here are indicated by the code letters "E" (Edward) and "C" (Crowns), starting with the first pane of the booklet, i.e. 3d., 1½d., 1d., ½d.

**Watermark Crowns (Nos. S4, S16, S28, S70), or graphite lines (Nos. S7, S18, S30, S72)**

| | | | |
|---|---|---|---|
| M10 | Dec 1958 | | |
| | (a) Combination ECEC | | |
| | (b) Combination CEEE | | |
| | (c) Combination CECE | 886,000 | 38·00 |
| | (d) Combination CEEC | | |
| | (e) Combination CECC | | |
| M11 | Jan 1959 | | |
| | (a) Combination CECC | 1,145,000 | 35·00 |
| M12 | Feb 1959 | 1,125,000 | 35·00 |
| M13 | Aug 1959 | 1,038,000 | 38·00 |
| | g. With graphite lines (issued 4.8.59) | 47,000 | £275 |
| M14 | Sept 1959 | 1,542,000 | 38·00 |
| | g. With graphite lines | 74,000 | £350 |

Paste-up books M1 to M4 (using 2s.6d. AVC to make up) each £200
M5 to M14 each £150
AVC books M1 to M14 each 20·00

**II. Brick-red Cover as Type C. Fully interleaved**
Watermark Crowns (Nos. S4, S16, S28, S70), graphite lines (Nos. S7, S18, S30, S72) or green phosphor (Nos. S9, S20, S32, S74)

| | | | |
|---|---|---|---|
| M15 | Oct 1959 | 1,016,000 | 38·00 |
| | g. With graphite lines | 74,000 | £350 |
| M16 | Nov 1959 | 2,287,000 | 38·00 |
| M17 | Dec 1959 | 1,027,000 | 38·00 |
| M18 | Jan 1960 | 752,000 | 38·00 |
| M19 | Feb 1960 | 750,000 | 38·00 |
| | g. With graphite lines | 37,600 | £325 |
| M20 | Mar 1960 | 966,000 | 38·00 |
| | g. With graphite lines | 39,600 | £400 |
| M21 | Apr 1960 | 941,000 | 38·00 |
| | g. With graphite lines | 38,200 | £325 |
| M22 | May 1960 | 911,000 | 38·00 |
| M23 | June 1960 | 982,000 | 38·00 |
| M24 | July 1960 | 989,200 | 38·00 |
| M25 | Aug 1960 | 897,000 | 38·00 |

| | | | |
|---|---|---|---|
| | p. With green phosphor bands (issued 14.8.60) | 39,800 | 75·00 |
| M26 | Sept 1960 | 1,326,600 | 38·00 |
| M27 | Oct 1960 | 1,343,400 | 38·00 |
| M28 | Nov 1960 | 2,068,200 | 38·00 |
| | p. With green phosphor bands | 11,900 | 80·00 |

Paste-up books M15 to M28 each £150
AVC books M15 to M28 each 10·00

**III. Brick-red Cover as Type D. Fully interleaved**
Watermark Crowns (Nos. S4 or S5, S16 or S17, S28 or S29, S70 or S71), green or blue phosphor (Nos. S9 or S10, S20 or S21, S32 or S33, S74 or S75)

| | | | |
|---|---|---|---|
| M29 | Dec 1960 | 905,200 | 40·00 |
| | p. With green phosphor bands | 31,800 | 85·00 |
| M30 | Jan 1961 | 731,800 | 38·00 |
| M31 | Feb 1961 | 727,000 | 38·00 |
| M32 | Mar 1961 | 754,600 | 32·00 |
| M33 | Apr 1961 | 760,800 | 38·00 |
| | p. With blue phosphor bands | 142,600 | 75·00 |
| M34 | May 1961 | 738,000 | 38·00 |
| M35 | June 1961 | 768,000 | 38·00 |
| M36 | July 1961 | 783,400 | 38·00 |
| | p. With blue phosphor bands | 7,800 | 75·00 |
| M37p | Aug 1961 | 747,400 | 38·00 |
| | (a) With green phosphor bands | 54,400 | 70·00 |
| | (b) With blue phosphor bands | | 80·00 |
| M38 | Sept 1961 | 513,600 | 38·00 |
| | p. With blue phosphor bands | 19,200 | 85·00 |
| M39 | Oct 1961 | 494,600 | 38·00 |
| | p. With blue phosphor bands | 18,800 | 80·00 |
| M40 | Nov 1961 | 467,600 | 38·00 |
| M41 | Dec 1961 | 356,800 | 38·00 |
| M42 | Jan 1962 | 447,000 | 38·00 |
| M43 | Feb 1962 | 654,200 | 38·00 |
| | p. With blue phosphor bands | 11,800 | 80·00 |
| M44 | Mar 1962 | 655,200 | 38·00 |
| | p. With blue phosphor bands | 19,400 | 80·00 |
| M45 | Apr 1962 | 569,600 | 38·00 |
| | p. With blue phosphor bands | 19,600 | 80·00 |
| M46 | May 1962 | 475,000 | 38·00 |
| | p. With blue phosphor bands | 27,000 | 80·00 |
| M47 | June 1962 | 468,400 | 38·00 |
| | p. With blue phosphor bands | 27,200 | 80·00 |
| M48 | July 1962 | 729,400 | 32·00 |
| M49 | Aug 1962 | 691,200 | 35·00 |
| | p. With blue phosphor bands | 28,800 | 80·00 |
| M50 | Sept 1962 | 687,400 | 38·00 |
| | p. With blue phosphor bands | 11,800 | 80·00 |
| M51 | Oct 1962 | 864,600 | 40·00 |
| | p. With blue phosphor bands | 35,200 | 80·00 |
| M52 | Nov 1962 | 1,125,600 | 38·00 |
| | p. With blue phosphor bands | 51,800 | 80·00 |
| M53 | Dec 1962 | 1,035,000 | 38·00 |
| | p. With blue phosphor bands | 19,200 | 80·00 |
| M54 | Jan 1963 | 499,400 | 38·00 |
| M55 | Feb 1963 | 462,400 | 35·00 |
| | p. With blue phosphor bands | 39,400 | 80·00 |
| M56 | Mar 1963 | 512,800 | 38·00 |
| | p. With blue phosphor bands | 39,200 | 80·00 |
| M57 | Apr 1963 | 512,800 | 38·00 |
| | p. With blue phosphor bands | 39,600 | 80·00 |
| M58 | May 1963 | 520,800 | 38·00 |
| | p. With blue phosphor bands | 19,400 | £275 |
| M59 | June 1963 | 532,400 | 38·00 |

|     |                              |           |       |
|-----|------------------------------|-----------|-------|
|     | p. With blue phosphor bands  | 19,800    | 55·00 |
| M60 | July 1963                    | 712,000   | 38·00 |
|     | p. With blue phosphor bands  | 17,800    | 80·00 |
| M61 | Aug 1963                     | 698,600   | 38·00 |
|     | p. With blue phosphor bands  | 19,800    | 80·00 |
| M62 | Sept 1963                    | 503,000   | 38·00 |
| M63 | Oct 1963                     | 660,400   | 38·00 |
| M64 | Nov 1963                     | 670,000   | 32·00 |
|     | p. With blue phosphor bands  | 39,400    | 80·00 |
| M65 | Dec 1963                     | 711,400   | 45·00 |
|     | p. With blue phosphor bands  | 19,350    | £180  |
| M66 | Jan 1964                     | 619,600   | 45·00 |
|     | p. With blue phosphor bands  | 67,000    | 60·00 |
| M67 | Mar 1964                     | 666,600   | 42·00 |
|     | p. With blue phosphor bands  | 30,400    | 80·00 |
| M68 | May 1964                     | 636,600   | 42·00 |
|     | p. With blue phosphor bands  | 46,600    | £110  |
| M69 | July 1964                    | 865,800   | 38·00 |
|     | p. With blue phosphor bands  | 27,400    | 80·00 |
| M70 | Sept 1964                    | 915,600   | 45·00 |
|     | p. With blue phosphor bands  | 39,800    | 80·00 |
| M71 | Nov 1964                     | 2,157,600 | 45·00 |
|     | p. With blue phosphor bands  | 99,200    | 60·00 |
| M72 | Jan 1965                     | 1,009,800 | 45·00 |
|     | p. With blue phosphor bands  | 50,000    | 60·00 |
| M73 | Mar 1965                     | 944,600   | 30·00 |
|     | p. With blue phosphor bands  | 38,200    | 60·00 |
| M74 | May 1965                     | 765,600   | 30·00 |
|     | p. With blue phosphor bands  | 58,200    | 60·00 |

Paste-up books M29 to M74 each £150
July 1965 (not issued) £250
AVC books M29 to M38 each 10·00
M39 to M42 each 50·00
M44 and M45 each 50·00
M46 to M74 each 10·00
3s. booklets were withdrawn from sale on 31 August 1965.

● ————————

## ▋ 3s.9d. Booklets

**Contents**: 18 × 2½d. in panes of six
Red Cover as Type B.

### A. Two interleaving pages, one at each end

**Watermark Tudor Crown (No. S51)**

|     |            |           |       |
|-----|------------|-----------|-------|
| G1  | Nov 1953   | 1,446,000 | 40·00 |
| G2  | Jan 1954   | 1,572,000 | 40·00 |
| G3  | Mar 1954   | 1,474,000 | 40·00 |
| G4  | Dec 1954   | 1,477,000 | 40·00 |
| G5  | Feb 1955   | 925,000   | 40·00 |
| G6  | Apr 1955   | 1,112,000 | 40·00 |
| G7  | June 1955  | 675,000   | 40·00 |
| G8  | Aug 1955   | 636,000   | 40·00 |

AVC books G1 to G4 each 30·00

**Tudor Crown, St. Edward's Crown and mixed watermarks
(see notes above No. F33)**

|     |                                                                                      |           |       |
|-----|--------------------------------------------------------------------------------------|-----------|-------|
| G9  | Oct 1955 (TTT) <br>(a) Combination TET <br>(b) Combination EET <br>(c) Combination EEE | 1,661,000 | 40·00 |
| G10 | Dec 1955 (TTT) <br>(a) Combination TET <br>(b) Combination EEE                         | 616,000   | 40·00 |

### B. Fully interleaved

**Watermark St. Edward's Crown (No. S53)**

|     |            |           |       |
|-----|------------|-----------|-------|
| G12 | Feb 1956   | 638,000   | 30·00 |
| G13 | Apr 1956   | 642,000   | 30·00 |
| G14 | June 1956  | 634,000   | 30·00 |
| G15 | Aug 1956   | 747,200   | 30·00 |
| G16 | Oct 1956   | 1,762,800 | 30·00 |
| G17 | Dec 1956   | 1,065,800 | 30·00 |
| G18 | Feb 1957   | 1,376,000 | 30·00 |
| G19 | Apr 1957   | 1,139,600 | 30·00 |
| G20 | June 1957  | 1,115,200 | 17·00 |
| G21 | Aug 1957   | 39,600    | 40·00 |

Paste-up book G12 (stapled to make up) £200
G13 to G21 each £150
AVC books G5 to G21 each 15·00
3s.9d. booklets were withdrawn from sale on 30 September 1957.

● ————————

# 4s.6d. Booklets

**Contents**: 18 × 3d. in panes of six

Type E. With GPO Cypher

Type F. With Post Office Crown symbol

## I. Purple Cover as Type B. Fully interleaved

### Watermark St. Edward's Crown (No. S68)

| | | | |
|---|---|---|---|
| L1 | Oct 1957 | 2,249,000 | 30·00 |
| L2 | Dec 1957 | 4,539,000 | 30·00 |
| L3 | Feb 1958 | 1,789,000 | 35·00 |
| L4 | Apr 1958 | 2,691,000 | 30·00 |
| L5 | June 1958 | 1,096,000 | 32·00 |
| L6 | Oct 1958 | 1,796,000 | 30·00 |
| L7 | Dec 1958 | 1,808,000 | 30·00 |

### Watermark Crowns (No. S70)

| | | | |
|---|---|---|---|
| L8 | Dec 1958 | (incl. Above) | £100 |

Paste-up books L1 or L2 (using 3s.9d. AVC books to make up) each £200
Paste-up books L3 to L8 each £150
Aug 1958 (not issued) £250
AVC books L1 to L8 each 20·00

## II. Purple Cover as Type C. Fully interleaved

### Watermark Crowns (No. S70) or graphite lines (No. S72)

| | | | |
|---|---|---|---|
| L 9 | Feb 1959 | (with L14) 2,260,000 | 30·00 |

| | | | |
|---|---|---|---|
| L10 | June 1959 | (with L16) 2,195,000 | 30·00 |
| L11 | Aug 1959 | | 1,710,000 | 30·00 |
| | g. With graphite lines | 97,600 | 45·00 |
| L12 | Oct 1959 | 1,852,000 | 45·00 |
| L13 | Dec 1959 | (with L17) 1,409,000 | 35·00 |

## III. Violet Cover as Type C. Fully interleaved
Watermark Crowns (No. S70), graphite lines (No. S72) or green phosphor (No. S74)

| | | | |
|---|---|---|---|
| L14 | Feb 1959 | (incl. in L9) | 45·00 |
| L15 | Apr 1959 | 2,137,000 | 35·00 |
| | g. With graphite lines | 99,200 | 30·00 |
| L16 | June 1959 | (incl. in L10) | 35·00 |
| | g. With graphite lines | 99,400 | 30·00 |
| L17 | Dec 1959 | (incl. in L13) | 35·00 |
| L18 | Feb 1960 | 1,801,000 | 35·00 |
| | g. With graphite lines | 79,600 | 35·00 |
| L19 | Apr 1960 | 1,730,000 | 35·00 |
| | g. With graphite lines | 78,800 | 35·00 |
| L20 | June 1960 | 1,832,000 | 35·00 |
| L21 | Aug 1960 | 1,771,600 | 35·00 |
| | p. With green phosphor bands | 39,800 | 60·00 |
| L22 | Oct 1960 | 2,723,600 | 35·00 |

Paste-up books L9 to L22 each £150
AVC books L9 to L14 and L16 to L22 each 10·00

## IV. Violet Cover as Type D. Fully interleaved
Watermark Crowns (No. S70 or S71), green or blue phosphor (Nos. S74, S75 or S76)

| | | | |
|---|---|---|---|
| L23 | Dec 1960 | 1,772,000 | 60·00 |
| L24 | Feb 1961 | 1,982,200 | 60·00 |
| | p. With green phosphor bands | 27,200 | 48·00 |
| L25 | Apr 1961 | 3,428,400 | 42·00 |
| | p. With blue phosphor bands | 297,400 | 45·00 |
| L26 | June 1961 | 1,825,600 | 42·00 |
| L27p | Aug 1961 | 2,679,800 | 42·00 |
| | (a) With green phosphor bands | } 63,120 | 70·00 |
| | (b) With blue phosphor bands | | 55·00 |
| L28 | Oct 1961 | 3,061,000 | 40·00 |
| | p. With blue phosphor bands | 31,400 | 55·00 |
| L29 | Dec 1961 | 1,942,800 | 40·00 |
| L30 | Feb 1962 | 2,405,200 | 40·00 |
| | p. With blue phosphor bands | 43,600 | 40·00 |
| L31 | Apr 1962 | 1,985,000 | 55·00 |
| | p. With blue phosphor bands | 75,400 | 55·00 |
| L32 | June 1962 | 2,190,600 | 55·00 |
| | p. With blue phosphor bands | 74,000 | 75·00 |
| L33 | Aug 1962 | 2,533,800 | 40·00 |
| | p. With blue phosphor bands | 83,600 | 80·00 |
| L34 | Oct 1962 | 3,525,400 | 40·00 |
| | p. With blue phosphor bands | 83,200 | £225 |
| L35 | Dec 1962 | 1,822,000 | 40·00 |
| | p. With blue phosphor bands | 82,200 | 55·00 |
| L36 | Feb 1963 | 2,352,600 | 40·00 |
| | p. With blue phosphor bands | 117,000 | 55·00 |
| L37 | Apr 1963 | 2,390,200 | 40·00 |
| | p. With blue phosphor bands | 119,000 | 55·00 |
| L38 | June 1963 | 2,873,600 | 40·00 |
| | p. With blue phosphor bands | 178,600 | 48·00 |
| L39 | Aug 1963 | 2,474,200 | 40·00 |
| | p. With blue phosphor bands | 111,000 | 60·00 |
| L40 | Oct 1963 | 1,829,200 | 40·00 |
| | p. With blue phosphor bands | 99,400 | 60·00 |
| L41 | Nov 1963 | 1,821,000 | 40·00 |
| | p. With blue phosphor bands | 99,600 | 60·00 |

| | | | |
|---|---|---:|---:|
| L42 | Dec 1963 | 2,431,400 | 40·00 |
| | p. With blue phosphor bands | 46,400 | £225 |
| L43 | Jan 1964 | 1,043,800 | 85·00 |
| L44 | Feb 1964 | 1,069,000 | 40·00 |
| | p. With blue phosphor bands | 87,000 | 48·00 |
| L45 | Mar 1964 | 1,014,200 | 80·00 |
| | p. With blue phosphor bands | 82,800 | £130 |
| L46 | Apr 1964 | 1,006,600 | 80·00 |
| | p. With blue phosphor bands | 62,400 | 55·00 |
| L47 | May 1964 | 1,028,800 | 40·00 |
| | p. With blue phosphor bands | 105,200 | 55·00 |
| L48 | June 1964 | 1,067,400 | 40·00 |
| | p. With blue phosphor bands | 70,400 | 55·00 |
| L49 | July 1964 | 1,673,600 | 40·00 |
| | p. With blue phosphor bands | 56,200 | 55·00 |
| L50 | Aug 1964 | 1,622,600 | 45·00 |
| | p. With blue phosphor bands | 78,200 | 40·00 |
| L51 | Sept 1964 | 1,561,200 | 55·00 |
| | p. With blue phosphor bands | 98,000 | 45·00 |
| L52 | Oct 1964 | 1,781,800 | 40·00 |
| | p. With blue phosphor bands | 197,800 | 55·00 |
| L53 | Nov 1964 | 1,686,000 | 40·00 |
| | p. With blue phosphor bands | 138,000 | 55·00 |
| L54 | Dec 1964 | 1,684,000 | 40·00 |
| | p. With blue phosphor bands | 119,200 | 55·00 |
| L55 | Jan 1965 | 1,519,200 | 32·00 |
| | p. With blue phosphor bands | 95,000 | 55·00 |
| L56 | Feb 1965 | 1,504,600 | 32·00 |
| | p. With blue phosphor bands | 94,200 | 55·00 |
| L57 | Mar 1965 | 1,479,600 | 35·00 |
| | p. With blue phosphor bands | 18,800 | £400 |
| L58 | Apr 1965 | 1,438,400 | 30·00 |

Paste-up books L23 to L58 each £150
L23 to L27 each 10·00
L28 to L31 each 50·00
L32 to L58 each 10·00
An edition dated MAY 1965 was prepared, but not issued, due
to the increase in letter rate from 3d. to 4d. on 17 May.
Paste-up May 1965 £250
AVC May 1965 £140

**Contents changed**: 12 × 4d., 6 × 1d. in panes of six
Slate-blue Cover as Type D

**Watermark Crowns (Nos. S17, S85), blue or violet phosphor
(Nos. S22, S23 or S24; S90, S91 or S92)**

| | | | |
|---|---|---:|---:|
| L59 | July 1965 (issued 26.7.65) | 2,191,600 | 30·00 |
| | p. With blue phosphor bands (issued 26.7.65) | 75,400 | 32·00 |
| L60 | Sept 1965 | 1,839,600 | 30·00 |
| | p. (a) With blue phosphor bands. | 200,800 | 32·00 |
| | p. (b) With violet 8 mm. phosphor bands | | 32·00 |
| L61 | Nov 1965 | 2,005,000 | 30·00 |
| | p. (a) With blue phosphor bands | 165,800 | 35·00 |
| | p. (b) With violet 8 mm. phosphor bands | | 32·00 |
| L62 | Jan 1966 | 1,671,000 | 24·00 |
| | p. (a) With blue phosphor bands | 334,600 | 25·00 |
| | p. (b) With violet 8 mm. phosphor bands | | 23·00 |
| L63 | Mar 1966 | 1,201,600 | 30·00 |
| | p. With violet 8 mm. phosphor bands | 153,200 | 30·00 |

| | | | |
|---|---|---:|---:|
| L64 | Jan 1967 | 98,800 | 24·00 |
| | p. With violet 8 mm. phosphor bands | 396,600 | 23·00 |
| L65p | Mar 1967 | 97,200 | 40·00 |
| | p. (a) With violet 8 mm. phosphor bands | 255,400 | 18·00 |
| | p. (b) With violet 9·5 mm. phosphor bands | | 18·00 |

**Watermark Crowns, violet 9·5 mm. phosphor (Nos. S24, S92)**

| | | | |
|---|---|---:|---:|
| L66p | May 1967 | 697,200 | 12·00 |
| L67p | July 1967 | 569,000 | 18·00 |
| L68p | Sept 1967 | 750,800 | 18·00 |
| L69p | Nov 1967 | 1,802,600 | 12·00 |
| L70p | Jan 1968 | 729,400 | 12·00 |
| L71p | Mar 1968 | 729,400 | 10·00 |

Paste-up books L59 (using 5s. AVC to make up) £200
L60 to L71 each £150
AVC books L59 to L71 each £10·00

## ■ 5s. Booklets

**Contents**: 12 × 2½d., 6 × 2d., 6 × 1½d., 6 × 1d., 6 × ½d. in panes of six
**Pattern book B** Dec 1952 (see notes)
(a) with red handstamp on cover £600
(b) without handstamp on cover £600

**I. Composite Booklets containing Stamps of King George VI and Queen Elizabeth II**

**A. Buff Cover as Type A. Not interleaved**
K.G. VI ½d. (No. Q3), 1d. (No. Q6), 2d. (No. Q12) and Q.E. II 1½d. (No. S25), 2½d. (No. S51)

| | | | |
|---|---|---|---|
| H1 | May 1953 | 1,309,000 | 48·00 |
| H2 | July 1953 | 1,716,000 | 50·00 |

**B. Buff Cover as Type A but with the addition of two interleaving pages, one at each end**
K.G. VI ½d. (No. Q3), 1d. (No. Q6), 2d. (No. Q12) and Q.E. II 1½d. (No. S25), 2½d. (No. S51)

| | | | |
|---|---|---|---|
| H3 | Sept 1953 | 1,070,000 | 50·00 |

**C. Buff Cover as Type B. Contents as No. H3**
K.G. VI ½d. (No. Q3), 1d. (No. Q6), 2d. (No. Q12) and Q.E. II 1½d. (No. S25), 2½d. (No. S51)

| | | | |
|---|---|---|---|
| H4 | Nov 1953 | 2,126,000 | 48·00 |
| H5 | Jan 1954 | 692,000 | 48·00 |

**D. Buff Cover as Type B.**
Contents as Nos. H4/5 but Q.E. II ½d. in place of K.G. VI ½d. K.G. VI 1d. (No. Q6), 2d. (No. Q12) and Q.E. II ½d. (No. S1), 1½d. (No. S25), 2½d. (No. S51)

| | | | |
|---|---|---|---|
| H6 | Mar 1954 | 16,000 | £400 |

**E. Buff Cover as Type B.**
Contents as No. H6 but Q.E. II 1d. in place of K.G. VI 1d. K.G. VI 2d. (No. Q12) and Q.E. II ½d. (No. S1), 1d. (No. S13), 1½d. (No. S25), 2½d. (No. S51)

| | | | |
|---|---|---|---|
| H7 | Mar 1954 | 160,000 | £225 |
| | a. Extra 1½d. pane | | £5500 |

**II. Booklets containing only Queen Elizabeth II Stamps**

**A. Buff Cover as Type B**
Watermark Tudor Crown (Nos. S1, S13, S25, S36, S51)

**A. Two interleaving pages, one at each end**

| | | | |
|---|---|---|---|
| H 8 | Mar 1954 | 1,092,000 | £170 |
| H 9 | May 1954 | 1,884,000 | 85·00 |
| H10 | July 1954 | 1,351,000 | 95·00 |
| H11 | Sept 1954 | 1,357,000 | 50·00 |
| H12 | Nov 1954 | 2,309,000 | 85·00 |

AVC books H4 to H12 each 40·00

**B. Fully interleaved**

| | | | |
|---|---|---|---|
| H13 | Jan 1955 | 1,349,000 | 85·00 |
| H14 | Mar 1955 | 1,450,000 | 75·00 |
| H15 | May 1955 | 1,461,000 | 75·00 |
| H16 | July 1955 | 1,460,000 | 75·00 |

> MIXED WATERMARKS. Nos. H17/19 and h21 exist with mixed Tudor Crown and St. Edward's Crown watermarks. The mixed watermarks are indicated by the code letters "T" (Tudor) and "E" (Edward) starting with the first pane of the booklet, i.e. 2½d. (2), 2d., 1½d., 1d., ½d.
> We only quote one price for each booklet and this is the minimum price. Some combinations are scarcer and worth more.

| | | | |
|---|---|---|---|
| H17 | Sept 1955 | | |
| | (a) Combination TTTETT | | |
| | (b) Combination TTTEET | | |
| | (c) Combination TTTETE | | |
| | (d) Combination TTEETT | | |
| | (e) Combination TTEEET | | |
| | (f) Combination TTEEEE | | |
| | (g) Combination TETETT | | |
| | (h) Combination TETEET | | |
| | (i) Combination TEEETT | | |
| | (j) Combination TETETE | | |
| | (k) Combination TEEETE | | |
| | (l) Combination ETTETT | | |
| | (m) Combination ETTEET | 1,328,000 | 40·00 |
| | (n) Combination ETEETT | | |
| | (o) Combination ETEEET | | |
| | (p) Combination EETETT | | |
| | (q) Combination EETEET | | |
| | (r) Combination EETETE | | |
| | (s) Combination EETEEE | | |
| | (t) Combination EEETTT | | |
| | (u) Combination EEETET | | |
| | (v) Combination EEETEE | | |
| | (w) Combination EEEETT | | |
| | (x) Combination EEEEET | | |
| | (y) Combination EEEEEE | | |

**Watermark St. Edward's Crown (Nos. S2, S14, S26, S37, S53)**

| | | | |
|---|---|---|---|
| H18 | Nov 1955 | | |
| | (a) Combination TTEEEE | | |
| | (b) Combination EETEEE | | |
| | (c) Combination TEEEEE | 2,147,000 | 42·00 |
| | (d) Combination EEEETE | | |
| | (e) Combination EEEEET | | |
| | (f) Combination ETEEEE | | 48·00 |
| H19 | Jan 1956 | | |
| | (a) Combination TTTEET | | |
| | (b) Combination EETETT | 1,337,000 | 55·00 |
| | (c) Combination EEEEET | | |
| H20 | Mar 1956 | 1,403,000 | 55·00 |
| H21 | May 1956 | 572,000 | |
| | (a) Combination EETETT | 572,000 | 55·00 |
| | (b) Combination EEEEET | | 36·00 |
| H22 | July 1956 | 1,465,190 | 48·00 |
| H23 | Sept 1956 | 1,589,000 | 48·00 |
| H24 | Nov 1956 | 2,430,600 | 48·00 |
| H25 | Jan 1957 | 100,000 | 60·00 |

Introduction of 2d. light red-brown (No. S38) in place of No. S37

| | | | |
|---|---|---|---|
| H26 | Jan 1957 | 1,417,800 | 48·00 |
| H27 | Mar 1957 | 1,435,400 | 60·00 |
| H28 | May 1957 | 1,375,200 | 50·00 |
| H29 | July 1957 | 1,453,600 | 42·00 |
| H30 | Sept 1957 | 2,104,600 | 42·00 |
| H31 | Nov 1957 | 1,708,400 | 42·00 |

**Contents changed**: 12 × 3d., 6 × 2½d., 6 × 1d., 6 × ½d. in panes of six

**Watermark St. Edward's Crown (Nos. S2, S14, S53, S68)**

| | | | |
|---|---|---|---|
| H32 | Jan 1958 | 1,528,000 | 42·00 |
| H33 | Mar 1958 | 442,000 | 42·00 |
| H34 | May 1958 | 795,000 | 42·00 |
| H35 | July 1958 (11.58) | | |

| | | | |
|---|---|---|---|
| | (a) Combination EEEEC | | |
| | (b) Combination EEECE | 1,313,000 | 30·00 |
| | (c) Combination EEECC | | |
| H36 | Nov 1958 | | |
| | (a) Combination EEECE | | |
| | (b) Combination EECEE | | |
| | (c) Combination EECEE | 1,235,000 | 30·00 |
| | (d) Combination CCEEE | | |
| | (e) Combination CCCEE | | |

MIXED WATERMARKS See notes above No. H17. The mixed watermarks here are indicated by the code letters "E" (Edward" and "C" (Crowns) starting with the first pane of the booklet, i.e. 3d. (2), 2½d., 1d., ½d..

### II. Blue Cover as Type C. Fully interleaved
Watermark Crowns (Nos. S4, S16, S55, S70), graphite lines (Nos. S7, S18, S59, S72) or green phosphor (Nos. S9, S20, S61, S74)

| | | | |
|---|---|---|---|
| H37 | Jan 1959 | | |
| | (a) Combination CCCCE | | |
| | (b) Combination CCCEC | 1,330,000 | 35·00 |
| | (c) Combination CCCEE | | |
| | (d) Combination CCECC | | |
| H38 | Mar 1959 | 895,000 | 42·00 |
| H39 | July 1959 | 1,122,000 | 42·00 |
| | g. With graphite lines (issued 21.8.59) | 46,200 | £150 |
| H40 | Sept 1959 | 1,541,000 | 42·00 |
| H41 | Nov 1959 | 1,340,000 | 42·00 |
| H42 | Jan 1960 | 1,092,000 | 42·00 |
| H43 | Mar 1960 | 1,042,000 | 42·00 |
| | g. With graphite lines | 38,000 | £170 |
| H44 | May 1960 | 1,023,000 | 50·00 |
| H45 | July 1960 | 1,104,000 | 50·00 |
| H46 | Sept 1960 | 1,158,800 | 60·00 |
| | g. With graphite lines | 65,999 | £170 |
| | p. With green phosphor bands | 39,600 | £120 |
| H47 | Nov 1960 | 1,308,400 | 55·00 |

Paste-up books H37 to H47 each £150
AVC books H37 to H47 each £15·00

### III. Blue Cover as Type D. Fully interleaved
Watermark Crowns (Nos. S4, S16, S55, S70) or blue phosphor with two bands on 2½d. (Nos. S10, S21, S62, S75)

| | | | |
|---|---|---|---|
| H48 | Jan 1961 | 1,344,600 | 60·00 |
| H49 | Mar 1961 | 2,382,800 | 60·00 |
| | p. With blue phosphor bands | 97,400 | £150 |
| H50 | May 1961 | 1,219,200 | 60·00 |
| H51 | July 1961 | 1,148,200 | 60·00 |
| | p. With blue phosphor bands | 7,200 | £200 |
| H52 | Sept 1961 | 1,728,600 | 60·00 |
| | p. With blue phosphor bands | 15,200 | £200 |
| H53 | Nov 1961 | 1,367,000 | 60·00 |
| H54 | Jan 1962 | 963,800 | 60·00 |
| | p. With blue phosphor bands | 38,600 | £200 |

Several examples of booklet No. H50 exist with pane 3 comprising No. S62 blue phosphor.

### Watermark Crowns
(Nos. S4 or S5, S16 or S17, S55 or S57, S70 or S71) or blue phosphor with one phosphor band on 2½d. (Nos. S10 or S11, S21 or S22, S63 or S65, S75 or S76)

| | | | |
|---|---|---|---|
| H55 | Mar 1962 | 1,006,200 | 60·00 |
| | p. With blue phosphor bands | 23,600 | £200 |
| H56 | May 1962 | 1,120,800 | 60·00 |
| | p. With blue phosphor bands | 50,800 | £180 |

| | | | |
|---|---|---|---|
| H57 | July 1962 | 1,309,600 | 60·00 |
| | p. With blue phosphor bands | 16,600 | £180 |
| H58 | Sept 1962 | 1,523,800 | 60·00 |
| | p. With blue phosphor bands | 49,800 | £200 |
| H59 | Nov 1962 | 1,543,200 | 60·00 |
| | p. With blue phosphor bands | 51,000 | £200 |
| H60 | Jan 1963 | 1,024,600 | 60·00 |
| | p. With blue phosphor bands | 38,800 | £500 |
| H61 | Mar 1963 | 1,116,800 | 60·00 |
| | p. With blue phosphor bands | 15,800 | £200 |
| H62 | May 1963 | 1,102,200 | 60·00 |
| | p. With blue phosphor bands | 78,600 | £200 |
| H63 | July 1963 | 1,456,400 | 60·00 |
| | p. With blue phosphor bands | 44,600 | £200 |
| H64 | Sept 1963 | 1,402,200 | 60·00 |
| | p. With blue phosphor bands | 36,200 | £200 |
| H65 | Nov 1963 | 1,400,000 | 60·00 |
| | p. With blue phosphor bands | 78,800 | £200 |
| H66 | Jan 1964 | 831,600 | 60·00 |
| | p. With blue phosphor bands | 43,000 | £120 |
| H67 | Mar 1964 | 760,200 | 60·00 |
| | p. With blue phosphor bands | 55,800 | £120 |
| H68 | May 1964 | 760,200 | 60·00 |
| | p. With blue phosphor bands | 66,000 | £200 |
| H69 | July 1964 | 1,647,200 | 60·00 |
| | p. With blue phosphor bands | 29,400 | £180 |
| H70 | Sept 1964 | 1,574,000 | 60·00 |
| | p. With blue phosphor bands | 38,400 | £180 |
| H71 | Nov 1964 | 1,152,400 | 55·00 |
| | p. With blue phosphor bands | 98,600 | £120 |
| H72 | Jan 1965 | 1,119,000 | 60·00 |
| | p. With blue phosphor bands | 55,200 | £120 |
| H73 | Mar 1965 | 657,600 | 50·00 |
| | p. With blue phosphor bands | 19,000 | £180 |
| H74 | May 1965 | 1,076,600 | 45·00 |
| | p. With blue phosphor bands | 56,800 | £120 |

Paste-up books H48 to H74 each £150
AVC books H48 to H52 each 15·00
H53 to H56 each 50·00
H57 and H58 each 15·00
H59 50·00
H60 to H74 each 15·00
5s. booklets were withdrawn from sale on 31 August 1965.

## 6s. Booklets

**Contents**: 18 × 4d. in panes of six
Claret Cover as Type D. Fully interleaved

### Watermark Crowns (No. S85), blue or violet phosphor (Nos. S90, S91 or S92)

| | | | |
|---|---|---|---|
| Q1 | June 1965 (issued 21.6.65) | 1,166,800 | 40·00 |
| | p. With blue phosphor bands (issued 21.6.65) | 101,800 | 40·00 |
| Q2 | July 1965 | 1,718,000 | 40·00 |
| | p. With blue phosphor bands | 136,200 | 40·00 |
| Q3 | Aug 1965 | 1,192,400 | 45·00 |
| | p. With blue phosphor bands | 87,600 | 48·00 |
| Q4 | Sept 1965 | 1,907,800 | 40·00 |
| | p. (a) With blue phosphor bands | 244,400 | 45·00 |
| | p. (b) With violet 8 mm. phosphor bands | | 45·00 |
| Q5 | Oct 1965 | 1,889,600 | 40·00 |
| | p. (a) With blue phosphor bands | 263,600 | 45·00 |
| | p. (b) With violet 8 mm. phosphor bands | | 45·00 |
| Q6 | Nov 1965 | 1,788,800 | 40·00 |
| | p. (a) With blue phosphor bands | 98,200 | 45·00 |
| | p. (b) With violet 8 mm. phosphor bands | | 45·00 |
| Q7 | Dec 1965 | 1,662,000 | 40·00 |
| | p. (a) With blue phosphor bands. | 93,000 | 45·00 |
| | p. (b) With violet 8 mm. phosphor bands | | 45·00 |
| Q8 | Jan 1966 | 1,114,800 | 42·00 |
| | p. (a) With blue phosphor bands. | 349,200 | 45·00 |
| | p. (b) With violet 8 mm. phosphor bands | | 45·00 |
| Q9 | Feb 1966 | 1,448,600 | 42·00 |
| | p. With violet 8 mm. phosphor bands | 116,800 | 45·00 |
| Q10 | Mar 1966 | 1,038,000 | 42·00 |
| | p. With violet 8 mm. phosphor bands | 122,400 | 45·00 |
| Q11 | Apr 1966 | 1,124,200 | 42·00 |
| | p. With violet 8 mm. phosphor bands | 119,600 | £120 |
| Q12 | May 1966 | 1,099,000 | 40·00 |
| | p. With violet 8 mm. phosphor bands | 121,000 | 55·00 |
| Q13 | June 1966 | 1,070,400 | 40·00 |
| | p. With violet 8 mm. phosphor bands | 121,000 | 45·00 |
| Q14 | July 1966 | 667,600 | 45·00 |
| | p. With violet 8 mm. phosphor bands | 46,800 | 65·00 |
| Q15 | Aug 1966 | 1,503,200 | 45·00 |
| | p. With violet 8 mm. phosphor bands | 42,400 | £180 |
| Q16 | Sept 1966 | 1,402,400 | 40·00 |
| | p. With violet 8 mm. phosphor bands | 227,200 | 40·00 |
| Q17 | Oct 1966 | 986,600 | 45·00 |
| | p. With violet 8 mm. phosphor bands | 227,200 | £120 |
| Q18 | Nov 1966 | 1,078,000 | 48·00 |
| | p. With violet 8 mm. phosphor bands | 271,200 | 40·00 |
| Q19 | Dec 1966 | 1,069,400 | 40·00 |
| | p. With violet 8 mm. phosphor bands | 270,500 | 45·00 |
| Q20 | Jan 1967 | 231,400 | 55·00 |
| | p. With violet 8 mm. phosphor bands | 622,400 | 55·00 |
| Q21 | Feb 1967 | 253,800 | 55·00 |
| | p. With violet 9·5 mm. phosphor bands | 566,200 | 40·00 |
| Q22 | Mar 1967 | 395,000 | 45·00 |
| | p. With violet 9·5 mm. phosphor bands | 580,800 | 40·00 |
| Q23 | Apr 1967 | 395,400 | 40·00 |
| | p. With violet 9·5 mm. phosphor bands | 632,200 | 40·00 |

### Watermark Crowns violet 9·5mm. phosphor (No. S92)

| | | | |
|---|---|---|---|
| Q24p | May 1967 | 1,612,600 | 40·00 |
| Q25p | June 1967 | 1,596,800 | 40·00 |
| Q26p | July 1967 | 776,600 | 45·00 |
| Q27p | Aug 1967 | 750,600 | 55·00 |

Paste-up books Q1 to Q2 (using 4s.6d. AVC to make up) each £200
Q4 (stapled to make up) £200
Q3 and Q5 to Q27 each £150
AVC books Q1 to Q27 each 15·00

## ▮ 10s. Booklets

**Contents:** 30 × 3d., 6 × 2d., 6 × 1½d., 6 × 1d., 6 × ½d. in panes of six

### I. Green Cover as Type D. Fully interleaved
Watermark Crowns (Nos. S4, S16, S28, S40, S70)

| X1 | No date (issued 10.4.61) | 902,000 | £150 |
|----|---------------------------|---------|------|
| X2 | Oct 1961 | 483,200 | £190 |

Paste-up books X1 or X2 each £400
AVC books X1 or X2 each £200
**Contents changed:** 30 × 3d., 6 × 2½d., 6 × 1½d., 6 × 1d. in panes of six

Watermark Crowns (Nos. S17, S29, S57, S71)

| X3 | Apr 1962 | 524,680 | £140 |
|----|----------|---------|------|
| X4 | Aug 1962 | 474,600 | £180 |
| X5 | Mar 1963 | 493,200 | £180 |
| X6 | July 1963 | 620,600 | £180 |
| X7 | Dec 1963 | 606,600 | £180 |
| X8 | July 1964 | 599,400 | £140 |
| X9 | Dec 1964 | 415,200 | £350 |

Paste-up book X3 or X4 each £300
X5 to X9 each £200
AVC books X3 or X4 each £200
X5 to X9 each 50·00
10s. booklets in this composition were withdrawn from sale on 31 August 1965.
**Contents changed:** 24 × 4d., 6 × 3d., 6 × 1d. in panes of six

### II. Ochre Cover as Type D. Fully interleaved

Watermark Crowns (Nos. S17, S71, S85)

| X10 | Aug 1965 (issued 23.8.65) | 854,200 | 38·00 |
|-----|---------------------------|---------|-------|
| X11 | Dec 1965 | 658,800 | 55·00 |
| X12 | Feb 1966 | 663,600 | 55·00 |
| X13 | Aug 1966 | 686,800 | 38·00 |
| X14 | Nov 1966 | 796,000 | 38·00 |

Watermark Crowns, violet phosphor with one side band on 3d. (Nos. S23 or S24, S78, S91 or S92)

| X15p | Feb 1967 | | |
|------|----------|---|---|
| | (a) With violet 8 and 4 mm. phosphor bands | 301,800 | 10·00 |
| | (b) With violet 9·5 and 4 mm. phosphor bands | | 10·00 |

Watermark Crowns, violet 9·5 mm. phosphor with one centre 4 mm. band on 3d. (Nos. S24, S79, S92)

| X16 p | Aug 1967 | 1,488,800 | 7·25 |
|-------|----------|-----------|------|
| X17 p | Feb 1968 | 474,400 | 9·00 |

Paste-up book X10 or X7 each £200
AVC books X10 or X17 each 20·00

## Section B.
## Machin £.s.d. Issues with Violet Phosphor Bands

> NOTE: All booklets in this Section are fully interleaved

## ▮ 2s. Booklets

**Contents:** 4 × 4d. in pane of four and 2 × 1d. and 2 × 3d. in pane of four arranged se-tenant horizontally
Orange-yellow Cover as Type C
PVA gum (Nos. U2, U10, U12)

| NP27 | May 1968 (issued 6.4.68) | 3,112,400 | 1·60 |
|------|--------------------------|-----------|------|
| NP28 | July 1968 | 1,971,685 | 1·40 |
| NP29 | Aug 1968 | | 5·25 |

2s. booklets containing 3d. stamps were withdrawn on 14 September 1968.
**Contents changed:** 6 × 4d. in pane of four and in pane of two plus two printed labels *se-tenant* vertically
Grey Cover as Type C
One centre phosphor band on *se-tenant* pane. PVA gum (Nos. U12, U13)

| NP30 | Sept 1968 (issued 16.9.68) | 2,497,400 | 1·10 |
|------|----------------------------|-----------|------|
| NP31 | Jan 1969 | 2,247,600 | £275 |

Change to one centre phosphor band on 4 × 4d. pane. PVA gum (No. U13)

| NP31a | Sept 1968 (issued 16.9.68)(incl. in NP30) | | £650 |
|-------|-------------------------------------------|---|------|
| NP32 | Nov 1968 | 2,397,400 | 1·10 |
| NP33 | Jan 1969(incl. in NP31) | | 1·10 |

Change to 4d. bright vermilion with one centre phosphor band. PVA gum (No. U14)

| NP34 | Mar 1969 (issued 3.3.69) | 1,952,000 | 1·25 |
|------|--------------------------|-----------|------|
| NP35 | May 1969 | 2,092,000 | 1·50 |
| NP36 | July 1969 | 436,000 | 2·00 |
| NP37 | Sept 1969 | 1,612,400 | 1·50 |
| NP38 | Nov 1969 | 1,470,400 | 1·50 |
| NP39 | Jan 1970 | 1,172,000 | 2·00 |
| NP40 | Mar 1970 | 1,168,600 | 2·00 |
| NP41 | May 1970 | 1,390,800 | 2·00 |
| NP42 | July 1970 | 1,023,800 | 2·25 |
| NP43 | Aug 1970 | 1,037,800 | 2·00 |
| NP44 | Oct 1970 | 2,544,600 | 2·00 |
| | b. Imprint error HARRISOU for HARRISON | | |
| NP45 | Dec 1970 | 2,273,400 | 2·00 |

## ■ **4s.6d. Booklets**

**Contents:** 12 × 4d., 6 × 1d. in panes of six

**I. Slate-blue Cover as Type D**
PVA gum (Nos. U2, U12)

| | | |
|---|---|---|
| LP45 May 1968 (issued 1.5.68) | 742,600 | 6·00 |

Type E. With GPO Cypher

Type F. With Post Office Crown Symbol

(Des. Stuart Rose)

(In Types E/F the design subject is changed from time to time and this is indicated in
brackets after the date)

**II. Blue Cover as Type E showing Ships**
PVA gum (Nos. U2, U12)

| | | |
|---|---|---|
| LP46 July 1968 (Cutty Sark) | 427,600 | 1·50 |

Change to one centre phosphor band on 4d. PVA gum (Nos.
U2, U13)

| | | |
|---|---|---|
| LP47 Sept 1968 (Golden Hind) (issued 16.9.68) | 1,052,800 | 2·00 |
| LP48 Nov 1968 (Discovery) | 1,009,000 | 2·00 |

Change to 4d. bright vermilion with one centre band. PVA
gum (No. U14)

| | | |
|---|---|---|
| LP49 Jan 1969 (Queen Elizabeth 2) (issued 6.1.69) | 775,200 | 3·25 |
| LP50 Mar 1969 (Sirius) | 1,105,800 | 3·00 |
| LP51 May 1969 (Sirius) | 993,200 | 2·50 |
| LP52 July 1969 (Dreadnought) | 932,000 | 3·00 |
| LP53 Sept 1969 (Dreadnought) | 1,318,600 | 5·00 |
| LP54 Nov 1969 (Mauretania) | 1,469,400 | 3·50 |
| LP55 Jan 1970 (Mauretania) | 1,046,600 | 5·00 |

| | | |
|---|---|---|
| LP56 Mar 1970 (Victory) | 872,400 | 4·00 |
| LP57 May 1970 (Victory) | 515,800 | 10·00 |

**III. Blue Cover as Type F showing Ships**
PVA gum (Nos. U2, U14)

| | | |
|---|---|---|
| LP58 Aug 1970 (The Sovereign of the Seas) | 412,600 | 3·75 |
| LP59 Oct 1970 (The Sovereign of the Seas) | 746,600 | 10·00 |

## 5s. Booklets

Type E. With GPO Cypher

Type F. With Post Office Crown Symbol

(Des. Stuart Rose)

**Contents**: 12 × 5d. in panes of six

**I. Cinnamon Cover as Type E showing English Homes**
PVA gum (No. U17)

| | | | |
|---|---|---|---|
| HP26 | Dec 1968 (Ightham Mote) (issued 27.11.68) | 978,000 | 2·40 |
| HP27 | Feb 1969 (Little Moreton Hall) | 1,510,200 | 2·40 |
| HP28 | Apr 1969 (Long Melford Hall) | 1,963,200 | 2·50 |
| HP29 | June 1969 (Long Melford Hall) | 1,821,000 | 2·50 |
| HP30 | Aug 1969 (Long Melford Hall) | 1,660,800 | 4·00 |

**II. Cinnamon Cover as Type F showing English Homes**
PVA gum (No. U17)

| | | | |
|---|---|---|---|
| HP31 | Oct 1969 (Mompesson House) | 2,251,200 | 2·50 |
| HP32 | Dec 1969 (Mompesson House) | 960,200 | 3·00 |
| HP33 | Feb 1970 (Cumberland Terrace) | 910,800 | 2·50 |

Type P

(Des. Peter Gauld)

Issued to publicise the Philympia International Philatelic Exhibition, London, September 1970

**III. Cinnamon Cover as Type P. Stitched in red**
PVA gum (No. U17)

| | | | |
|---|---|---|---|
| HP34 | (no date) (issued 3.3.70) | 1,019,800 | 3·00 |

**IV. Cinnamon Cover as Type F showing English Homes**
PVA gum (No. U17)

| | | | |
|---|---|---|---|
| HP35 | June 1970 (The Vineyard, Saffron Walden) | 1,814,400 | 3·50 |
| HP36 | Aug 1970 (The Vineyard, Saffron Walden) | 2,076,800 | 4·75 |
| HP37 | Oct 1970 (Mereworth Castle) | 3,301,400 | 4·50 |
| HP38 | Dec 1970 (Mereworth Castle) | 5,517,680 | 4·75 |

Paste-up books HP26 or HP27 (using 4s.6d. AVC to make up) £200
HP28 to HP38 each £150
AVC books HP27 to HP38 10·00

## ■ 6s. Booklets

Contents: 18 × 4d. in panes of six

### I. Claret Cover as Type D
Gum arabic (No. U11 (1))

| QP28 | Sept 1967 (issued 21.9.67) | 1,345,000 | 55·00 |
| QP29 | Oct 1967 | 1,487,400 | 55·00 |
| QP30 | Nov 1967 | 1,522,200 | 55·00 |
| QP31 | Dec 1967 | 1,531,000 | 55·00 |
| QP32 | Jan 1968 | 1,251,400 | 50·00 |

Change to 4d. deep olive-brown. Gum arabic (No. U11 (2))

| QP33 | Feb 1968 | 1,314,400 | 50·00 |
| QP34 | Mar 1968 | 1,090,600 | 20·00 |
| QP35 | Apr 1968 | 1,127,800 | 42·00 |
| QP36 | May 1968 | 1,398,000 | 21·00 |

Change to PVA gum (No. U12 (2))

| QP37 | May 1968 (incl. in QP36) | | £500 |

Paste-up books QP28 to QP31 each £150
QP32 (stapled to make up) £200
QP33 to QP37 each £150
AVC books QP28 to QP37 each 8·00

Type E. With GPO Cypher

Type F. With Post Office Crown Symbol

(Des. Stuart Rose)

### II. Orange-red Cover as Type E showing Birds
PVA gum (No. U12 (2))

| QP38 | June 1968 (Kingfisher) (issued 4.6.68) | 1,212,000 | 2·50 |
| QP39 | July 1968 (Kingfisher) | 1,195,000 | 13·00 |
| QP40 | Aug 1968 (Peregrine Falcon) | 1,223,800 | 2·00 |

Change to one centre phosphor band. PVA gum (No. U13)

| QP41 | Sept 1968 (Peregrine Falcon) (issued 16.9.68) | 1,010,200 | 2·10 |
| QP42 | Oct 1968 (Pied Woodpecker) | 1,277,800 | 2·10 |
| QP43 | Nov 1968 (Pied Woodpecker) | 1,006,200 | 2·25 |
| QP44 | Dec 1968 (Great Crested Grebe) | 975,600 | 2·25 |
| QP45 | Jan 1969 (Barn Owl) | 1,017,000 | 3·50 |

Change to 4d. bright vermilion with one centre phosphor band. PVA gum (No. U14)

| QP46 | Feb 1969 (Barn Owl) (issued 20.2.69) (PPP) | 3750 | 4·25 |
| | (a) Combination GGP | | £170 |
| | (b) Combination GPG | | £170 |
| | (c) Combination GPP | | 80·00 |
| | (d) Combination PGG | 1,035,200 | £125 |
| | (e) Combination PGP | | 80·00 |
| | (f) Combination PPG | | 80·00 |
| | (g) Combination GGG | | £225 |
| QP47 | Mar 1969 (Jay) (PPP) | | 37·00 |
| | (a) Combination GGP | | £170 |
| | (b) Combination PGP | | 80·00 |
| | (c) Combination PPG | 424,400 | 80·00 |
| | (d) Combination GPP | | 80·00 |
| | (e) Combination GPG | | £170 |
| | (f) Combination GGG | | £225 |
| QP48 | May 1969 (Jay) | 533,800 | 4·25 |
| QP49 | July 1969 (Puffin) | 498,400 | 3·50 |
| QP50 | Sept 1969 (Puffin) | 506,200 | 6·00 |

### III. Orange-red Cover as Type F showing Birds
PVA gum (No. U14)

| QP51 | Nov 1969 (Cormorant) | 472,600 | 4·25 |
| QP52 | Jan 1970 (Cormorant) | 487,800 | 5·00 |
| QP53 | Apr 1970 (Wren) | 512,800 | 4·25 |
| QP54 | Aug 1970 (Golden Eagle) | 570,600 | 4·25 |
| QP55 | Oct 1970 (Golden Eagle) | 754,800 | 4·25 |

Paste-up books QP38 to QP55 each £150
Mar 1970 (not issued) £250
AVC books QP38 to QP43 each 10·00
QP44 25·00
QP45 to QP55 each 10·00

## ■ 10s. Booklets

Type E I

Type E II

Pictorial Cover with GPO Cypher

(Des. Stuart Rose)

Two types of Cypher:
Type I. GPO in clear letters. 10s. Booklets XP4/5
Type II. GPO in black letters. 10s. Booklets XP6/10
**Contents:** 24 × 4d., 6 × 3d., 6 × 1d. in panes of six
Bright Purple Cover as Type E I showing Explorers
PVA gum (Nos. U2, U9, U12)

| | | | |
|---|---|---|---|
| XP4 | MAY 1968 (Livingstone) (issued 25.3.68) | 713,200 | 6·00 |
| XP5 | AUG 1968 (Livingstone) | 39,497 | 6·00 |

**Contents changed:** 12 × 5d., 14 × 4d., 4 × 1d., in panes of six and one horizontally *se-tenant* pane of 2 × 4d., and 4 × 1d. Yellow-green Cover as Type E II showing Explorers
PVA gum (Nos. U3, U13, U17)

| | | | |
|---|---|---|---|
| XP6 | Sept 1968 (Scott) (issued 16.9.68) | 1,513,400 | 4·75 |

Change to 4d. bright vermilion but *se-tenant* pane comprises 1d. with two phosphor bands and 4d. with one left side phosphor band. PVA gum (Nos. U2, U14, U16, U17). For booklets with mixed gum, see note above No. QP46

| | | | |
|---|---|---|---|
| XP 7 | Feb 1969 (Mary Kingsley) (issued 6.1.69) | 2,338,200 | 3·50 |
| XP 8 | May 1969 (Mary Kingsley) (PPPPP) | } 1,165,200 | 4·75 |
| | (a) Combination PPPGP | | 70·00 |
| | (b) Combination PPGPP | | £200 |
| XP 9 | Aug 1969 (Shackleton) | 1,765,600 | 4·75 |
| XP10 | Nov 1969 (Shackleton) | 1,176,000 | 7·25 |

Type F

(Des. Stuart Rose)

Pictorial Cover with Post Office Corporation Crown Symbol

Yellow-green Cover as Type F showing Explorers
PVA gum (Nos. U2, U14, U16, U17)

| | | | |
|---|---|---|---|
| XP11 | FEB 1970 (Frobisher) (issued 2.2.70) | 490,200 | 7·25 |
| XP12 | NOV 1970 (Captain Cook) | 737,400 | 7·25 |

Paste-up books XP4 tp X912 each    £200
May 1970 (not issued)    £300
AVC books XP4 to X912 each    12·00
●————————

## Publicity proof covers and related material

All proofs are booklet cover size unless otherwise stated.

## 1. Cover proofs for issued booklets

### 4s. 6d. Proofs

**Blue card**
(a) As Type E

| Cutty Sark, Golden Hind, Discovery, Queen Elizabeth II | each 30.00 |
|---|---|

(b) As Type E but with Type F value setting

| Queen Elizabeth 2, Sirius, Dreadnought, Mauretania, Victory | each 40.00 |
|---|---|

**White glazed art paper**
(a) As Type E

| (i) Cutty Sark (10cm square) | 50.00 |
| (ii) Golden Hind, Discovery, Queen Elizabeth II | each 30.00 |

### 5s. Proofs

**Cinnamon card**
(a) As Type E

| Ightham Mote, Little Moreton Hall | each 50.00 |
|---|---|

**White glazed art paper**
(a) As Type E

| Ightham Mote, Little Moreton Hall | each 50.00 |
|---|---|

### 6s. Proofs

**Orange-red card**
(a) As type E

| Kingfisher, Peregrine Falcon, Pied Woodpecker, Great Crested Grebe, Barn Owl, Jay | each 30·00 |
|---|---|

(b) As Type E but with Type F value setting

| Kingfisher, Peregrine Falcon, Pied Woodpecker, Great Crested Grebe, Jay, Puffin | each 60·00 |
|---|---|

**White glazed art paper**
(a) As Type E

| (i) Kingfisher, Peregrine Falcon, Barn Owl (10cm square) | each 50·00 |
| (ii) Pied Woodpecker, Great Crested Grebe, Jay | each 30·00 |

### 10s. Proofs

**Bright purple card**
(a) As Type EI but with Type EII GPO Cypher

| Livingstone, Scott, Shackleton, Cook | each 40·00 |
|---|---|

(b) As Type EII but with Type EI stamp contents

| Livingstone, Scott, Kingsley, Frobisher, Cook | each 60·00 |
|---|---|

**White glazed art paper**
(a) As Type EI but with Type EII GPO Cypher

| Livingstone, Scott, Shackleton, Cook | each 40·00 |
|---|---|

**White card**
(c) As Type EII

| Scott, Shackleton, Kingsley, Frobisher, Cook | each 60·00 |
|---|---|

## 2. Cover proofs for booklets not issued

### 4s. 6d. Proof

White glazed art paper, as Type F

| Swallow | £120 |
|---|---|

### 5s. Proof

White glazed art paper, as Type F

| The Red House | £700 |
|---|---|

### 10s. Proofs

| Bright purple card, as Type EI but with Type EII GPO Cypher  Drake | £100 |
| White glazed art paper, as Type EI but with Type EII GPO Cypher  Drake | £100 |
| White card, as Type EII  Drake | £120 |

## 3. Composite proof

White glazed art paper, as Type F (18cm by 21cm)

| 10s. Cook and Drake, 6s. Curlew and Golden Eagle | £800 |
|---|---|

## 4. Poster Proof (PL(S) 331)

White glazed art paper (21cm by 28cm) illustrating six covers

| 4s. 6d. Queen Elizabeth 2 and Sirius, as Type E but with Type F value setting | |
| 6s. Barn Owl and Jay, as Type E but with Type F value setting | |
| 10s. Kingsley, as Type EII | |
| 5s. Little Moreton Hall, as Type E | £600 |

## 5. Preliminary Proofs and Essays

| 5s. Proof on cream paper, The Red House, as Type F (marked "5A") | £500 |
| 10s. Proof on Bright purple card, Livingstone, as Type EI, 120% booklet size | £500 |
| 10s. Essay on white paper, Kingsley with volcano and palm tree, no contents line, 120% booklet size | £500 |
| 10s. Essay on cream paper, palm tree and Drake ship (inverted), no contents line, 120% booklet size | £500 |
| 10s. Essay on cream paper, Frobisher, no contents line, 133% booklet size | £500 |
| 10s. Essay on cream paper, Cook, no contents line, 114% booklet size | £500 |

## 6. Zinc Metal Printing Blocks ("Zincos")

| 4s. 6d. Golden Hind, Discovery, Queen Elizabeth II | each £400 |
| 5s. The Red House | £500 |
| 6s. Great Crested Grebe, Jay | each £400 |
| 10s. Scott, Shackleton, Cook, Drake | each £400 |

■ **£1 Booklet ( Stamps for Cooks)**

Type X

**Contents**: 18 × 5d., 36 × 4d., 6 × 1d., in panes of fifteen and one horizontally *se-tenant* pane of 3 × 5d., 6 × 4d., and 6 × 1d. There are 12 recipes on interleaving pages and on *se-tenant* labels attached to each pane.

**Pattern book** (April 1969)(see notes)

Full colour cover showing cooking ingredients on ladle and "Stamps for cooks" "20s." £2000

Full Colour Cover as Type X size 6 × 2⁷/₈ in. showing Baked Stuffed Haddock

Pane of fifteen 5d. has two phosphor bands, panes of fifteen 4d. have one centre phosphor band but *se-tenant* pane has two phosphor bands on 1d. and 5d. and one side band on 4d. (three stamps with band at left and three stamps with band at right)

| | | | |
|---|---|---:|---:|
| ZP1 | (no date) (issued 1.12.69) | | |
| | (stapled) | 10,848 | £400 |
| | (s) Each stamp overprinted "Specimen" 14×2 mm. | | £5750 |
| ZP1a | As last but booklet is sewn with thread | 374,902 | 13·00 |
| | (as) Each stamp cancelled with Philatelic Bureau postmark of 8 June 1971. | | £2200 |
| | (at) Stamps overprinted double-line "SPECIMEN" 72×13 mm | | £7500 |

Examples of this booklet are known with one or two colours omitted from the cover.

Upon issue in 1969, examples of SPIs were provided to the advertising contractor for presentation as specimens to commercial advertising agencies for future editions of £1 books. During 1971, when a future edition was planned, examples of Nos. ZP1as and ZP1at were similarly provided to the advertising contractor.

AVC book (as ZP1a without black binding) £100

# APPENDIX HB
Postage Rates

Postage rates from 1635 have been researched from official records and the following extract is reproduced with kind permission of the Post Office. The rates given apply only to the period covered by this Catalogue.

## Letter Post
The Treasury was empowered to regulate rates of postage, and subsequent changes were made by Treasury Warrant

| Date | Rates of Charge | |
|---|---|---|
| 1 May 1952 | 2oz. | 2½d. |
| | 4oz. | 3d. |
| | Then 1d. for each additional 2oz. | |
| 1 January 1956 | 2oz. | 2½d. |
| | Then 1½d. for each additional 2oz. | |
| 1 October 1957 | 1oz. | 3d. |
| | 2oz. | 4½d. |
| | Then 1½d. for each additional 2oz. | |
| 17 May 1965 | 2oz. | 4d. |
| | Each additional 2oz. up to 1lb. 2d. | |
| | Each additional 2oz. thereafter 3d. | |
| 3 October 1966 | 2oz. | 4d. |
| | Each additional 2oz. up to 1lb. 2d. | |
| | Each additional 2oz. up to 1lb. 8oz. 3d. | |
| | Over 1lb. 8oz. up to 2lb. 3s.6d. | |
| | Each additional 1lb. 2s. | |

## Introduction of the first and second class services for letters and cards.

| Date | Weight not exceeding | First Class | Second Class |
|---|---|---|---|
| 16 September 1968 | 4oz. | 5d. | 4d. |
| | 6oz. | 9d. | 6d. |
| | 8oz. | 1s. 0d. | 8d. |
| | 10oz. | 1s. 3d. | 10d. |
| | 12oz. | 1s. 6d. | 1s. 0d. |
| | 14oz. | 1s. 9d. | 1s. 2d. |
| | 1lb 0oz. | 2s. 0d. | 1s. 4d. |
| | 1lb 2oz. | 2s. 3d. | 1s. 6d. |
| | 1lb 4oz. | 2s. 6d. | 1s. 7d. |
| | 1lb 6oz. | 2s. 9d. | 1s. 8d. |
| | 1lb 8oz. | 3s. 0d. | 1s. 9d. |
| | 2lb 0oz. | 4s. 0d. | Not admissible over 1½lbs. |
| | Each additional 1lb. 2s. | | |

## Postcards
From 1925 the maximum size allowed was 57/8 × 4¹/8 and the minimum size was 4 × 2¾ .

| Date | Charge |
|---|---|
| 1 May 1940 | 2d. |
| 1 October 1957 | 2½d. |
| 17 May 1965 | 3d. |

## Printed Papers

| Date | Rates of Charge | |
|---|---|---|
| 1 June 1951 | 4oz. | 1½d. |
| | Then ½d. for each additional 2oz. up to 2lb. | |
| 1 January 1956 | 2oz. | 1½d. |
| | Then 1d. for each additional 2oz. | |
| 1 June 1956 | 4oz. | 2d. |
| | Then 1d. for each additional 2oz. | |
| 1 October 1957 | 2oz. | 2d. |
| | 4oz. | 4d. |
| | Then 1d. for each additional 2oz. | |
| 1 October 1961 | 2oz. | 2½d. |
| | 4oz. | 4d. |
| 17 May 1965 | Not over 2oz. | 3d. |
| | Not over 4oz. | 5d. |
| | Each additional 2oz. | 1d. |

## Newspaper Post
From 1870 the charge had been ½d. per copy irrespective of weight, but from 1 November 1915 the maximum weight permitted was 2lb.

| Date | Charge Per Copy not exceeding | |
|---|---|---|
| 1 July 1940 | 4oz. | 1½d. |
| | Then ½d. for each additional 4oz. | |
| 1 June 1956 | 6oz. | 2d. |
| | Then 1d for each additional 6oz. | |
| 1 October 1957 | 6oz. | 2½d. |
| | Then 1½d. for each additional 6oz. | |
| 1 October 1961 | 6oz. | 3d. |
| | Then 1½d. for each 6oz. | |
| 17 May 1965 | 2oz. | 3d. |
| | 4oz. | 5d. |
| | Then 1d. for each additional 2oz. Per copy regulation abolished | |

## Articles for the Blind
This service was made free of charge from 17 May 1965 (maximum weight 15lb.).

| Date | Rates of Charge | |
|---|---|---|
| 1 July 1940 | 2lb. | ½d. |
| 12 April 1954 | 8lb. | 1½d. |
| | 15lb. | 2½d. |
| | 5lb. | 1d. |
| | 11lb. | 2d. |
| | 5lb | 1d. |
| | 11lb. | 2d. |
| | 2lb. | ½d. |
| | 8lb. | 1½d. |
| | 15lb. | 2½d. |

Note that the rates were unchanged in 1954 but certain details of the regulations were amended, including thr fact that the rates were extended to mail to the Irish Republic.

## Express Service

**Service 1.** Express by special messenger all the way.

| Date | Charges | Notes |
|---|---|---|
| 1934 | 6d. per mile plus cost of special conveyance if used. Weight fee (for packets over 1lb.) 3d. | Charge for additional articles 1d. per article after the first. Waiting fee 2d. for each 10 minutes after the first 10 minutes |
| 1 January 1956 | 1s. per mile plus cost of special conveyance if used | Additional articles 2½d. for each item beyond the first. Waiting fee 4d. for each 10 minutes after the first 10 minutes |
| 1 October 1957 | As above | Additional articles 3d. for each item beyond the first |
| 17 May 1965 | 3s. per mile plus cost of special conveyance if used | Each additional article 4d. for each item beyond the first. Waiting fee 1s. for each 10 minutes after the first 10 minutes |

**Service 2.** Special Delivery at the request of the sender. Post Office messenger from the delivery office after transmission by post.

| Date | Charges | Notes |
|---|---|---|
| 1 January 1956 | Full postage plus special fee of 1s. (from 1934 6d.). | If a special conveyance was used the actual cost, or if that was unknown, 1s. per mile |
| 17 May 1965 | Full postage plus special fee of 3s. | As above but 6s. per mile |
| 16 September 1968 | As above but only for first class service. | |

There was also a Limited Sunday Special Delivery Service. Charges were as for Service 2 except the special fee was 1s.6d. in 1934; 3s. from 1 January 1956 and 9s. from 17 May 1965 in addition to full postage.

The service providing for the express delivery of a message received by telephone was withdrawn on 30 December 1955.

**Service 3.** Express delivery all the way at the request of the addressee. Charges were the same as for Service 1. Additional articles 2d. for every ten beyond the first (from 1934 1d.). From 17 May 1965 this charge was increased to 6d. for every ten after the first.

## Railex

This service was introduced on 1 January 1934. It provided for the conveyance of a postal packet to a railway station by Post Office messenger for despatch on the first available train, and for its immediate delivery by Post Office messenger from the station of destination.

| Date | Charge | |
|---|---|---|
| 1 July 1940 | Not exceeding 2oz. | 3s. 0d. |
| | Over 2oz. and up to 1lb | 3s. 6d. |
| 1 January 1956 | Not over 2oz. | 6s. 0d. |
| | Not over 1lb | 7s. 0d. |
| 17 May 1965 | Charge per packet | 20s. 0d. |
| | (irrespective of weight but not exceeding 1lb.) | |

## Official Parcel Post

This service had first been introduced on 1 August 1883.

| Date | | Rates of Postage |
|---|---|---|
| 31 March 1952 | 2lb. | 11d. |
| | 3lb. | 1s. 1d. |
| | 4lb. | 1s. 3d. |
| | 5lb. | 1s. 5d. |
| | 6lb. | 1s. 7d. |
| | 7lb. | 1s. 9d. |
| | 8lb. | 1s. 10d. |
| | 11lb. | 1s. 11d. |
| | 15lb. | 2s. 0d. |
| 7 April 1953 | 2lb. | 1s. 0d. |
| | 3lb. | 1s. 2d. |
| | 4lb. | 1s. 4d. |
| | 5lb. | 1s. 6d. |
| | 6lb. | 1s. 8d. |
| | 7lb. | 1s. 10d. |
| | 8lb. | 1s. 11d. |
| | 11lb. | 2s. 0d. |
| | 15lb. | 2s. 1d. |
| 12 April 1954 | 2lb. | 1s. 1d. |
| | 3lb. | 1s. 3d. |
| | 4lb. | 1s. 6d. |
| | 5lb. | 1s. 8d. |
| | 6lb. | 1s. 10d. |
| | 7lb. | 2s. 0d. |
| | 8lb. | 2s. 1d. |
| | 11lb. | 2s. 3d. |
| | 15lb. | 2s. 4d. |
| 1 January 1956 | 2lb. | 1s. 3d. |
| | 3lb. | 1s. 5d. |
| | 4lb. | 1s. 8d. |
| | 5lb. | 1s. 11d. |
| | 6lb. | 2s. 1d. |
| | 7lb. | 2s. 3d. |
| | 8lb. | 2s. 6d. |
| | 11lb. | 2s. 8d. |
| | 15lb. | 2s. 9d. |
| 1 June 1956. | 2lb. | 1s. 4d. |
| | 3lb. | 1s. 6d. |
| | 4lb. | 1s. 9d. |
| | 5lb. | 2s. 0d. |
| | 6lb. | 2s. 3d. |
| | 7lb. | 2s. 6d. |
| | 8lb. | 2s. 9d. |
| | 15lb. | 3s. 0d. |
| 1 October 1957 | 2lb. | 1s. 6d. |
| | 3lb. | 1s. 9d. |
| | 4lb. | 2s. 0d. |
| | 5lb. | 2s. 3d. |
| | 6lb. | 2s. 6d. |
| | 7lb. | 2s. 9d. |
| | 8lb. | 3s. 0d. |
| | 11lb. | 3s. 3d. |
| | 15lb. | 3s. 6d. |
| 1 October 1961 | 2lb. | 2s. 0d. |
| | 3lb. | 2s. 3d. |
| | 4lb. | 2s. 6d. |
| | 5lb. | 2s. 9d. |
| | 6lb. | 3s. 0d. |
| | 7lb. | 3s. 3d. |
| | 8lb. | 3s. 6d. |
| | 11lb. | 3s. 9d. |
| | 15lb. | 4s. 0d. |
| 29 April 1963. | 2lb. | 2s. 0d |

| Date | Rates of Postage | |
|---|---|---|
| | 3lb. | 2s. 3d. |
| | 4lb. | 2s. 6d. |
| | 5lb. | 2s. 9d. |
| | 6lb. | 3s. 0d. |
| | 8lb. | 3s. 6d. |
| | 10lb. | 4s. 0d. |
| | 12lb. | 4s. 6d. |
| | 15lb. | 5s. 0d. |
| | 18lb. | 5s. 9d. |
| | 22lb. | 6s. 6d. |
| | Increased weight limit of 22 lbs. intro-duced 18 February 1963 | |
| **17 May 1965** | 2lb. | 2s. 9d. |
| | 3lb. | 3s. 0d. |
| | 4lb. | 3s. 3d. |
| | 6lb. | 3s. 6d. |
| | 8lb. | 4s. 0d. |
| | 10lb. | 4s. 6d. |
| | 14lb. | 5s. 6d. |
| | 18lb. | 6s. 6d. |
| | 22lb. | 7s. 6d. |
| **3 October 1966** | (Ordinary Rate) | |
| | 1½lb. | 2s. 6d. |
| | 2lb. | 3s. 0d. |
| | 6lb. | 4s. 6d. |
| | 10lb. | 6s. 0d. |
| | 14lb. | 7s. 6d. |
| | 18lb. | 9s. 0d. |
| | 22lb. | 10s. 6d. |
| | (Local delivery) As for ordinary less 1s.0d. at each step. | |

The Local Parcel Delivery comprised all places which had, in their local address, the same post town name as that of the office of posting.

# Further Reading

The following list is representative of the major works relating to Queen Elizabeth II pre-decimal issues, stamp booklets, postmarks and postal history. Originally culled in part from *A List of Books on the Postal History, and Adhesive Postage and Revenue Stamps of Great Britain*, compiled by Arnold M. Strange (2nd edition, 1971, Great Britain Philatelic Society, London). Later publications have been included.

## GENERAL

**Alderfer, David and Rosenblum, Larry.** *Introduction to the Stamps of Great Britain.* (2004, Amos Press, Sidney, Ohio, USA)

**Allen, Giles.** *Special Stamp History: 1953 Coronation Issue* (1997, National Postal Museum, London.)

**Allen, Giles.** *The Wildings: The First Elizabeth II Definitives* (2002, British Philatelic Bulletin Publication No 9, Royal Mail, London)

**Allen, Giles.** *The First Elizabeth II Castle High Value Definitives* (2005, British Philatelic Bulletin Publication No 11, Royal Mail, London)

**Bater, Gerry and The Lord Spens.** *The Queen Elizabeth II Waterlow Castle High Values, 1955-1958.* (1990. The G.B. Overprints Society.)

**Furfle, Michael.** *British Postage Due Mail, 1914-1971.* (1993. The Author, Middx.)

**Gentleman, David.** *Artwork* (2002, Ebury Press, London)

**Hine, I. S. and Loveland, R. A. Great Britain, Queen Elizabeth II.** *Check List of Photogravure Cylinder Numbers, 1952-1963.* (1964, A. L. Bert.)

**J.L. Shelley** *Simplified Catalogue of Varieties on Queen Elizabeth II Postage Stamps.* (11th Edn. 1968. Shelley Stamps, London. Supplement 1969/70.)

**Langston, Colin M.** *Catalogue of Flaws on Q.E. G.B. Sheet Stamps.* (1966. The Author, London.)

**Langston, Colin M.** *A Priced Catalogue and Guide to Collecting Queen Elizabeth Great Britain Stamp Booklets.* March 1953 to December 1963. (1964. The Author, London.)

**Langston, Colin M.** *The Complete List of Flaws on Queen Elizabeth Great Britain (1st Design) Stamps from Booklets and Coils.* (1969. The Author, London.)

**Langston, Colin M. and Corliss, H. C.** *Stamps of Great Britain Issued in Rolls and the Machines which Use Them.* An Historical Survey including a Check List of the Rolls issued since 1938. (1961. The Authors, London.)

**Mackay, James A.** *British Stamps.* (1985. Longman Group Ltd., London.)

**Machin, Arnold.** *Artist of an Icon: The Memoirs of Arnold Machin* (2002, Frontier Publishing, Kirstead, Norfolk)

**Morgan, Glenn H.** *British Stamp Exhibitions* (1995, The Author, London.)

**Myall, D. G. A.** *The Deegam Se-tenant Catalogue of G.B. Elizabethan Definitives.* (1979. The Author, Bridport, Dorset.)

**Myall, D. G. A.** *The Deegam Catalogue of Elizabethan Coil Leaders.* (1987. The Author, Bridport, Dorset.)

**Myall, D.G.A.** *The Complete Deegam Machin Handbook* (2003, 3rd edition, The Author, Bridport, Dorset. Published in printed & electronic versions. Supplement published 2005)

**Pierron, Tom.** *The 2005 Catalogue of Great Britain Errors & Varieties* (2005, 2nd edition, Baccic Multimedia. No place stated. Published in printed and electronic versions)

**Potter, David.** *British Elizabethan Stamps.* (1971. B.T. Batsford, London.)

**Rigo de Righi, A. G.** *The Stamps of Royalty; British Commemorative Issues for Royal Occasions, 1935-1972.* (1973. The National Postal Museum, London.)

**Rose, Stuart.** *Royal Mail Stamps. A Survey of British Stamp Design.* (1980. Phaidon Press, Oxford.)

**The Shalan Catalogue.** *A Guide to the Missing Phosphor Lines Issues of Queen Elizabeth II Great Britain.* (3rd. Edn. 1971. Shelley Stamps, and B. Alan Ltd., London.)

**Sweet, Fay.** *Queen Elizabeth II: A Jubilee Portrait in Stamps* (2002, Royal Mail & The British Library, London).

**West, Richard and Muir, Douglas N.** *The Story of Definitive Stamps* (1993, Royal Mail, London)

**Wijman, J. J.** *Postage Stamps of Great Britain and their History.* (1986. The Author, Netherlands.)

**Williams, L. N. and M.** *Commemorative Postage Stamps of Great Britain.* (1967. Arco Publications, London.)

## POST OFFICE BOOKLETS OF STAMPS

**Alexander, Jean and Newbery, Leonard F.** *British Stamp Booklets.* Part 1, Series 1: Part 2, Series 1/2; Part 3, Series 3/5; Part 4, Series 6: Part 5, Series 7; Part 6, Series 8/9: Part 7, Series 10/11, Part 8, Appendix A and B, Part 9, Appendix C, Addenda & Corrigenda and Index (1987-97 in nine parts. The Great Britain Philatelic Society, London.) Parts 4/7 contain information on booklets issued from 1951/70.

## POSTAL HISTORY AND POSTMARKS

**Awcock, P. G.** *Automatic Letter Sorting in the United Kingdom.* (7th. Edn. 1985. The Author, Haywards Heath.)

**Bennett, J. Bruce, Parsons, Cyril, R. H., and Pearson, G. R.** *Current Machine Postmarks of the United Kingdom.* (1963. British Postmark Society, London.)

**Dagnall, H.** *The Mechanised Sorting of Mail.* (1976. The Author, Leicester.)

**Daunton, M. J.** *Royal Mail: The Post Office since 1840.* (1985. The Athlone Press, London.)

**Farrugia, Jean.** *A Guide to Post Office Archives.* (1986. The Post Office, London.)

**Holland, F. C.** *Introduction to British Postmark Collecting.* (1971.)

**Langston, Colin M.** *Surcharge and Explanatory Dies of Great Britain.* (1964. The Author.)

**Mackay, James A.** *The Parcel Post of the British Isles.* (1982. The Author, Dumfries.)

**Mackay, James A.** *Registered Mail of the British Isles.* (1983. The Author, Dumfries.)

**Mackay James A.** *Scottish Postmarks 1693-1978.* (1978. The Author, Dumfries.)

**Mackay James A.** *English and Welsh Postmarks since 1840.* (1980. The Author, Dumfries.)

**Mackay, James A.** *British Post Office Numbers 1924-1969.* (1981. The Author, Dumfries.)

**Mackay, James A.** *Surcharged Mail of the British Isles.* (1984. The Author, Dumfries.)

**Mackay, James A.** *Official Mail of the British Isles.* (1983. The Author, Dumfries.)

**Mackay, James A.** *Machine Cancellations of Scotland.* (1986. The Author, Dumfries.)

**Mackay, James A.** *Postal History Annual.* (From 1979. The Author, Dumfries.)

**Mackay, James A.** *Scotlands Posts (2000.* The Author, Glasgow)

**Muir, Douglas N. and Robinson Martin.** *An Introduction to British Postal Mechanisation.* (1980. Postal Mechanisation Study Circle, Henley-on-Thames, Oxon. Supplements 1981, 1983 and 1992.)

**Parsons, Cyril R. H., Peachey, Colin G. and Pearson, George R.** *Local Publicity Slogan Postmarks 1963-1969.* (1981. 2nd edn. The Authors, Herts.)

**Parsons, Cyril R. H., Peachey, Colin G. and Pearson, George R.** *Slogan Postmarks of the Seventies.* (1980. The Authors, London.)

**Parsons, Cyril R.H., Peachey, Colin G. and Pearson, George.** *Collecting Slogan Postmarks 1917-69.* (1986. The Authors, Aylesbury.)

**Pask, Brian and Peachey, Colin, G.** *Twenty Years of First Day Postmarks.* (1983. British Postmark Society, Herts.)

**Peach, Jack.** *U.K.* Machine Marks. (1982. 2nd Edn. Vera Trinder Ltd., London.)

**Peachey, Colin G.** *In-depth U.K.* Slogan Postmark Listings: Details of All Towns Using Multi-Town Slogan Postmarks in the U.K. Over Four Decades 1960-1999. (1996. The Author, Hemel Hempstead.)

**Pearson, George R.** *Special Event Postmarks of the United Kingdom, Vol.* II 1963-1983. (1996. British Postmark Society, Hemel Hempstead, Herts.)

**Pearson, George R.** *Special Event Postmarks of the United Kingdom.* Vol. I The Early Years 1851-1962 (1991 4th. Edn. British Postmark Society, Hemel Hempstead, Herts.)

**Reynolds, Paul.** *The Machine Cancellations of Wales 1905-1985.* (1985. Welsh Philatelic Society, Swansea.)

**Swan, V.** *British Slogan Cancellations, 1917-1960.* (1960. The Author, Alton.)

**Wellsted, Hilary.** *Express Service 1891-1971.* (1986. Postal History Society, Tonbridge.)

**Whitney, Dr. J. T., Peachey, Colin G. and Crookes, V. Brian.** *Collect British Postmarks.* (1997 7th Edn. British Postmark Society, Hemel Hempstead, Herts.)

**POSTAL RATES**

**Johnson, Robert and Peet, Gordon.** *British Postal Rates 1937 to 2000.* (2000)

Est 1856

# STANLEY GIBBONS

# About Us

## Our History
Edward Stanley Gibbons started trading postage stamps in his father's chemist shop in 1856. Since then we have been at the forefront of stamp collecting for over 150 years. We hold the Royal Warrant, offer unsurpassed expertise and quality and provide collectors with the peace of mind of a certificate of authenticity on all of our stamps. If you think of stamp collecting, you think of Stanley Gibbons and we are proud to uphold that tradition for you.

## 399 Strand
Our world famous stamp shop is a collector's paradise, with all of our latest catalogues, albums and accessories and, of course, our unrivalled stockholding of postage stamps.

www.stanleygibbons.com          shop@stanleygibbons.co.uk          +44 (0)20 7836 8444

## Specialist Stamp Sales
For the collector that appreciates the value of collecting the highest quality examples, Stanley Gibbons is the only choice. Our extensive range is unrivalled in terms of quality and quantity, with specialist stamps available from all over the world.

www.stanleygibbons.com/stamps          shop@stanleygibbons.co.uk          +44 (0)20 7836 8444

## Stanley Gibbons Auctions and Valuations
Sell your collection or individual rare items through our prestigious public auctions or our regular postal auctions and benefit from the excellent prices being realised at auction currently. We also provide an unparalleled valuation service.

www.stanleygibbons.com/auctions          auctions@stanleygibbons.co.uk          +44 (0)20 7836 8444

## Stanley Gibbons Publications
The world's first stamp catalogue was printed by Stanley Gibbons in 1865 and we haven't looked back since! Our catalogues are trusted worldwide as the industry standard and we print countless titles each year. We also publish consumer and trade magazines, Gibbons Stamp Monthly and Philatelic Exporter to bring you news, views and insights into all things philatelic. Never miss an issue by subscribing today and benefit from exclusive subscriber offers each month.

www.stanleygibbons.com/shop          orders@stanleygibbons.co.uk          +44 (0)1425 472 363

## Stanley Gibbons Investments
The Stanley Gibbons Investment Department offers a unique range of investment propositions that have consistently outperformed more traditional forms of investment, from capital protected products with unlimited upside to portfolios made up of the world's rarest stamps and autographs.

www.stanleygibbons.com/investment          investment@stanleygibbons.co.uk          +44 (0)1481 708 270

## Fraser's Autographs
Autographs, manuscripts and memorabilia from Henry VIII to current day. We have over 60,000 items in stock, including movie stars, musicians, sport stars, historical figures and royalty. Fraser's is the UK's market leading autograph dealer and has been dealing in high quality autographed material since 1978.

www.frasersautographs.com          sales@frasersautographs.co.uk          +44 (0)20 7557 4404

## stanleygibbons.com
Our website offers the complete philatelic service. Whether you are looking to buy stamps, invest, read news articles, browse our online stamp catalogue or find new issues, you are just one click away from anything you desire in the world of stamp collecting at stanleygibbons.com.  Happy browsing!

www.stanleygibbons.com

# Great Britain Specialised Vol 3

## From Stanley Gibbons, THE WORLD'S LARGEST STAMP STOCK

**Priority order form – Four easy ways to order**

Phone: 020 7836 8444      Overseas: +44 (0)20 7836 8444

Fax:      020 7557 4499      Overseas: +44 (0)20 7557 4499

Email:  lmourne@stanleygibbons.co.uk

Post:    Lesley Mourne, Stamp Mail Order Department, Stanley Gibbons Ltd, 399 Strand, London, WC2R 0LX, England

## Customer Details

Account Number .................................................................................................

Name .................................................................................................................

Address .............................................................................................................

..........................................................................................................................

Postcode ........................................... Country ...............................................

Email..................................................................................................................

Tel No. ........................................... Fax No. ...................................................

## Payment details

Registered Postage & Packing £3.60

O  Please find my cheque/postal order enclosed for £.........................................................
    Please make cheques payable to Stanley Gibbons Ltd.
    *Cheques must be in £ sterling and drawn on a UK bank*

O  Please debit my credit card for £............................................................ in full payment.
    O Mastercard      O VISA      O Diners      O AMEX      O Switch

    Card Number

    CVC Number              Issue No (Switch)

    Start Date (Switch & Amex)          /          Expiry Date          /

Signature ..................................................................... Date ...............................

# Great Britain Specialised Vol 3 Catalogue

## From Stanley Gibbons, THE WORLD'S LARGEST STAMP STOCK

| Condition (mint/UM/used) | Country | SG No. | Description | Price | Office use only |
|---|---|---|---|---|---|
| | | | | | |
| | | | | | |
| | | | | | |
| | | | | | |
| | | | | | |
| | | | | | |
| | | | | | |
| | | | | | |
| | | | | | |
| | | | | | |
| | | | | | |
| | | | | | |
| | | | | | |
| | | | | | |
| | | | | | |
| | | | | | |
| | | | | | |
| | | | | | |
| | | | | | |
| | | | | | |
| | | | | | |
| | | | | | |
| | | | | | |
| | | | | POSTAGE & PACKING | £3.60 | |
| | | | | GRAND TOTAL | | |

Minimum price. The minimum catalogue price quoted in 10p. For individual stamps, prices between 10p and 95p are provided as a guide for catalogue users.
The lowest price charged for individual stamps or sets purchased from Stanley Gibbons Ltd is £1.

## Please complete payment, name and address details overleaf